Jan 4,

O. T. Herrell
501 S. Knight Ave
Park Ridge, Ill

THE THEORY OF ECONOMETRICS

By

HAROLD T. DAVIS

NORTHWESTERN UNIVERSITY

THE PRINCIPIA PRESS, INC.
BLOOMINGTON, INDIANA

SET UP AND PRINTED
IN THE UNITED STATES OF AMERICA
BY
THE DENTAN PRINTING COMPANY
COLORADO SPRINGS, COLORADO

To My Friend

ALFRED COWLES

This Book is Dedicated in Appreciation for what he had Done for Econometrics

TABLE OF CONTENTS

ECONOMIC STATICS

CHAPTER 1

PRELIMINARY CONCEPTS

CHAPTER 2

THE NATURE OF WEALTH AND INCOME

CHAPTER 3

THE CONCEPT OF UTILITY

Page

CHAPTER 4

SUPPLY AND DEMAND CURVES

CHAPTER 5

THE THEORY OF PURE EXCHANGE

CHAPTER 6

THE THEORY OF MONOPOLY AND DUOPOLY

CHAPTER 7

PRODUCTION AND ALLIED FUNCTIONS

Page

CHAPTER 8

BUDGETS

CHAPTER 9

THE THEORY OF EQUILIBRIUM

CHAPTER 10

TAXATION

ECONOMIC DYNAMICS

CHAPTER 11

THE GROWTH OF POPULATION AND INDUSTRY

CHAPTER 12

THE EQUATION OF EXCHANGE

Page

CHAPTER 16

TIME SERIES AND THEIR CORRELATION

CHAPTER 17

DYNAMIC CONCEPTS OF SUPPLY AND DEMAND

CHAPTER 18

THE DYNAMICS OF ECONOMIC TIME SERIES

CHAPTER 19

THE THEORY OF BUSINESS CYCLES

Page

CHAPTER 20

INTERNATIONAL EXCHANGE

TABLES

PREFACE

The principal difference between an exact science and an inexact one is that the former has defined and measured its variables and has ascertained certain fundamental relationships between them. Thus it may be seen that the evolution of a science from its initial imperfections requires years of patient assembling of data; it forces the invention of new mathematical methods for their interpretation; its creators must pass through many struggles to define the most useful variables and to discover their interrelationships.

This has been the stony path followed by all high scientific achievement, and it must also be the path that is finally taken by disciplines known collectively as the social sciences. Economics is one of these, and during the past half century it has been evolving slowly into an exact science. To note this progress we need merely compare the knowledge of economic phenomena available to W. S. Jevons and his school in 1870 with that available to modern students. Slowly the veil of the past has been pushed back. Each year adds something to our knowledge of the behavior of prices, of production, and of other concomitants of the function which measures the economic well-being of people of other times. Concurrent with this assembling of basic data there has been a steady growth in our knowledge of mathematical disciplines necessary to their analysis and interpretation. Thus we may observe that modern statistics is almost wholly a development of the present century.

In view of these facts the author has undertaken the task of setting forth certain aspects of the knowledge which has been gained in the evolution of economics into an exact science. Since the newly-coined term "econometrics" connotes better than either "mathematical economics" or "statistical economics" the measure of his task, this word has been adopted as a descriptive title. As one may infer, it implies that the phenomena of economics are to be investigated through their statistics, and such patterns as may be observed are to be described in mathematical terms and by means of mathematical equations. Although this may remove the book from the reach of some who do not know the language of mathematics, there seems to be no other way in which so large an area can be exactly surveyed.

In earlier days, when economists were scarcely aware of the power of the mathematical method, Alfred Marshall found it the better policy to place his equations in a small appendix toward the end of his treatise on economics. In recent times this appendix has come to be regarded by many as his most valuable contribution to the subject. Other writers, such as Vilfredo Pareto and Léon Walras, more boldly mingled their equations with the body of their text. Their work necessarily lacked in popular appeal, although their books are now placed among the classics of the subject. A. A. Cournot, who published in 1838 his famous *Researches into the Mathematical Principles of the Theory of Wealth,* complained sadly a third of a century later that his work was sterile, and he attempted to revive interest in it by a volume written in more popular language. But during the course of the century that has passed since the publication of Cournot's volume, there has come new knowledge. Today modern writers turn for inspiration to the discarded masterpiece of Cournot and it has served as a guide to many who have sought to explain the interrelationships of economic variables.

Therefore, without apology, the author offers this attempt to survey a considerable part of economic phenomena by the most recent data and the best methods of analysis known to modern workers. Where data are available to him, he has used them freely; where they are lacking, he has indicated the present status of the problem. Mathematics has been employed freely where it has been needed.

In the course of writing the present volume the author discovered that studies in economics fell naturally into two parts, one concerned with phenomena independent of the time variable and the other concerned with the analysis of data varying with time. This observation suggested that the book be divided into two parts, one devoted to economic statics, and the other to economic dynamics. But it was then discovered that the first of these two divisions was more highly developed than the other, probably because of its longer history. Thus, economic statics may be said to have originated with Cournot's *Theory of Wealth* in 1838, while economic dynamics is essentially a development of the present century.

It soon became apparent to the author that some extensive coordination of the material on time series was necessary before the second part of the book could be completed satisfactorily. It was necessary, therefore, to interrupt the writing of the present volume and to prepare a second work on the subject of economic dynamics. This work, *The Analysis of Economic Time Series,* is now completed and available as a monograph of the Cowles Commission for Research in Economics. The author has borrowed heavily from the material in this treatise. Much of the analysis and many of the charts have been reproduced in the present work. Since *The Analysis of Economic Time Series,* however, was written as a treatise, and the present volume as a text, the material in the latter has been treated less completely as to its details and the reader is referred to the larger work for a more extensive analysis of some of the problems.

In the course of writing the present book the author has become indebted to many people. Among these particularly to be mentioned is Mr. Alfred Cowles, president of the Cowles Commission for Research in Economics, who put the laboratory and other facilities of the Commission at the disposal of the author, and also gave him encouragement in other ways to carry on the work.

All of the charts in the present volume which are reproduced from *The Analysis of Economic Time Series* were done under the careful supervision of D. H. Leavens, of the Cowles Commission. In checking certain parts of the proof, and in many other ways, the author has found himself especially indebted to Mr. Leavens. The laboratory staff of the Cowles Commission also has been indispensable in many details of the work. Forrest Danson and Miss Emma Manning made numerous computations for the examples used in the book. Miss Kathryn Withers assisted in the preparation of the charts and Miss Mary Jo Lawley helped in the preparation of the manuscript for the press.

To Professor Gerhard Tintner of Iowa State College the author is particularly indebted. Professor Tintner has read the proof in its entirety and has made many very useful suggestions. His wide acquaintance with the literature of economics has made his criticism of the material of great value.

The author has also received many suggestions from Dr. C. F. Roos, former research director of the Cowles Commission, and from Professor T. O. Yntema, the present research director. The published works of both of them have been frequently consulted. The manuscript has been read also in part by Professor Francis McIntyre, Dr. J. Marschak, and Dr. Victor Smith, all of whom have made valuable critical contributions to the work.

In connection with some of the most difficult parts of the analysis of time series the author is indebted especially to Professor Ragnar Frisch of Oslo, Norway, to Dr. A. Wald, and to Herbert E. Jones, research associate of the Cowles Commission. The latter, in particular, contributed essentially to the theory of serial correlation as it is presented in this book.

During the course of the preparation of the manuscript the author moved to Northwestern University. A new statistical laboratory was made available to him for his work and this has been of great value in carrying out many of the computations in the book. The author wishes to express his appreciation to Professor E. J. Moulton, and, to others in the administrative staff who have made this laboratory possible.

Many students have assisted in computations in various parts of the book. The drawings not taken from *The Analysis of Economic Time Series* were made by Miss Vera Fisher, who also prepared an earlier mimeographed edition of the work.

Parts of the manuscript have been examined also by visitors to the annual conferences of the Cowles Commission in Colorado Springs and the critical advice from many of these has been very helpful. During the course of these conferences the author listened to some 200 lectures covering nearly every phase of economic activity. To a certain extent the present work is an attempt by the author to put in systematic form the ideas gathered during the course of this exceptional experience.

In conclusion the author must extend his thanks to the Principia Press, and to its editor, Professor J. R. Kantor, from whom he has received courtesies too numerous to mention. The manuscript has been put in type by the Dentan Printing Company of Colorado Springs, who, as usual, have made the task of producing the book a pleasure instead of a burden.

H. T. DAVIS.

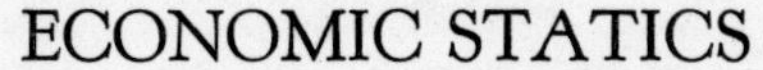

ECONOMIC STATICS

CHAPTER 1

PRELIMINARY CONCEPTS

1. Economics and Human Welfare

Economics may be defined as that field of knowledge which investigates the laws of the production, distribution, and consumption of goods. At first sight it might appear from this definition that economics is a branch of engineering and, therefore, the subject might be approached entirely from a study of the behavior of material things. Since engineering has reached a high degree of perfection, one might then be led to assume that the science of economics has attained a similar perfection. But observation of the devastating crises which so often engulf communities and nations shows too clearly how slight a control we have of the forces of economics.

There exists a human side to the problem which makes it difficult to state precisely the laws of economics. The vagaries of human beings, both as individuals and as collections of individuals, are reflected in the variations that are seen day by day, month by month, and year by year in the indexes which measure price, production, interest rates, volume of sales, etc. Economics is thus regarded by many as a study of human wants and satisfactions as these relate to the production, distribution, and consumption of goods. Thus we find that Alfred Marshall (1842–1924) in the beginning of his *Principles of Economics* states: "Political economy or economics is a study of mankind in the ordinary business of life; it examines that part of individual and social action which is most closely connected with the attainment and with the use of the material requisites of well being. Thus it is on the one side a study of wealth; and on the other, and more important side, a part of the study of man." This human aspect of the study will appear in many places in the book.

Since economics thus appears to be a study of human wants and satisfactions, the question naturally arises as to the tools which shall be used in exploring the problems of this science and the form in which the laws shall be stated. One is met by the insistent observation of some economists that the erratic element in economic studies finds its origin in the erratic psychology of human beings and that this element is not amenable to exact measurement. Structure which is observed in certain economic time series over one period may be submerged in another period by an unaccountable caprice of human behavior. The phenomenon of the great bull market, which began in 1926 and culminated in 1929, is an example in point. The memory is still vivid of the destruction which this catastrophic event caused to numerous theories of economic behavior. No indication of the imminence of this great inflation is to be found in the structure of the economic time series in the years prior to 1926. The phenomenon was clearly monetary in its origin, since its most striking characteristic was an abnormal increase in the velocity of money. But the causes which led to the observed velocity must be sought for in the obscure realm of human behavior.

Since economics must thus be regarded as the study of man himself in relation to his wants and satisfactions, it seems important to take this point of view as a fundamental one in establishing the postulates of the theory of economic behavior. Such a basis is found in the concept of utility, which will be more fully developed in a later chapter. By the utility of a group of things we shall mean, in a technical sense, the pleasure which their possession and use occasions. Similarly, we shall mean by *disutility* the lack of pleasure, or the dissatisfaction, caused by the possession of a group of things. Work is regarded in economics as an example of a disutility; the reason why things are made, one may argue, is because the use of them causes more satisfaction than the work necessary to create them occasions dissatisfaction.

By thus employing the concepts of utility and disutility, it will be possible to relate in a most intimate manner the cause of things in the material world with the people who employ them. On the other hand, the principal disadvantage of creating a theory of economics on the basis of these concepts is found in the great difficulty encountered in measuring them. Units of satisfaction and dissatisfaction have never been defined, and in some discussions it will be necessary to attain exact calculations only by the use of indirect methods.

2. Measurement in Economics

In this book we shall adopt the hypothesis that the phenomena of economics, as they apply to sufficiently large collections of individuals, are amenable to measurement. When we say this we do not mean that the measurement is as exact as that found in the physical sciences, but merely that there exist determinate values which may be ascertained within definite limits of error.

The reason for this hypothesis goes back to a dictum by Lord Kelvin (1824–1907), which should always be kept in mind by those who would bring a set of concepts within the domain of Science. Thus Lord Kelvin affirmed: "I often say that when you can measure what you are speaking about, and express it in numbers, you know something about it; but when you cannot measure it, when you cannot express it in numbers, your knowledge is of a meager and unsatisfactory kind."[1] In so far, therefore, as we shall fail to clothe our ideas in exact mathematical form, our subject will fail to attain the strict requirements of science. It is for this reason that we have adopted the word *econometrics*, rather than economics, for those concepts of human behavior, as such behavior relates to the use and enjoyment of goods, when they have been put into mathematical form and subjected to the test of statistical data.

A second assumption that will be made in this book affirms that there exists for the phenomena of economics a structural relationship. That is to say, the activity of large groups of people in relation to their wants and satisfactions is not indeterminate and random. Underlying the vagaries of individual human action there is a trend and structure for the activity of the group. It is the purpose of econometrics to ascertain and to formulate this relationship in precise mathematical language.

Alfred Marshall (1842–1924), who, although not essentially a mathematician, knew the value of mathematics in scientific argument and used it as occasion arose, has put the matter thus:

> The chief use of pure mathematics in economic questions seems to be in helping a person to write down quickly, shortly, and exactly, some of his thoughts for his own use; and to make sure that he has enough, and only enough, premises for his conclusions.

Antoine Augustin Cournot (1801–1877), who may be said to have initiated mathematical economics in his celebrated volume published in France in 1838, *Researches into the Mathematical Principles of the Theory of Wealth,* states the following proposition:

> I have said that most authors who have devoted themselves to political economy seem also to have a wrong idea of the nature of the applications of mathematical analysis to the theory of wealth. They imagine that the use of symbols and formulas could only lead to numerical calculations, and as it was clearly perceived that the subject was not suited to such a numerical determination of values by means of theory alone, the conclusion was drawn that the mathematical apparatus, if not liable to lead to erroneous results, was at least idle and pedantic. But those skilled in mathematical analysis know that its object is not simply to calculate numbers, but that it is also employed to find the relations between mag-

---

[1] *Popular Lectures and Addresses by Lord Kelvin,* London, 1889, Vol. 1, p. 73. See also *The Life of Lord Kelvin,* by S. P. Thompson, 1910, Vol. 2, p. 792.

nitudes which cannot be expressed in numbers and between *functions* whose law is not capable of algebraic expression. Thus the theory of probabilities furnishes a demonstration of very important propositions, although, without the help of experience, it is impossible to give numerical values for contingent events, except in questions of mere curiosity, such as arise from certain games of chance. Thus, also, theoretical Mechanics furnishes to practical Mechanics general theorems of most useful application, although in almost all cases recourse to experience is necessary for the numerical results which practice requires.

The employment of mathematical symbols is perfectly natural when the relations between magnitudes are under discussion; and even if they are not rigorously necessary, it would hardly be reasonable to reject them, because they are not equally familiar to all readers and because they have sometimes been wrongly used, if they are able to facilitate the exposition of problems, to render it more concise, to open the way to more extended developments, and to avoid the digressions of vague argumentation.

The use of mathematical methods in economics is today supplemented by a tool which was not available to Cournot and, indeed, was scarcely available in any modern sense before the beginning of the present century. This tool is the collection of statistical data, which has been assembled by many agencies and which affords an opportunity for the numerical verification of economic postulates. Simultaneously with the collection of data there has been developed a very extensive and adequate theory of statistics.

3. The Role of Postulates in Economics

In some disciplines of knowledge which do not pretend to have a scientific background, one not infrequently hears discussions about the *truth* of certain propositions. But more scientific fields, particularly in recent years, have come to recognize that truth, if it exists at all, is an elusive entity and difficult to find. Propositions which were believed to be completely valid in one period of scientific development, have sometimes been replaced by others, or have been modified in some essential particular by the discovery of new facts.

Because of this *relativity of truth,* science today is largely formulated in terms of postulates, that is to say, affirmations which are to be assumed as temporary propositions that account for existing facts, or which may be admitted as the basis of further argument. Newton's law of gravitation is an example of a postulate which has played a long and conspicuous part in the history of physics and astronomy. The statement that it is a postulate, and not an absolute truth or law of nature, has been strikingly revealed in recent years by the modifications, both in fact and theory, which have been imposed upon the law by Einstein's theory of relativity.

The empirical nature of scientific truth often comes as something of a shock to those uninitiated in the history of science. This point of view, which we might call scientific empiricism, is often attained by them only after a considerable struggle with the basic concepts of some scientific discipline. Mathematics was one of the first sciences to recognize this postulational approach to knowledge, the first notable example being found in the subject of geometry. It is instructive to give a brief résumé of the history of this example.

In Euclid's *Elements,* written between 330 and 320 B. C., the statement is made that through a point external to a given straight line only one parallel to the given line can be drawn. Although numerous attempts were made to *prove* the *truth* of this statement, it was not until the early years of the nineteenth century that the conclusion was reached that the statement could not be proved. This remarkable idea seemed to occur almost simultaneously in various parts of the mathematical world, to K. F. Gauss (1777–1855) in Germany, to N. Lobatschevski (1793–1856) in Russia, and to W. Bolyai (1775–1856) in Transylvania. As a consequence a new non-Euclidean geometry was created which affirmed the postulate that through a point external to a given line not one but many parallel lines can be drawn to the given line. Later G. F. B. Riemann (1826–1866) indicated that a third possibility existed and that another geometry, now commonly referred to as Riemannian, could be constructed on the postulate that no line could be drawn through the given point parallel to the given line.

The interest for us in this example is found in its indication of the necessity of a postulational form for the statement of scientific laws. Thus also in economics we must formulate the basic principles in terms of postulates, not as inevitable truths of human action, but as statements which conform to the existing facts. Then, if new observations of economic data are at variance with the laws which we have formulated, these statements or postulates may be changed without the fear that we are modifying fundamental truths. In other words, the use of the postulational method gives a sort of elasticity to scientific reason. This is particularly valuable in the early stages of of a science, where new facts may necessitate the frequent modification of existing theories.

As an example of the application of the postulational method the reader is referred to the next chapter in which the distribution of income in a large economic system is studied. This distribution will be found to vary greatly from what one would expect it to be on the ordinary assumption that the distribution is due to chance. Obviously some theoretical formulation of the curve of income is required, and this must be stated in postulational form. It is also important to have some theory to account for the theoretical pattern, and this again requires assumptions which must lead by mathematical reasoning to the postulated curve. Once such a theory has been formulated, scientific inquiry must be directed to the question of the reasonableness and consistency of the system which has been constructed.

4. *Economic Statics*

The phenomena of economics have long been recognized as possessing characteristics similar to those observed in the phenomena of mechanics. This does not mean merely that an analogy exists between these two branches of knowledge so remote in essential character from one another. Rather we observe that the mathematical theory which formulates the data of one discipline is similar in character to that which formulates the other. The same mathematical equations appear and the consequence of this is that the same mathematical functions will describe the behavior of essentially different and unrelated phenomena.

Irving Fisher, in his classical essay *Mathematical Investigations in the Theory of Value and Prices,* written under the stimulus of Josiah Williard Gibbs (1839–1903) and published in 1892, gave a table of mechanical analogies, which has been very suggestive in directing attention to the possibilities of constructing a dynamics of economics. We reproduce an abbreviation of the table which Fisher suggested:

In mechanics	*In economics*
A particle	An individual
Space	Commodity space
Force	Marginal utility
Work	Disutility
Energy	Utility
Total work	Total disutility, or the integral of marginal disutility
Total energy	Total utility, or the integral of marginal utility
Net energy	Net utility
Equilibrium of forces	Equilibrium of utility

One frequently hears the objection that by following the model of physics, such as is implied by the above table of correspondences, we are dealing with invalid analogies, but this objection can be refuted on two grounds. The first is that all applications of interpretive methods to physical phenomena are themselves at heart logical *isomorph-*

isms. Thus the differential equation

$$\frac{d^2u}{dt^2} + k^2u = 0 \ ,$$

which describes the motion of a swinging pendulum, is a mathematical abstraction which is finally justified by the fact that the values of u are highly correlated with the measurements of the physical displacements of the bob over an interval of time.

On the empirical assumption that isomorphisms are given validity only by final reference to data, we are justified in following the model of mechanics, thermodynamics, or any other physical discipline, provided only that the isomorphism is established by the stubborn facts of statistical verification.

The second argument, which seems to refute the charge of dealing with invalid analogies, is found in the observation that all sciences, when they reach the stage which justifies an attempt at mathematical formulation, seek in some manner to find what we may call the *extremal conditions* which characterize their data. Something is either to be maximized or minimized in the complex of defined concepts which differentiate one science from another. Since the mathematical theory of extremals is a unique theory, whether it be applied to point functions or to such functionals as appear in the calculus of variations, it is but natural that the equations of one science should bear a close resemblance to those of another.

As an example, let us cite the profit integral which we shall discuss at greater length later in the book. This integral is defined as follows:

$$\Pi = \int_{t_0}^{t_1} [y(t)\, p(t) - Q(u)]\, dt \ ,$$

where $y(t)$ is the amount of some commodity purchased at price $p(t)$, and $Q(u)$ is the cost of manufacturing and marketing u units. One theory of economics assumes that business men are always seeking to maximize this integral. But mathematically the method of maximizing the profit integral introduces the same concepts in economics as the minimizing of the action integral introduces in the theory of mechanics. One might then be inclined to say than an analogy exists, whereas the fact is merely that the two disciplines are unified by a common mathematical process.[2]

In this book, then, we shall find it useful to follow somewhat the tradition of mechanics, a subject which has been divided conveniently

[2] See the author's article: "Mathematical Adventures in Social Science," *American Mathematical Monthly*, Vol. 44, 1938, pp. 93–104.

into the two branches of *statics* and *dynamics*. As the first of these words implies, the theory of statics deals with problems of equilibrium, wherein the variations occasioned by the flow of time are not considered. On the other hand, the theory of dynamics treats of the motion of bodies (kinematics) and the action of forces which produce changes in the motion (kinetics). Thus we see that dynamics is essentially a theory of the variations which take place in time. As one might surmise, there is considerable interrelationship between statics and dynamics, although, for the most part, problems belonging to one of these disciplines are easily recognized from those belonging to the other.

In the following pages we shall endeavor to make a similar division of the subject of economics into two parts, namely, *economic statics* and *economic dynamics.* Problems in economic statics are problems connected with equilibrium conditions, which do not involve essentially variations in the time variable. On the other hand, economic phenomena which depend upon their sequence in time, such for example as those found in the theory of business cycles, are to be regarded as belonging to economic dynamics.

As an example of a problem in economic statics, let us consider the relationship between price and demand as it has been considered in classical economics. One observes readily that as a general thing demand will vary inversely with prices. That is to say, certain commodities will be purchased in greater amounts when prices are low than when prices are high. Theoretically the curve of this variation, or the functional relationship between the amount demanded and the price, is a reasonably permanent structure of the economic system, varying little with time. It may be regarded as a static relationship. Unfortunately the actual construction of a curve of demand is difficult to accomplish since the data available for this purpose come to us in the form of a time sequence. The ingenuity of scientific workers in this field has been devoted to the problem of eliminating the influence of the time variable from the desired static relationship between the amount demanded and the price.

Other problems in economic statics may be mentioned. For example, the distribution of incomes in an economy, that is to say, the number of people in each income class, is a reasonably permanent pattern and may be described by a curve which depends little upon the variable of time. The theory of pure exchange between buyers and sellers in a market depends upon the curves of supply and demand and consequently is a theory of economic statics. Similarly, the concept of utility is independent of time and can be characterized fully by consumer preferences. Although the problems of monopoly and duopoly, and the related problems of production, may change from one period to another, the classical theory of these domains of economics are formulated on the assumption that the patterns of purchasing and selling behavior remain invariant with respect to the variable of time.

Family budgets may change from year to year, but it is reasonable to assume that the annual expenditures of families at different levels of incomes will vary little with the business cycle. Incomes of individuals may change with time, and there is a constant contraction or expansion in the spending habits of most families as the vicissitudes of fortune redistribute the annual incomes, but it is probably true that the pattern of expenditure for different levels remains invariant. It is thus apparent that the problem of family budgets is a problem in economic statics.

As a general proposition, we may then affirm that those problems which are concerned with equilibrium in the economy, that is to say, problems which may be described in terms of mathematical models that do not introduce the variable of time, belong to the domain of economic statics. One of the most general of such theories is the concept of equilibrium introduced by Léon Walras (1834–1910) in his classical treatise entitled *Elements d'économie politique pure ou théorie de la richesse sociale,* (1874), the fifth edition of which appeared in 1926. This equilibrium theory of economics was later the basis of much of the thought of Vilfredo Pareto (1848–1923), who somewhat extended the concepts of Walras. Trained as an engineer, Pareto's thesis had been a study of the mathematical theory of the equilibrium of elastic bodies and one of his major contributions to knowledge was his extension of this subject to the social sciences.

5. *Time Series*

For the most part any system of dynamics applicable to economics must be a theory which accounts for the changes observed in economic time series. It is necessary, therefore, to acquire some appreciation of the meaning and significance of the problems associated with such series.

By a *time series* in economics we shall mean a set of data relating to some economic variable which has been arranged in a sequence of time, as, for example,

$$y_1, y_2, y_3, \cdots, y_t, \cdots,$$

where the subscripts refer to units of time. These intervals may be days, weeks, months, or years, depending upon the phenomenon that is being investigated. It is unusual to consider intervals smaller than days, although the behavior of prices in the stock market has been recorded in units as short as 20 minutes. It is also unusual to have intervals greater than a year, although in studies of long secular movements, ten-year averages have been employed, since such averages tend to smooth out the shorter and often inconsequential variations of the data.

It will be convenient occasionally to regard the data as continuous in time. In this case the time sequence is replaced by the functional notation

$$y = y(t) ,$$

where t is regarded as a continuous variable over some specified range $(t_0 \leqq t \leqq t_1)$.

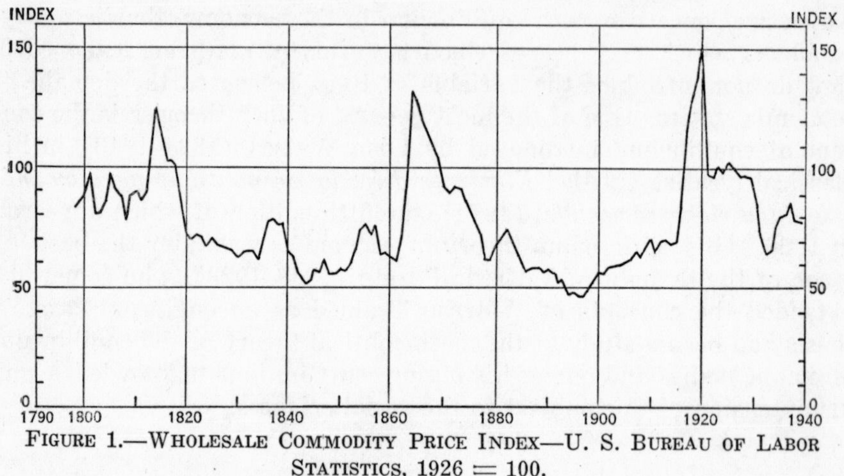

FIGURE 1.—WHOLESALE COMMODITY PRICE INDEX—U. S. BUREAU OF LABOR STATISTICS, 1926 = 100.

For an example of a characteristic time series in economics, the student is referred to Figure 1, which shows the behavior of the wholesale commodity index over the period from 1797 to 1940. This is one of the longest series available to us and the variations in it are connected with some of the most dramatic events in American history. The effect of the War of 1812, the Civil War, and the first World War are clearly revealed by the inflationary peaks of 1814, 1864, and 1920. The period of wildcat speculation which marked the administration of Andrew Jackson from 1829 to 1837 was followed by the period of panic in 1843. The long deflation which followed the Civil War finally terminated in the depression of 1893–1896. We also observe the spectacular decline in prices in 1920, which so violently disturbed our agricultural economy, and the second dramatic deflation, that characterized the depression which began in 1929 and reached its bottom in 1932. It is not our purpose here to discuss the economic aspects of this instructive series, but merely to give an example which exhibits many of the characteristics of the data to be studied in economic dynamics.

The variables useful in representing economic phenomena are frequently expressed as index numbers. By an *index number* we shall mean a value, generally expressed as a percentage, which is designed to indicate the level at any given date of the items of a time series. For example, if we say that the level of wholesale prices in 1939 was 70, when the level of prices of 1926 was 100, we mean that on the average the prices of the first year were 70% of the prices of the second. This does not mean that all prices in 1939 were 70% of all prices in 1926, but that the average prices had this relationship to one another.

The theory of the construction of index numbers will be deferred to a later chapter, but it is sufficient for our present purpose to note their use in connection with economic time series. Although index numbers are applied to various economic variables, their greatest use is in connection with prices.

In spite of the fact that time series are of fundamental importance in the discussion of many phenomena in economics, their availability is of comparatively recent origin. Early economists were sadly hampered in their work by the scarcity of good data. It may be fairly stated that competent series were almost non-existent before the beginning of the twentieth century, and the relatively slow development of a realistic understanding of the working of economic laws is to be attributed to the fact that good data have been available for only a few years. Today, however, numerous agencies have been developed for the collection of data and many of our series have been extended over intervals as long as a century.

6. *Economic Dynamics*

By the term *economic dynamics* we shall mean that branch of economics which treats of the variation in economic time series (economic kinematics), and the nature of the forces which produce these observed variations (economic kinetics).

We shall mention briefly a few of the problems which belong essentially to economic dynamics. The first of these is the theory of the growth of population upon which depends the growth of many of the time series especially important to general economic well-being. As the population grows so also must increase the production of agriculture and the industrial capacities of the nation. Otherwise prevailing standards of living cannot be maintained. An adequate theory of these phenomena is essential to an understanding of the basic economics of a country. In Figure 2 we find represented the Standard Statistics index of industrial production in the United States. We observe the steady growth of industry from 1885 to its peak value in

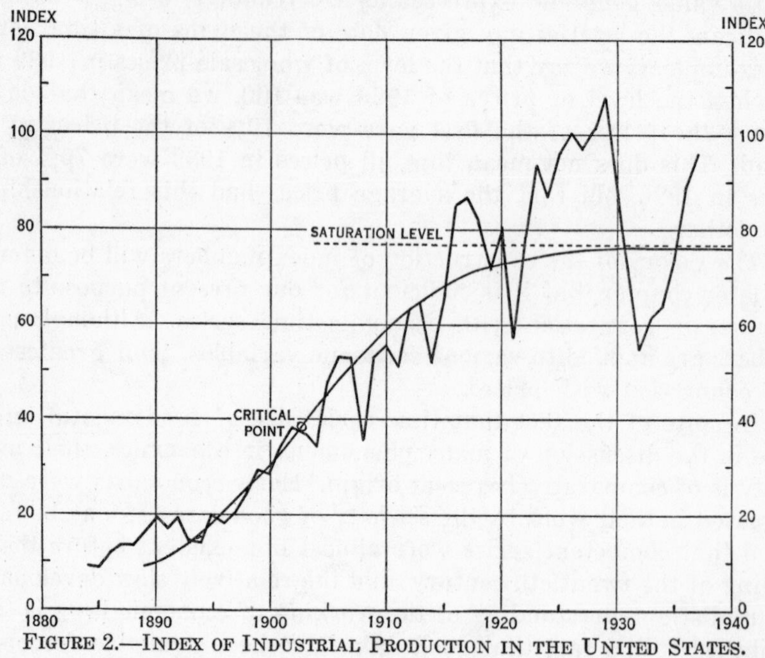

FIGURE 2.—INDEX OF INDUSTRIAL PRODUCTION IN THE UNITED STATES.

1929, then the effect of the depression years which followed, and finally the apparent leveling-off as production reached maturity in the United States. This phenomenon of growth, from origin to maturity, which we shall designate as *logistic* in character from the mathematical curve used to describe it, is typical of both population and production. An adequate discussion of the phenomenon involves a dynamical theory, which we shall describe in detail in a later chapter.

A large body of literature has grown up around the subject of *business cycles,* a term applied to the more or less periodic alternations of business between prosperity and depression. As an example of what is meant by such movements, let us consider Figure 3, which shows the Cowles Commission-Standard Statistics index of industrial stock prices from 1871 to 1938.

In this series we note first the existence of a *secular trend*, that is to say, a persistent tendency for stock prices to advance throughout the period under observation. This tendency, called by Carl Snyder the *inertia* of economic series, is not always positive, nor is it represented always by a straight line. In the second place, we observe a more or less regular oscillatory movement of the index about the line

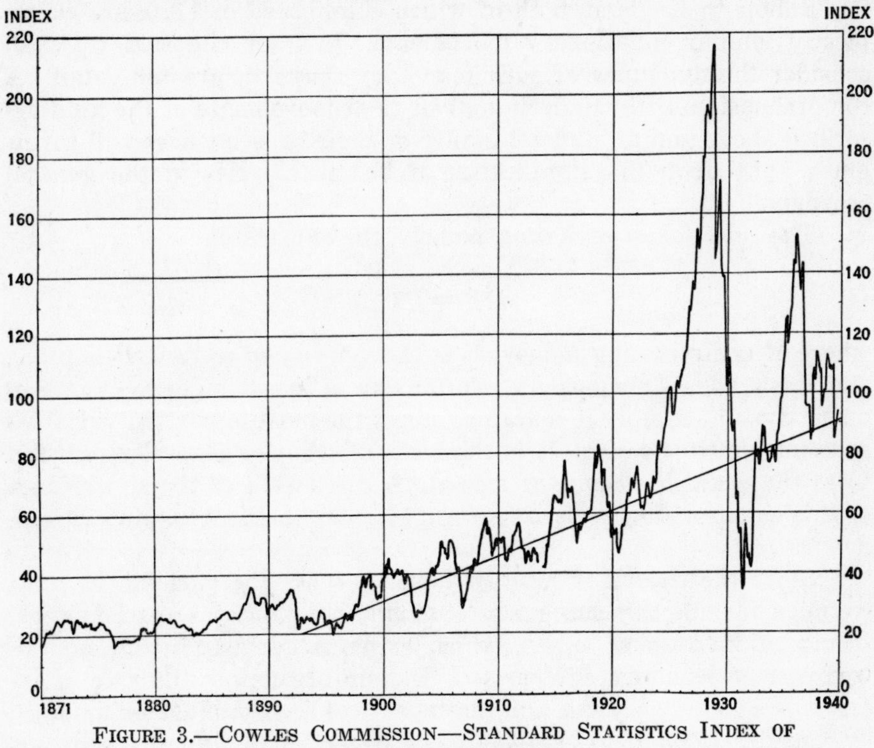

FIGURE 3.—COWLES COMMISSION—STANDARD STATISTICS INDEX OF INDUSTRIAL STOCK PRICES.

of trend over the years from 1895 to 1925. These variations from prosperity to depression and back again are measures of the normal cycle of business, which, it will be observed in the period under discussion, had an average length of approximately 40 months. This fairly periodic movement is commonly referred to as the 40-month cycle.

In the period around the year 1926 we observe the origin of an extraordinary phenomenon, which is now referred to as the *great bull market*, namely an inflationary movement which carried the industrial stock market indexes from an average value of about 70 to the unprecedented value of approximately 215. The subsequent collapse of values reduced the indexes to the exceedingly low figure of 30 in the depression years of 1932 and 1933. Although these abnormal inflationary and deflationary movements are comparatively rare in economic history, they carry with them dramatic consequences. The tulip mania, which swept Holland in 1637, and the two contemporary phenomena known as the Mississippi Scheme in France and the South Sea Bubble in England, both of which culminated in 1720, are examples of similar inflationary movements. In later chapters we shall consider the dynamics of such monetary crises in greater detail. A comprehension of the underlying causes of movements of the kind described above and an understanding of their consequences will throw much light upon the significance of business cycles in the general economy.

The *equation of exchange,* namely, the expression

$$MV = PT ,$$

where M is circulating money, V is the velocity of money, P is price, and T is trade, is obviously a relationship of great importance in economic dynamics, since it contains four of the most important variables in economic time series. It is the basis of what is generally referred to as the *quantity theory of money.* A discussion of the significance of this equation forms an important chapter in the dynamics of economics.

Since the theory of interest depends upon the variable of time, we must include this subject in economic dynamics. A mathematical theory of investment exists, which explains adequately the capitalized cost of economic enterprises. But unfortunately the rate of interest is seldom constant, and mathematical models must be modified by considerations of the economic consequences of a fluctuating market for money. These problems will be considered in some detail later in the book.

Closely related to the theory of interest and investment is the problem of insurance. Here also there exists a satisfactory mathematical theory, partly empirical in character where it depends upon statistical tables of experience, and partly mathematical where it depends upon the computation of values under a fixed rate of interest. But in this problem, as in all others which depend upon the changing patterns of economic time series, there intrude considerations of a strictly dynamical character as we shall indicate in a later chapter.

Among other topics in economic dynamics we find the problems of supply and demand as they depend upon changes in the level of prices. Closely related to them we meet the problem of international trade, which is connected in an intimate manner with the ebb and flow of economic variables.

Economic dynamics is by no means so thoroughly developed as the subject of economic statics, a proposition that may be readily surmised from a casual survey of the graphs of the time series which we have exhibited in this chapter. But out of the large number of variables that have been investigated in recent years, a few dominating ones have been found, which appear to carry with them most of the important variations of the economic system. Hence there exists real confidence that further study of the phenomena of time series will ultimately create a thoroughly satisfactory theory of economic dynamics.

PROBLEMS

1. Represent graphically some set of economic data over the period from 1900 to 1910. Do you observe movements which could be described as cyclical? How would you characterize the trend?

2. Graph some economic time series over the period from 1920 to 1930. What characteristic features do you observe in the series?

3. Represent graphically some set of economic data from 1930 to 1940. Compare the characteristic movements of this period with those of the periods covered in problems 1 and 2.

4. The following table gives the index numbers (Base = 1716–17) of commodity prices in Paris during the John Law expansion called the Mississippi Scheme. Graph these data, which are taken from E. J. Hamilton, "Prices and Wages at Paris under John Law's System," *The Quarterly Journal of Economics*, Vol. 51, 1936, pp. 42–70. Compare the French expansion with our own in the period around 1929.

Year	Jan.	Feb.	Mar.	April	May	June	July	Aug.	Sept.	Oct.	Nov.	Dec.
1711	123.2	114.4	115.1	108.7	111.1	105.8	104.0	115.6	113.3	111.9	112.0	124.6
1712	134.9	133.5	126.5	131.1	124.3	125.5	126.1	118.7	128.6	127.5	142.6	141.3
1713	146.9	147.4	138.6	142.2	137.7	137.7	138.4	144.1	139.7	139.1	154.6	159.7
1714	163.7	165.2	168.1	154.7	149.3	141.5	145.8	146.8	155.3	149.0	150.6	148.4
1715	139.6	128.4	123.3	118.9	113.4	115.5	106.3	106.2	108.7	108.9	104.2	104.5
1716	102.7	102.9	100.1	101.6	100.7	99.4	98.1	94.6	99.7	107.5	107.6	105.5
1717	105.8	104.4	100.3	100.9	98.0	98.6	96.0	95.5	93.7	93.4	94.7	95.9
1718	96.0	97.6	93.8	90.6	92.7	92.3	96.8	102.9	100.6	107.5	109.4	112.1
1719	111.6	114.3	107.5	109.0	106.9	111.7	116.1	119.7	124.9	120.1	129.3	136.3
1720	171.1	171.1	180.4	191.2	189.7	183.8	190.6	190.5	203.7	199.6	198.8	164.2
1721	162.8	149.4	142.6	137.6	130.1	132.3	124.9	133.4	136.0	134.5	133.0	137.2
1722	140.7	136.6	139.2	149.1	139.7	136.6	134.4	138.7	143.8	151.8	153.5	160.0
1723	161.7	156.8	151.4	156.7	163.9	156.3	156.6	159.5	163.0	174.8	175.2	180.4
1724	181.8	178.9	166.9	171.9	162.9	149.5	142.8	144.5	152.0	159.4	163.3	169.0
1725	169.7	161.4	163.7	151.1	146.6	144.1	147.0	144.6	164.2	159.4	155.7	158.0

5. Make a list of ten economic variables and discuss from your personal knowledge the characteristic behavior of two of them.

6. The following two postulates, quoted from R. D. Carmichael's *The Logic of Discovery*, Chicago, 1930, p. 102, are attributed to J. Rueff, who makes them basic in the theory of economics as developed in his book, "*Des sciences physiques aux sciences morales*, Paris, 1922:

"I. The need which we have for certain merchandise decreases when the quantity which we have of it increases.

"II. Each individual possesses wealth in a finite quantity and seeks by means of exchanges to acquire wealth in different objects in such a way as to bring to a maximum the sum of the respective utilities of the various sorts of things which he comes to possess."

Discuss this system of postulates. Would you make any additions or modifications in it? Does it seem to be sufficient to account for all economic behavior?

7. The logic of Aristotle is founded essentially upon the following three postulates:

(1) The postulate of identity: "A is A". (2) The postulate of contradiction: "A is B" and "A is not B" cannot hold simultaneously. (3) The postulate of the excluded middle: Of the two propositions "A is B" and "A is not B", one must hold irrespective of the nature of A and B.

Are these self evident truths? Can you think of any exceptions to the third postulate? Non-aristotelean logics have been recently constructed and discussed. Are such logics *illogical?*

8. Is the subject of mechanics an experimental or a deductive science? Discuss. How is force defined? Is this definition empirical, or a logical necessity?

9. The solution of the differential equation

$$\frac{d^2y}{dt^2} + b\frac{dy}{dt} + cy = 0$$

is given by the function

$$y = Ae^{rt} + Be^{st},$$

where A and B are arbitrary constants, and where r and s are roots of the equation:

$$r^2 + br + c = 0 .$$

Discuss this solution when $b = 0$, for the following cases: (1) c is positive; (2) c is negative; (3) $c = 0$.

10. If in problem 9 the variable y describes the movement of some economic time series, which would you say from an observation of the graphs of economic data would be the most realistic case among the three cases given above?

11. In problem 9, if b is not zero, what would be the most probable sign for this constant, if y is to describe the movement of an economic time series?

12. How should one proceed to test the validity of the proposition that business men seek to maximize profits? Do you believe that business attemps to maximize the profit integral, or merely the profit function, namely, $\pi = yp - Q(u)$? What is the difference between these problems?

CHAPTER 2.

The Nature of Wealth and Income

1. The Nature of Wealth

At the basis of our economic system lies the concept of wealth. Although one at first thought would assume that the wealth of a man consisted of his possessions in material goods, it is clear that this definition is too restrictive in some respects. The possession of unproductive land or the ownership of property whose present or expected yield is less than the cost of maintenance, are liabilities difficult to construe as wealth. On the other hand, the possession of a special ability may earn a good livelihood for the possessor, and a computation of the present value of the income which may be derived from it shows that it is convertible into material goods and hence into material wealth. Much wealth is also psychic in its character as, for example, the value that is given to paintings, jewelry, and other possessions which have little material usefulness.

We shall define wealth to be all "consumable utilities, which require labor for their production and can be appropriated and exchanged." It is clear that this definition is sufficiently broad to include the wealth which is psychic in its character, as well as the wealth of material possession. It excludes the natural wealth which all of us possess in the free benefits of nature, since this, not being the product of labor, is scarcely to be regarded as part of the subject matter of economics.

Since further classification is desirable in arguments about wealth, it will be useful to consider wealth as consisting of *goods,* the word being used in a general sense, which are of two categories. Thus we have, in the first place, goods which are material and external, and, in the second place, goods which are personal. Material goods may also be subdivided into two classes, namely, those which are transferable, and those which are not transferable. Personal goods are of two classes also, one being external and the other internal. External goods may be either transferable or not transferable, but internal goods may never be transferred.

Marshall, adopting the ideas of earlier economists, has also defined goods as belonging to different orders.[1] For example, *goods of*

[1] See his *Principles of Economics.*

the first order are those which satisfy wants directly, such as food, clothing, dwellings, etc. Such goods are conveniently designated as *consumer's goods. Goods of the second order* are those which contribute to the manufacture of consumers' goods. For example, farms, which produce food, factories which make clothing, lumber mills which contribute to the construction of dwellings, are goods of second order. In the field of psychic wealth we would classify the possession of a voice for singing as a good of first order. The conservatory which trains the voice would be classified under the category of goods of the second order. It is clear that *goods of third order* would be those which contribute to the manufacture of goods of the second order; *goods of the fourth order* those which contribute to the creation of goods of the third order, etc. It is convenient to refer to goods of second and higher orders as *production or producers' goods.* They are also commonly designated as *capital goods.*

The word *capital* has been introduced into economics to designate that part of wealth which has been reserved to increase wealth. Capital thus is almost synonymous with what we have called producers' goods, since it is only through producers' goods that wealth may be created.

It is rather difficult to estimate the actual value of wealth and consequently much more attention has been paid to the statistics of income. However, certain approximations have been made for the wealth of the United States for the years from 1912 to 1935. In the table which gives these estimates there is also shown the ratio of wealth to annual income and the ratio of annual income to wealth. The second coefficient might be called the *efficiency of wealth,* since it measures the power of wealth to produce income.[2]

Year	Wealth in Billions of Dollars	Ratio of Wealth to Income	Ratio of Income to Wealth	Year	Wealth in Billions of Dollars	Ratio of Wealth to Income	Ratio of Income to Wealth
1912	186.3	5.86	0.171	1924	337.9	4.85	0.206
1913	192.5	5.71	0.175	1925	362.7	4.70	0.213
1914	192.0	6.00	0.167	1926	356.5	4.54	0.220
1915	200.2	5.80	0.172	1927	346.4	4.49	0.223
1916	251.6	5.69	0.176	1928	360.1	4.47	0.224
1917	351.7	6.61	0.151	1929	361.8	4.57	0.219
1918	400.5	6.65	0.150	1930	323.1	4.48	0.223
1919	431.0	6.40	0.156	1931	275.1	4.58	0.219
1920	488.7	6.58	0.150	1932	246.4	5.30	0.189
1921	317.2	6.03	0.166	1933	252.3	5.68	0.176
1922	320.8	5.20	0.192	1934	289.2	5.74	0.174
1923	339.9	4.87	0.205	1935	308.9	5.63	0.178

[2] The estimates of total wealth to 1930 are from the National Industrial Conference Board; thereafter from Standard Statistics, who modified the estimates to take account of the change in the price level.

In order that one may get a more precise idea as to exactly what is meant by wealth in this table, let us consider the distribution for 1922. This estimate was made by the United States Bureau of the Census, which allocated wealth to 21 separate categories as shown in the following table:

Type of Wealth	Value in Millions of Dollars	Per Cent of total	Type of Wealth	Value in Millions of Dollars	Per Cent of total
Real property taxed	155,909	48.60	Pipe lines	500	0.16
Real property exempt	20,506	6.39	Shipping canals	2,951	0.92
Livestock	5,807	1.81	Privately owned water works	361	0.11
Farm implements, etc.	2,605	0.81	Privately owned electric light and power	4,229	1.32
Gold and silver coins and bullion	4,278	1.33	Agricultural products	5,466	1.71
Manufactured machinery, tools, etc.	15,783	4.92	Manufactured products	28,423	8.86
Railroads and their equipment	19,951	6.22	Imported merchandise	1,549	0.48
Motor vehicles	4,567	1.42	Clothing, personal ornaments, furniture, etc.	39,816	12.41
Street railways	4,878	1.52	Other products	730	0.23
Telegraph systems	204	0.07			
Telephone systems	1,746	0.54			
Pullman and other private property not owned by railroads	545	0.17	Totals	320,804	100.00

There is no reason to believe that the percentages as given above have appreciably changed during the past few years.

2. *The Nature of Income*

The nature of income is not easily attained as one may see from the constant controversy that is waged over what is to be included in income-tax returns.[3] It will be sufficient for our purpose to define the income of an individual as that quantity of goods and services, measured in terms of a money unit, which he has received during some period of time as a result of the expenditure of disutility or the employment of capital during that time. It is customary to denote the first category of income as *wages and salaries* and the second category as the *return from investment.* The total income of all its citizens is known as the total income of the state.

Capital gains, that is to say, that part of the earnings of capital which is returned to capital, is not to be regarded as income. Capital gains increase the wealth of a country, but they do not increase the income until such time as they have been used or distributed.

[3] A very penetrating analysis of this problem has been given by Irving Fisher in his extensive monograph: "Income in Theory and Income Taxation in Practice," *Econometrica,* Vol. 5, 1937, pp. 1–55.

It will be seen readily that income may be estimated in two ways. The first and most obvious way would be to determine income from reports on income received by individuals. Such an estimate would be constructed from income-tax returns, from studies on the wages and salaries paid by corporations, schools, government bureaus, factories, etc., from the profits of agriculture, from fisheries, and from other similar enterprises.

In the last analysis, however, income can never be greater than the actual wealth produced. Hence we can also esimate income from the total value of goods and services produced in a given period of time. This estimate would be made from reports on the amount of raw materials which have been manufactured and transported, from the estimates of coal and metals which have been mined, from crop reports, from the production of the lumber industry, from the statistics of the building trades, and from similar data on other enterprises.

These estimates are naturally difficult to obtain with any degree of completeness and considerable error may be anticipated in arriving at the total income of a country from either of these methods. Comprehensive attempts, however, have been made to evaluate the income of the United States by both of these means and unusually consistent results have been attained.

The following figures on the income in the United States were obtained from estimates made by the National Industrial Conference Board,[4] the data for the years 1929–1935 being revisions by J. A.

Year	Income in Billions of Dollars	Population in Thousands	Per Capita Income in Dollars	Year	Income in Billions of Dollars	Population in Thousands	Per Capita Income in Dollars
1909	27.2	90,691	300	1924	69.6	112,079	615
1910	30.1	91,072	326	1925	77.1	114,867	671
1911	29.4	93,682	314	1926	78.5	116,532	674
1912	31.8	95,097	334	1927	77.2	118,197	653
1913	33.7	96,512	350	1928	80.5	119,861	671
1914	32.0	97,927	327	1929	79.1	121,526	651
1915	34.5	99,343	347	1930	72.2	122,775	588
1916	44.2	100,758	439	1931	60.1	124,070	484
1917	53.2	102,173	521	1932	46.5	124,822	373
1918	60.2	103,588	581	1933	44.4	125,693	353
1919	67.4	105,003	642	1934	50.4	126,425	399
1920	74.3	105,711	697	1935	54.9	127,172	432
1921	52.6	107,833	486	1936	62.4	128,429	486
1922	61.7	109,248	562	1937	67.8	129,257	525
1923	69.8	110,664	626	1938	64.2	130,215	493

[4] Except for the years 1936, 1937, and 1938, which are from the U. S. Department of Commerce.

Slaughter in his volume, *Income Received in the Various States 1929–1935,* New York City, 1937. These data are graphically shown in Figure 4.

But data on total income, however interesting they may be as indicators of the prosperity of a nation and of its relative economic importance, must be exhibited in terms of their partial origins in order to show the nature of income and the part which it plays in the well-

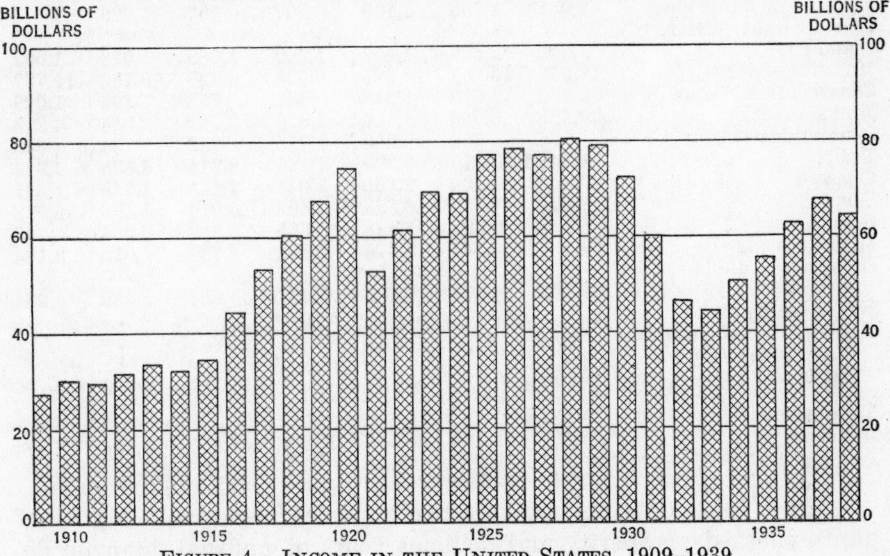

FIGURE 4.—INCOME IN THE UNITED STATES, 1909–1939.

being of groups in different social orders. The following table shows the distribution of the total income for the years 1929–1935 according to income types:

INCOME DISTRIBUTED ACCORDING TO TYPE*
Unit: Millions of Dollars

Type of Income	1929	1930	1931	1932	1933	1934	1935
Salaries and wages	50,611	46,201	38,643	29,752	27,858	31,225	34,223
Entrepreneurial income	13,118	11,277	8,955	6,712	7,018	8,127	9,247
Dividends	5,763	5,631	4,179	2,626	2,102	2,338	2,648
Interest	3,994	4,156	4,024	3,756	3,361	3,154	2,945
Net rents and royalties	1,188	884	618	448	473	589	693
Other accountable income	4,561	4,163	3,736	3,232	3,608	5,063	5,284
Net adjustment for international balance of payments of dividends and interest	—133	—127	— 37	— 20	— 31	— 69	— 96
Total accountable income	79,101	72,186	60,117	46,506	44,389	50,426	54,944

* This table is adapted from Slaughter, **op. cit.**, p. 5. The item "Other accountable income" includes pensions, compensation for injuries, interest on mortgages on owned homes, net rent of rented homes, relief payments, and governmental rental and benefit payments to farmers.

Turning to the production of incomes, we obtain the following table which exhibits the classes of industry from which the income has been derived:

INCOME DISTRIBUTION ACCORDING TO PRODUCTION*
Unit: Millions of Dollars

Industrial Origin	1929	1930	1931	1932	1933	1934	1935
Agriculture	8,720	6,761	4,476	3,040	3,771	4,644	5,498
Mining and quarrying	2,051	1,703	1,190	807	797	1,025	1,074
Electric light, power, and gas	1,299	1,469	1,402	1,269	1,089	1,028	1,002
Manufacturing	18,059	15,958	12,376	8,528	8,428	10,190	11,727
Construction	3,225	2,910	1,945	932	762	866	1,028
Transportation	6,525	6,046	5,146	4,022	3,733	4,014	4,253
Communications	926	966	903	785	712	734	748
Trade	11,446	10,779	9,331	7,145	6,214	6,885	7,314
Finance	3,140	2,904	2,636	2,041	1,483	1,349	1,321
Service	8,378	7,889	6,889	5,409	5,016	5,395	5,913
Government	6,197	6,395	6,438	6,365	6,063	6,354	6,745
Miscellaneous	4,706	4,371	3,684	2,952	2,744	2,950	3,134
Other accountable income	4,561	4,163	3,736	3,232	3,608	5,063	5,284
Net adjustment for international balance of payments of dividends and interest	—133	—127	— 37	— 20	— 31	— 69	— 96
Total accountable income	79,101	72,186	60,177	46,506	44,389	50,426	54,944

* This table is adapted from Slaughter, op. cit., p. 6.

Since these data pertain to a period which began with a year of unprecedented prosperity and includes years of unusual financial depression, it is illuminating to observe that the ratios of the incomes by classes to the total annual income changed but little. This quite remarkable stability is revealed in the following two tables of percentages:

INCOME DISTRIBUTED ACCORDING TO TYPE
Percentage of type to total income

Type of income	1929	1930	1931	1932	1933	1934	1935
Salaries and wages	63.98	64.00	64.28	63.97	62.76	61.92	62.29
Entrepreneurial income	16.58	15.62	14.90	14.43	15.81	16.12	16.83
Dividends	7.29	7.80	6.95	5.65	4.74	4.64	4.82
Interest	5.05	5.76	6.69	8.08	7.57	6.25	5.36
Net rents and royalties	1.50	1.23	1.03	0.96	1.07	1.17	1.26
Other income less net adjustments	5.60	5.59	6.15	6.91	8.06	9.90	9.44
Totals	100.00	100.00	100.00	100.00	100.00	100.00	100.00

We thus observe that there is a sort of internal stability to the data on incomes, which appears to be independent of the actual level or of wide fluctuations in the business cycle. The problem of the dis-

INCOME DISTRIBUTED ACCORDING TO PRODUCTION
Percentage of origin to total income

Industrial Origin	1929	1930	1931	1932	1933	1934	1935
Agriculture	11.02	9.37	7.45	6.54	8.50	9.21	10.01
Mining and quarrying	2.59	2.36	1.98	1.74	1.80	2.03	1.95
Electric light, power, etc.	1.64	2.04	2.33	2.73	2.45	2.04	1.82
Manufacturing	22.83	22.11	20.59	18.34	18.99	20.21	21.34
Construction	4.08	4.03	3.24	2.00	1.72	1.72	1.87
Transportation	8.25	8.38	8.56	8.65	8.41	7.96	7.74
Communications	1.17	1.34	1.50	1.69	1.60	1.46	1.36
Trade	14.47	14.93	15.52	15.36	14.00	13.65	13.31
Finance	3.97	4.02	4.38	4.39	3.34	2.68	2.40
Service	10.59	10.92	11.46	11.63	11.30	10.70	10.76
Government	7.83	8.85	10.71	13.68	13.66	12.60	12.28
Miscellaneous	5.96	6.06	6.13	6.34	6.17	5.84	5.71
Other income less net adjustments	5.60	5.59	6.15	6.91	8.06	9.90	9.44
Totals	100.00	100.00	100.00	100.00	100.00	100.00	100.00

tribution of incomes with respect to type and production classes thus seems to belong to economic statics. In the next few sections we shall see that this stability also holds in a remarkable manner with respect to individual levels of income.

3. *The Distribution of Incomes—Pareto's Law*

The first extensive discussion from the statistical point of view of the problem of how income is distributed among the citizens of a state was made by Vilfredo Pareto (1848–1923), disciple of Léon Walras (1834–1910), and his successor in the chair of Political Economy at the University of Lausanne. The first chapter of the second book of Pareto's *Cours d'économie politique*, published in 1897, is devoted to this problem.[5] By ingenious reasoning and on the basis of data collected from numerous sources, Pareto arrived at a formulation of his famous law of the distribution of incomes. This law we have cast somewhat precisely in the following statement:

In all places and at all times the distribution of income in a stable economy, when the origin of measurement is at a sufficiently high income level, will be given approximately by the empirical formula

$$y = a\,x^{-\nu}, \tag{1}$$

where y *is the number of people having the income* x *or greater, and* ν *is approximately 1.5.*[6]

[5] Volume 2, pp. 299–345.

[6] The phrase "in a stable economy" has been interpolated by the present writer and should not be ascribed to Pareto. By a stable economy is meant one that is not verging upon revolution or civil war, as measured by political disturbances, civil riots, and the like. The consequences of this interpolation will be developed later.

Pareto was well aware of the importance of this discovery as is proved by the following comment about it:

> These results are very remarkable. It is absolutely impossible to admit that they are due only to chance. There is most certainly a cause, which produces the tendency of incomes to arrange themselves according to a certain curve. The form of this curve seems to depend only tenuously upon different economic conditions of the countries considered, since the effects are very nearly the same for the countries whose economic conditions are as different as those of England, of Ireland, of Germany, of the Italian cities, and even of Peru.[7]

The law of Pareto, because of its rigid and uncompromising form and because also of the great generality of its statement, has been vigorously attacked. It obviously strikes at the most fundamental tenets of socialism and must be reckoned with in all propositions which underlie attempts to formulate a regimented social order. The law has been subjected to careful scrutiny by a number of scientific investigators, and considerable objection has been raised to it in its rigid form. No one, however, has yet exhibited a stable social order, ancient or modern, which has not followed the Pareto pattern at least approximately.

The problem of the distribution of incomes may be formulated in three questions as follows:

First. What is the frequency function for the total distribution of incomes from the poorest member of society to the wealthiest?

Second. Does this distribution appear to be an inevitable one, or may its form be governed by the type of society from which the income is derived?

Third. Can any a priori reason be given for the form of the frequency function?

In order to formulate our ideas with precision, let us assume that a population of N individuals is to be distributed with respect to their possession of a quantity of a variable x, and let the distribution function be designated by $\phi(x)$. Furthermore, we shall let the lowest measure of the range of x be A and the highest B.

If we define $\phi(x)$ to be the total number of individuals who possess the measure between x and $x + dx$, then the number of those who have the measure x or lower is given by the integral

$$Y(X) = \int_A^X \phi(x)\, dx .$$

Obviously we have $Y(B) = N$; moreover, $N - Y(X)$ is the ac-

[7] *Cours*, Vol. 2, p. 312.

cumulated frequency of the population. That is to say, this function gives the number of individuals who have the measure X or greater. If we designate this accumulated frequency by $y(X)$, we shall have

$$y(X) = N - Y(X) = \int_X^B \phi(x)\, dx\,.$$

It is this function which Pareto assumed has the form $y = aX^{-\nu}$, $\nu = 1.5$, provided X is sufficiently large. Under this assumption we should then obtain

$$\phi(X) = -dy/dX = a\nu X^{-\nu-1}\,.$$

Taking logarithms of both $y(X)$ and $\phi(X)$, we have

$$\log y = \log a - \nu \log X\,, \tag{2}$$

$$\log \phi = \log (a\nu) - (\nu + 1) \log X\,. \tag{3}$$

Hence, if the functions are graphically represented on double logarithmic paper, or what is the same thing, if their logarithms are graphed against the logarithms of X, then the graphs will be straight lines and the ratios of the respective slopes will be $\nu/(\nu + 1)$.

4. Income Data

A number of attempts have been made to obtain the data on the incomes of individuals from the lowest income levels to the highest. One of the most comprehensive of these studies was that made by the National Bureau of Economic Research, who published their estimates of the distribution of income among personal-income recipients in the United States for the year 1918.[8]

Their table, an abbreviation of which appears below, gives a carefully determined estimate of the income of 37,569,060 persons, somewhat more than one-third of the total population, although the incomes of 2,500,000 soldiers, sailors, and marines are excluded. The range of income extends from an average negative income of −\$625 to incomes in excess of \$4,000,000.

From the complete table of data we find that the average income is \$1543 and that the modal income is \$957. Since the estimated population of the United States in 1918 was 103,588,000, we obtain an

[8] *Income in the United States, Its Amount and Distribution, 1909–1919*. National Bureau of Economic Research, Vol. 1, New York, 1921, 152 pp.; Vol. 2, 1922, 440 pp. For the data, see Vol. 1, pp. 132–133.

Income Class	Class Mark	Number of Persons	Total Income
Under zero	....	200,000	\$ —125,000,000
\$ 0– \$ 500	250	1,827,554	685,287,806
500– 1,000	750	12,530,670	9,818,678,617
1,000– 1,500	1,250	12,498,120	15,295,790,534
1,500– 2,000	1,750	5,222,067	8,917,648,335
2,000– 3,000	2,500	3,065,024	7,314,412,994
3,000– 5,000	4,000	1,383,167	5,174,090,777
5,000– 10,000	7,500	587,824	3,937,183,313
10,000– 25,000	17,500	192,062	2,808,290,063
25,000– 50,000	37,500	41,119	1,398,785,687
50,000– 100,000	75,000	14,011	951,529,576
100,000– 200,000	150,000	4,945	671,565,821
200,000– 500,000	250,000	1,976	570,019,200
500,000–1,000,000	750,000	369	220,120,399
1,000,000 and over	.....	152	316,319,219
Totals		37,569,060	\$57,954,722,341

average per-capita income of \$560 and a modal per-capita income of \$347. The extraordinary spread of income is readily seen from the fact that if these data were graphed on an arithmetic scale with one-eighth of an inch equal to \$1000, a chart 42 feet long would be required for their representation.

The almost fantastic spread of the income from the average is revealed in a computation of the second, third, and fourth moments about the mean, the unit being \$1,000. These values are as follows:

$$\mu_2 = 32.1367\,, \qquad \mu_3 = 40165.4694\,, \qquad \mu_4 = 77{,}281{,}288.7\,.$$

From these moments we compute the standard error, the skewness, and the kurtosis of the distribution to be respectively

$$\sigma = 5.6689, \qquad S = \mu_3/(2\sigma^3) = 11.0253\,, \qquad E = \beta_2 - 3 = 74{,}826\,,$$

where we use the customary notation $\beta_2 = \mu_4/\sigma^4$.

These values show how hopeless is the task of attempting to graduate the data by any of the curves of Pearson type. This comment is quite significant, since the problem invoked by the distribution of incomes is thus shown to be essentially different from that of the usual frequency distributions which arise in biology for which the Pearson types were primarily designed. The extraordinary difference between biometric frequencies and income frequencies is found in the general observation that in the former, even in cases of extreme skewness, it is unusual to find any member of the distribution more than 4σ from the mean. In the case of income data, extreme individuals are found more than 700σ from the mean.

This difference can be illustrated by considering the distribution of height, which is governed by glandular secretions, whose variation in individuals follows the normal curve. Thus the data on the measurement of nearly a million men, as reported by the medical division of the United States army during the world war, show that the average height is 67.49 inches, and that the standard error is 4.03 inches. From this we see that the probability of a man attaining a height of $67.49 + 4\sigma = 83.61$ inches is very small, approximately 6 in 100,000. But if the hormones of growth were distributed according to the law of incomes, essentially the same probability would lead one to expect giants as tall as $67.49 + 2827.00 = 2894$ inches $= 241$ feet.

The problem of estimating the number of income-recipients in classes below $2,000 is much more difficult that that of estimating the number in classes above $2,000, since income-tax returns are available in the case of the latter. Moreover, the definition of income received is also difficult to state precisely for the classes below the median. Thus one may properly assume that the poorest person in an economy is the vagabond, who exists by pilferage and begging. His income is the lowest possible for existence and no one should be regarded as having a lower economic status measured in terms of income than this man. This was Pareto's point of view, but the fact that negative incomes are included in the table prepared by the National Bureau of Economic Research shows that the estimators assumed otherwise.

Obviously the matter depends primarily upon the definition employed for income as it refers to the lowest income class. In this book it will be convenient to hold to Pareto's view and we shall assume that the lowest admissible income is that of subsistence, a value which we have estimated to be about $196 per capita in 1918. This income we shall refer to as the *wolf point,* since it is the amount of goods and services necessary to sustain life. Below this point the wolf, which lurks so close to the doors of those in the neighborhood of the modal income, actually enters the house.[9]

For a business man, who has a net loss in any year, we can assume that he still has a positive real income, which, even in bad periods, is far above the subsistence level. This income is derived either from a transfer of savings into the income stream, or from the use of borrowed funds. Thus no one in the economy will be represented as having had an income less than that of the vagabond at the wolf point. Obviously our graduation of the data, on this assumption, will

[9] Compare this estimate with the emergency level of income given in Chapter 8.

diverge sharply from that reported in the frequency range below the mode.

5. *The Pareto Distribution*

We shall refer to that part of the distribution of income frequencies which lies sufficiently far beyond the mode to be graduated by the curve

$$y = a\,x^{-\nu}\,, \tag{4}$$

as *the Pareto distribution.*

Taking logarithms of both sides of (1) we obtain

$$\log y = \log a - \nu \log x\;; \tag{5}$$

from which it is observed that if the logarithms of the frequencies are plotted against the logarithms of the incomes, or what is the same thing, if the data are graphed on double-logarithmic paper, the Pareto distribution will appear as a straight line with negative slope.

In order to exhibit the technique of fitting (4) to the income data given in the preceding section, we first form the cumulative frequency table for the data given there, the first two classes being omitted.

Income in Dollars (x)	Cumulative Frequency, y (unit 1,000)	$\log x$	$\log y$	$(\log x)\cdot(\log y)$	$(\log x)^2$
500	35,541	2.69897	4.55073	12.28228	7.28444
1,000	23,010	3.00000	4.36192	13.08576	9.00000
1,500	10,512	3.17609	4.02169	12.77325	10.08755
2,000	5,290	3.30103	3.72346	12.29125	10.89680
3,000	2,225	3.47712	3.34733	11.63907	12.09036
5,000	842	3.69897	2.92531	10.82063	13.68238
10,000	254	4.00000	2.40483	9.61932	16.00000
25,000	62	4.39794	1.79239	7.88282	19.34188
50,000	21	4.69897	1.32222	6.21307	22.08032
100,000	7	5.00000	0.84510	4.22550	25.00000
200,000	2	5.30103	0.30103	1.59577	28.10092
Totals		42.75012	29.59601	102.42872	173.56465

Employing the method of least squares, we form from the above totals the following normal equations for the determination of $\log a$ and ν:

$$11 \log a - \;\; 42.75012\,\nu = \;\; 29.59601\,,$$

$$42.75012 \log a - 173.56464\,\nu = 102.42873\,.$$

From these equations we compute

$$\log a = 9.28462, \quad \nu = 1.69672 \log x .$$

and the desired curve, in logarithmic form, is thus found to be

$$\log y = 9.28462 - 1.69672 \log x .$$

The following table of values has been computed to exhibit the closeness with which the cumulative frequency is represented by the curve. Both the computed and the observed values are graphically represented on double logarithmic paper in Figure 5.

Income x	y observed	y computed
500	35,541	50,722
1,000	23,010	15,648
1,500	10,512	7,864
2,000	5,290	4,827
3,000	2,225	2,426
5,000	842	1,020
10,000	254	315
25,000	62	66
50,000	21	21
100,000	7	6
200,000	2	2

PROBLEMS

1. The following data on national income in 1929 have been given by V. von Szeliski (see *Econometrica*, Vol. 2, 1934 pp. 215–216):

Income Class	Number in each class	Cumulative	Per Cent of total	Income in Millions	Cumula-tive	Per Cent of total
Under $1,000	15,472,560	48,500,000	100.0	$9,567	$90,500	100.0
1,000– 2,000	20,117,510	33,027,440	68.1	29,487	80,933	89.4
2,000– 3,000	8,962,940	12,909,930	26.6	21,462	51,446	56.8
3,000– 4,000	1,994,920	3,946,990	8.13	6,773	29,984	33.1
4,000– 5,000	720,210	1,952,070	4.02	3,216	23,211	25.6
5,000– 10,000	770,909	1,231,860	2.54	5,339	19,995	22.1
10,000– 25,000	339,871	460,951	0.950	5,032	14,656	16.2
25,000– 50,000	77,039	121,080	0.250	2,623	9,624	10.6
50,000– 100,000	28,021	44,041	0.0909	1,908	7,001	7.73
100,000– 250,000	11,648	16,020	0.0330	1,749	5,093	5.63
250,000– 500,000	2,842	4,372	0.00891	911	3,334	3.70
500,000–1,000,000	973	1,530	0.00316	663	2,433	2.68
1,000,000 and over	557	557	0.00115	1,770	1,770	1.96

Using the method described in this section, show that the equation $\log y = 11.91 - 1.48 \log x$ fits the data.

2. Graphically represent the data of problem 1, using a log-log scale, and show how well the equation $\log y = 11.91 - 1.48 \log x$ fits them.

6. *The Statistical Verification of Pareto's Distribution*

In view of the great economic importance of the Pareto distribution and of its social significance, it will be worth while to consider how far it may be regarded as having been verified by statistical use.

Since Pareto's formulation assumes a statistical constancy for ν, it is interesting to examine the data from which he derived his law.

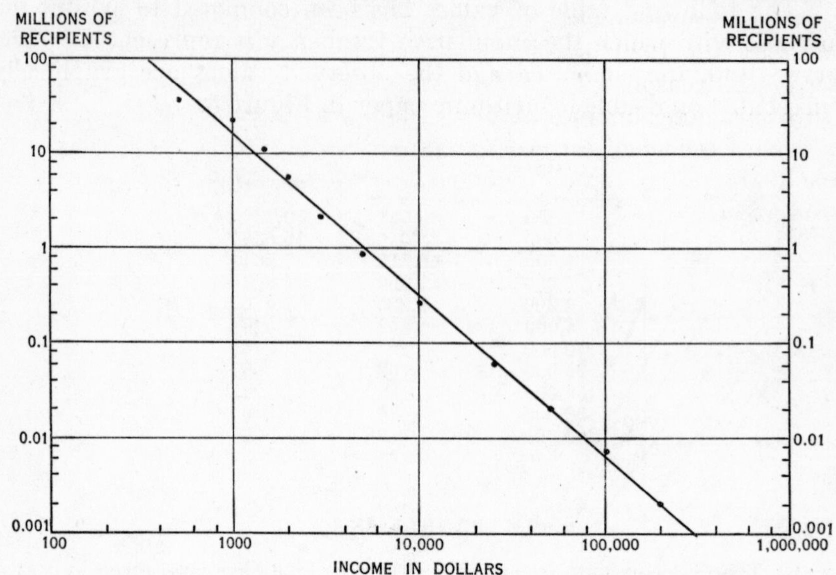

FIGURE 5.—CUMULATIVE FREQUENCY DISTRIBUTION OF INCOMES IN UNITED STATES, 1918, ON LOG-LOG SCALE.

We now have much better statistics about the distribution of income in modern societies than were available to Pareto, but his data with respect to older states have never been surpassed. The following table summarizes his computations, which, it will be observed, extend in time from 1471 to 1894 and in geographical distribution from Peru in the eighteenth century to the wealthy commonwealths of Europe.

Country	ν	Country	ν	Country	ν
England (1843)	1.50	Saxony (1880)	1.58	Basel	1.24
(1879–80)	1.35	(1886)	1.51	Paris (rents)	1.57
(1893–94)	1.50				
Prussia (1852)	1.89	Florence	1.41	Augsburg (1471)	1.43
(1876)	1.72	Perugia (city)	1.69	(1498)	1.47
(1881)	1.73	Perugia (country)	1.37	(1512)	1.26
(1886)	1.68	Ancona, Arezzo,		(1526)	1.13
(1890)	1.60	Parma, Pisa	1.32	Peru (at the end of	
(1894)	1.60	Italian cities	1.45	the 18th century)	1.79

The following table exhibits the stability of the coefficient ν for data on incomes in the United States over the period from 1914 to 1919:[10]

ν	1.56	1.42	1.42	1.54	1.69	1.73	Average = 1.56
Year	1914	1915	1916	1917	1918	1919	$\sigma_\nu = 0.12$

These figures may be supplemented by a computation on the income data for 1929, where the value of ν was found to equal 1.48. There is no reason to believe that a significant change has occurred in this parameter during the depression or afterwards, although there has been a tendency for it to increase as the tax burden has grown since 1933.

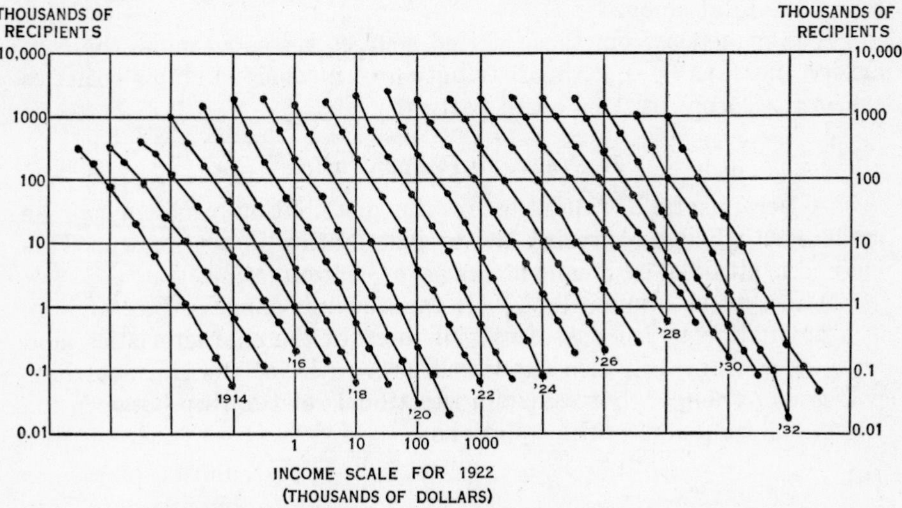

FIGURE 6.—COMPARISON OF INCOME DISTRIBUTION IN THE UNITED STATES, 1914–1933.

Cumulated frequencies, both scales logarithmic. The vertical lines are one cycle apart, as are the horizontal ones, the scale shifting one-half cycle to the right for each successive year. The point nearest the date in each case measures the number of incomes in excess of $1,000,000 in that year.

N. O. Johnson, in an elaborate investigation of the Pareto law, plotted income-tax data on double-logarithmic paper for the years from 1914 to 1933. The value of the slopes of the lines as shown in Figure 6 are given in the following table:[11]

[10] From F. R. Macaulay's study on *Income in the United States—Its Amount and Distribution*, Vol. 2, New York, 1922, Publication No. 2 of the National Bureau of Economic Research, Inc.

[11] Taken from N. O. Johnson, "The Pareto Law," *The Review of Economic Statistics*, Vol. 19, 1937, pp. 20–26.

Year	ν	Year	ν	Year	ν	Year	ν
1914	1.54	1919	1.71	1924	1.67	1929	1.42
1915	1.40	1920	1.82	1925	1.54	1930	1.62
1916	1.34	1921	1.90	1926	1.55	1931	1.71
1917	1.49	1922	1.71	1927	1.52	1932	1.76
1918	1.65	1923	1.73	1928	1.42	1933	1.70

It is evident from these data and also from the accompanying graph that the variation of ν from Pareto's estimate of 1.5 was slight and within statistical error. One also notes that there was a tendency for the distribution of incomes to become more concentrated in times of prosperity and less concentrated in times of depression. The data include only about 2,000,000 income recipients per year, perhaps one-twentieth of the total, but their combined income was perhaps a quarter of the total amount.

The evidence from these varied sources seems to make the conclusion inescapable that the distribution of incomes in stable societies conforms closely to the Pareto pattern.

7. *Curves of Concentration*

A very useful formulation of the distribution problem can be made even when the precise law of distribution is not known. This method is attained by means of *curves of concentration.*

Thus, let us assume that p_x is the amount, expressed as a ratio, of a population which possesses x or more of the characteristics, and let q_x be the amount, also expressed as a ratio, of the characteristic possessed. Then, if there exists a functional relationship between the two variables p and q, the equations

$$p = p_x\,, \quad q = q_x\,, \tag{6}$$

form a parametric system for determining it.

If the law of distribution is sufficiently well known, then x may be eliminated from (6) and we have the equation

$$q = f(p)\,. \tag{7}$$

The straight line, $q = p$, is called the *line of equal distribution.* Since the range of p and q is from 0 to 1, this is the diagonal of a square with unit sides.[12]

Another formulation, which is often useful in application to income data, may be given to (6). Let us designate by N_x that part of of a population N which possesses at least x of a characteristic, and

[12] In case negative amounts of x are possessed, q may have a value smaller than zero. Such negative amounts are apt to be small compared with the total and can usually be neglected.

and let I_x be the amount of the characteristic possessed by N_x. If N is the total population and I the total amount, then we have

$$(8) \qquad p_x = \frac{N - N_x}{N}, \quad q_x = \frac{I - I_x}{I}.$$

Curves of this form were suggested for the representation of the distribution of income almost simultaneously by M. O. Lorentz, C. Gini, and others.[13]

In order to illustrate the application of (8), let us assume that N_x is represented by a Pareto distribution; that is to say,

$$(9) \qquad \log N_x = A - \nu \log x.$$

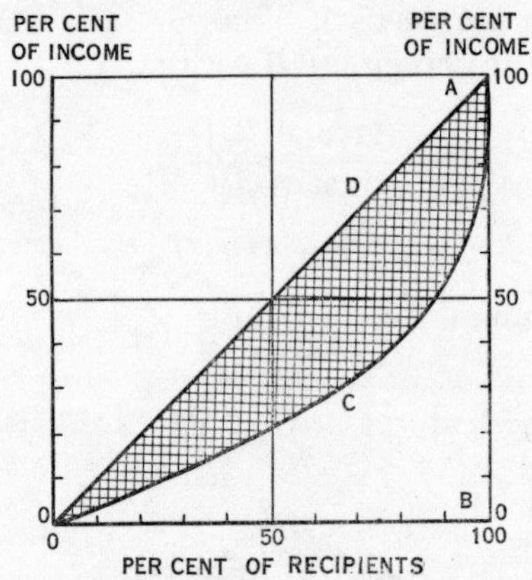

FIGURE 7.—DIAGRAM OF INCOME CONCENTRATION.

Since $-dN_x/dx$ is the frequency, it is clear that we shall have

$$I_x = \int_x^{x_1} \left(- \frac{dN_x}{dx} \right) x \, dx,$$

where x_1 is the limit of the distribution. Applying this to the Pareto distribution and assuming that $x_1 = \infty$, we get

$$(10) \qquad \log I_x = B - (\nu - 1) \log x.$$

Eliminating $\log x$ from (9) and (10), we obtain the relationship

$$(11) \qquad \frac{N_x}{N} = \left(\frac{I_x}{I} \right)^\delta, \text{ where } \delta = \frac{\nu}{\nu - 1}.$$

This is derived, of course, upon the assumption that (9) applies over the entire range of incomes, an assumption that obviously is not warranted for incomes below the mode.

[13] See *Bibliography* at the end of this chapter.

Upon using (8), we find the following relationship between p and q:

$$q = 1 - (1 - p)^{1/\delta} . \tag{12}$$

Assuming the Pareto value of 1.5 for ν, we have $\delta = 3$; hence, equation (12) reduces to

$$q = 1 - (1 - p)^{1/3} .$$

The graph of this function is compared with the line of equal distribution in Figure 7.

As a measure of the difference between distributions, Gini has proposed a concentration ratio, which we designate as ρ. This ratio is defined as the area between the line OA and the curve OCA, divided by the area of the triangle OBA; that is,

$$\rho = \frac{\text{Area } ACOD}{\text{Area } AOB} ,$$

$$= 2 \text{ Area } ACOD .$$

Using (12) to define OCA, we have

$$ACOB = \int_0^1 q\, dp = \int_0^1 [1 - (1 - p)^{1/\delta}]\, dp = 1/(1 + \delta) .$$

Hence we get

$$\rho = 2\, [\tfrac{1}{2} - 1/(1 + \delta)]$$

$$= \frac{\delta - 1}{\delta + 1} = \frac{1}{2\nu - 1} .$$

This function is observed to vary from 0 to 1 as δ varies from 1 to ∞. For the Pareto value $\delta = 3$, the concentration ratio equals $\frac{1}{2}$.[14]

Over the period available to statistical observation the ratio of concentration for the United States has fluctuated around the Pareto value of 0.50. Using Johnson's data we see that the smallest concentration was in 1921, a year of unusual financial crisis, when $\rho =$ 0.3571. The largest value was in 1916 during the period of rapidly

[14] H. Mendershausen has suggested as an alternative measure of concentration the expression $\beta = 1 - M/E$, where M is the median income and E is the "equatorial income." If incomes, ordered by size, are cumulated, the equatorial income is the one which divides the total income into two equal parts. For the distribution of Section 4, $M = 1140$ and $E = 1647$. Hence we get $\beta = 0.3078$, which may be compared with $\rho = 0.4271$ for the same data. See *Report of the Fifth Annual Research Conference of the Cowles Commission*, 1939, pp. 63–65.

increasing prices when $\rho = 0.5952$. One may also observe that the concentration ratio appears to increase during periods of prosperity and to fall during periods of depression. Thus we find $\rho = 0.5435$ in 1929 at the time of the great bull market, but this concentration had declined to $\rho = 0.4167$ by 1933, a year of great financial difficulty. In a later chapter we shall have more to say about the significance of these changes in the concentration of income.

PROBLEMS

1. Assuming that $\nu = 2$, compute δ and graph the curve of concentration (12).

2. From the results of problem 1, compute the concentration ratio.

3. Graph the concentration ratio as a function of δ.

4. Graph the concentration ratio as a function of ν.

5. Assuming that $N_x = 100 - x^2$, $0 \leqq x \leqq 10$, compute p_x and q_x as defined by (8).

6. Represent graphically the curve of concentration as defined by problem 5, and show that $q = p^{3/2}$.

7. Compute the concentration ratio for problem 6.

8. Assuming that

$$N_x = 1 - \sqrt{\frac{2}{\pi}} \int_0^x e^{-\frac{1}{2}x^2}\, dx\,,$$

prove that

$$p_x = \sqrt{\frac{2}{\pi}} \int_0^x e^{-\frac{1}{2}x^2}\, dx\,, \quad q_x = 1 - e^{-\frac{1}{2}x^2}.$$

From tables of the probability function and of the probability integral, graph the curve

$$q = q_x\,, \quad p = p_x\,.$$

8. *The General Distribution Function*

A number of attempts have been made to state formulas which would represent not merely the tail of the distribution of incomes, but which would also graduate the distribution down to a threshold value. This value, the *wolf point,* designated by c, is very small when compared with the total range and may be introduced into the formula for the Pareto distribution without essentially affecting the graduation.

The problem, then, is to determine the function $\phi(x)$ of Section 3, which has the following properties:

(A) $\phi(c) = 0$, where c is the wolf point.

(B) There exists a modal income, x_0, small in comparison with the range, such that $\phi(x_0)$ is a maximum.

(C) For large values of x, the distribution function is approximately represented by Pareto's formula; that is to say,

$$\phi(x) \backsim A(x-c)^{-\mu},$$

where $\mu = \nu + 1$ approximately equals 2.5, and where the symbol $\backsim$ means "is asymptotic to."

(D) The integral $\phi(x)$ over the total range of income (A,B) is equal to the total income population, N; that is,

$$\int_A^B \phi(x)\,dx = N. \tag{13}$$

A number of attempts have been made to construct a function which would have some of the characteristics enumerated above and which would fit reasonably well the observed distributions of income. Pareto, himself, recognized the inadequacy of his formula and made some attempt to improve it. L. Amoroso, D. C. Champernowne, and R. Gibrat have suggested formulas of considerable interest.[15] In particular, Gibrat published an extensive study in a volume entitled *Les inégalites économiques,* which appeared in 1931. His formula for representing the accumulated frequencies took the following interesting form:

$$y = \frac{N}{\sqrt{2\pi}} e^{-\frac{1}{2}z^2},$$

$$z = a\log(x-k) + b.$$

This logarithmic expression of the normal law of statistics fits rather well the observed distribution of incomes, although it does not actually lead to the Pareto law. Thus, for large values of x, the Pareto formula

$$y = A(x-c)^{-\nu}$$

leads to the ratio

$$\frac{y'}{y} = -\frac{\nu}{(x-c)}$$

whereas Gibrat's formula has the form

[15] See the *Bibliography* for these references.

$$\frac{y'}{y} = \frac{ab}{(x-k)} + \frac{a^2 \log(x-k)}{(x-k)} .$$

Computation shows that the second term is not negligible when the formula is applied to the income data used in this chapter.

We shall now develop a new function to represent the distribution of incomes. For this purpose, let us assume that there are N individuals in a population, and that they are to be distributed into the income classes $z_1, z_2, z_3, \cdots$, the potential number in each class being $N_1, N_2, N_3, \cdots$. If the division is sufficiently small between classes, and if N is sufficiently large, then the distribution may be regarded as being essentially a continuous one.

Now let us consider a typical class z, to which N_z individuals aspire to belong. If the total income for the class is I_z, then there will be $P_z = I_z/z$ places in the class to be filled.

But we know from the theory of probability that the number of ways in which P places can be assigned to N individuals is given by

$$Q = \frac{(N+P-1)!}{N!(P-1)!} .$$

For example, if $N=5$ and $P=3$, there are $Q=7!/(5!\cdot 2!)=21$ ways in which the individuals can be assigned to the three places. Some of these assignments are 5 in the first place and none in the other two; 4 in the first place, 1 in the second, 0 in the third, etc.

Introducing Stirling's approximation

$$n! \backsim n^n e^{-n} \sqrt{2\pi n}$$

for the evaluation of the factorials in Q, we readily compute

$$\begin{aligned} \log Q \backsim & (N+P-1) \log(N+P-1) - (N+P-1) + \tfrac{1}{2} \log(N+P-1) \\ & - N \log N + N - \tfrac{1}{2} \log N - (P-1) \log(P-1) \\ & - \tfrac{1}{2} \log(2\pi) - \tfrac{1}{2} \log(P-1) . \end{aligned}$$

Taking derivatives of both sides of this expression with respect to P, we obtain

$$\frac{1}{Q}\frac{dQ}{dP} \backsim \log(N+P-1) - \log(P-1) + \frac{1}{2(N+P-1)} + \frac{1}{2(P-1)} .$$

Since, by assumption, both N and P are large we may neglect the last two terms of this expression and we may also replace $P-1$ by P without essentially altering the relationship. Thus, replacing the approximation symbol with the sign of equality, we write

(14) $$\frac{1}{Q}\frac{dQ}{dP} = \log(N+P) - \log P \,.$$

We now introduce the assumption that the rate of change of Q with respect to P varies directly with Q, but inversely as the size of the income class z, measured from the wolf point; that is

(15) $$\frac{dQ}{dP} = \frac{bQ}{z}\,, \quad z = x - c \,.$$

There is no direct statistical evidence to support this assumption, except the actual form of the distribution curve itself. However, it seems reasonable to believe that the shifting of income recipients from one income class to another takes place more rapidly in numerically large income groups than in numerically small income groups, and that there is a rather remarkable class stability at high income ranges. Equation (15) expresses these assumptions in the simplest possible mathematical form. If the formulation of the distribution problem should prove unsatisfactory for data other than those used in this chapter, it is upon this question that more careful investigation should be made.

Eliminating $(1/Q)\,(dQ/dP)$ between (14) and (15), solving for P, and introducing the subscript z, we finally obtain

$$P_z = \frac{N_z}{e^{b/z} - 1}.$$

From the well-known expansion

$$\frac{t}{e^t - 1} = 1 - \tfrac{1}{2}t + B_1\, t^2/2! - B_2\, t^4/4! + B_3\, t^6/6! - \cdots \,,$$

where $B_1 = 1/6$, $B_2 = 1/30$, $B_3 = 1/42$, $B_4 = 1/30, \cdots$ are the *Bernoulli numbers,* we see that equation (4) can be written

$$P_z = N_z\left(\frac{z}{b} - \frac{1}{2} + \frac{B_1\, b}{2!\, z} - \frac{B_2\, b^3}{4!\, z^3} + \cdots\right).$$

But we know that as z increases P_z approaches the Pareto distribution $A\, z^{-\mu}$, $\mu = \nu + 1$, which means that $N_z = A\, b\, z^{-n}$, $n = \mu + 1$. Hence, replacing Ab by a, and P_z by ϕ, we obtain the desired formula for the frequency distribution; namely,

(16) $$\phi = \frac{a}{z^n}\,\frac{1}{(e^{b/z} - 1)}\,, \quad z = x - c \,.$$

We shall show in the next section that this function satisfies the conditions given in our initial set of postulates.

9. *Properties of the General Distribution Function*

In this section we shall discuss some of the properties of the general distribution function

$$(17) \qquad \phi = \frac{a}{z^n} \frac{1}{(e^{b/z} - 1)} , \qquad z = x - c ,$$

which we derived in the preceding section.

In the derivation of the function we have shown that

$$(18) \qquad \phi \backsim \frac{a}{b} z^{-\mu} ,$$

for large values of z. Hence formula (17) will graduate the Pareto tail of the income distribution.

Moreover, if z is a small positive value, then 1 in the denominator of equation (17) can be neglected in comparison with $e^{b/z}$ and we have the following approximation when x is close to the wolf point c:

$$(19) \qquad \phi \backsim \frac{a}{z^n} e^{-b/z} .$$

But as $z \to 0$, that is to say, when $x \to c$, both $e^{-b/z}$ and z^n approach zero. But since the former function dominates the latter, the limiting value of ϕ is zero. Hence postulate (A) of Section 8 is satisfied.

The maximum value of ϕ is obtained by equating the derivative of (17) to zero. Thus we get

$$(20) \qquad \frac{d\phi}{dz} = z^{\mu} (\phi^2/a) [e^{b/z} (b/z - n) + n] = 0 .$$

From this equation we then derive the condition that ϕ have a maximum value. A brief calculation shows that z must satisfy the equation

$$(21) \qquad z = \frac{b}{n - p} ,$$

where p is the real nontrivial solution of the equation

$$(22) \qquad p\, e^{-p} = n\, e^{-n} .$$

If we abbreviate the right-hand member of this equation by m, that is, if $n e^{-n} = m$, then p may be approximated by the series

$$(23)\qquad p = m + m^2 + \frac{3}{2}m^3 + \frac{8}{3}m^4 + \frac{125}{24}m^5 + \cdots .$$

Designating the value obtained from (22) by z_0 and the corresponding value of ϕ by ϕ_0, we then obtain as the value of the maximum frequency the quantity

$$(24)\qquad \phi_0 = a\, b^{-n}\, p\,(n-p)^{\mu} = \frac{ap}{n-p}\, z_0^{-n} = \frac{ap}{b}\, z_0^{-\mu} .$$

Since only one real nontrivial solution exists for (22), there is a unique maximum frequency and hence one modal income.

Returning to equation (17) let us multiply numerator and denominator by b/z. Then if we use the abbreviation $b/z = t$, the function can be written in the following convenient form

$$(25)\qquad \phi = N(z)\,\frac{t}{e^t - 1},$$

where we write

$$(26)\qquad N(z) = \frac{a}{b} z^{-\mu} .$$

The total distribution is obtained from the integral of (17). The value of this integral may be shown to equal

$$(27)\qquad \int_0^\infty \phi(z)\, dz = a\, b^{-\mu}\, \Gamma(\mu)\, \zeta(\mu) = N ,$$

where $\Gamma(\mu)$ is the Gamma function and $\zeta(\mu)$, the Riemann Zeta function, is defined by the series

$$\zeta(\mu) = 1 + \frac{1}{2^\mu} + \frac{1}{3^\mu} + \frac{1}{4^\mu} + \cdots .$$

Similarly the total income is given by the following integral:

$$(28)\qquad \int_0^\infty \phi(z)\, z dz = a\, b^{-\nu}\, \Gamma(\nu)\, \zeta(\nu) = I .$$

In the evaluation of the parameters for an actual graduation of income data, it is necessary to know the values of $\Gamma(x)$ and $\zeta(x)$. The following brief table of the two functions is sufficient for this purpose:

x	$\Gamma(x)$	Δ	x	$\zeta(x)$	Δ
1.1	0.95135	—0.03318	1.1	10.58445	—4.99287
1.2	0.91817	—0.02070	1.2	5.59158	—1.65963
1.3	0.89747	—0.01021	1.3	3.93195	—0.82640
1.4	0.88726	—0.00103	1.4	3.10555	—0.49317
1.5	0.88623	0.00729	1.5	2.61238	—0.32661
1.6	0.89352	0.01512	1.6	2.28577	—0.23148
1.7	0.90864	0.02274	1.7	2.05429	—0.17206
1.8	0.93138	0.03039	1.8	1.88223	—0.13248
1.9	0.96177	0.03823	1.9	1.74975	—0.10482
2.0	1.00000	0.04649	2.0	1.64493	—0.08471
2.1	1.04649	0.05531	2.1	1.56022	—0.06978
2.2	1.10180	0.06491	2.2	1.49054	—0.05812
2.3	1.16671	0.07546	2.3	1.43242	—0.04908
2.4	1.24217	0.08717	2.4	1.38334	—0.04185
2.5	1.32934	0.10028	2.5	1.34149	—0.03601
2.6	1.42962	0.11507	2.6	1.30548	—0.03122
2.7	1.54469	0.13180	2.7	1.27426	—0.02723
2.8	1.67649	0.15087	2.8	1.24703	—0.02390
2.9	1.82736	0.17264	2.9	1.22313	—0.02107
3.0	2.00000	0.19762	3.0	1.20206	—0.01868

It will be observed from equations (25) and (26) that the significant parameters for the actual evaluation of the frequency function are b and a/b. But these are readily computed by means of equations (27) and (28). Thus eliminating a between these two equations, we obtain

$$b=\frac{\Gamma(\mu)\ \zeta(\mu)}{\Gamma(\nu)\ \zeta(\nu)}\frac{I}{N}\,. \tag{29}$$

Using this value we then obtain from equation (27)

$$\frac{a}{b}=\frac{N\,b^{\nu}}{\Gamma(\mu)\ \zeta(\mu)}\,. \tag{30}$$

It is also instructive to observe that both the modal income and the modal frequency, given respectively by equations (21) and (24), are evaluated directly by these formulas. Replacing (29) in (21) we obtain

$$z_0=\frac{\Gamma(\mu)\ \zeta(\mu)}{(n-p)\ \Gamma(\nu)\zeta\ (\nu)}\frac{I}{N}\,. \tag{31}$$

Moreover, eliminating a and b from the first equation in (8), we obtain

$$\phi_0=\frac{\Gamma(\nu)\ \zeta(\nu)}{[\Gamma(\mu)\ \zeta(\mu)]^2}p\,(n-p)^{\mu}\frac{N^2}{I}\,. \tag{32}$$

If we assume that the distribution is strictly Paretean, namely, that $\nu = 1.5$, then these formulas can be simplified. Substituting numerical values for the Gamma and Zeta functions in (29), we obtain

$$b = 0.77023 \frac{I}{N}. \tag{33}$$

Similarly, equation (30) reduces to the numerical form

$$\frac{a}{b} = 0.37915\, I\sqrt{I/N}. \tag{34}$$

In order to evaluate the numerical coefficient in (31), we must first compute p. This is readily found from equation (23) to be $p = 0.11905$. Substituting this value in (31), we then obtain

$$z_0 = 0.29578\, b = 0.22782 \frac{I}{N}. \tag{35}$$

Similarly equation (34) reduces to

$$\phi_0 = 1.82135 \frac{N^2}{I}. \tag{36}$$

PROBLEMS

1. Make a table showing the 21 ways in which individuals can be assigned to 3 places, if $N = 5$ and $P = 3$.

2. Using $\nu = 1.40$, evaluate p from equation (23).

3. Substitute the value obtained from problem 2 in equations (31) and (32), and evaluate both z_0 and ϕ_0 in terms of I and N. How do these values compare with those obtained from the Pareto distribution?

4. Using $\nu = 1.60$, evaluate p from equation (23).

5. Substitute the value obtained from problem (4) in equations (31) and (32) and evaluate both z_0 and ϕ_0 in terms of I and N. How do these values compare with those obtained from the Pareto distribution?

6. Assuming that the distribution of von Szeliski given in the first list of problems in this chapter is essentially Paratean, since $\nu = 1.48$, compute z_0 and ϕ_0 from equations (35) and (36).

10. Statistical Determination of the Distribution Function

From the formulas given in the preceding section, in particular (29), (30), (31), and (32), it is clear that the parameters of the general distribution function can be determined as soon as we know I, N, and ν. It may be readily suspected, however, that the practical adjusting of the parameters to an actual distribution could be improved by some statistical considerations.

As an example of the application of the formulas let us adjust the distribution function to the data given in Section 4. We observe that $I = \$57{,}954{,}722{,}341$ and that $N = 37{,}569{,}060$. In Section 5 we have already made a statistical determination of ν and found the value

$$\nu = 1.69672 \, .$$

From the table of Section 9 we immediately determine the following values: $\Gamma(\nu) = 0.9081$, $\zeta(\nu) = 2.0582$, $\Gamma(\mu) = 1.5408$, $\zeta(\mu) = 1.2753$. The value of b is then determined from formula (29) and found to be

$$b = 1622 \, .$$

Since a/b is in general a large number we evaluate its logarithm by taking logarithms of both sides of equation (30). We thus obtain

$$\log\ (a/b) = 12.72803 \, .$$

In order to compute the modal income we must first determine p. From $n = \mu + 1 = 3.69672$, we find $m = n\, e^{-n} = 0.09169$. Substituting this value in formula (23) of Section 9 we compute $p = 0.10148$. It then follows from formula (21), or from formula (31), which is equivalent, that

$$z_0 = \$451 \, .$$

Since the actually observed modal income is \$957, as stated in Section 4, the wolf point is thus seen to be $c = 957 - 451 = \$506$. Since the estimated population in 1918 was 103,588,000 and since our data report the income of 37,569,060 persons, there is an average of 2.75 people depending upon each income. Hence the per capita wolf point is \$184, a value that does not seem to be unrealistic, since it is hard to believe that a single person could have survived in 1918 without receiving at least as many goods and services as would have been purchased by this sum.

From formula (24), or from formula (32), which is equivalent, we now compute the modal frequency. This is found to be

$$\phi_0 = 37{,}710 \, .$$

It will be observed that this frequency assumes a range in the data of only one dollar, obviously too narrow for statistical verification. The data of the National Bureau of Economic Research which we are using give frequencies for intervals of \$100 in the neighborhood of the modal income. Hence, if we multiply ϕ_0 by 100 we may compare the estimated frequency of 3,771,000 with the observed modal, frequency of 3,144,722. The discrepancy in these figures may be attributed principally to the fact that the National Bureau assumed the existence of incomes below the wolf point, which would tend to reduce frequencies in the neighborhood of the mode.

If units of \$100 are used for the income range, then the value of b must be divided by 100 and the logarithm of a/b must be reduced by 2ν, as one observes from equation (30). We should then have the values $b = 16.22$, and $\log (a/b) = 9.33459$.

From statistical considerations based upon the entire frequency distribution given by the National Bureau, considerations too lengthy to be discussed here,[16] some adjustments in the values of b and of

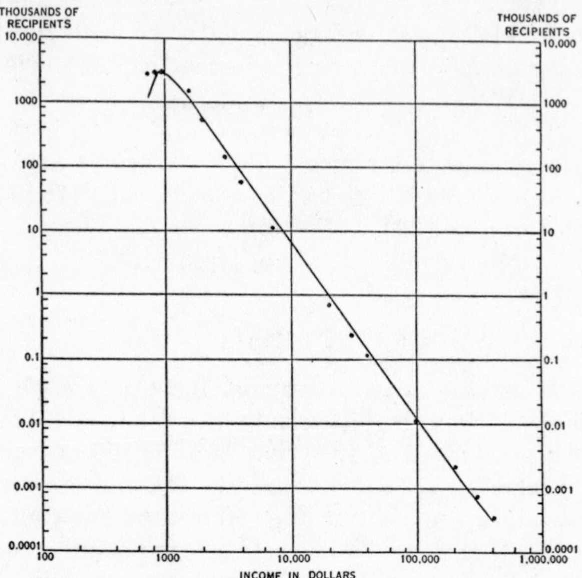

FIGURE 8.—FREQUENCY DISTRIBUTION OF INCOMES IN THE UNITED STATES, 1918.

$\log(a/b)$ were found desirable. These adjusted values were

$$b = 15.043 , \qquad \log (a/b) = 9.16749 .$$

Using these values we may obtain a modal income (in dollars) of $z_0 = \$418$ and a wolf point of \$539, the per capita value of which is

[16] These computations will be found in the author's book: *The Analysis of Economic Time Series*, The Principia Press, 1941, Chapter 9.

$196. The adjustment has been made so that the computed and observed modal frequencies are essentially equal.

The graduation of the observed frequency distribution is accomplished by means of formula (25). For this comparison we shall use the adjusted estimates of b and log (a/b) and compute values of $\phi(x)$ at various points of the income range from $x = 7.5$ to $x = 4000.5$, the unit of income being $100. These values are given in the following table and the closeness of the fit at and beyond the mode is graphically represented in Figure 8. The discrepancy below the mode is again to be attributed to the definition of income for low income classes.

x	Φ(computed)	Φ(observed)	x	Φ(computed)	Φ(observed)
7.5	1,122,435	2,668,466	200.5	942	663
8.5	2,667,070	3,013,034	300.5	313	248
9.5	3,143,365	3,144,722	400.5	143	118
15.5	1,245,979	1,512,649	1000.5	12.04	11.90
20.5	566,752	549,787	2000.5	1.84	2.09
30.5	180,277	142,802	3000.5	0.61	0.73
40.5	80,079	55,904	4000.5	0.28	0.33
70.5	16,806	11,118			

PROBLEMS

1. Estimate by interpolation the modal income in 1929 from von Szeliski's data given in the first list of problems in this chapter. Noting that the total population in 1929 was approximately 121,526,000, estimate the per capita income at the mode.

2. From the results of problem 6, Section 9, and from the estimate obtained in problem 1 of this section, compute the per capita wolf point in 1929.

3. Obtain from formulas (33) and (34) of Section 9, the values of b and a/b for the income data of 1929. Using these values compute $\phi(t)$ at $t = \$9,500$ the unit range being $100. Does your estimate appear to agree with the value estimated from the table?

11. *The Generalized Law of Inequality*

Having in preceding sections given theoretical and statistical validity to the Pareto pattern of income distribution, we shall attempt to explain this distribution as a special case of a more general law of inequality, which we shall refer to as the *law of the distribution of special abilities*. This thesis was first advanced by Carl Snyder at the Research Conference of the Cowles Commission for Research in Economics in 1936 and has since been elaborated in two chapters of his recent book on *Capitalism the Creator*. The same idea had also occurred at about the same time to the author of this work and statistical evidence was at hand to support the proposition.

The generalized law makes the following assumptions:

(1) The variable x is the measure of a measurable ability possessed by a total group of N individuals.

(2) The variable x has a range, which, for practical measurements, may be regarded as infinite at one end. For example, in the case of incomes, there is no upper bound to one's possible income and the actual range from near zero to more than $4,000,000 may be regarded statistically as essentially an infinite one.

(3) Each unit of x is comparable with every other unit. Thus, in playing billiards, the addition of one billiard to a run of x is no more difficult than the addition of one billiard to a run of x'. In golf, however, the reduction of a stroke at the level 125 is very much simpler than the reduction of a stroke at the level 70. In the case of income, while it may be argued that the addition of one dollar at a level of $100,000 is obviously easier than the addition of one dollar at the level of $1,000, it is not improbable that to *earn and keep* a dollar, that is, to add one dollar to actual income, is approximately the same at each level. At least, since the Pareto law holds for income distributions, it would appear that this proposition has an empirical validity. One of the strongest arguments against the use of the Binet I. Q. test of intelligence for high levels is found in the fact that abilities measured by it conform to the normal curve. It seems clear that the addition of a unit to a score at a high level is considerably more difficult than the addition of a unit at a low level.

The proposition may then be stated that, *under the assumptions given above, the distribution of* N *individuals will approximate a Pareto distribution when* x *is sufficiently large.*

In support of this thesis we shall submit data from the game of billiards, data showing the ability to write mathematical papers, and data showing the distribution of values to a corporation of the members of its executive staff as measured in terms of salary incomes. This evidence will be further supported by some significant results obtained by A. J. Lotka in a study of scientific productivity.[17]

Records kept over a number of years by Dean C. E. Edmondson of Indiana University on the ability of the members of the faculty to play billiards was kindly put at the disposal of the author. The group, consisting of 79 members, had played billiards for a sufficiently long period to have reached approximately the upper bound of their curves of learning. It is obvious that the upper range of the data is infinite, that the ability to make billiards is measured by the average number

[17] "The Frequency Distribution of Scientific Productivity," *Journal of the Washington Academy of Sciences*, Vol. 16, 1926, pp. 317–323.

made in a given number of innings, and that the difficulty of adding one billiard to a score is the same at any level. Hence, the 79 members of the group should be distributed in a Pareto curve. The unit used is the number of billiards made in 50 innings; the mode is around 50, and the standard error approximately 10. The data are given in the following table:

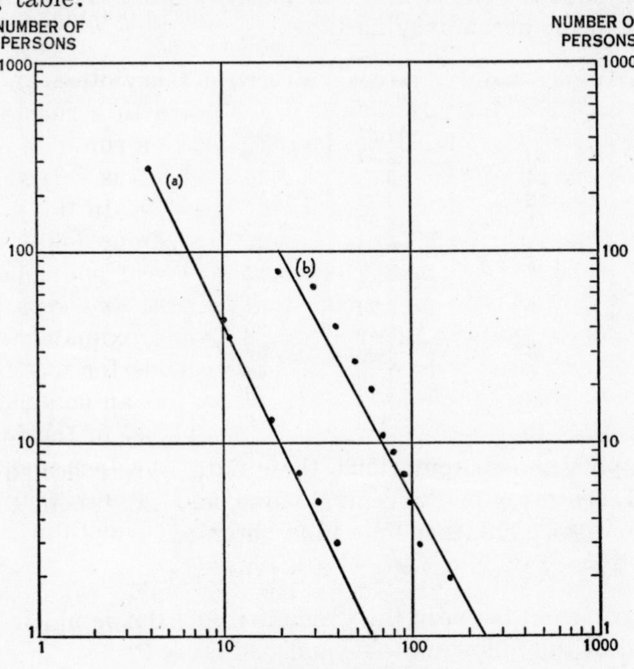

FIGURE 9.—CUMULATIVE FREQUENCY DISTRIBUTIONS OF MATHEMATICAL CONTRIBUTIONS (a) AND OF BILLIARD SCORES (b).

No. of billiards in 50 innings	Accumulated Frequency	Per Cent of total	No. of billiards in 50 innings	Accumulated Frequency	Per Cent of total
20	79	100.00	80	9	11.39
30	66	83.54	90	7	8.86
40	41	51.90	100	5	6.33
50	27	34.18	110	3	3.80
60	19	24.05	160	2	2.53
70	11	13.95	280	1	1.27

When these data are graduated by the parabolic curve, we get

$$\log y = 4.44919 - 1.867 \log x \, .$$

It will be seen from the chart (Figure 9) that the fit is reasonably good except at the upper end. But this is to be expected since a score of 20 billiards is far below the modal class.

An accumulation similar to that observed in the billiard data is furnished by a distribution submitted by Arnold Dresden at the twenty-fifth anniversary meeting of the Chicago section of the American Mathematical Society. Dresden's paper exhibited the productivity of 278 authors in the writing of mathematical papers. In all, 1102 papers were produced. The data are themselves interesting and they are reproduced in the accompanying table.[18]

No. of Contributions (x)	No. of Persons Contributing	Per Cent of total	No. of Contributions (x)	No. of Persons Contributing	Per Cent of total
1	133	47.84	14	1	0.36
2	43	15.47	15	1	0.36
3	24	8.63	16	2	0.72
4	12	4.32	19	1	0.36
5	11	3.96	20	1	0.36
6	14	5.04	21	1	0.36
7	5	1.80	24	1	0.36
8	3	1.08	27	1	0.36
9	9	3.24	32	1	0.36
10	1	0.36	35	1	0.36
11	3	1.08	39	1	0.36
12	5	1.80	42	1	0.36
13	1	0.36	70	1	0.36
			Totals	278	100.02

To simplify the computations, these data were collected into intervals of 7, centering on the central value, and a parabolic curve was fitted to their accumulation. We thus obtained

$$\log y = 3.74877 - 2.11012 \log x \, .$$

The agreement between the graduated and the actual frequencies is exhibited in the following table and in Figure 9:

x	y (actual)	y (computed)	x	y (actual)	y (computed)
4	278	301	39	3	2
11	36	36	46	1	2
18	13	13	53	1	1
25	7	6	60	1	1
32	5	4	67	1	1

An interesting verification of the general thesis of the Pareto

Salary Group	No. of Individuals	Salary Group	No. of Individuals
\$ 5,000– 9,999	1,363	\$50,000–59,999	8
10,000–14,999	173	60,000–69,999	1
15,000–19,999	67	70,000–79,999	8
20,000–29,999	42	80,000–99,999	1
30,000–39,999	9	100,000 and over	2
40,000–49,999	4	Total	1,678

[18] "A Report on the Scientific Work of the Chicago Section, 1897–1922," *Bulletin of the American Math. Soc.*, Vol. 28, 1922, pp. 303–307.

distribution of special abilities is given in the following data published in the 28th annual report of the General Motors Corporation for the year ending December 31, 1936. This report shows the salary schedule for the executive administrative staff of the corporation.

These data are first arranged in an accumulated frequency table as shown and a parabolic curve is fitted to them. We thus obtain the equation

$$\log y = 10.83006 - 2.067 \log x \, .$$

Salary (x)	Number (y)	Salary (x)	Number (y)
$ 5,000	1,678	$ 50,000	20
10,000	315	60,000	12
15,000	142	70,000	11
20,000	75	80,000	3
30,000	33	100,000	2
40,000	24		

Our conclusion from this result would be that the distribution of salaries in a successful corporation like General Motors tends toward the Pareto pattern. High executive ability is a rare talent and it must be properly recognized if the corporation which employs it, is to maintain its competitive efficiency.

Other examples in kind could be cited in support of the thesis developed here. One of the most instructive is due to A. J. Lotka whose study has already been referred to. Lotka made a count of the number of names in the decennial index of *Chemical Abstracts*, 1907–1916, against which appeared 1, 2, 3, etc. entries. The letters *A* and *B* of the alphabet only were considered. A second count (of the entire alphabet) was also made for the name index of Auerbach's *Geschichtstafeln der Physik* (J. A. Barth, Leipzig, 1910), which covered the entire range of history up to and including 1900.

Lotka found that the parabolic function

$$f = 56.69/n^{1.888}$$

gave an excellent graduation of the percentage of people contributing articles to chemical literature, and that the function

$$f = 600/(\pi^2 n^2)$$

similarly fitted the frequency distribution (in percentage) for the production of papers in physics.

On the basis of these results Lotka was led to speak of the "inverse-square law of scientific production," according to which "the proportion of all contributors who contribute a single item should be just over 60 per cent."

An interesting attempt has recently been made by C. H. Boissevain to give a genetic basis to the thesis which has been advanced in this section.[19] Boissevain's assumption is that special abilities are the products of several genetic factors. For example, the ability to play billiards is undoubtedly derived from good eyesight combined with good muscular coordination. Hence the deviation of the ability to play billiards from the normal pattern comes about through the combination of independent factors derived from the compounding of two or more normal distributions. In support of this theory Boissevain exhibited frequency tables based upon the compounding of two, three, and four factors with normal distributions.

PROBLEMS

1. In graduating the data on the ability to play billiards, we found the value $\nu = 1.867$. Using this value, compute p by means of equation (23) of Section 9.

2. Using $\nu = 1.867$, evaluate $\Gamma(\nu)$, $\zeta(\nu)$, $\Gamma(\mu)$, and $\zeta(\mu)$.

3. From the computations of problems 1 and 2, evaluate z_0 and ϕ_0 for the game of billiards. For this purpose use formulas (31) and (32) of Section 9, noting that I equals the total number of billiards scored.

4. Can the concept of a wolf point be extended to the game of billiards? Estimate its value from the results of problem 3 and discuss its meaning.

5. Assuming the inverse square law of ability, that is to say, assuming $\nu = 2$, compute formulas analogous to (33), (34), (35), and (36) of Section 9.

12. Conclusions

From many varied sources we have found that the accumulated frequency curve of distributions of people arranged according to some special ability can be graduated by a parabolic curve, whose coefficient is nearly 2. From this we may safely conclude that such distributions cannot be described in terms of the theory of the normal probability curve and that the ordinary laws of chance are disturbed by another law operative in the case of special abilities.

Since the data which pertain to incomes are also graduated by a parabolic curve it is reasonable to assume that the ability to accumulate wealth is an ability not dissimilar to those which appear in games of skill and in the production of scientific literature. The fact that the essential coefficient in the latter cases is approximately 2, while the coefficient in income distributions is approximately 1.5 is no argu-

[19] "Distribution of Abilities Depending upon two or more Independent Factors," *Metron*, Vol. 13, 1939, pp. 49-58.

ment against the general thesis. This discrepancy may be accounted for easily by denying the strict equivalence of one dollar earned and kept at any level of the income distribution.

Our general conclusion would be, then, that the Pareto distribution of income is a necessary phenomenon of any stable economic state. The reason for the distribution must be sought in the mysterious realm of human psychology which accounts for the existence and distribution of special abilities.

SELECTED BIBLIOGRAPHY OF THE DISTRIBUTION OF INCOME

D'ADDARIO R. "Sulla curva dei redditi di Amoroso," *Annali dell 'Istituto di Statistica*, Bari, Vol. 10, 1936, pp. 1–57.

AMMON, O. *Die Gesselschaftsordnung und ihre natürlichen Grundlagen.* First ed., Jena, 1895; 3rd ed., 1900, viii + 408 pp.

AMOROSO, L. "Ricerche intorno alla curva dei redditi," *Annali di matematica,* Vol. 2, 4th series, 1924–25, pp. 123–160.

BAXTER, R. D. *National Income: The United Kingdom.* London, 1868, 100 pp.

BORTKIEWICZ, L. VON. "Die Desparitätsmasse der Einkommensstatistik," *Bulletin de l'institut international de statistique,* Vol. 25, 1931, pp. 189–298.

BRESCIANI-TURRONI, C. (1) "On Pareto's Law," *Journal of the Royal Statistical Society,* Vol. 100, 1937, pp. 421–432.

(2) "Annual Survey of Statistical Data," *Econometrica,* Vol. 7, 1939, pp. 107–133.

CASTELLANO, V. "Sulle relazioni tra curve di frequenza e curve di concentrazione e sui rapporti di concentrazione correspondenti a determinate distribuzioni," *Metron,* Vol. 10, No. 4, 1933, pp. 3–60.

CZUBER, E. *Beitrag zur Theorie der statistischer Reihen.* Versicherungswissenschaftliche Mitteilungen. Neue Folge, 9 Band, 2 Heft, Wien, 1914.

DALTON, H. (1) "The Measurement of the Inequality of Incomes," *Economic Journal,* Vol. 30, 1920, pp. 348–361.

(2) *Inequality of Incomes.* First ed., London, 1920; 2nd end., 1925, xiii + 360 pp. + appendix of 16 pp.

DARMOIS, G. "Distributions statistiques rattachées a la loi de Gauss et la répartition des revenus," *Econometrica,* Vol. 1, 1933, pp. 159–161.

DAVIS, H. T. (1) "The Significance of the Curve of Income," *Abstracts of Papers Presented at the Research Conference Held by the Cowles Commission,* 1938, pp. 19–22.

(2) "Relationship between the Distribution of Income and Total Real Income," *Ibid.,* 1939, pp. 76–77.

FRÉCHET, M. "Sur les formules de répartition des revenus," *Revue de l'institut international de statistique,* 7 annee, 1939, pp. 32–38.

GALTON, SIR FRANCIS. *Hereditary Genius. An Inquiry into its Laws and Consequences.* New York, 1869, xxvii + 379 pp.

GIBRAT, R. *Les inégalites économiques.* Paris, 1931, 296 pp.

GINI, C. (1) The Contributions of Italy to Modern Statistical Methods," *Journal of the Royal Statistical Society,* Vol. 89, 1926, pp. 703–724.

(2) "Sul massimo degli indici di variabilità assoluta e sulle sue applicazioni ogli indici di variabilità relativa e al rapporto di concentrazione," *Metron,*

Vol. 8, 1930, No. 3, pp. 3–65.

(3) "Intorno alle curve di concentrazione," *Metron*, Vol. 9, 1932, Nos. 3–4, pp. 3–76.

(4) "Di una estensione del concetto di scostamento medio," *Atti del R. Istituto Veneto*, 1917–18.

(5) "On the Measure of Concentration with Special Reference to Income and Wealth," *Abstracts of Papers Presented at the Research Conference . . . Held by the Cowles Commission, . .* 1936, (Colorado College Publication, General Series No. 208) pp. 73–80.

JOHNSON, N. O. (1) "The Brookings Report on Inequality in Income Distribution," *Quarterly Journal of Economics*, Vol. 49, 1935, pp. 718–724.

(2) "The Pareto Law," *Review of Economic Statistics*, Vol. 19, 1937, pp. 20–26.

KING, W. I. (1) *The National Income and its Purchasing Power*. National Bureau of Economic Research, New York, 1930, 394 pp.

(2) *Wealth and Income of the People of the United States*, New York, 1915, xxiv + 278 pp.

KUZNETS, S. *The National Income, 1929–1932*. Sen. Doc. 124, 73rd Congress, 2nd Sessions, Washington, D. C., 1934, xi + 261 pp. Summarized in *Bulletin 49*, National Bureau of Economic Research, 1934.

LEVEN, M. (with H. G. MOULTON and C. WABRURTON), *America's Capacity to Consume*. The Brookings Institution, Washington, D. C., 1934, xi + 272 pp.

LORENZ, M. O. "Methods of Measuring the Concentration of Wealth," *Publications of the American Statistical Association*, Vol. 9 (New series), 1905, pp. 209–219.

MACAULAY, F. R. "The Personal Distribution of Income in the United States," Part 3, pp. 341–425 of *Income in the United States—Its Amount and Distribution*, Vol. 2, New York, 1922, Publication No. 2 of the National Bureau of Economic Research, xiv + 440 pp.

MARCH, L. "Quelques exemples de distribution de salaires," *Journal de la Société de Statistique de Paris*, 1898.

MARSCHAK, J. *Elastizität der Nachfrage*. Tübingen, 1931, p. 83 et seq.

MACGREGOR, D. H. "Pareto's Law," *Economic Journal*, Vol. 46, 1936, pp. 80–87.

MOULTON, H. G. (see Leven, M.).

PARETO, V. (1) "Aggiunta allo studio sulla curva delle entrate," *Giornale degli Economisti*, 1897.

(2) *Cours d'économie politique*. Lausanne, 1897. Book 2, Part 1, Chapter 1.

(3) *Manuel d'économie politique*. Paris, 1909; 2nd ed., 1927. Chapter 7; in particular, pp. 390 *et seq.*

PIETRA, G. "Delle relazioni tra gli indici di variabilità," *Atti del R. Istituto Veneto*, 1914–15 (two notes).

PIGOU, A. C. *The Economics of Welfare*. First ed., London, 1920; 4th, ed., 1932, Part 4, Chapter 2, pp. 647–655.

POWERS, L. G. "Factors Producing Unequal Wealth Distribution and Ownership and Measurements of their Influence," *Journal of the American Statistical Association*, Vol. 23, 1928, pp. 417–428.

RICCI, U. "L'indice di variabilità e la curva dei redditi," *Giornale degli Economisti*, 1916.

SAIBANTE, M. (1) "I profitti delle società per azioni e la concentrazione dei capitali industriali," *Metron*, Vol. 6, No. 1, 1926, pp. 165–201.

(2) "La concentrazione della popolazione," *Metron*, Vol. 7, No. 2, 1928, pp. 53–99.

SHIRRAS, G. F. "The Pareto Law and the Distribution of Income," *Economic Journal*, Vol. 45, 1935, pp. 663–681.

SNYDER, C. (1) "The Pareto Curve and its Significance for our Time," *Report of the Research Conference of the Cowles Commission*, 1937, p. 61.

(2) *Capitalism the Creator*. New York, 1940, xii + 473 pp. In particular, Chapters 14 and 15.

STAEHLE, H. "Short-Period Variations in the Distribution of Incomes," *Review of Economic Statistics*, Vol. 19, 1937, pp. 133–143.

TUCKER, R. S. "The Distribution of Income Among Income Taxpayers in the United States, 1863–1935," *Quarterly Journal of Economics*, Vol. 52, 1938, pp. 547–587.

VINCI, F. (1) "La concentrazione dei capitali delle nostre società ordinarie per azioni," *Rivista della società commerciali*, Anno 8, Fesc. 3, 1918.

(2) "Recenti vedute sulla legge di distribuzione dei redditi," in *Problemi di finanza fascista*, Bologna, 1937, p. 332.

WARBURTON, C. (see Leven, M.)

WIJK, J. VAN DER. *Incomens—en Vermogensverdeling.* (*Distribution of Incomes and Fortunes*). Haarlem, 1939. Publication No. 26 of the Netherlands Economic Institute. xv + 295 pp. This contains a five page summary in English.

WOLD, H. "A Study on the Mean Difference, Concentration Curves, and Concentration Ratio," *Metron*, Vol. No. 2, 1935, pp. 39–58.

YNTEMA, D. B. "Measures of the Inequality in the Personal Distribution of Wealth or Income," *Journal of the American Statistical Association*, Vol. 28, 1933, pp. 423–433.

YOUNG, A. A. "Do the Statistics of the Concentration of Wealth in the United States Mean What they are Commonly Assumed To Mean?" *Journal of the American Statistical Association*, Vol. 15 (new series), 1917, pp. 476–484.

CHAPTER 3

THE CONCEPT OF UTILITY

1. *Historical Summary*

From one very important point of view economics may be regarded as the science of human satisfactions. Thus we find W. Stanley Jevons affirming in his *Theory of Political Economy* (p. 39):

> But it is surely obvious that Economics does rest upon the laws of human enjoyment; and that, if those laws are developed by no other science, they must be developed by economists. We labor to produce with the sole object of consuming, and the kinds and amounts of goods produced must be determined with regard to what we want to consume. Every manufacturer knows and feels how closely he must anticipate the tastes and needs of his customers: his whole success depends upon it; and, in like manner, the theory of Economics must begin with a correct theory of consumption.

We shall begin by considering the concept invoked by the word, *utility,* or as some writers prefer to say, *ophelimity,* which is derived from the Greek equivalent for utility. By either of these words we shall mean a measure of the satisfaction enjoyed in the possession and use of certain specified quantities of a number of economic goods. This satisfaction is obviously psychic in character and as yet there exists no objective measure for it. For the present discussion we shall assume that the measure applies to a single individual, rather than to a community, or to the average individual of a community.

We shall also assume, in order to establish a basis for our discussion, that utility is a function of the quantities of the goods possessed, and that it may be mathematically specified by the ordinary functional notation

$$U = U(x_1, x_2, \cdots, x_n)\,, \tag{1}$$

where $x_1, x_2, \cdots, x_n$ designate the quantities of the n goods possessed by the individual.

Since the idea of a function of utility may seem abstract and unrealistic to the reader, it is perhaps wise to begin with an account of the historical origins of the concept. In this manner we may reach, perhaps, a more satisfactory appreciation of the value of the idea in economic arguments.

Apparently the concept originated in a theory of moral expectation which was advanced by Daniel Bernoulli (1700–1782) in his *Specimen Theoriae Novae de Mensura Sortis,* published in 1738. This theory was proposed to explain a perplexing problem in the calculus of probabilities, which was called the St. Petersburg paradox.

In the theory of probability the *mathematical expectation* (E) of one who has the probabilities p_i of gaining amounts x_i is defined to be the sum

$$E = \sum p_i x_i = \int_b^a p(t)\, x(t)\, dt \,, \tag{2}$$

the integral, of course, being used in the case of continuous probabilities.

For example, if two dice are to be thrown and A is to receive \$100 if the sum is 7 and \$50 if the sum is 9, then his mathematical expectation is

$$E = \$100 \times \frac{6}{36} + \$50 \times \frac{4}{36} = \$22.22 \,,$$

since the probability of throwing a 7 with two dice is 6/36 and the probability of throwing a 9 is 4/36.

The theory of life insurance is founded upon the concept of mathematical expectation, which is a sufficient indication of its importance in economics. Thus we have from the *American Experience Table* (See Chapter 14) the probability that a man age 25 will fail to survive to age 26 is 0.0080645. Hence, neglecting considerations of interest, the amount necessary to insure him for one year for \$1,000 is the mathematical expectation, $E = \$1{,}000 \times 0.0080645 = \$8.06$.

The St. Petersburg paradox is important in the theory of probability because it implies a criticism of the concept of mathematical expectation. The paradox was submitted by Nicolas Bernoulli (1695–1726) to Pierre Remond de Montmort (1678–1719). It may be stated as follows:

Suppose that A and B are playing a game in which B is to toss a coin until it falls heads. If it falls heads for the first time on the nth toss, then A pays B the sum of 2^{n-1} dollars. What amount should B pay A for the privilege of playing the game?

The mathematical expectation is the sum of the series

$$E = 1 \cdot \tfrac{1}{2} + 2(\tfrac{1}{2})^2 + 4(\tfrac{1}{2})^3 + 8(\tfrac{1}{2})^4 + \cdots , \tag{3}$$

which has the value ∞.

This is obviously an absurd answer. Thus Georges Louis Leclerc, Comte de Buffon (1707–1788), quoted by A. De Morgan (1806–1871) in his treatise *On Probabilities,* tabulated the results of 2048 games for which was paid \$10,057, or an average of \$4.91 per game. Although the possibility always exists that a phenomenal run of luck may lead to a phenomenal winning, it is easily proved that in 2^n games, the average amount paid per game will be slightly in excess of $\frac{1}{2}n$ dollars. How then shall we explain the paradox?

One solution that has been offered is based on the observation that A's fortune is finite, and hence B does not have a chance to win an infiite amount. Thus if A's wealth is 2^p dollars, then the series defining the expectation becomes

$$E=1\cdot\tfrac{1}{2}+2(\tfrac{1}{2})^2+4(\tfrac{1}{2})^3+8(\tfrac{1}{2})^4+\cdots+2^p(\tfrac{1}{2})^{p+1}+2^p(\tfrac{1}{2})^{p+2}+\cdots$$
$$=\tfrac{1}{2}(p+2)\ .$$

For example, if A's fortune were $2^{10} = 1024$ dollars, then B's expectation would equal $E = \frac{1}{2}(10 + 2) = \$6.00$; and if A were a millionaire, that is, if $p=20$, then B's expectation would equal \$11.00.

But does it seem to the reader that he would be willing to play a single game with one man for one price and the same game with another for a different and much larger price? Obviously some psychological considerations must be imposed. This was the point of view of Bernoulli, who said that the difficulty in the paradox resided not so much with A's fortune as with B's. Even assuming that A's capacity to pay was adequate, nevertheless B would first consult his own financial status before purchasing a very small chance of winning a very large amount.

Bernoulli found it necessary to inquire into the problem of how much satisfaction there would be to a man in adding an increment of wealth to his personal fortune. Bernoulli's famous postulate assumes that *the satisfaction which a man has in adding an increment of wealth,* dx , *to his fortune of* x *units, is directly proportional to* dx *and inversely proportional to* x . In other words, if we call this added increment of satisfaction an increment of utility and designate it by dU, then Bernouli's assumption takes the form

$$dU=\mu\frac{dx}{x}\ , \tag{4}$$

where μ is a constant.

Therefore, the total utility would be equal to the integral of this amount, or

$$U=\mu\int_{x_0}^{x}\frac{dx}{x}=\mu\log(x/x_0)\ , \tag{5}$$

where x_0 is a threshold amount which measures the origin of the function. In the theory of Bernoulli the value of x_0 was regarded as an amount necessary to sustain life, for, as he remarks, "no man is absolutely destitute unless he is dying of hunger."

But what shall we really understand by U and in terms of what units shall we measure it? Following the pattern of the physicists we should set up a standard of measurement and in terms of this standard define units of utility. As the physicist speaks of *joules of energy,* we should also have *bernoulli's of satisfaction.* But, alas, the problem belongs to psychology and this subject has not yet produced an objective measure of human emotions satisfactory for our purpose.

Bernoulli proceeded next to define *moral expectation* in contrast to *mathematical expectation.* This concept is formulated as follows:

If a man has an initial fortune of a dollars, and if a probability, p, exists that he may increase his fortune by x dollars, then the moral expectation, ΔU, is equal to

$$\Delta U = U(x+a) - U(a) = p\,\mu[\log(x+a) - \log a] ,$$

that is,

$$\Delta U = \log(1 + x/a)^p . \tag{6}$$

In order to convert moral expectation into monetary units, Bernoulli then introduced the concept of a *moral fortune,* F_M, which he defined to be

$$F_M = \mu[\log(X+a) - \log a] , \tag{7}$$

where X is the real increment equivalent to his real expectation.

Equating moral expectation to moral fortune, that is, setting $\Delta U = F_M$, and solving for X, we obtain as the money equivalent of the expectation the following value:

$$X = a[(1 + x/a)^p - 1] . \tag{8}$$

More generally, if probabilities $p_1, p_2, \cdots, p_n$ exist that a man will add respectively $x_1, x_2, \cdots, x_n$ dollars to his initial fortune a, and if the probabilities form a complete mutually exclusive set, that is, if $p_1 + p_2 + p_3 + \cdots + p_n = 1$, then the moral expectation is given by

$$E_M = \mu[p_1 \log(x_1 + a) + p_2 \log(x_2 + a) + \cdots \\ + p_n \log(x_n + a) - \log a] .$$

Equating this to moral fortune and solving for X, we obtain as the money equivalent of the expectation the following:

$$(9) \qquad X = [(x_1 + a)^{p_1}(x_2 + a)^{p_2}(x_3 + a)^{p_3} \cdots (x_n + a)^{p_n}] - a\,.$$

In the case of continuous probabilities, mathematical expectation as defined in equation (2), is replaced by the integral of moral expectation, namely,

$$(10) \qquad E_M = \mu \int_a^b p(t) \log[1 + x(t)/a]\, dt\,.$$

The equivalent money value of this expectation is then given by

$$X = a[e^{E_M} - 1]\,.$$

We shall now consider two examples illustrating the analysis which we have just given.

Example 1. A life insurance company uses as its basic charge for the insurance of a life from age 25 to age 26 for \$1,000 the mathematical expectation \$8.0645. This amount is quoted to any individual irrespective of his total fortune. Compare the attitude toward insurance of two men of age 25, one who has a fortune of \$1,000 and the other a fortune of \$10,000.

Solution. Designating the moral expectations of the two men by ΔU_1 and ΔU_2 respectively, and assuming that μ is the same for both, we first compute the ratio

$$r = \frac{\Delta U_1}{\Delta U_2} = \frac{\log 2}{\log 1.1} = \frac{0.30103}{0.04139} = 7.273\,.$$

We thus conclude that the satisfaction of the poorer man is more than seven times that of the richer man in the ownership of a life insurance policy for \$1.000. But before we can conclude that the poor man spends proportionately more for life insurance than the rich man, we must next examine the money values set by both men on their moral expectations.

Employing formula (10), in which a is first set equal to \$1,000, and then to \$10,000, we find the respective values to be

$$X_1 = \$5.61\,, \qquad X_2 = \$7.69\,.$$

Hence we see that, in spite of the poor man's desire for insurance, he cannot afford to pay as much for it as the rich man. We might tentatively conclude from this that people in the higher income levels would devote a larger percentage of their income to the purchase of insurance, but that this percentage would not tend to vary greatly from one income level to another.

In a survey of personal budgets, which we shall discuss more completely in Chapter 8, the following expenditures for insurance were observed in the budgets of Chicago families:

Income Level	Per Cent of Money Income	Income Level	Per Cent of Money Income	Income Level	Per Cent of Money Income
\$500– 750	5.3	\$1750–2000	5.5	\$3500– 4000	6.4
750–1000	5.6	2000–2250	5.7	4000– 5000	6.6
1000–1250	5.1	2250–2500	5.7	5000– 7500	7.5
1250–1500	5.0	2500–3000	5.5	7500–10000	7.4
1500–1750	4.7	3000–3500	5.5	over 10000	9.6

The conclusion which we reached above seems to be substantiated by this table. The poor man, in spite of his desire for insurance, cannot afford to devote as large a part of his income to this purchase as he would like to do.

Example 2. Discuss the St. Petersburg paradox from the point of view of the Bernoulli theory.

Solution. Under the conditions of the game described above, we find that Bernoulli's solution, that is to say, the price to be charged for a single game, is given by formula (9) in which we write $p_r = (\frac{1}{2})^r$ and $x_r = 2^{r-1}$, and allow n to become infinite. If, under these conditions, we abbreviate the right member of (9) by $X(a)$, then we shall have

$$X(0) = 1^{1/2}\, 2^{1/4}\, 4^{1/8}\, 8^{1/16} \cdots = 2 .$$

If, however, we observe that

$$\lim_{a=\infty} a[\log(X+a) - \log a] = \lim_{a=\infty} a \log(1 + X/a)$$

$$= \lim_{a=\infty} a\left[\frac{X}{a} + \frac{X^2}{2a^2} + \cdots\right] = X ,$$

we then obtain the limiting value

$$X(\infty) = p_1 x_1 + p_2 x_2 + \cdots + p_n x_n + \cdots .$$

From the first of these values of $X(a)$ we see that a man of zero wealth will be unwilling to pay more than \$2 per game. The value for $X(\infty)$ merely shows that an assumption of infinite wealth in the Bernoulli theory reduces it to the ordinary theory of mathematical expectation.

As a matter of fact, the increase in $X(a)$ with increasing a is very slow, as one may see from the values

$$X(10) = 3 , \quad X(100) = 4.333 , \quad X(1000) = 6 .$$

It has been pointed out by Karl Menger,[1] that the paradox is actually not explained by the Bernoulli suggestion. If we use continuous probabilities, then conditions equivalent to those of the original problem are found by setting $p(t) = e^{-at}$, and $x(t) = e^{at}$ in the integral of (2). But for these same values, the integral which defines E_M in (10) converges. However, as Menger points out, values of $p(t)$ and $x(t)$ are easily written down for which neither (2) nor (10) converge.

2. *Equi-expectancy Curves*

We shall find it convenient a little later to discuss the nature of *indifference curves* and *indifference surfaces,* that is to say, loci along which utility is constant. In view of the discussion of the last section, it is possible to relate this concept to that of *equi-expectancy curves,*

[1] "Das Unsicherleitsmoment in der Wertlehre", *Zeitschrift für Nationalökonomie,* Vol. 5, 1934, pp. 459–485.

or loci along which either mathematical expectation, or moral expectation, is constant.

Let us ask the question whether one would prefer to have ten tickets out of twenty in a lottery with a prize of \$20, or ten tickets out of one hundred in a lottery with a prize of \$100?

In order to answer the question proposed we compute the mathematical expectations: $E_1 = \frac{1}{2} \times 20 = 10$, $E_2 = 0.1 \times 100 = 10$, and thus we see that one proposition is equal to the other. There is thus nothing to choose between them.

As a matter of fact, we can let $E = 10$ in the equation

$$E = px \,, \tag{11}$$

and then obtain other values of x corresponding to values of p between 0 and 1 , which would give other equivalent propositions. Equation (11) then defines a set of indifferent propositions; hence the equi-

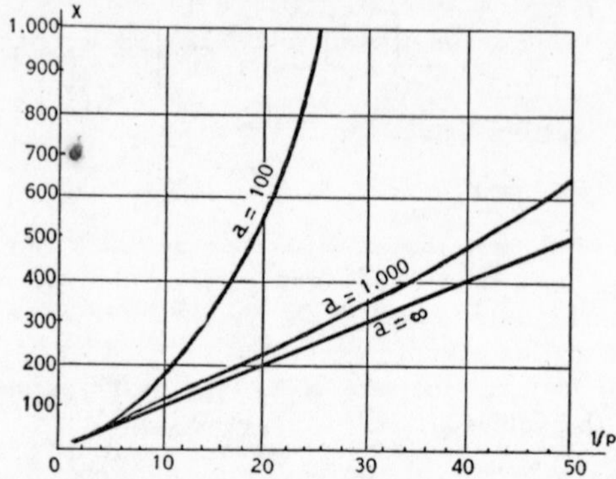

FIGURE 10.—EQUI-EXPECTANCY CURVES AT DIFFERENT LEVELS OF FORTUNE (a).

lateral hyperbolas obtained by letting E assume various values would give a set of equi-expectancy curves. Such a set of curves is called an *indifference map*.

Let us now carry the matter to an extreme case and compare the proposition of holding one ticket out of 10,000 in a lottery with a prize of \$100,000 with the proposition of holding half the tickets in a lottery with a prize of \$20. Although the mathematical expectations in both cases are the same, the two propositions seem to be psychologically different. It does not seem plausible that a person of moderate means would part with \$10 as readily for the remote contingency of winning a fortune as he would for an even chance of doubling his money.

In such a judgment as the one discussed in the preceding paragraph, it is clear that the status of a person's wealth would play some part in the matter. At any rate, let us assume that judgment would be formed on the basis of moral expectation rather than mathematical expectation. Thus we return to formula (8) of Section 1, in which we replace X by E so that it may be compared with equation (11) to which it reduces when $a = \infty$.

The curve defined by the relationship

$$E = a[(1 + x/a)^p - 1] , \tag{12}$$

when E is kept constant and x and p are allowed to vary, is called an equi-expectancy curve.

We shall consider the two cases (1) when $a = 100$, and (2) when $a = 1000$. Assuming that $E = 10$, we compute the accompanying table, which compares the moral expectations at different levels of wealth with the equivalent mathematical expectation.

$1/p$	Value of x $a = 100$	Value of x $a = 1000$	Value of x $a = \infty$
1	10.00	10.00	10
2	21.00	20.10	20
3	33.10	30.30	30
4	46.41	40.60	40
5	61.05	51.01	50
6	71.16	61.52	60
8	114.36	82.86	80
10	159.37	104.62	100
20	572.75	220.19	200
30	1,644.94	347.85	300
40	4,425.26	488.86	400
50	11,639.09	644.63	500
60	30,348.02	686.60	600
80	204,740.02	1,216.72	800
100	1,377,961.25	1,704.81	1,000
150	....	3,448.42	1,500
200	....	6,316.02	2,000

We see from this table that for probabilities which are not too small the theory of mathematical expectation is a good approximation to moral expectation, the approximation improving as the percentage of one's total fortune, which is risked, diminishes.

Unfortunately there are no data available which will serve as a statistical check for these results. It seems reasonable to believe, however, that the average man would need to be spurred by extremely high stakes before he would risk one-tenth of his entire capital in a one-hundred-to-one chance.

The relationship between the three columns in the table is graphically represented in Figure 10.

PROBLEMS

1. If a man age 40 has a fortune of \$10,000, and if his expectation of life for a single year is 0.9902, compare his moral expectation in the purchase of an insurance policy of \$1,000 with the net annual premium.

2. From formula (12) of Section 2, compute and graph the curve corresponding to the case $a = 200$.

3. A man with a capital of \$1,000 purchases three stocks in which his expectations are ½ that he will make \$400, 1/3 that he will make \$600, and 1/5 that he will make \$1,000. What should he pay for these expectations on the basis of moral expectation?

4. Verify the value $X(100) = 4.333$ given in the second illustrative example of Section 1.

3. *The Utility of Money*

From the foregoing discussion we have seen how the value of an addition to one's wealth has come to be associated with one's total fortune. Although the idea has not yet been subjected to adequate statistical analysis, it is, nevertheless, a very useful one and will be adopted in this book as suggesting an important clue to the behavior of people with respect to their expenditure of money.

Let us now make the assumption that the marginal utility of money. The function $F(W)$ is undefined, but it must have the proper-

$$\frac{dU}{dW} = \mu F(W) , \tag{13}$$

where μ is a parameter which measures one's personal generosity, or free-handedness, and where $F(W)$ is a function depending upon one's total liquid wealth, W; that is to say, his wealth easily converted into money. The function $F(W)$ is undefined, but it must have the properties

$$\text{(a)} \quad \lim_{W=\infty} F(W) = 0 \; ; \qquad \text{(b)} \quad \lim_{W=W_0} F(W) = \infty \; , \tag{14}$$

where W_0 is a threshold value, closely related to the *wolf point* discussed in Chapter 2.

Bernoulli, as we have seen, assumed that $F(W) = 1/(W - W_0)$; on the other hand, Charles Jordan has suggested the formula, $F(W) = 1/(W - W_0)^2$, and Ragnar Frisch the function, $F(W) = 1/\log(W/W_0)$. The formula of Jordan assumes that we reach money satiation more rapidly than is assumed by the formula of Bernoulli, while the formula of Frisch assumes that the approach to money satiation is relatively slow. Jordan arrived at his formula through a study of the utility involved in the purchase of life insurance, while Frisch found arguments for his formulation in considerations relating to the index of the cost of living.

Total money utility is then given by the integral

$$U(W) = \int_a^W F(W)\,dW\,,$$

where a is some value greater than W_0.

We shall designate the marginal utility of money by λ, a symbol which is commonly used for it in economic literature. From assumption (b) above it is clear that λ, regarded as a function of W, has a critical value at $W = W_0$, where it becomes infinite. This may be interpreted to mean that an individual at such a critical value will be under such psychic strain that he will cease to function as a rational being. The increase in suicides during financial crises is material evidence that great psychic shocks occur to individuals when their marginal utilities of money are evaluated in the neighborhood of their respective critical points.

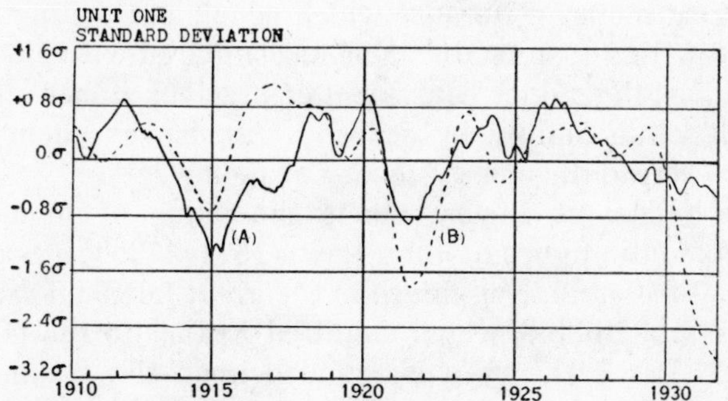

FIGURE 11.—SUICIDE AND BUSINESS CONDITIONS ILLUSTRATING THE EXISTENCE OF THE CRITICAL POINT IN THE MARGINAL UTILITY OF MONEY

Curve (A) is the inverted suicide index, based on the death rates in ten cities of the Middle Atlantic Region. Curve (B) is the index of business.—From Dublin and Bunzel: *To Be or Not To Be.*

Figure 11, reproduced from *To Be or Not To Be,* by L. I. Dublin and Bessie Bunzel, New York, 1933, exhibits the remarkable correlation between business conditions and the inverted suicide rate. The coefficient of correlation between the suicide rate for white males, ages 1–74, in the United States from 1911 to 1931, and the Index of General Business Conditions was -0.66; the correlation between the business index and the total monthly suicide rate was -0.47.

We may conclude from all of this that the concept of a marginal utility of money, residing though it does in the relatively unexplored domain of psychic behavior, furnishes a mathematical formulation of a real human potential. A theory of value, founded upon this concept, should give us insight into the real phenomena of a realistic economy.

4. The Value of Money

The value of money has always been a puzzling concept in economics. One school of thought has assumed that the value of money can be measured in terms of the amount of energy which it will purchase. Thus for $100 one can obtain a certain number of ergs of manual work, a certain number of kilowatts of electricity, a certain number of thermal units of coal, or a quantity of goods created by the expenditure of a specified number of man-hours of labor. But if strict account is taken of these erg-equivalents, it will be found that this theory is untenable. Thus the number of ergs of energy actually expended in skilled professional services has no relationship to the number of ergs expended in the money equivalent of common manual labor. The great money difference which people are willing to pay for goods marked with a fashionable label as compared with similar goods without the label, the money equivalent of precious stones and of other objects given value mainly by scarcity, furnish excellent examples with which to refute the energy theory of money.

Another fallacious theory about the value of money centers around the romantic figure of John Law (1671–1729), a Scotch financier, who was the dominating figure in the great financial crisis known as the Mississippi Bubble, which engulfed France in the period from 1716 to 1720. Law's theory was founded upon the assumption that scarcity of money restricts commerce, and that this scarcity can be remedied by the issue of paper currency against physical wealth. That is to say, he assumed that the value of money is determined by the ratio of its quantity to the value of the physical holdings of a country. The fallacy was dramatically exhibited by the spectacular collapse of the Mississippi scheme in 1720.

In this book we shall assume that *the value of money is measured by its marginal utility*. In this way the concept of the value of money is, on the one hand, intimately related to physical wealth, and, on the other, it takes account of those psychic elements which give extravagant money equivalents to objects of small intrinsic usefulness.

An amusing and instructive story by O. Henry illustrates this point. In his work entitled *Gentle Grafters,* the confidence men who are the heroes of the book are called gentle, because they seek to exchange their worthless goods for their victims' cash by a strict equating of utilities. For example, a man places in their hands a sum of \$5,000 for safekeeping. Wishing to appropriate this sum they seek to determine its utility to the owner. When he tells them that he is planning to bet the sum upon a horse race, the utility of the money is determined. They reason that the utility of \$5,000 bet on a horse race is approximately equivalent to five shares of stock in a corporation, which has an issue of 1,000 shares of stock with nominal value of \$1,000 per share. Hence, equating the utilities, they print 1,000 shares of stock and leave their victim in the possession of five of them.

5. *The Utility of Goods*

It is useful to extend the concept of utility to goods, an extension which we have already indicated in Section 1. In order to limit our preliminary ideas to the simplest case, let us consider the utility for a single variable. If x is, let us say, the number of ties a man possesses, then $U(x)$ will measure the pleasure which he derives from the possession of them. But after he has purchased a certain number of ties, let us say 20, then the addition of another tie to his stock will add very little to his satisfaction. On the other hand, if the man possesses but a single tie, then the addition of a second will materially increase his satisfaction. We may thus regard $U(x)$ as a function, which, while it increases, in general, as x increases, tends asymptotically to an upper limit. Actually, after a certain point, $U(x)$ might decline in value. It is possible, for example, that the man whom we have just discussed might find the possession of too many ties a burden instead of a pleasure. The old story of King Midas and the golden touch is a case in point.

A function, $U(x)$, such as we have described, can be characterized by its first derivative. Thus we see that dU/dx, after a certain value of x, would continually decrease toward zero. W. S. Jevons in his *Theory of Political Economy* (1871), which first introduced the concept of utility into English economics, refers to dU/dx as *the degree of utility*, and the value of this derivative at the last element of x which is consumed as *the final degree of utility*. Today we refer to dU/dx as the *marginal utility* of x. Jevons states the following as a fundamental postulate: "We may state as a general law, that *the degree of utility varies with the quantity of the commodity, and ultimately decreases as that quantity increases.*"

The idea of utility is easily extended to more than one good. Thus, we may designate by the expression

$$U = U(x_1, x_2, \cdots, x_n)$$

the utility of owning, or consuming, n goods in the amounts $x_1, x_2, \cdots, x_n$.

The function thus defined may be regarded as a surface in the space of n variables. This space we shall call a *commodity space,* and we shall assume that we can move continuously from one point $(x'_1, x'_2, \cdots, x'_n)$ in it to another point $(x''_1, x''_2, \cdots, x''_n)$.

It will be convenient, also, to assume that U has derivatives at least as high as order two, so that we can evaluate

$$(15) \qquad U_i = \frac{\partial U}{\partial x_i}, \quad U_{ij} = \frac{\partial^2 U}{\partial x_i \partial x_j}.$$

The quantity U_i is called the *marginal utility* of the goods x_i.

Clearly the increment of utility, dU, can be written

$$(16) \qquad dU = \frac{\partial U}{\partial x_1} dx_1 + \frac{\partial U}{\partial x_2} dx_2 + \cdots + \frac{\partial U}{\partial x_n} dx_n$$

$$= U_1 \, dx_1 + U_2 \, dx_2 + \cdots + U_n \, dx_n.$$

Total utility can then be expressed as the integral

$$(17) \qquad U = \int_C U_1 \, dx_1 + U_2 \, dx_2 + \cdots + U_n \, dx_n,$$

where C is some path in the space of the commodities $x_1, x_2, \cdots, x_n$.

In the case of the simple utility function, $U(x)$, discussed above, it was assumed that after some value of x, the derivative, dU/dx, became a decreasing function of the variable. This assumption is equivalent to stating that the second derivative, d^2U/dx^2, was negative.

In the general case, the Jevons' postulate may be stated as the assumption that $U(x_1, x_2, \cdots, x_n)$ is a *convex function.* Analytically this is equivalent to stating that the quadratic form

$$(18) \qquad d^2U = \sum u_{ij} \, dx_i \, dx_j$$

must be *negative definite.*

A quadratic form is said to be *definite* if it assumes only values of one sign for all permissible values of the variables, the case where all the variables are zero being excepted. The form is *negative definite* if it assumes only negative values.

It is proved in higher algebra that the condition that d^2U shall be negative definite is that the leading principal minors of the determinant $|U_{ij}|$, that is to say, the minors which have as their diagonal the diagonal elements of $|U_{ij}|$, shall be alternately negative and positive.

Explicitly this condition becomes

$$(19)\quad U_{11} < 0\,, \quad \begin{vmatrix} U_{11} & U_{12} & U_{13} \\ U_{21} & U_{22} & U_{23} \\ U_{31} & U_{32} & U_{33} \end{vmatrix} < 0\,, \text{etc.}$$

$$\begin{vmatrix} U_{11} & U_{12} \\ U_{21} & U_{22} \end{vmatrix} > 0\,, \quad \begin{vmatrix} U_{11} & U_{12} & U_{13} & U_{14} \\ U_{21} & U_{22} & U_{23} & U_{24} \\ U_{31} & U_{32} & U_{33} & U_{34} \\ U_{41} & U_{42} & U_{43} & U_{44} \end{vmatrix} > 0, \text{etc.}$$

It will be useful to us later to observe that the plane tangent to the utility surface at a commodity point $(x^{(0)}{}_1\,, x^{(0)}{}_2\,, \cdots, x^{(0)}{}_n)$ is expressed in terms of the marginal utilities evaluated at the point, that is, $U^{(0)}{}_1\,, U^{(0)}{}_2\,, \cdots, U^{(0)}{}_n$. In terms of these quantities we have as the equation of the tangent plane

$$(20)\qquad (x_1 - x_1{}^{(0)})\,U_1{}^{(0)} + (x_2 - x_2{}^{(0)})\,U_2{}^{(0)} + \cdots \\ + (x_n - x_n{}^{(0)})\,U_n{}^{(0)} = U - U^{(0)}\,.$$

Let us now consider the change in the utility function when there is a change in the amounts purchased of two goods only. Without loss of generality, these may be assumed to be the goods designated by x_1 and x_2. If we further assume that there is neither loss nor gain in utility in this transaction, we shall then have

$$dU \equiv U_1\,dx_1 + U_2\,dx_2 = 0\;;$$

that is to say, we obtain

$$\frac{dx_1}{dx_2} = \frac{U_2}{U_1}.$$

The ratio, $r_{21} = U_2/U_1$, is called the *marginal rate of substitution of* x_1 *for* x_2.

Let us now consider two examples illustrating the theory of this section.

Example 1. We shall derive the conditions under which

$$U = x^a\,y^b\,z^c$$

may serve as a utility function.

Solution. Designating the marginal utilities by U_i, $i = 1, 2, 3$, we compute

$$U_1 = a\,x^{a-1}\,y^b\,z^c = \frac{a}{x}U\,, \quad U_2 = \frac{b}{y}U\,, \quad U_3 = \frac{c}{z}U\,.$$

The determinant $|U_{ij}|$ is then seen to equal

$$\begin{vmatrix} \dfrac{a(a-1)}{x^2}U & \dfrac{ab}{xy}U & \dfrac{ac}{xz}U \\ \dfrac{ab}{xy}U & \dfrac{b(b-1)}{y^2}U & \dfrac{bc}{yz}U \\ \dfrac{ac}{xz}U & \dfrac{bc}{yz}U & \dfrac{c(c-1)}{z^2}U \end{vmatrix}\,.$$

The convexity conditions (19) are then easily reduced to the following inequalities:

$$\text{(21)} \qquad a(a-1) < 0\,, \; ab(a+b-1) < 0\,, \; abc(a+b+c-1) < 0\,.$$

These are the desired conditions under which the given function may represent utility. It is clear that all the inequalities are satisfied provided a, b, and c are positive and their sum is less than one.

As a corollary we observe that if $c = 0$, then the convexity conditions reduce to the first two inequalities. Although we shall find it convenient later in simple illustration to assume a utility function of the form $U = xy$, it is clear from the above analysis that this function does not satisfy the convexity conditions, and hence would not be a realistic representation of actual utility.

Example 2. Discuss the function

$$U = -(x^2 + y^2 + 2z^2 + 3w^2) + 24x + 32y + 40z + 84w$$

as a representation of utility.

Solution. Designating the marginal utilities by U_i, $i = 1, 2, 3, 4$, we compute:

$$U_1 = 24 - 2x\,, \qquad U_2 = 32 - 2y\,, \qquad U_3 = 40 - 4z\,, \qquad U_4 = 84 - 6w\,.$$

From these values we compute the elements of the determinant $|U_{ij}|$ and thus obtain

$$\begin{vmatrix} -2 & 0 & 0 & 0 \\ 0 & -2 & 0 & 0 \\ 0 & 0 & -4 & 0 \\ 0 & 0 & 0 & -6 \end{vmatrix}$$

The principal minors of this determinant are respectively -2, 4, -16, and 96; hence the quadratic form (18) is negative definite, and the convexity conditions are satisfied.

The plane tangent to the utility surface at the point x_0, y_0, z_0, w_0 is readily computed to be

$$U = x(24 - 2x_0) + y(32 - 2y_0) + z(40 - 4z_0) + w(84 - 6w_0)$$
$$+ 24x_0 + 32y_0 + 40z_0 + 84w_0 + U_0 .$$

PROBLEMS

1. Write three functions which would serve, in theory at least, to measure the utility of one commodity. For example, $U = A \log(x/a)$ is such a function. Why?

2. If a man's desire to add dy units of a commodity to his present holding of y units is given by $dW = m\, dy/y$, and if his pleasure in adding dx units of money to his present capital of x is given by $dU = \mu dx/x$, compute the relationship between x and y on the assumption that $U + W = C$, where C is a constant.

3. Discuss the conditions under which

$$U = ax^2 + 2bxy + cy^2 + 2dx + 2ey + f$$

can serve as a utility function.

4. Give $U = x^a y^b$, $a < 1$, $a + b < 1$, prove that this function satisfies the convexity conditions imposed upon the utility function.

5. Show that $U = ax + by + c(xy)^m$ satisfies the convexity conditions provided $c > 0$, and $m < \frac{1}{2}$.

6. Compute the marginal rate of substitution for (1) the utility function given in problem 3; (2) the utility function given in problem 4.

7. If a utility function is given by $U = U(x,y)$, is $\log U(x,y)$ also a utility function?

8. If $U = x + y + (xy)^{\frac{1}{2}}$, compute the tangent plane at the point $U = 7$, $x = 1$, $y = 4$.

6. *Indifference Surfaces and Lines of Preference*

The basis of hedonistic philosophy, which we may tentatively assume as the philosophy which governs economic activity, is found in the assumption that a person always seeks to increase his utility.

We shall assume, therefore, that if a person is given a free choice in the matter of the ownership or use of goods, he will, as an average economic individual, accumulate this ownership, or use, along the path which offers him a maximum increase in utility.

The development of a proper mathematical picture of hedonistic behavior begins with the concept of an indifference surface. Thus if $U(x_1, x_2, \cdots, x_n)$ is the utility function associated with a commodity space of n goods, then the equation

$$U(x_1, x_2, \cdots, x_n) = k, \tag{22}$$

where k is a constant, defines an *indifference surface* in the space. No point on the surface will be preferred to any other point, since for every set of values which satisfies the equation the utility is the same.

If k is assumed to vary, then a series of indifference surfaces will be obtained and the totality of such surfaces is said to form an *indifference map*. We should observe that when only two variables are involved, equation (22) defines an *indifference curve* instead of a surface.

Let us now consider the marginal utilities

$$U_i = \frac{\partial U}{\partial x_i} . \tag{23}$$

It will be convenient to think of these as components of a vector in the direction defined by the infinitesimal vector $(dx_1, dx_2, dx_3, \cdots, dx_n)$. In the language of vector analysis it is customary to refer to such a vector as a *gradient*, and to designate it symbolically as follows:

$$\text{grad } U = (U_1, U_2, \cdots, U_n) . \tag{24}$$

Since the direction cosines of the normal to the tangent plane of the surface (22) are proportional to the marginal utilities, one observes that the gradient vector points in the direction of this normal

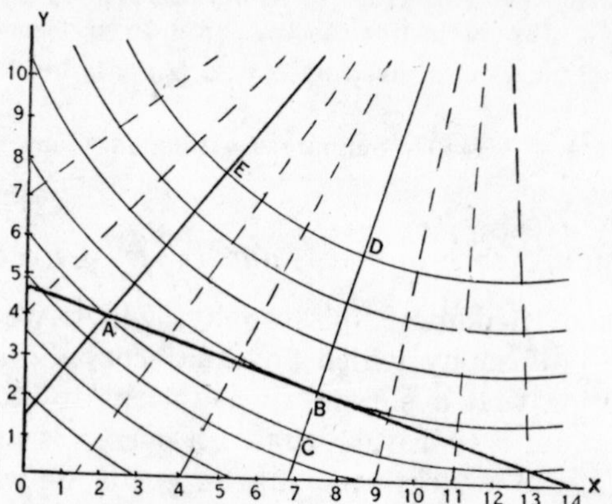

FIGURE 12.—INDIFFERENCE MAP SHOWING PREFERENCE CURVES AND BUDGET LINES.

line and hence indicates the direction of the maximum change of utility. The direction thus indicated is called the *preference direction* of the individual and is the direction in which he will acquire commodities if his choice is unrestricted by other considerations.

A line drawn through successive points of an indifference map in the direction of preference is called a *preference line*. The totality of such lines is called a *preference map*.

From differential geometry it is seen that the system of differential equations which defines a preference map is the following set of equations:

$$(25) \qquad \frac{dx_1}{U_1}=\frac{dx_2}{U_2}=\frac{dx_3}{U_3}=\cdots=\frac{dx_n}{U_n}.$$

Example. As an example, let us compute the indifference map and the preference map associated with the utility function

$$U(x,y)=24x+32y-x^2-y^2.$$

Solution. If we set $U(x,y)=k$, then we see that the indifference lines are the arcs, which lie in the first quadrant, of the circles

$$(x-12)^2+(y-16)^2=400-k.$$

In Figure 12 these are the curves ED, AC, etc.

Since the marginal utilities are given by

$$U_1=24-2x, \qquad U_2=32-2y,$$

we see that the differential equation of the preference lines is the following:

$$\frac{dx}{24-2x}=\frac{dy}{32-2y}.$$

The general integral of this equation, namely,

$$y-16=m(x-12),$$

shows that the preference lines are straight lines through the point $(12,16)$. In Figure 12 these are the lines AE, BD, etc.

In recent econometric literature it has become common practice to refer to the utility function as a *choice-indicator,* or more briefly, as an *indicator,* provided the function increases monotonically as one moves from one indifference surface to another that is preferred to the first. When the indicator characteristic of the utility function is the predominately useful one the function is often represented in the notation,[2]

$$I=I(x_1, x_2, \cdots, x_n).$$

PROBLEMS

1. Graph the indifference lines associated with the utility function

$$U=180x+384y-9x^2-16y^2.$$

2. Make a preference map for the utility function of problem 1.

3. Graph the indifference lines associated with the utility function $U=xy$. Determine the preference lines and construct a preference map.

4. Make an indifference map for $U=x^{1/3}\,y^{1/3}$.

5. Show that the preference lines for the utility function of problem 4 are equilateral hyperbolas.

[2] See, for example, R. Frisch and A. Wald. [*Bibliography,* Frisch (6) and Wald.]

6. If $U = u(x,y)$ is a utility function, and if $I(U)$ is an indicator, prove that

$$\frac{\partial^2 I}{\partial^2 x} = I'(U)\frac{\partial^2 U}{\partial^2 x} + I''(U)\left(\frac{\partial U}{\partial x}\right)^2.$$

7. If $(x-a)^2 - k(y-b)^2 = R^2$ forms a set of preference lines as k varies, show that the marginal rate of substitution defined in Section 5 is given by

$$r_{21} = \frac{(x-a)(y-b)}{(x-a)^2 - R^2}.$$

8. If $U = u(x,y)$ is a utility function, and if $I = I(U)$ is an indicator, prove that $U_1/U_2 = I_1/I_2$, where the subscripts denote differentiation with respect to x and y.

7. *The Budget Equation*

Let us now consider an individual's relationship to his own utility surface, when this relationship is restrained by the limitations imposed by his budget. That is to say, let us suppose that an individual finds himself in possession of the amounts $Q_1, Q_2, Q_3, \cdots, Q_n$ of a set of commodities, the prices of which are respectively $P_1, P_2, P_3, \cdots, P_n$. We shall assume that the individual can freely exchange one commodity for another at the quoted prices. Our problem, then, is to determine whether he can increase his utility, subject to the condition of a fixed budget, which is constant and equal to

$$E_0 = \sum P_i Q_i, \tag{26}$$

where E_0 is used to designate the expenditure of the individual.

Analytically the problem reduces to that of maximizing the utility function

$$U = U(x_1, x_2, \cdots, x_n), \tag{27}$$

subject to the restraint imposed by the *budget plane*

$$E \equiv \sum P_i x_i = E_0. \tag{28}$$

The desired maximization is attained by means of the theory of Lagrangian multipliers, which, with sufficient generality for the present problem, may be formulated as follows:

Given a function $U = U(x_1, x_2, \cdots, x_n)$ of n variables, which are connected by the m distinct relations

$$F_1(x_1, x_2, \cdots, x_n) = 0, \quad F_2(x_1, x_2, \cdots, x_n) = 0, \quad \cdots, F_m(x_1, x_2, \cdots, x_n) = 0;$$

then, in order to find the values of $x_1, x_2, \cdots, x_n$ which may render this function a maximum or a minimum, we must equate to zero the partial derivatives of the auxiliary function

$$U + \lambda_1 F_1 + \lambda_2 F_2 + \cdots + \lambda_m F_m ,$$

where $\lambda_1 , \lambda_2 , \cdots , \lambda_m$, the Lagrangian multipliers, are constants.[3]

In the present instance, since we have only the one restraint condition, we write

$$\frac{\partial}{\partial x_i}(U + \lambda_1 E) = 0 , \quad \text{that is,} \quad U_i + \lambda_1 P_i = 0 .$$

Letting i assume the values from 1 to n, we may write these equations in the following form

$$\frac{U_1}{P_1} = \frac{U_2}{P_2} = \frac{U_3}{P_3} = \ldots = \frac{U_n}{P_n} = -\lambda_1 . \tag{29}$$

Since these ratios are all positive, it is clear that $-\lambda_1$ is also positive. We shall therefore replace it by λ, and identify this parameter with the marginal utility of money.

Equations (29), which are thus seen to define a set of necessary conditions for the existence of an extremal, are among the most important in economics. They are basic in all problems of exchange in static economics.

Example. As an example, let us assume that the utility of a man, A, with respect to two commodities X and Y, is defined by the same function used in the example of the preceding section, namely,

$$U(x, y) = 24x + 32y - x^2 - y^2. \tag{30}$$

Let us assume further that A possesses 2 units of X worth \$2 per unit, and 4 units of Y worth \$6. If the sum, $2 \times 2 + 4 \times 6 = 28$, is all that A can allow for the purchase of the two commodities, then his budget equation is given by

$$2x + 6y = 28 . \tag{31}$$

We now seek to find the combination, that is to say, the number of units of X and Y, which will give the maximum satisfaction to A subject to the restraint imposed by his budget.

Solution. Since the marginal utilities are respectively

$$U_1 = 24 - 2x , \qquad U_2 = 32 - 2y ,$$

conditions (29) reduce to

$$\frac{24 - 2x}{2} = \frac{32 - 2y}{6} ;$$

[3] For a proof of this see E. Goursat: (Hedrick translation) *A Course in Mathematical Analysis*, Vol. 1, 1904, pp. 128–129.

that is to say, to the straight line

$$3x - y = 20. \tag{32}$$

In Figure 12 it will be observed that this is the equation of the preference line through the point B, that is to say, the point where the budget line, AB, is tangent to one of the curves of constant utility.

The gain in utility of position B over position A is represented by the distance BC. In order to compute this difference in utility, we first solve for the intersection between (31) and (32). This we find to be the point (7.4, 2.2). Substituting this point in the utility function, we then obtain as the desired difference the following:

$$\Delta U = U(7.4, 2.2) - U(2, 4) = 188.4 - 156 = 32.4 .$$

PROBLEMS

1. An individual is at the point (2,4) on the indifference map for the utility function: $U = 180x + 384y - 9x^2 - 16y^2$. If the prices per unit of the commodities are respectively \$2 and \$6, determine his point of preference and compute the resulting change in utility.

2. Consider the individual of problem 1 with respect to an indifference map constructed from the utility function: $U = xy$. Determine his point of preference. Compare the utilities of the initial point and of the point of preference.

3. Compute the preference point of the individual of problem 1 with respect to an indifference map constructed from the utility function: $U = x^{1/3}y^{1/3}$.

8. *The Weber-Fechner Law and its Relationship to the Utility Concept*

In the first section of this chapter we have indicated how Bernoulli was led to the concept of the marginal utility of money. His assumption, as we have seen, took the form: $dU/dW = \mu/W$. It is perhaps more than coincidence that experimental studies in psychology tend to confirm Bernoulli's assumption.

This interesting relationship between the concepts of utility and psychological measurement is found in what is called the *Weber-Fechner law,* which proposes to formulate more or less exactly the connection between change of stimulus and change of sensation.

This "psycho-physical" law, first enunciated by E. H. Weber (1795–1878), was extensively studied by G. T. Fechner (1801–1887), who gave it a precise formulation. In its simplest form the law may be stated as follows: "In order that the intensity of a sensation may increase in arithmetical progression, the stimulus must increase in geometrical progression".

To reduce this to a simple formula, let S measure the intensity of a sensation, and let R measure the stimulus necessary to produce the sensation. Then dS/dt will be the increase in S per unit of time produced by dR/dt ; from hypothesis we have

$$\frac{dS}{dt} = c \,, \qquad \frac{dR}{dt} = c' R \,.$$

Hence, eliminating dt , we get

$$\frac{dS}{dR} = k \frac{1}{R} \,, \qquad k = c/c' \,;$$

which leads by integration to the formula

$$S = k \log (R/R_0) \,.$$

Although the sensations contemplated by the psychologists were those of weight, sound, light, and so on, there is no reason why S might not be extended to include the sensation of pleasure, as this psychic variable is stimulated by different things. For example, we might include the sensation of pleasure which is derived from the receipt of money, or from the possession of a bank account. From this point of view the money utility as postulated by Bernoulli is a special case of the Weber-Fechner law.

Attempts have been made to construct the utility function of n independent goods from the Weber-Fechner law by assuming that the sensations of pleasure derived from the ownership of each separate item are additive. Thus, if we make the assumption that total sensation is composed linearly of each separate sensation, that is, if

$$S = S_1 + S_2 + \cdots + S_n \,,$$

where we abbreviate $S_i = c_i \log (x_i/x_i^0)$, then we should have as the total sensation

$$\begin{aligned} S &= \sum c_i \log (x_i/x_i^0) \\ &= \log (x_1^{c_1} x_2^{c_2} x_3^{c_3} \cdots x_n^{c_n}) + S_0 \,. \end{aligned}$$

Hence, replacing $S - S_0$ by $\log (U - U_0)$, we obtain as the form of the utility function the following product:

$$U - U_0 = x_1^{c_1} x_2^{c_2} x_3^{c_3} \cdots x_n^{c_n} \,. \tag{33}$$

Some attempts have been made by L. L. Thurstone to test statistically this approach to the problem of utility.[4] However, the data which he employed were obtained subjectively, and hence the conclu-

[4] "The Indifference Function," *Journal of Social Psychology*, Vol. 2, 1931, pp. 139–167.

sions seem to be prejudiced by an assumption of those very elements of the theory which are to be tested.

The direct measurement of utility, however, is admittedly a very difficult matter. There is some indication, nevertheless, that further development in the field of bio-chemistry may throw considerable light on the matter, since progress has been made in recent years in correlating emotional responses of various kinds with changes in certain glandular secretions of the body.

In this book, however, we shall not reject the concept of utility because emotional responses cannot be measured in absolute terms. Certain inferences follow from the assumption of the existence of a utility function in problems of economic exchange, and some of these inferences are amenable to statistical measurement. Moreover, when necessity demands an explicit formulation of utility, it will be convenient to assume that the functional representation of utility is approximated by the Weber-Fechner law. Measurable results seem to indicate that this assumption does not lead to unrealistic conclusions.

9. *The Indeterminacy of Indifference*

One interesting contribution obtained from a consideration of the psychological aspects of the utility function is associated with what

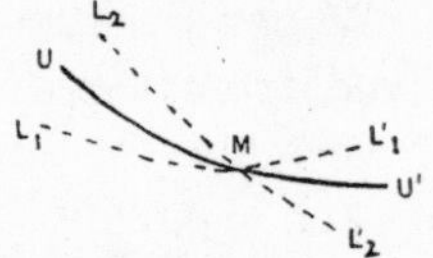

FIGURE 13.—CURVES ILLUSTRATING THE INDETERMINACY OF INDIFFERENCE.

we might call the *indeterminacy of indifference.*

Thus it is found from psychological experiments that if two objects weigh respectively W and $W + \Delta W$ pounds, an individual cannot detect the difference between them when ΔW remains smaller than a determinate *threshold value.* Hence, there is a complete indeterminacy of choice within the threshold limits.

It is obvious that this psychological experiment has an immediate implication in the theory of indifference, since choice, if limited by too small a difference between the alternatives, is also indeterminate.

A theory of such indeterminacy has been considered by N. Georgescu-Roegen, in a theoretical paper of much interest.[5] Thus he criticizes the following two postulates implicitly assumed by the analytical theory of utility:

---

[5] "The Pure Theory of Consumer's Behavior," *Quarterly Journal of Economics,* Vol. 50, 1936, pp. 545–593.

(1) There is a unique combination which will separate the non-preferred combinations from the preferred ones.

(2) The limiting directions of the slopes of the indifference element in either direction from an indifference point are vertically opposite.

The author reaches the conclusion that if an individual is at a point M on his curve of indifference, represented by UU' in Figure 13, and if he wishes to change his position by moving along the curve, then the indeterminacy in satisfaction for a sufficiently small change in stimulus permits the individual to move with indifference along any path between a lower limiting line L_1L_1' and an upper limiting line $L_2L'_2$, provided the distance is sufficiently short. Indeterminacy in indifference is thus an *im klienen* phenomenon, which, borrowing the word from F. W. Taussig, the author calls a *penumbra*.[6]

As a result of this argument the following conclusions are reached:

> The penumbra of demand makes way for an explanation of many facts that are observed in actual markets. In this way we may account for certain aspects of the imperfections of markets.
>
> The general means used by the entrepreneurs for inducing people to buy more of one commodity — which necessarily implies loss of some others — might be separated into two groups: those that aim at influencing the position of the buyer within the existing penumbra and those that seek to modify his tastes. The immediate task of the salesman, special sales, loss leaders, etc. belong to the first group. The second group consists mainly of advertising on a large scale and for a long time, in other words, consists of real propaganda to convince buyers of the advantages of consuming more of the advertised commodity.
>
> Stable commodities, like meat, bread, milk, etc., that are more regularly consumed and consequently experimented with longer, will naturally present a smaller threshold and thus a smaller penumbra of demand. This seems to be in complete agreement with the fact that the first group of actions on the part of the seller is practically absent in the marketing of these commodities. Such actions will be especially important and conspicuous in the case of those commodities whose use is less frequent.
>
> There is thus a sense in which two different commodities, not necessarily competitive, can be considered as competing against each other in the short run as well as in the long.

10. *Utility as a Functional*

In preceding sections of this chapter we have assumed that there existed a function,

---

[6] "Is Market Price Determinate?" *Quarterly Journal of Economics,* Vol. 35, 1921, p. 394.

$$U = U(x_1, x_2, \cdots, x_n),$$

which represented the utility to an individual of the use of n kinds of goods in the amounts specified by the variables $x_1, x_2, \cdots, x_n$. We also observed the difficulties connected with the explicit determination of such a function and noted that the observable values were the ratios of the marginal utilities, since U_i/U_j, under the limitations imposed by the budget equation, was the ratio P_i/P_j.

Hence, if we set up the differential of U, in terms of the marginal utilities, that is, if we write

$$dU = U_1\,dx + U_2\,dx + \cdots U_n\,dx, \tag{34}$$

then the total utility may be defined by the integral

$$U = \int_C U_1\,dx + U_2\,dx + \cdots + U_n\,dx, \tag{35}$$

where C is some path through the commodity space from an initial position A to a second position B.

But there is no way of knowing a priori whether a second path, C', from A to B will give the same value to U, unless we make the assumption that dU is, indeed, the differential of a point function in the variables. If, however, we regard utility as primarily defined by the integral given in (35), then the assumption that every path between A and B gives a unique value to U is a highly restricted one, which can be tested only by a realistic investigation of statistical data not available at the present stage of economic knowledge.

If U, as defined by (35), has a unique value for all paths between the points A and B, then U is said to be a *point function,* or more briefly, a *function* of the variables involved. Otherwise, U is said to be a *functional.*

Questions presented by the definition of utility as an integral were considered by Pareto as the result of a suggestion made by Vito Volterra, the father of the modern theory of functionals.

Thus, defining utility by the integral

$$I = \int A\,dx + B\,dy + \cdots + M\,dt,$$

which is merely the same thing as U defined by (35) above only in different notation, Pareto in his *Manuel d'économie politique* (p. 556) says:

> If one then considers a commodity path, which departing from a point $x, y, \ldots, t$, returns again to this point, one says that he has traversed a *closed*

cycle provided he returns to this point with the same index of ophelimity with which he left it. This case corresponds to indifference in the order of consumption.

One will say that he has traversed an *open cycle,* if he returns to the point of departure with an index of ophelimity different from that with which he departed. This case corresponds to that in which the order of consumption influences the pleasure which it occasions.

We can illustrate this difference by means of the two forms

$$dU = y\,dx + x\,dy\,, \qquad dU = y\,dx - x\,dy\,.$$

In the first instance U is a point function, which has the explicit value $U = xy + K$, where K is an arbitrary constant. The integral

$$(36) \qquad U = \int_A^B y\,dx + x\,dy\,,$$

where C is any path in the xy-plane from a point A to a second point B, yields a unique value.

In the second instance, however, there is a great difference. If we evaluate

$$(37) \qquad U = \int_A^B y\,dx - x dy$$

over two paths between A and B the difference between the two values of the integral will be *numerically equal to twice the area included between the paths.*

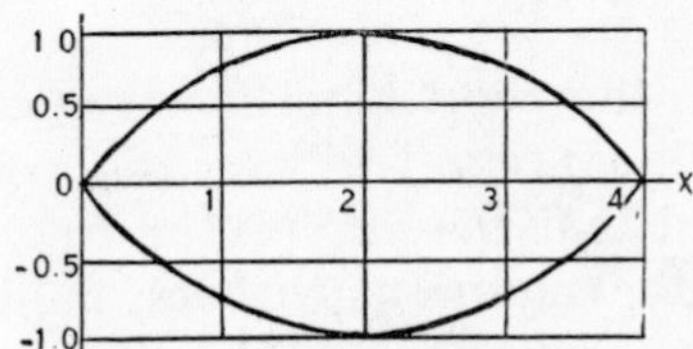

FIGURE 14.—INTEGRATION PATHS.

Example. As an example, let us consider the values of U obtained when the integration is over the parabola, $y = -\frac{1}{4}x(x-4)$, and then over the parabola, $y = \frac{1}{4}x(x-4)$, between the points $(0, 0)$ and $(4, 0)$, as shown in Figure 14.

Solution. We thus obtain, $dy = (1 - \frac{1}{2}x)\,dx$, for the first parabola, and hence $dU_1 = \frac{1}{2}x^2 dx$. From this it follows that

$$U_1 = \int_0^4 (x^3/12)\,dx = 16/3\,.$$

Similarly we find $U_2 = -16/3$, and hence we obtain $U_1 - U_2 = 32/3$, which is twice the area inclosed by the two curves.

On the other hand, let us evaluate $dU = y\,dx + x\,dy$ over the same two parabolas. For the first we obtain $dU_1 = (2x - 3x^2/4)\,dx$, and for the second dU_2

$= (3x^2/4 - 2x)\,dx$. Integrating both of these expressions from 0 to 4, we obtain identical values, namely, zero.

If the value of the integral (35) is zero for any closed path C, then the differential form defined by (34) is said to be *exact.*

Criteria for the exactness of a differential form may be obtained from what is called the generalized formula of Stokes, which may be stated as follows:

(38)

$$\int_C U_1\,dx_1 + U_2\,dx_2 + \cdots + U_n\,dx_n \equiv \int\int_G \sum_{ij} \left(\frac{\partial U_i}{\partial x_j} - \frac{\partial U_j}{\partial x_i}\right) dx_i\,dx_j\,.$$

The path C for the line integral is some closed path in the commodity space $(x_1, x_2, \cdots, x_n)$; the integration for the second integral is taken over any cap, or hypersurface, G, bounded by the closed path C. The proof of this famous identity belongs to advanced mathematics, but its applicability in the problem before us is readily understood.

Referring to the right hand member of the identity, we see that the general criteria for the exactness of the differential form (34) are given by the conditions

$$\frac{\partial U_i}{\partial x_j} - \frac{\partial U_j}{\partial x_i} = 0, \quad i, j = 1, 2, \cdots, n\,. \tag{39}$$

These conditions make the right hand member of (38) vanish identically, and hence the line integral will vanish over any closed path.

It will be observed that the differential form (34) can be made integrable, under certain conditions through multiplication by a factor r of the n variables. Conditions (39) are then replaced by

$$\frac{\partial (r\,U_i)}{\partial\,x_j} - \frac{\partial (r\,U_j)}{\partial\,x_i} = 0\,. \tag{40}$$

In the case of three variables it can be shown that the existence of such an integrating factor reduces to the following single condition upon the marginal utilities

$$U_1\left(\frac{\partial U_3}{\partial x_2} - \frac{\partial U_2}{\partial x_3}\right) + U_2\left(\frac{\partial U_1}{\partial x_3} - \frac{\partial U_3}{\partial x_1}\right) + U_3\left(\frac{\partial U_2}{\partial x_1} - \frac{\partial U_1}{\partial x_2}\right) = 0\,. \tag{41}$$

Thus, let us write conditions (40) for the case of three variables in the following explicit form:

$$r\left(\frac{\partial U_2}{\partial x_1}-\frac{\partial U_1}{\partial x_2}\right)+U_2\frac{\partial r}{\partial x_1}-U_1\frac{\partial r}{\partial x_2}=0\,,$$

$$r\left(\frac{\partial U_3}{\partial x_2}-\frac{\partial U_2}{\partial x_3}\right)+U_3\frac{\partial r}{\partial x_2}-U_2\frac{\partial r}{\partial x_3}=0\,,$$

$$r\left(\frac{\partial U_1}{\partial x_3}-\frac{\partial U_3}{\partial x_1}\right)+U_1\frac{\partial r}{\partial x_3}-U_3\frac{\partial r}{\partial x_1}=0\,.$$

If the first of these equations is multiplied by U_3, the second by U_1, and the third by U_2, and if then the resulting equations are added, there is obtained equation (41) multiplied by r. Since r cannot be identically zero, condition (41) follows as a natural consequence.

It will be clear from this discussion that the conditions of integrability impose stringent conditions upon the marginal utilities. Hence the assumption that there exist utility surfaces along which we move with indifference is by no means obvious a priori.

PROBLEMS

1. Evaluate the line integral

$$I=\int 3x^2y^2dx+2x^3ydy$$

from the point (2,2) to the point (3,6) along a straight line connecting the two points and along the parabola: $y=x^2-x$. Show that the values thus obtained are equal.

2. Evaluate the line integral

$$I=\int 2x^2ydx+3xydy$$

along the same two paths as those given in problem 1. Show that these values are unequal.

3. What integrating factor will render the differential in the integral of problem 2 exact?

4. Test the following for integrability.

$$dU=(U-U_0)\left(\frac{dw}{w}+\frac{dx}{x}+\frac{dy}{y}+\frac{dz}{z}\right).$$

Prove that an integrating factor is $w^2x^2y^2z^2$.

5. Given

$$dU=yz\,dx+xz\,dy+xy\,dz\,,$$

find an integrating factor which makes dU exact. Hence construct indifference surfaces and preference lines. Does the utility function satisfy the condition of convexity?

6. Prove that the differential corresponding to the utility function derived from the Weber-Fechner law is given by the following:

$$dU=(U-U_0)\left[\frac{c_1\,dx_1}{x_1}+\frac{c_2\,dx_2}{x_2}+\cdots+\frac{c_n\,dx_n}{x_n}\right].$$

7. Find the conditions which will assure convexity for the Weber-Fechner utility function.

8. If total sensation is assumed to be the product of individual sensations, what would be the form assumed by the general Weber-Fechner law?

9. Specialize the result obtained in problem 8 to two sensations, and test the utility function for convexity.

10. Prove that the integrability conditions for the general differential form

$$dU = \Sigma\, U_i\, dx_i$$

are given by

$$U_i(U_{jk} - U_{kj}) + U_j(U_{ki} - U_{ik}) + U_k(U_{ij} - U_{ji}) = 0.$$

SELECTED BIBLIOGRAPHY ON THE THEORY OF UTILITY (OPHELIMITY)

ALLEN, R. G. D. (1) (with A. L. Bowley). *Family Expenditure.* London, 1935, viii + 145 pp. In particular the *Mathematical Appendix,* pp. 127–145.

(2) "A Note on the Determinateness of the Utility Function," *Review of Economic Studies,* Vol. 2, 1934–35, pp. 155–158.

(3) "Professor Slutsky's Theory of Consumers' Choice," *Review of Economic Studies,* Vol. 3, 1935–36, pp. 120–129.

(4) "The Nature of Indifference Curves," *Review of Economic Studies,* Vol. 1, 1933–34, pp. 110–121.

(5) "A Comparison between Different Definitions of Complementary and Competitive Goods," *Econometrica,* Vol. 2, 1934, pp. 168–175.

(6) [See J. R. Hicks].

(7) "On the Marginal Utility of Money and Its Application," *Economica,* Vol. 13, 1933, pp. 186–209.

BERNADELLI, HARRO. [See E. H. Phelps Brown].

BERNOULLI, DANIEL. "Specimen Theoriae Novae de Mensura Sortis," *Commentarii Acad. Petrop.,* Vol. 5, 1730–1731, published 1738, pp. 175–192. See I. Todhunter, *A History of the Mathematical Theory of Probability,* Cambridge and London, 1865, Chap. 11.

BIRCK, L. V. *The Theory of Marginal Value.* London, 1922, viii + 351 pp.

BÖHM-BAWERK, E. VON. (1) *Grundzüge der Theorie des Wirtschaftlichen Güterwerts,* Reprinted by the London School of Economics, 1932, from the *Jahrbücher für Nationalökonomie und Statistik,* New Series, Vol. 13, 1886, pp. 1–88, 477–541.

(2) *The Positive Theory of Capital.* Translated by W. Smart, 1890 and 1923, xl + 428 pp.

BOWLEY, A. L. (1) *The Mathematical Groundwork of Economics,* Oxford, 1924, viii + 98 pp.

(2) [See R. G. D. Allen (1)].

BROWN, E. H. PHELPS. "Notes on the Determinateness of the Utility Function," *The Review of Economic Studies,* Vol. 2, 1934–35, pp. 66–77. Part I by E. H. Phelps Brown, pp. 66–69; Part II by Harro Bernadelli, pp. 69–75; Part III by O. Lange, pp. 75–77.

DAVIS, H. T. (1) "Mathematical Adventures in Social Science," *American Mathematical Monthly,* Vol. 45, 1938, pp. 93–104.

(2) "The *Fonctionelle* Nature of Utility. *Third Annual Report of the Conference of the Cowles Commission for Research in Economics,* 1937, pp. 73–79.

DIVISIA, F. *Economique rationnelle.* Paris, 1927, xxxii + 443 pp. In particular pp. 367–433.

EDGEWORTH, F. Y. (1) *Mathematical Psychics.* London, 1881, viii + 150 pp.

(2) *Papers Relating to Political Economy.* Vol. 1, London, 1925, pp. 111-142.

EVANS, G. C. *Mathematical Introduction to Economics.* New York, 1930, xi + 177 pp. In particular Chapters 11 and 12.

FISHER, IRVING. (1) *Mathematical Investigations in the Theory of Value and Prices.* New Haven, 1925, 126 pp. Reprint of an article originally published in the *Transactions of the Connecticut Academy,* Vol. 9, 1892.

(2) "A Statistical Measure for Measuring 'Marginal Utility' and Testing the Justice of a Progressive Income Tax." From *Economic Essays Contributed in Honor of John Bates Clark.* New York, 1927, pp. 157-193.

FRISCH, RAGNAR. (1) *New Methods of Measuring Marginal Utility.* Tübingen, 1932, 142 pp.

(2) "Sur un problème d'économie pure," *Norsk Mathematisk Forenings Skrifter,* Series 1, No. 16, 1926.

(3) [See J. Moret (2)].

(4) "Der Einflusz der Veränderungen der Preisniveaus auf den Grenznutzen des Geldes," *Zeitschrift für Nationalökonomie,* 1931.

(5) "Statikk og Dynamikk . . . ," *Nationalökonomisk Tidsskrift,* Kobenhavn, 1928.

(6) "Annual Survey of General Economic Theory: The Problems of Index Numbers," *Econometrica,* Vol. 4, 1936, pp. 1–38.

GEORGESCU-ROEGEN, N. (1) "The Pure Theory of Consumer's Behavior," *Quarterly Journal of Economics,* Vol. 50, 1936, pp. 545–593.

(2) "Note on a Proposition of Pareto," *Quarterly Journal of Economics,* Vol. 49, 1935, pp. 706–714.

GOSSEN, H. H. (1) *Entwicklung der Gesetze des menschlichen Verkehrs und der daraus flieszenden Regeln für menschliches Handeln.* 1st ed., 1853, 3rd ed. Berlin, 1927, xxiii + 277 pp.

HICKS, J. R. "A Reconsideration of the Theory of Value," Part I by J. R. Hicks, *Economica,* Vol. 1 (2nd series), 1934, pp. 52–76; Part II by R. G. D. Allen, *Ibid,*, pp. 196–219.

HOTELLING, HAROLD. (1) "Edgeworth's Taxation Paradox and the Nature of Demand and Supply Functions," *Journal of Political Economy,* Vol. 40, 1932, pp. 577–616.

(2) "Demand Functions with Limited Budgets," *Econometrica,* Vol. 3, 1935, pp. 66–78.

JEVONS, W. S. *Theory of Political Economy.* First ed., London, 1871; 4th ed., 1911, 1924, 1931, lxiv + 339 pp. In particular, Chap. 3.

JOHNSON, W. E. "The Pure Theory of Utility Curves," *Economic Journal,* Vol. 23, 1913, pp. 483–513.

JORDAN, CHARLES. "On Daniel Bernoulli's 'Moral Expectation' and on a New Conception of Expectation," *American Mathematical Monthly,* Vol. 31, 1924, pp. 183–190.

KNIGHT, F. H. (1) "Marginal Utility Economics," *Encyclopedia of the Social Sciences,* Vol. 5, pp. 357–363.

(2) *Risk, Uncertainty and Profits.* New York, 1921; Reissued in 1933 and 1935 by the London School of Economics, xl + 381 pp.

LANGE, O. (1) "The Determinateness of the Utility Function," *Review of Economic Studies*, Vol. 1, 1933–34, pp. 218–225.

(2) [See E. H. Phelps Brown].

LEONTIEF, W. "Composite Commodities and the Problem of Index Numbers," *Econometrica*, Vol. 4, 1936, pp. 39–59.

LOTKA, A. J. "An Objective Standard of Value Derived from the Principle of Evolution," *Journal of the Washington Academy of Sciences*, Vol. 4, 1914, pp. 409–418, 447–457, 499–500.

MACVANE, S. M. "Marginal Utility and Value," *Quarterly Journal of Economics*, Vol. 7, 1893, pp. 255–285.

MARSCHAK, J. *Elastizität der Nachfrage*. Tübingen, 1931, xix + 114 pp. In particular, Chapters 12, 13, 14.

MARSHALL, ALFRED. *Principles of Economics*. 8th ed., London, 1936. In particular Book 3, Chap. 6, pp. 124–137. Also the *Mathematical Appendix*.

MAYER, J. "Pseudo-scientific Method in Economics," *Econometrica*, Vol. 1, 1933, pp. 418–428.

MENGER, CARL. *Grundsätze der Volkswirtschaftslehre*. 1871; Reissued by the London School of Economics as Vol. 1 of the *Collected Works of Carl Menger*, 1934, xlx + 288 pp.

MORET, J. (1) *L'emploi des mathématiques en économie politique*. Paris, 1915, 271 pp. In particular, chapters 4 and 5 of Part 3.

(2) (With Ragnar Frisch). "Methodes nouvelles pour mesurer l'utilité marginale," *Revue d'Économie politique*, 1931, pp. 5–32.

PABST, W. R. *Butter and Oleomargarine*. Columbia University Studies, 1937, v + 112 pp.

PANTALEONI, M. *Principii di economia pura*. Milano, 1889; second ed., 1931, 428 pp.

PARETO, V. (1) *Manuel d'économie politique*. 1st ed., Paris, 1909; 2nd ed., 1927, 694 pp. In particular the appendix, p. 538 et. seq.

(2) *Cours d'économie politique*, 2 vols., Lausanne, 1896–97.

RICCI, U. "Die Kurve des Geldnutzens und die Theorie des Sparens," *Zeitschrift für Nationalökonomie*, Vol. 3, 1932.

ROSENSTEIN-RODAN, P. N. "Grentznutzen," *Handwörterbuch der Staatswissenschaften*, 4th ed.

RUEFF, J. *From the Psysical to the Social Sciences*. Baltimore, 1929, 159 p.

SCHULTZ, HENRY. (1) "Interrelations of Demand," *Journal of Political Economy*, Vol. 41, 1933, pp. 468–512.

(2) "Interrelations of Demand, Price and Income," *Journal of Political Economy*, Vol. 43, 1935, pp. 433–481.

(3) "Frisch on the Measurement of Utility," *Journal of Political Economy*, Vol. 41, 1933, pp. 95–116.

SLUTSKY, E. "Sulla teoria del bilancio del consumatre," *Giornale degli Economisti*, Vol. 51, 1915, pp. 1–26.

STAEHLE, H. "A Development of the Economic Theory of Price Index Numbers," *Review of Economic Studies*, Vol. 2, 1934–35, pp. 163–188.

WALD, A. "The Approximate Determination of Indifference Surfaces by Means of Engel Curves," *Econometrica*, Vol. 8, 1940, pp. 144–175.

WALRAS, L. *Elements d'économie politique pure*. 1874; 5th ed., Paris and Lausanne, 1926, xx + 487 pp. In particular pp. 72–88.

WAUGH, F. V. "The Marginal Utility of Money in the United States from 1917 to 1921 and from 1922 to 1932," *Econometrica*, Vol. 3, 1935, pp. 376–399.

WEINBERGER, O. *Mathematische Volkswirtschaftslehre.* Leipzig and Berlin, 1930, xiv + 241 pp. In particular, pp. 134–140.

WICKSELL, K. (1) *Über Wert, Kapital and Rente.* Jena, 1893, xvi + 143 pp. Reprinted in 1933 by the London School of Economics.

(2) *Lectures on Political Economy.* Vol. 1, London, 1934, xix + 299 pp. In particular, pp. 13–100.

WICKSTEED, P. H. *The Common Sense of Political Economy and Selected Papers.* Vol. 1 and 2, London, 1935, xxx + 871 pp. In particular, pp. 401–490, 759–765.

VON WIESER, F. (1) *Social Economics.* Translated by A. F. Hinrichs, New York, 1927, xxii + 470 pp.

(2) *Natural Value.* 1889; English edition, 1938, xlv + 243 pp.

CHAPTER 4

SUPPLY AND DEMAND CURVES

1. *Notation*

One of the most basic concepts in economic statics is that of supply and demand. Thus Marshall says in his *Principles of Economics* (p. 83):

> There is . . . a good deal of general reasoning with regard to the relation of demand and supply which is regarded as a basis for the practical problems of value, and which acts as an underlying backbone, giving unity and consistency to the main body of economic reasoning. Its very breadth and generality mark it off from the more concrete problems of distribution and exchange to which it is subservient.

We shall first define a few symbols, which are generally employed in the discussion of supply and demand and the related theory of costs and profits. Thus we may let p equal the price of a commodity x, y the amount of the commodity purchased, and $Q(u)$ the cost of manufacturing and marketing u units of x. We may then speak of y as the *demand,* the product

$$R = yp$$

as the *total revenue* from the sale of the commodity, and the quantity

$$\pi = yp - Q(u)$$

as the *profit function.*

2. *The Concept of Demand*

Limiting ourselves to a single commodity for the sake of simplicity, let us first consider the problem of demand. If a given commodity were freely distributed, that is to say, without a price being charged for it, then a certain amount y_0 would be demanded. This value is naturally finite, but for many commodities it would be large, as one can see by considering the amount of water used by a community, where the water supply is not metered, or where the annual rent is negligible. The value y_0 may be called the *maximum demand.*

If, however, a price is charged for the commodity, then amounts smaller than y_0 would be demanded, and if the price became sufficiently great, the demand would fall to zero. Let us call this price the *price of zero demand,* and let us designate it by p_0. If, then, the price, p, be plotted against the demand, y, the resulting curve would resemble I in Figure 15.

3. *The Concept of Supply*

It is clear that there will exist in connection with demand a second consideration, namely, the availability of supplies to satisfy the demand. This availability is closely related to the price, since, for any commodity there exists a price, P_0, below which it is unprofitable to produce it. Let us call P_0 the *price of zero supply.* In general, the available supply, which we shall designate by u, will increase with an increasing price, as is exhibited by curve II in Figure 15. This is certainly true for manufactured goods, where natural limitations are not imposed as in the annual growth of agricultural commodities. It is clear that the supply curve does not continue indefinitely upwards, since the supply of most goods is limited. And even under the conditions of an unlimited supply, the curve would not, in general, continue

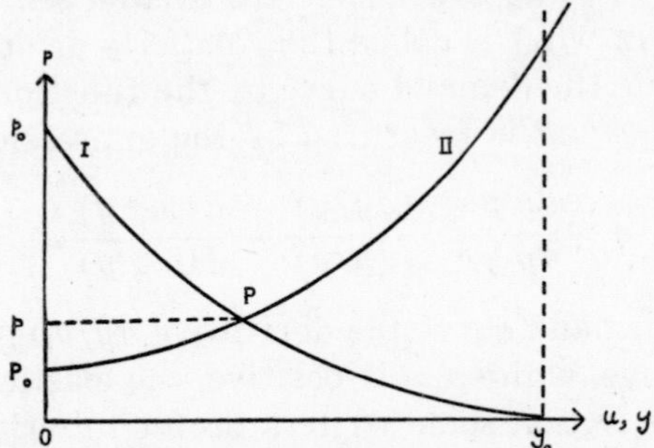

FIGURE 15.—SUPPLY AND DEMAND CURVES. CURVE I IS DEMAND: $y = y(p)$; CURVE II IS SUPPLY: $u = u(p)$.

beyond the point of maximum demand.

It is probable, also, that the curve of supply is mathematically more complex than that of demand in some respects. For example, it has been observed that some supply curves may actually turn back with increasing price; or, in other words, that prices may rise so high that available supply will diminish instead of increase. This anomalous situation may be illustrated by the supply of labor. Thus, it is possible to imagine that wages might increase to a point, where labor could earn enough for its standard of living with shorter hours of work, and it might then prefer leisure to more work at any price. Mathematically this situation would be described by means of a double-valued function of price.

4. *The Concept of Price*

Market price is defined as the ordinate of P, where the curves of supply and demand cross. The point P is a position of equilibrium, that is to say, the place where supply equals demand,

$$y = u .$$

It is obvious from any casual survey of economic data that the point P is not a stable one, since it varies from one period to another. We shall consider later the dynamics of the point P, but in the present discussion the assumption is made that we are regarding a stable situation with fixed curves of supply and demand, and a unique intersection.

5. *The Elasticity of Demand*

Casual observation will show that the demand for some goods is much more sensitive to price changes than are other goods. Hence it is desirable to have some exact measure of this sensitivity, and this measure is found in what is called the *elasticity of demand.*

If we designate the demand curve by the function $y = y(p)$, then the *elasticity of demand* is measured by the expression

$$\eta = \frac{dy}{dp}\frac{p}{y} = \frac{(dy/y)}{(dp/p)} = \frac{d(\log y)}{d(\log p)} . \tag{1}$$

Since in the demand curve the derivative dy/dp, which measures the slope, is negative, while p/y is positive, the elasticity is a negative quantity. For this reason some writers prefer to write the ratio with a negative sign. It will be observed that η is a pure number.

If the demand curve is a straight line,

$$\frac{y}{y_0} + \frac{p}{p_0} = 1 ,$$

then the elasticity is given by the formula

$$\eta = \frac{-(y_0 - y)}{y} = -\frac{p}{(p_0 - p)} .$$

If the elasticity of demand is a constant, η_0, then we have

$$\frac{dy}{y} = \eta_0 \frac{dp}{p} ,$$

from which we get by integration

$$\log y = \eta_0 \log p + \log C\,,$$

or in the sometimes more convenient form

$$y = Cp^{\eta_0}\,. \tag{2}$$

From this equation we derive the observation that the elasticity of demand is a constant, if the demand curve is a simple parabolic curve. In particular, if $\eta_0 = -1$, then the demand curve is an equilateral hyperbola.

The concept of the elasticity of demand is due to Augustin Cournot in his *Mathematical Principles of the Theory of Wealth* published in 1838, although he never used the phrase itself. Employing the notation of the present work in order to avoid confusion, we shall quote the original passage of Cournot:

> Since the (demand) function $y(p)$ is continuous, the function $py(p)$, which expresses the total value of the quantity annually sold, must be continuous also. This function would equal zero if p equals zero, since the consumption of any article remains finite even on the hypothesis that it is absolutely free; or, in other words, it is theoretically always possible to assign to the symbol p a value so small that the product $py(p)$ will vary imperceptibly from zero. The function $py(p)$ vanishes also when p becomes infinite, or, in other words, theoretically a value can always be assigned to p so great that the demand for the article and the production of it would cease. Since the function $py(p)$ at first increases, and then decreases as p increases there is therefore a value of p which makes this function a maximum, and which is given by the equation
>
> $$y(p) + py'(p) = 0\,, \tag{3}$$
>
> in which y', according to Lagrange's notation, denotes the differential coefficient of the function y.

Although the elasticity of demand is not explicitly considered in this passage, we observe that equation (3) is equivalent to setting η equal to minus one. The implications of this equation will be considered in the next section.

6. *Cournot's Point*

Let us now consider the elasticity of demand in the form

$$\eta = \frac{py'}{y} = \frac{p}{yp'(y)}\,,$$

and let us evaluate it at the point defined by equation (3) of the preceding section. It is immediately seen that we obtain the value $\eta = -1$. The point, designated by P_c, at which the elasticity of demand equals -1, is called *Cournot's point*. One observes from equation (2) of the preceding section that the demand curve for which every point is a Cournot point is the equilateral hyperbola, $y = Cp^{-1}$.

One sees from an inspection of Figure 16 that P_C defines the maximum area $Op_cP_Cy_c$ that can be formed by lines parallel respectively to the price and demand axes which intersect on the demand curve. This area,

$$R = yp \, ,$$

as we have seen in the first section, is important in economics since it represents the *total revenue* of the quantity sold.

The equation of the tangent line through P_C is given by

$$y - y_c = -\frac{y_c}{p_c}(p - p_c) \, .$$

If now we first set $p = 0$ and then $y = 0$ in this equation, we find for the intercepts OA and OB the quantities $2y_c$ and $2p_c$ respectively. From these values we immediately derive the fact that the ratio $(P_CA)/(P_CB)$ equals 1; that is to say, this ratio is numerically equal

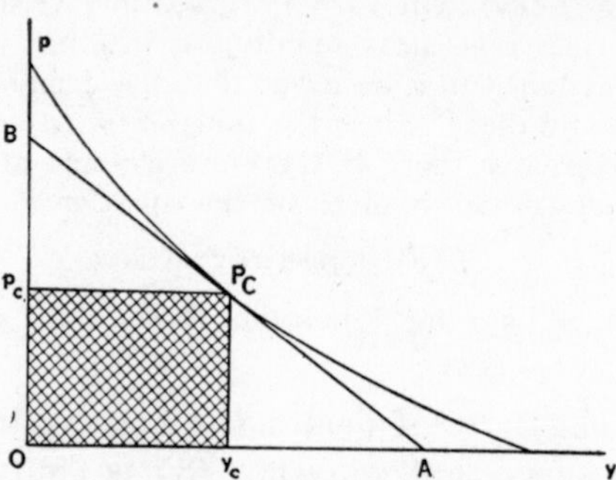

FIGURE 16.—DEMAND CURVE SHOWING TOTAL REVENUE AND COURNOT'S POINT, P_C.

to the elasticity of demand for the point P_C. This conclusion, true in the specific case of the Cournot point, is also true in general; it can be formulated in the following theorem, which is due to Alfred Marshall:

If P *is any point on the demand curve and if* A *and* B *are the points of intersection of the tangent through* P *with the demand and price axes respectively, then the ratio* (PA)/(PB) *is numerically equal to the value of the elasticity of demand at the point* P.

Proof: Let (p_1, y_1) be the coordinates of the point P on the curve of demand. Then the equation of the tangent through P will be

$$y - y_1 = \left(\frac{dy}{dp}\right)_1 (p - p_1),$$

where $(dy/dp)_1$ is the value of the derivative at the point P. Noting the relationship $(dy/dy)_1 = (y_1\eta_1)/p_1$, we see that the equation of the tangent can be written

$$y - y_1 = \frac{y_1\eta_1}{p_1}(p - p_1).$$

Hence, setting first p and then y equal to zero, we obtain the corresponding ordinate and abscissa; that is

$$OA = y_1(1 - \eta_1), \qquad OB = (\eta_1 - 1)p_1/\eta_1.$$

From these values we then compute

$$PA = \sqrt{\eta_1^2 y_1^2 + p_1^2}, \qquad PB = \frac{\sqrt{\eta_1^2 y_1^2 + p_1^2}}{|\eta_1|}.$$

The desired ratio is then found to be

$$(PA)/(PB) = |\eta_1|.$$

PROBLEMS

1. Compute the elasticity of demand for the curve

$$p = \frac{a}{b + cy}.$$

2. Determine the elasticity of demand, first as a function of y, and then as a function of p, for the curve

$$p = (y - a)^2.$$

3. Show that for the demand function of problem 1, Cournot's point is at infinity.

4. Compute Cournot's point for the demand function of problem 2.

5. Given the demand function

$$p = \frac{10}{5 + 2y},$$

compute the elasticity of demand both as a function of y and as a function of p and graph both functions.

6. Compute the ratio $(PA)/(PB)$ for the demand function of problem 2 and show that it is equal to the elasticity of demand at P. Show that at Cournot's point the absolute value of this ratio equals 1.

7. Show that Cournot's point for the function

$$p = \frac{k}{a + by + cy^2}$$

is given by

$$p = \frac{k\sqrt{c}}{b + 2\sqrt{ac}}, \qquad y = \sqrt{a/c}.$$

8. If the demand function is given by

$$p = \frac{a}{y + b} - c,$$

compute the maximum revenue.

9. Find the maximum revenue possible under the demand function

$$p = a \log(b/y).$$

10. If the demand prices for two competing goods are defined by the following equations.

$$p_1 = a_1 - b_1 y_1 - c_1 y_2\,, \qquad p_2 = a_2 - b_2 y_1 - c_2 y_2\,,$$

find the amounts demanded which correspond to maximum joint revenue. That is to say, find values of y_1 and y_2 such that the function

$$R = p_1 y_1 + p_2 y_2$$

is maximized.

7. *Relationship Between the Demand Curve and the Utility Function*

In view of the fact that direct measures of utility have never been made, while some progress has been attained in the statistical determination of demand, it is interesting to establish the mathematical relationships which exist between the two concepts. These relationships throw considerable light upon the difficulties inherent in the problem of the statistical measurement of demand.

Let us begin by assuming that an individual B is in the possession of α units of a commodity X and β units of a commodity Y. We shall further assume that Y is money and that the price of a unit of X is p. Hence the relationship between x units of the first commodity and y units of money is given by the equation

$$y = px\,. \tag{4}$$

Let us further assume that $V = V(x,y)$ is B's utility function, and that his curves of indifference are given by

$$V(x,y) = k\,. \tag{5}$$

Let us now consider the function

$$V'(x,y) = V(\alpha + x, \beta - y), \tag{6}$$

which gives B's utility after he has gained x units of X in exchange for y units of Y.

Referring to the theory of Lagrange multipliers developed in Section 7 of Chapter 3, we see that B's utility will be maximized subject to the restraint condition (4) provided the following conditions are satisfied:

$$V'_x - \lambda p = 0, \qquad V'_y + \lambda = 0, \tag{7}$$

where the subscripts x and y indicate that the partial derivatives of $V'(x,y)$ have been taken; that is

$$V'_x = \frac{\partial}{\partial x} V'(x,y), \qquad V'_y = \frac{\partial}{\partial y} V'(x,y).$$

If the parameter λ is eliminated from (7), we obtain the following equation, which must be satisfied by B's utility function (6):

$$V'_x(x,y) + pV'_y(x,y) = 0. \tag{8}$$

If y is now eliminated from (4) and (8), a relationship is obtained between p and x, which is the desired demand curve for B. This we can write in the form

$$p = f(x). \tag{9}$$

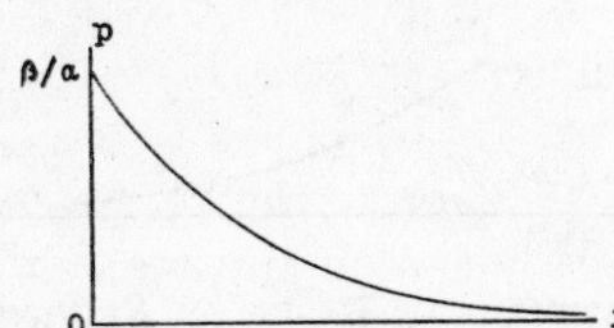

FIGURE 17.—HYPERBOLIC DEMAND CURVE.

Example 1. As an example, let us assume that B's utility function is of the form $V(x, y) = xy$. From this we get

$$V'(x, y) = (\alpha + x)(\beta - y),$$

and equation (8) becomes

$$(\beta - y) - p(\alpha + x) = 0.$$

Eliminating y between this equation and (4), we obtain the equation of the curve of demand in the form

$$p = \frac{\beta}{\alpha + 2x}.$$

It is immediately seen that for $x = 0$, we have $p_0 = \beta/\alpha$; the demand curve takes the form shown in Figure 17.

Example 2. In Section 9 of Chapter 3 we saw that the Weber-Fechner law suggested that the general form of the utility function might be

$$V(x, y) = x^m y^n .$$

It seems desirable, therefore, to determine the form of the demand curve on this assumption.

From the function $V'(x, y) = (\alpha + x)^m (\beta - y)^n$, we immediately obtain from (8) the following equation:

$$m(\alpha + x)^{m-1} (\beta - y)^n - pn(\alpha + x)^m (\beta - y)^{n-1} = 0 ;$$

which, when the common term is factored out, becomes

$$m(\beta - y) - pn(\alpha + x) = 0 .$$

Eliminating y by means of (4), we obtain as the equation of the demand curve the following:

$$p = \frac{m\beta}{n\alpha + (m+n)x} . \tag{10}$$

For $x = 0$, we have $p_0 = m\beta/(n\alpha)$, and when $x \to \infty$, we see that $p \to 0$. We also note that p_0 must be positive and hence, since both α and β are positive, the signs of m and n must be the same. Consequently the denominator of p cannot vanish and the curve of demand must resemble that given in Figure 18.

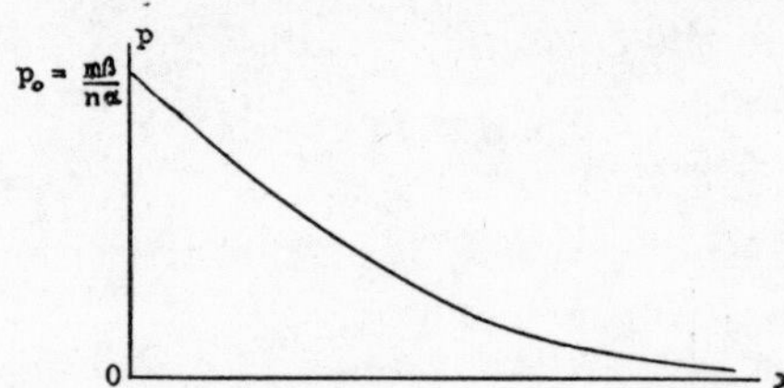

FIGURE 18.—DEMAND CURVE BASED ON FECHNER'S LAW.

It is instructive to evaluate the elasticity of demand for the general demand curve given by (10). For this purpose we first compute the slope

$$p'(x) = -\frac{m+n}{n\alpha + (m+n)x} p(x) .$$

From this the elasticity of demand is immediately found to be

$$\eta = -\frac{n\alpha + (m+n)x}{(m+n)x} = -\left[1 + \frac{n\alpha}{(m+n)x}\right] .$$

We thus observe that the absolute value of the elasticity of demand continually diminishes as x increases, and that Cournot's point, defined by $\eta = -1$, is at infinity. Thus, for this curve of demand, there exists no finite point for which the revenue is a maximum.

8. Relationship Between the Supply Curve and the Utility Function

Just as in the case of demand it is possible to derive the supply curve if the utility function of the producer is known. In order to exhibit the details of this analysis, let us assume that an individual A is in possession of a units of a commodity X and b units of a commodity Y. We shall assume that Y is money and that the price of a unit of X is p. Hence the relationship between x units of X and y units of Y is given, as in the previous case, by the equation

$$y = px . \tag{11}$$

Let us assume that $U = U(x,y)$ is A's utility function and that his indifference curves are given by

$$U(x,y) = k . \tag{12}$$

Let us further consider the function

$$U'(x,y) = U(a - x, b + y). \tag{13}$$

which measures A's utility when he has supplied x units of X in exchange for y units of Y.

As in the case of demand, his utility will be maximized subject to (11) provided

$$U'_x - \lambda p = 0 , \qquad U'_y + \lambda = 0 , \tag{14}$$

where the subscripts indicate that partial derivatives of $U'(x,y)$ with respect to x and y have been taken.

Eliminating the parameter λ from (14), we obtain the following equation, which must be satisfied by A's utility function (13):

$$U'_x(x,y) + pU'_y(x,y) = 0 . \tag{15}$$

If y is now eliminated between (11) and (15), a relationship is obtained between p and x which is the desired equation of the supply curve. This we can write in the form

$$p = g(x). \tag{16}$$

Example. As an application of this analysis, let us derive the supply curve which corresponds to the utility function suggested by the Weber-Fechner law. That is to say, we assume that the utility function has the form

$$U(x, y) = x^{\mu} y^{\nu} .$$

Solution. From the Weber-Fechner function we obtain

$$U'(x, y) = (a - x)^{\mu} (b + y)^{\nu} ,$$

and equation (15) becomes

$$-\mu(a-x)^{\mu-1}(b+y)^{\nu}+p\nu(a-x)^{\mu}(b+y)^{\nu-1}=0.$$

Removing the common factor, we then obtain

$$-\mu(b+y)+p\nu(a-x)=0.$$

The supply curve, obtained through the elimination of y by means of (11), is then found to be

$$(17) \qquad p=\frac{b\mu}{\nu a-(\mu+\nu)x}.$$

The price corresponding to zero supply is given by setting $x=0$ in (17); that is to say, $p_0=b\mu/(a\nu)$. Since this price must be positive it is clear that μ and ν must have the same sign. This leads us to a curious property of the supply curve, which was not possessed by the corresponding curve of demand. Thus we observe that there exists an upper bound to the amount that will be supplied at any price, since we have $p=\infty$, when $x=x_{\infty}=(\nu a)/(\mu+\nu)$. This characteristic of the supply curve is shown in Figure 19.

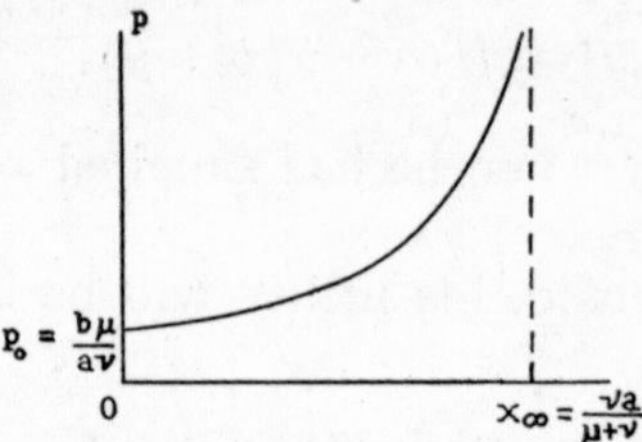

FIGURE 19.—SUPPLY CURVE BASED ON FECHNER'S LAW.

Since the actual price at which trade is consummated is given by the intersection of the curves of supply and demand, we can obtain this price by eliminating x from equation (17) of this section and equation (10) of Section 7. We thus find

$$(18) \qquad p=\frac{(m\beta)(\mu+\nu)+(\mu b)(m+n)}{(\nu a)(m+n)+(n\alpha)(\mu+\nu)}.$$

The corresponding value of x is readily obtained by eliminating p from the two equations. Thus the quantity actually exchanged is found to be

$$(19) \qquad x=\frac{\nu m a\beta-\mu n\alpha b}{(b\mu)(m+n)+(\beta m)(\mu+\nu)}.$$

Since x must be a positive quantity, it is clear that we must impose the restriction that the numerator of the fraction is positive; that is, $\nu m a\beta>\mu n\alpha b$.

If the simplifying assumption is made that $\mu=m$ and $\nu=n$, then equations (18) and (19) reduce to the following:

$$p=\frac{m}{n}\frac{(b+\beta)}{(a+\alpha)},$$

$$x = \frac{n}{m+n}\frac{(a\beta - \alpha b)}{(b+\beta)}, \quad a\beta > \alpha b:$$

As in the case of demand, we may define an elasticity of supply, ε, as the quotient

$$\text{(20)} \qquad \varepsilon = \frac{dx}{dp}\frac{p}{x} = \frac{(dx/x)}{(dp/p)} = \frac{d(\log y)}{d(\log p)}.$$

If we define $p(x)$ by (17), we readily compute

$$p'(x) = \frac{(\mu+\nu)b\mu}{[\nu a - (\mu+\nu)x]^2} = \frac{\mu+\nu}{\nu a - (\mu+\nu)x}p.$$

Hence the elasticity of supply becomes

$$\varepsilon = \frac{\nu a - (\mu+\nu)x}{(\mu+\nu)x} = -\left[1 - \frac{\nu a}{(\mu+\nu)x}\right].$$

PROBLEMS

1. If A's utility function is $U(x,y) = 2Gx + 2Fy - Ax^2 - 2Hxy - By^2$, and if B's utility function is $V(x,y) = 2G'x + 2F'y - A'x^2 - 2H'xy - B'y^2$, show that the supply and demand curves are given respectively by the following equations:

$$x = \frac{Aa + Hb - C + p(F - Ha - Bb)}{A - 2Hp + Bp^2},$$

$$\text{and } x = \frac{G' - A'\alpha - H'\beta + p(H'\alpha + B'\beta - F')}{A' - 2H'p + B'p^2}.$$

2. Note that in problem 1, if $H = 0$, the supply curve is of the form

$$x(1 + cp^2) = -d + ep,$$

where we use the abbreviations:

$$c = \frac{B}{A}; \quad d = \frac{G - Aa}{A}, \quad e = \frac{F - Bb}{A}.$$

Then, if p_0 is the price of zero supply, and if p_1 is the price where the derivative dp/dx becomes infinite, prove that

$$p_1 = p_0 + (p_0^2 + c^{-1})^{\frac{1}{2}}.$$

3. Derive the supply curve which corresponds to the utility function

$$U(x,y) = 480x + 208y - 5x^2 - y^2,$$

where the initial point of the seller is given by the coordinates $a = 8$, $b = 4$. Show that $p = 2$, when $x = 0$, and that $p = 5$, when $x = 10$. Prove that the supply curve is defined by a double-valued function, which turns back when $p > 5$.

4. Derive the demand curve which corresponds to the utility function

$$V(x,y) = 32x + 22y - x^2 - y^2,$$

where the initial point of the buyer is given by the coordinates $\alpha = 4$, $\beta = 8$. Show that $p = 4$ when $x = 0$, and that $x = 12$, when $p = 0$.

5. Graph the supply and demand functions obtained in the two preceding problems. From your graph determine the point of intersection and compare the utilities of buyer and seller at this point with the initial utilities.

9. The Statistical Determination of Demand and Supply Curves

Although numerous attempts have been made in recent times to determine the shape of both demand and supply curves, the problem has presented many obstacles. Perhaps the first to make a serious effort to surmount the difficulties were H. L. Moore and R. A. Lehfeldt. The former published his results in *Economic Cycles: Their Law and Cause,* a small volume which appeared in 1914, and which is now regarded as a classic in the subject. The latter considered the problem of demand in a paper entitled "The Elasticity of Demand for Wheat", which was also published in 1914. In the introduction to his paper Lehfeldt makes the following remarks:

> The writer can remember, as a student, meeting with the 'entropy' as a mysterious abstraction, enshrined in the writings of Lord Kelvin and others, but which no one dreamed of vulgarizing by the attachment of numerical values. Now every engineer's pocket-book contains tables of the entropy of different substances, and that most useful quantity is made available to the vulgar.
>
> Elasticity of demand, or of supply, as defined in theoretical writings on economics is an equally important quantity; but when, after hearing about curves of demand, the student comes with the question, 'How are these curves obtained?' one has to confess that they are not obtained, but rest in the limbo of abstractions. It would seem, therefore, that the roughest attempt to measure a coefficient of elasticity would be better than none, and would serve to make the concept of more real use.

From ordinary data it is obviously very difficult to construct a curve either of demand or of supply because both prices and production are given to us as separate values arranged in a time sequence. Such a sequence, as we have pointed out in Chapter 1, is called a *time series.* In order to obtain the pertinent data for, let us say, the demand for milk, it would be necessary to experiment with several communities, isolated from one another and from the general market. Then, if the price of milk were changed from one community to another, the resulting per capita demand would supply ideal data for the construction of the classical demand curve. But such an ideal experiment is impossible to perform. We have as our *observable* only the actual market price at a single point in time associated with a single visible supply and a single visible demand. What we actually need is a number of simultaneous prices together with the concomitant demands and their supplies.

But from two time series, one of price and the other of production, it is usually possible to make a reasonable approximation of either the demand curve or the supply curve, but not both, according to a theory advanced by E. J. Working. The possibility of constructing such curves depends upon the stability of either the demand curve or the supply curve with respect to the other. The argument then proceeds as follows. Price is the intersection of the two curves, and this price is observed at different periods of time for different levels of supply. Now if it happens that the demand curve is fixed, or at least varies little from one time to another, as might reasonably be the case with agricultural commodities, while the supply curve shifts with the changing conditions of production, then the observed price would appear as the intersection of the varying supply curve with the fixed demand curve. The situation would then be that shown in Figure 20.

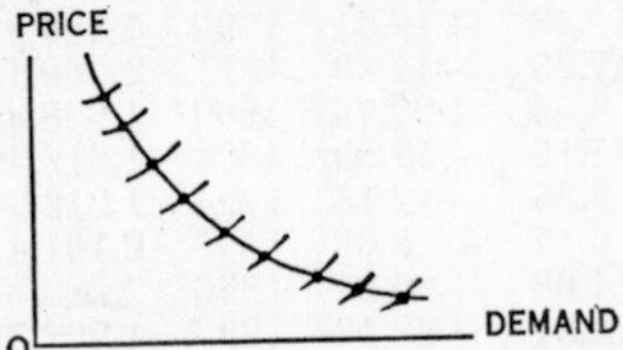

FIGURE 20.—FIXED DEMAND CURVE WITH VARYING SUPPLY CURVE.

Let us now assume that, on the contrary, the demand curve is variable, while the supply curve is constant. This would be the case presumably in the steel industry, or in most industrial production, where the capacity to produce is large, but where the demand fluctuates with general business conditions. In this case price would appear as the intersection of the varying demand curve with the fixed curve of supply. The situation is represented in Figure 21.

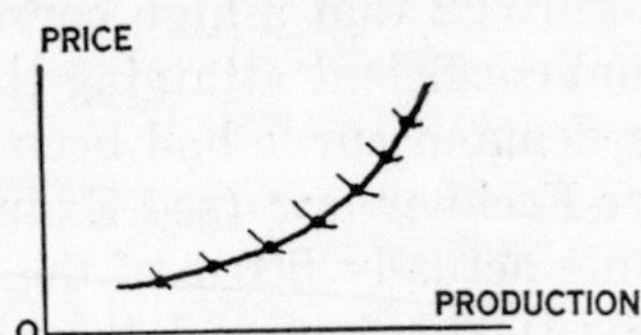

FIGURE 21.—FIXED SUPPLY CURVE WITH VARYING DEMAND CURVE.

An instructive example of these possibilities was given by H. L. Moore in his *Economic Cycles: Their Law and Cause,* to which reference has already been made. Recognizing the validity of the assumption that in studying a particular problem in economics *all other things must be equal,* the classical principle of *ceteris paribus,* Moore believed that much of the variability occasioned by random causes should be eliminated by correlating the relative changes of price with the corresponding relative changes in production. That is to say, he correlated the ratios

$$y = \frac{\Delta p}{p}\,, \quad \text{and} \quad x = \frac{\Delta u}{u}\,,$$

where p is price and u is production. We give in the accompanying table his data for the study of the demand for corn.

Year	Production in bushels Unit: 1000	Av. Price per bushel	$\Delta p/p$	$\Delta u/u$	Year	Production in bushels Unit: 1000	Av. Price per bushel	$\Delta p/p$	$\Delta u/u$
1866	867,946	47.4			1889	2,112,892	28.3	+ 6.29	—17.01
1867	768,320	57.0	—11.48	+19.41	1890	1,489,970	50.6	—29.48	+78.80
1868	906,527	46.8	+17.99	—17.89	1891	2,060,154	40.6	+38.27	—19.76
1869	874,320	59.8	— 3.55	+27.78	1892	1,628,464	39.4	—20.95	— 2.96
1870	1,094,255	49.4	+25.15	—17.39	1893	1,619,496	36.5	— .55	— 7.36
1871	991,898	43.4	— 9.35	—12.15	1894	1,212,770	45.7	—25.11	+25.21
1872	1,092,719	35.3	+10.17	—18.66	1895	2,151,139	25.3	+77.37	—44.64
1873	932,274	44.2	—14.68	+25.21	1896	2,283,875	21.5	+ 6.17	—15.02
1874	850,148	58.4	— 8.81	+32.13	1897	1,902,968	26.3	—16.68	+22.33
1875	1,321,069	36.7	+55.39	—37.16	1898	1,924,185	28.7	+ 1.11	+ 9.13
1876	1,283,828	34.0	— 2.82	— 7.36	1899	2,078,144	30.3	+ 8.00	+ 5.57
1877	1,342,558	34.8	+ 4.57	+ 2.35	1900	2,105,103	35.7	+ 1.30	+17.82
1878	1,388,219	31.7	+ 3.40	— 8.91	1901	1,522,520	60.5	—27.67	+69.47
1879	1,547,902	37.5	+11.50	+18.30	1902	2,523,648	40.3	+65.75	—33.39
1880	1,717,435	39.6	+10.95	+ 5.60	1903	2,244,177	42.5	—11.07	+ 5.46
1881	1,194,916	63.6	—30.42	+60.61	1904	2,467,481	44.1	+ 9.95	+ 3.76
1882	1,617,025	48.5	+35.33	—23.74	1905	2,707,994	41.2	+ 9.75	— 6.58
1883	1,551,067	42.4	— 4.08	—12.58	1906	2,927,416	39.9	+ 8.10	— 3.16
1884	1,795,528	35.7	+15.76	—15.80	1907	2,592,320	51.6	—11.45	+29.32
1885	1,936,176	32.8	+ 7.83	— 8.12	1908	2,668,651	60.6	+ 2.94	+17.44
1886	1,665,441	36.6	—13.98	+11.59	1909	2,772,376	59.6	+ 3.89	— 1.65
1887	1,456,161	44.4	—12.57	+21.31	1910	2,886,260	48.0	+ 4.11	—19.46
1888	1,987,790	34.1	+36.51	—23.20	1911	2,531,488	61.8	—12.29	+28.75

It is clear from Figure 22 that a high correlation exists between the two ratios, the actual coefficient attaining the value —0.789. It is also apparent that if a demand curve had been employed of the type suggested by the Weber-Fechner law (see Example 2, Section 7), instead of the straight line actually fitted to the data, then the agreement between the theoretical curve and the observed values would have been extremely good. The equation of the actual regression line obtained by Moore is the following:

$$y = -0.8896x + 7.79\,.$$

Moore then assumed that this is the equation for linear demand,

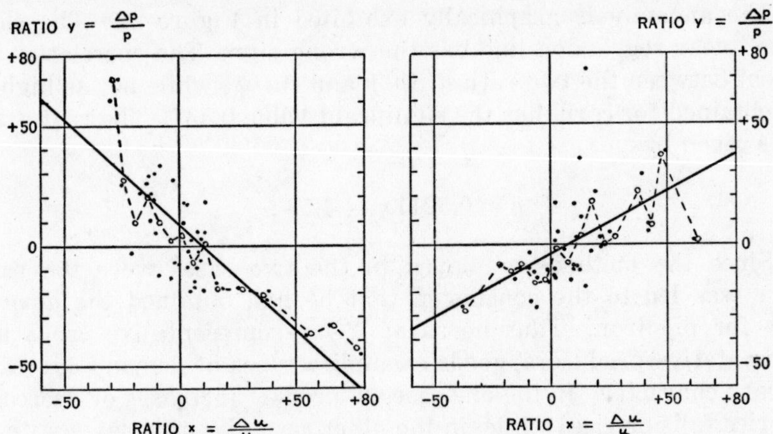

FIGURE 22.—STATISTICAL DEMAND AND SUPPLY CURVES. THE FIRST FIGURE SHOWS THE DEMAND CURVE FOR CORN; THE SECOND FIGURE SHOWS THE SUPPLY CURVE FOR PIG IRON.

not precisely in the classical sense, perhaps, but at least a good statistical approximation to it.

But a curious anomaly soon appeared. Moore next applied his method of correlating price and production ratios to obtain the "demand" curve for pig iron. The data which he employed are given in the accompanying table.

MOORE'S RATIOS FOR THE CHANGE IN PRODUCTION AND PRICE OF PIG IRON

Year	$\Delta p/p$	$\Delta u/u$	Year	$\Delta p/p$	$\Delta u/u$
1871	+ 5.57	+ 2.52	1892	— 8.91	+10.59
1872	+39.51	+49.33	1893	— 8.09	—22.19
1873	—12.57	+ .47	1894	—14.32	— 6.55
1874	—26.79	— 6.25	1895	+ 8.64	+41.87
1875	—14.14	—15.70	1896	— 3.55	— 8.71
1876	—10.61	— 7.66	1897	—10.43	+11.94
1877	— 9.99	+10.59	1898	— .60	+21.97
1878	— 9.39	+11.32	1899	+73.67	+15.70
1879	+22.68	+19.17	1900	+ 1.51	+ 1.23
1880	+28.72	+39.86	1901	—17.36	+15.15
1881	—14.82	+ 8.06	1902	+35.80	+12.24
1882	+ 3.15	+11.56	1903	—10.07	+ 1.05
1883	—15.87	— .58	1904	—23.99	— 8.40
1884	— 9.95	—10.84	1905	+17.22	+39.37
1885	—10.75	— 1.29	1906	+16.85	+10.07
1886	+ 5.95	+41.61	1907	+16.86	+ 1.87
1887	+11.95	+12.92	1908	—26.44	—38.19
1888	—13.32	+ 1.14	1909	+ 1.83	+61.87
1889	— 2.72	+17.16	1910	— 2.08	+ 5.85
1890	+ 3.37	+21.03	1911	— 8.66	—13.38
1891	— 9.85	—10.03	1912	+ 4.40	+25.70

The anomaly is graphically exhibited in Figure 22. The slope of the linear regression line has the wrong sign. The correlation coefficient between the two ratios, $\Delta p/p$ and $\Delta u/u$, while not as high as that obtained for corn, has the significant value 0.537. The regression line is given by

$$y = 0.5211x - 4.58\,.$$

Since the methods employed in the two cases were the same Moore was led to the conclusion that he had obtained the *demand curve* for pig iron. Thus he says: "Our representative crops and representative producers' goods exemplify types of demand curves of contrary character. In the one case, as product increases or decreases the price falls or rises while, in the other case, the price rises with an increase of the product and falls with its decrease."

If one assumes that agricultural commodities are associated with their price in essentially the same way as manufactured goods are associated with their price, then it is much more sensible to interpret the two contradictory results in the light of the hypothesis advanced by Working. In the case of corn the demand curve was fixed and the supply curve varied, while in the case of pig iron, the supply curve remained stable, and demand varied. Hence, we obtained in the first instance an approximation to the classical curve of demand, and in the second an approximation to the curve of supply.

10. The Relationship Between Supply and Demand Functions and Time Series

The most complete discussion of the relationship between static supply and demand functions and the items of time series from which they are to be statistically determined, is to be found in the monumental treatise by the late Henry Schultz entitled: *The Theory and Measurement of Demand.* This volume superseded a former work by the same author on the subject *Statistical Laws of Demand and Supply, with Special Application to Sugar,* which appeared in 1928. In this section we shall summarize some of the conclusions reached by Schultz in his study of this problem.

We may observe that four hypotheses can be made about the supply and demand functions: (1) that the supply curve remains fixed with time, but the demand curve varies; (2) that the demand curve is fixed, while supply varies; (3) that both supply and demand curves vary; (4) that neither of the curves is variable.

In order to fix our ideas more precisely, let us assume that the first case prevails. For simplicity of description, we may assume that the supply curve is the straight line

$$p = u \,, \tag{21}$$

and that prices are observed to be simply periodic with time; that is to say, they can be described by the function

$$p(t) = p_0 + A \sin kt. \tag{22}$$

If, then, the demand curve is also linear, let us say, of the form

$$p + mu = a \,, \quad m > 0 \,, \tag{23}$$

it is clear that the parameters m and a must be functions of time. Although the parameters cannot be explicitly determined, we can eliminate p and u between (21), (22), and (23) and hence obtain the following time relationship which they must satisfy:

$$\frac{a}{1+m} = p_0 + A \sin kt \,.$$

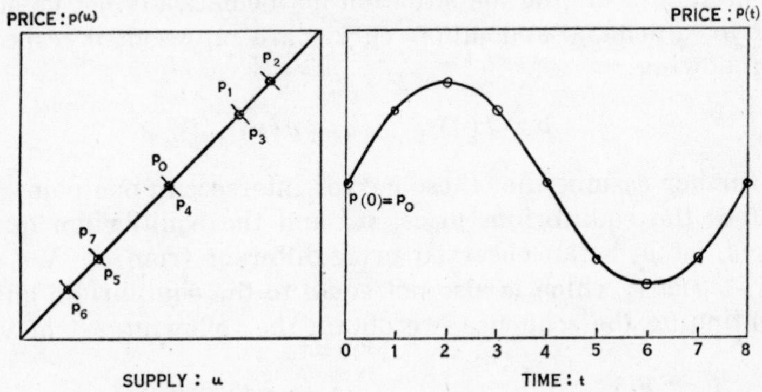

FIGURE 23.—DIAGRAM SHOWING HOW A FIXED SUPPLY CURVE MAY BE DETERMINED IF DEMAND CHANGES WITH TIME. THE FIRST FIGURE SHOWS THE SUPPLY CURVE: $p = u$. THE SECOND FIGURE SHOWS THE TIME-PRICE CURVE: $p = p_0 + A \sin kt$.

Since the supply curve remains fixed, while the curve of demand varies with time, one observes that the intersection of these two curves will exhibit the variable price originally postulated. Conversely, the graph of the price-production points will lie along the supply curve and thus determine it. The situation is graphically exhibited in Figure 23.

The same argument prevails if the demand curve remains fixed, while the supply curve varies. If the observed price changes with time, then the intersections of the demand curve with the variable supply curve will yield a set of points from which the demand curve can be constructed.

If both supply and demand vary, however, then the situation becomes indeterminate and there is no possibility of computing either the demand curve or the supply curve from the data of time series.

The fourth possibility remains, namely, where both supply and demand are fixed. In this case the price would be rigidly established at the intersection of the two curves and we should not note in the time series any substantial variation from the equilibrium price, p_0.

There do not appear to be many such inelasticities of price in economics. Most prices change from week to week and month to month, these variations often being of considerable magnitude. Hence, even though supply and demand curves were fixed, we might expect prices to vary from the equilibrium price, and this in turn would cause a dislocation of the equilibrium quantity, q_0, which is both demanded and supplied.

In order to examine the situation mathematically, let us suppose that the fixed demand and supply curves are represented respectively by the following:

$$p = f(q) , \qquad q = g(p) .$$

Let us further assume that these curves intersect in one point, which determines the equilibrium price, p_0, and the equilibrium quantity, q_0. Then, let p_1 be an observed price different from p_0. We should have $q_1 = g(p_1)$, which is also not equal to the equilibrium quantity, q_0. Continuing the sequence, we obtain the following set of values:

$$\begin{aligned} p &= p_1 , & q_1 &= g(p_1) , \\ p_2 &= f(q_1) , & q_2 &= g(p_2) , \\ p_3 &= f(q_2) , & q_3 &= g(p_3) , \\ p_4 &= f(q_3) , & q_4 &= g(p_4) , \\ &\cdots & &\cdots \end{aligned}$$

If, finally, the functions are such that some p_r corresponds to p_1, then obviously the sequence $p_1, p_2, p_3, \cdots, p_r = p_1$, and so on, is cyclical in character. The situation is schematically represented in Figure 24. This is known as the *cobweb* theory of price.

The remarks of Schultz about this situation are as follows:[1]

Thus far we have assumed that the two unknown curves (of demand and supply) remain fixed and have shown that, when an interval elapses between changes in price and corresponding changes in supply, it is possible to deduce both curves statistically. This conclusion also holds even when both curves are subject to secular movements, the necessary conditions being (1) that the curves retain their shape, (2) that each curve shift in some regular manner, and (3) that there exist a time interval between changes in price and changes in supply.

The importance of such a demand-supply relationship lies in that it admits of a straightforward statistical "verification." If by corresponding prices and output (consumption for synchronous years, or other intervals) we obtain a high negative correlation; and if by correlating the same data but with out-put lagged by, say, one year, we get a high positive correlation; *and if these correlations have meaning in terms of the industry or commodity under consideration*, the statistical demand and supply curves thus obtained are probably very close approximations to the theoretical curves. It is assumed, of course, that the data have been adjusted for secular changes and other disturbing factors.

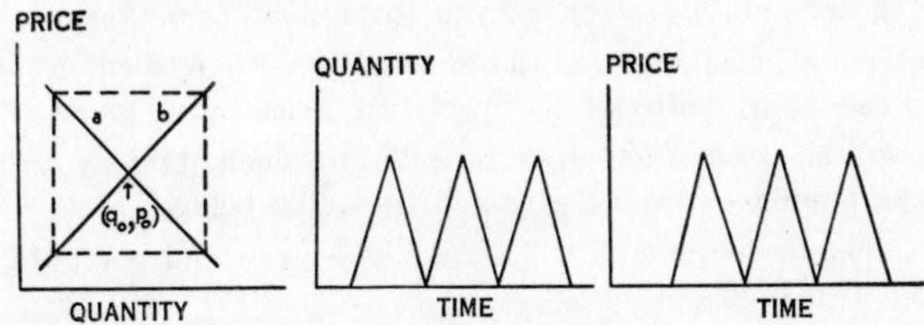

FIGURE 24.—DIAGRAM ILLUSTRATING THE TIME-PRICE RELATIONSHIP WHEN NEITHER THE DEMAND CURVE (a) NOR THE SUPPLY CURVE (b) VARIES.

The situation thus commented upon is not unlike that of the stranger in Aesop's fable, who aroused the suspicion of his host because he blew hot to warm his hands and then blew cold to cool his porridge. It seems, indeed, a curious circumstance that the same time series could be used to evaluate both curves of supply and demand. It is reasonable to suppose, however, that when agricultural prices are high, the farmers will plant more acres during the next season in the hope that they may profit from a continuation of the prevailing price level. On the other hand, for the same reason, they may be expected to plant fewer acres during the season which follows a period of low prices. Thus, in one case, a surplus is created, and in the other a deficiency. From his studies, Schultz reached the conclusion that sugar was one commodity in which both demand and supply curves were fixed.

[1] See *The Theory and Measurement of Demand*, pp. 78–79.

PROBLEMS

1. Fit a curve of the form $y = k(x + 45)^n$ to the price and production relatives for corn given in Section 9.

2. From the data on the production of corn given in Section 9, estimate the elasticity of the demand for corn.

3. Let us assume that the demand curve is fixed and of the form $p = (u - a)^2$, and let us assume further that the supply curve is variable with time, but linear. If prices are observed to vary sinusoidally in time, determine the intersections of the supply curve with the demand curve for one complete cycle of prices.

4. Given the demand curve $p = 5/(1 + q)$ and the supply curve $p = q$, show that if prices are displaced from the equilibrium value, they will always tend to return to this value. Illustrate this process by assuming an initial demand price of 1, that is, let $q = 4$. With this price, compute supply, namely, $q = p = 1$. Substitute this in the demand function to obtain the new demand price, hence the new supply, etc.

5. Employing the price-production data for corn given in the preceding section, compute the demand curve for corn in the following manner:

(a) Correct the price data for the general price movement by dividing each item by the corresponding value of the wholesale price index given below.

(b) Correct the production data by dividing each item by the corresponding values of the population index given in the table below .

(c) Shift the production data forward one year and compute the correlation between the two series.

(d) Make a scatter diagram of the price-production (shifted) data, and fit a straight line to the points.

PRICE-POPULATION INDEXES FROM 1866 TO 1913
1926 = 100

Year	Price	Population	Year	Price	Population	Year	Price	Population
1866	120	30	1882	74	45	1898	49	63
1867	111	31	1883	69	46	1899	52	64
1868	108	32	1884	64	47	1900	56	65
1869	103	32	1885	58	48	1901	55	67
1870	92	33	1886	56	49	1902	59	68
1871	89	34	1887	58	50	1903	60	69
1872	93	35	1888	59	51	1904	60	71
1873	91	36	1889	56	53	1905	60	72
1874	86	37	1890	56	54	1906	62	74
1875	81	38	1891	56	55	1907	65	75
1876	76	39	1892	52	56	1908	63	76
1877	73	40	1893	53	57	1909	68	78
1878	62	41	1894	48	59	1910	70	79
1879	61	42	1895	49	60	1911	65	80
1880	69	43	1896	47	61	1912	69	82
1881	70	44	1897	47	62	1913	70	83

6. Work problem 5 as before except shift price one year ahead of production. What conclusion do you draw from this analysis?

7. Gregory King, presumably using data pertaining to the agricultural economy of the sixteenth and seventeenth centuries, stated that the defect in a harvest raises the price of corn in the following proportions:

Defect in Harvest:	0.1	0.2	0.3	0.4	0.5
Proportional Rise in Price:	0.3	0.8	1.6	2.8	4.5

Verify Yule's statement (see *Bibliography*) that this relationship, often called the *Gregory King law*, is exactly given by the equation

$$y = -2.33x + 0.05x^2 - 0.00167x^3 ,$$

where x is the defect, assumed negative and expressed as a per cent, and y is the increase in price, also expressed as a per cent. Do the data of Section 9 tend to confirm the law?

SELECTED BIBLIOGRAPHY ON SUPPLY AND DEMAND

BEAN, L. H. (1) "The Farmer's Response to Price," *Journal of Farm Economics*, Vol. 11, 1929, pp. 368–385.

(2) (with G. B. THORNE) "The Use of 'Trends in Residuals' in Constructing Demand Curves," *Journal of the American Statistical Association*, Vol. 37, 1932, pp. 61–67.

BOWLEY, A. L. *The Mathematical Groundwork of Economics*. Oxford, 1924, viii + 98 pp. In particular, pp. 10–12, 32–34, 44.

CLARK, J. M. "The Bullion Market and Prices: An Inductive Study of Elasticity of Demand." Appendix to "Possible Complications of the Compensated Dollar." *American Economic Review*, Vol. 3, 1913, pp. 584–588.

COURNOT, A. A. *Recherches sur les principes mathématiques de la théorie des richesses*. Paris, 1838, xi + 198 pp. English translation by N. T. Bacon, New York, 1897, xxiv + 213 pp. In particular, Chapter 4.

EZEKIEL, MORDECAI. (1) "Statistical Analysis and the 'Laws' of Price," *Quarterly Journal of Economics*, Vol. 42, 1928, pp. 199–227.

(2) "Preisvoraussage bei landwirtschaftlichen Erzeugnissen," *Veröffentlichungen der Frankfurter Gesellschaft für Konjunkturforschung*, Bonn, 1930, 32 pp.

FRISCH, R. "Pitfalls in the Statistical Construction of Demand and Supply Curves," *Veröffentlichungen der Frankfurter Gesellschaft für Konjunkturforschung*, New Series, Heft 5, Leipzig, 1933, 39 pp.

JEVONS, W. S. *Theory of Political Economy*. First ed., London, 1871; 4th ed., 1911, 1924, 1931, lxiv + 339 pp. In particular, p. 157 et seq.

LEHFELDT, R. A. "The Elasticity of Demand for Wheat," *Economic Journal*, Vol. 24, 1914, pp. 212–217.

LEONTIEF, W. "Ein Versuch zur statistischen Analyse von Angebot und Nachfrage," *Weltwirtschaftliches Archiv*, Vol. 30, 1929, 53 pp.

MARSHALL, ALFRED. *Principles of Economics*. 8th ed., London, 1936. In particular, Books 3 and 5, and the *Mathematical Appendix*.

MOORE, H. L. (1) "Elasticity of Demand and Flexibility of Prices," *Journal of the American Statistical Association*, Vol. 18, 1922, pp. 8–19.

(2) *Forecasting the Yield and Price of Cotton*. New York, 1917.

(3) *Synthetic Economics*. New York, 1929, vii + 186 pp. In particular, Chapters 3, 4, and 6.

(4) *Economic Cycles: Their Law and Cause*. New York, 1914, viii + 149 pp. In particular, Chapters 4 and 5.

MORETTI, V. "Sopra alcuni problemi di dinamica economica," *Giornale degli economisti e rivista di statistica,* Vol. 44, 1929, pp. 450–488.

MOSAK, J. L. Interrelation of Production, Price, and Derived Demand," *Journal of Political Economy,* Vol. 46, 1938, pp. 761–787.

PEARSON, F. A. (See G. F. WARREN).

PIGOU, A. C. (1) "A Method of Determining the Numerical Value of Elasticities of Demand," *Economic Journal,* Vol. 20, 1910, pp. 636–640.

(2) "The Statistical Derivation of Demand Curves," *Economic Journal,* Vol. 40, 1930, pp. 384–400.

(3) *The Economics of Welfare.* 4th ed., London, 1932, xxxi + 837 pp. In particular, Appendix II, pp. 782–788.

RICCI, U. "Elasticità dei bisogni, della demanda e dell' offerta," *Giornale degli economisti e rivista di statistica,* Vol. 65, 1924.

ROY, RENÉ. (1) "La demande dans ses rapports avec la répartition des revenues," *Metron,* Vol. 8, 1930, pp. 101–153.

(2) "Les lois de la demande," *Revue d'économie politique,* Vol. 45, 1931, pp. 1190–1218.

SCHULTZ, H. (1) "The Statistical Measurement of the Elasticity of Demand for Beef," *Journal of Farm Economics,* Vol. 6, 1924, pp. 254–278.

(2) *Statistical Laws of Demand and Supply, with Special Application to Sugar.* Chicago, 1928, xix + 228 pp.

(3) "Der Sinn der statistischen Nachfragekurven," *Veröffentlichungen der Frankfurter Gesellschaft für Konjunkturforschung.* First Series, Heft 10, 1930, 99 pp.

(4) *The Theory and Measurement of Demand.* Chicago, 1938, xxxi + 817 pp.

STAEHLE, H. "Die Analyse von Nachfragekurven in ihre Bedeutung für die Konjunkturforschung," *Veröffentlichungen der Frankfurter Gesellschaft für Konjunkturforschung.* First series, Heft 2, 1929, 48 pp.

STIGLER, G. "The Limitations of Statistical Demand Curves," *Journal of the American Statistical Association,* Vol. 34, 1939, pp. 469–481.

THORNE, G. B. (See L. H. BEAN).

WARREN, G. F. (1) (with F. A. PEARSON). *Interrelationships of Supply and Price.* Bulletin 466 Cornell Uni. Agricultural Experiment Station, 1928, 144 pp.

(2) (with F. A. PEARSON). *Prices.* New York, 1933, vi + 386 pp.

(3) (with F. A. PEARSON). *Gold and Prices.* New York, 1935, vii + 475 pp.

WORKING, E. J. "What do Statistical 'Demand Curves' Show?" *Quarterly Journal of Economics,* Vol. 41, 1927, pp. 212–235.

WORKING, H. "The Statistical Determination of Demand Curves." *Quarterly Journal of Economics,* Vol. 39, 1925, pp. 503–543.

YULE, G. U. "Crop Production and Prices: A Note on Gregory King's Law," *Journal of the Royal Statistical Society,* Vol. 78, 1915, pp. 296–298.

CHAPTER 5

The Theory of Pure Exchange

1. *The Theory of Exchange*

One of the most fundamental concepts in economics is that of *exchange*, by which is meant the act of giving or taking one thing in return for an equivalent. In days before the use of money became as general as it is now in all civilized countries, exchange was equivalent to barter, where one good was traded directly for another. But in modern countries in all transactions of exchange there intervenes the use of money; that is to say, equivalent amounts of different goods are measured in terms of a common unit. This unit has generally been a certain number of grains of gold; in some countries and at different times it has been a defined weight of silver, copper, or other metal. In modern society the tendency has been to replace gold by fiduciary currency, the value of which depends upon the stability of the credit of the government that issues it. A more extensive account of these matters will be found in Chapter 12.

In this chapter we shall discuss the mathematical aspect of pure exchange and postpone to a later place a consideration of the data which interpret the problem of a real exchange in a real economy. We have already considered in Chapter 4 those parts of the theory which were necessary to explain the existence of curves of demand and supply. The ensuing discussion will deepen and generalize the theory which was developed there.

2. *The Bargaining Locus*

In order to understand the principle of pure exchange, let us consider the case of two traders, A and B. Let us assume that the trade concerns two commodities X and Y, and that A possesses amounts a and b of X and Y respectively, while B possesses them in the amounts α and β.

Let us construct for A a set of indifference curves, which, as we have seen, are curves along which his utility function $U(x, y)$ is constant. That is to say, we write

$$U(x, y) = k\,, \tag{1}$$

where k is a parameter which assumes positive values and represents the amount of utility which A possesses for any point on the curve. His initial point will be (a, b) and his initial utility becomes

$$U_0 = U(a, b) . \tag{2}$$

In similar fashion we construct a set of indifference curves for B, which we represent by the function

$$V(x, y) = k' . \tag{3}$$

B's initial position will be

$$V_0 = V(\alpha, \beta) . \tag{4}$$

Now A and B proceed to trade, the former giving up ξ units of X from his supply a, and adding η units of y to his supply b. Hence, after the trading, A's position on the indifference map will be $a - \xi$, $b + \eta$, while B's position will be $\alpha + \xi$, $\beta - \eta$.

It is clear that a trade will be consummated provided values of ξ and η can be found such that the following inequalities are satisfied:

$$U(a - \xi, b + \eta) > U_0 , \quad V(\alpha + \xi, \beta - \eta) > V_0 . \tag{5}$$

In general, the units of X and Y are not equivalent, and there will exist between them a ratio of trade expressed by the equation

$$\eta/\xi = p . \tag{6}$$

In particular, if Y is money, then p is the price of X. But if Y is not money, then p may be expressed as the ratio of the prices of the two commodities. Thus if p_x is the price of X and p_y is the price of Y, then one obtains

$$p = p_x/p_y . \tag{7}$$

By means of (6) we can express A's position on the indifference map in terms of one of the parameters ξ or η. Thus A's position after trading will be $a - \xi$, $b + p\xi$, while B's position will be $\alpha + \xi$, $\beta - p\xi$.

Let us now define a locus by means of the equations

$$x = a - \xi , \quad y = b + p\xi ,$$

in terms of the parameter ξ. The elimination of ξ gives the line

$$y - b = p(x - a) , \tag{8}$$

which, it is observed, depends upon the parameter p. This ratio of exchange, as we see from the constant fluctuation of prices, is subject to change. Bargaining usually focuses upon the problem of reaching some mutual agreement as to the value that is to be assigned to it.

Now the line defined by equation (8), when graphed upon A's indifference map, is tangent to one of A's indifference loci at some point (x_1, y_1). As p varies this point of tangency varies and traces a curve, which we shall designate as A's bargaining locus. It is obvious that A will wish to attain a value of the ratio, p, which will yield him the largest possible utility.

If the equation of the utility function is explicitly known, then A's bargaining locus may be computed. The equation of a tangent to the curve defined by $U(x, y) = k$, in terms of the point of tangency (x_1, y_1) is given by

$$(9) \qquad \frac{\partial U(x_1, y_1)}{\partial x_1}(x - x_1) + \frac{\partial U(x_1, y_1)}{\partial y_1}(y - y_1) = 0 .$$

Regarding this, now, as an equation in x_1, y_1, we require that it pass through the point (a, b); that is, we set $x = a$, $y = b$. Hence, dropping subscripts from x_1 and y_1, we obtain as A's bargaining locus the equation:

$$(10) \qquad (x - a) U_x(x, y) + (y - b) U_y(x, y) = 0 ,$$

where $U_x(x, y)$ and $U_y(x, y)$ designate respectively the partial derivatives of $U(x, y)$ with respect to x and y.

Similarly, the equation

$$(11) \qquad (x - \alpha) V_x(x, y) + (y - \beta) V_y(x, y) = 0$$

is B's bargaining locus.

Example. As an example, let us assume that A's initial position is the point $a = 10$, $b = 14$, and that his utility function is

$$U(x,y) = 40x + 40y - x^2 - y^2 .$$

Substituting these values in equation (10), we obtain as his bargaining locus

$$(x - 10)(x - 20) + (y - 14)(y - 20) = 0 ;$$

that is to say, the circle

$$(x - 15)^2 + (y - 17)^2 = 34 .$$

Similarly, let B's initial position be the point $\alpha = 16$, $\beta = 8$, and assume that his utility function is

$$V(x, y) = xy .$$

From (11) we immediately obtain

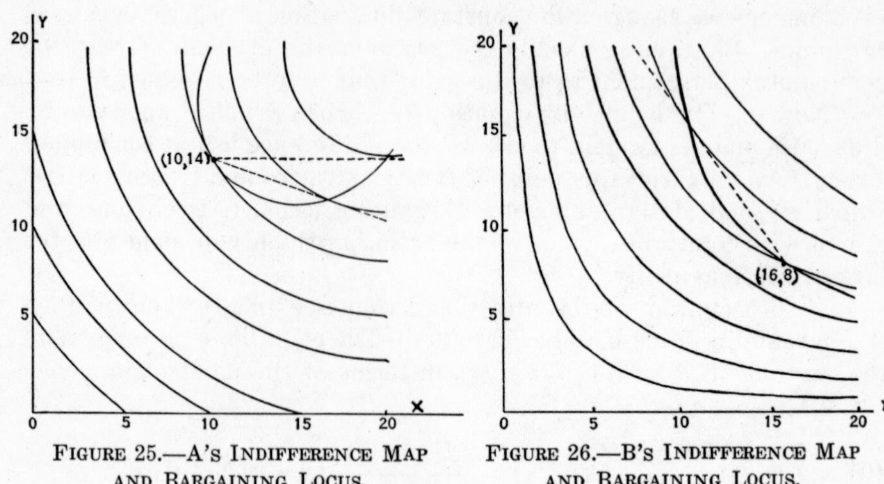

FIGURE 25.—A'S INDIFFERENCE MAP AND BARGAINING LOCUS.

FIGURE 26.—B'S INDIFFERENCE MAP AND BARGAINING LOCUS.

$$(x-16)y+(y-8)x=0\,;$$

that is to say, B's bargaining locus is the hyperbola

$$y=\frac{4x}{x-8}\,.$$

The two utility maps and the respective bargaining loci are graphically represented in Figures 25 and 26. It will be observed that tangents drawn from the initial points to the indifference lines intersect the bargaining loci at the points of contact.

PROBLEMS

1. If A's utility function is

$$U(x,y)=60x+120y-2x^2-3y^2,$$

show that his bargaining locus is an ellipse. If A's initial position is the point $a=8$, $y=10$, determine the ellipse explicitly. Graph both the bargaining locus and the indifference curve which passes through the initial point.

2. If B's utility function is

$$V(x,y)=x+y+2x^{\frac{1}{2}}y^{\frac{1}{2}},$$

and if his initial position is the point $\alpha=9$, $\beta=4$, show that his bargaining locus is the curve defined by the equation

$$(x+y-13)x^{\frac{1}{2}}y^{\frac{1}{2}}+2xy-9y-4x=0\,.$$

3. Referring to problem 2, observe that the relationship between x, y, and V can be written

$$y=(V^{\frac{1}{2}}-x^{\frac{1}{2}})^2.$$

Letting V assume the values 9, 16, 25, 36, and 49, construct a set of five indifference curves. Finally, draw the tangent lines from the point $x=9$, $y=4$ to these curves and through the points of tangency construct graphically a smooth curve. Show that the curve so constructed is the bargaining locus defined in problem 2.

4. If A's utility function is defined by

$$U = Ax^2 + 2Hxy + By^2 + 2Fx + 2Gy + 2C\,,$$

show that his bargaining locus is (a) an ellipse if Ψ and $\theta\ \Delta$ are less than 0; (b) a hyperbola if $\Phi > 0$, $\Delta \neq 0$; (c) a parabola if $\Phi = 0$, $\Delta \neq 0$: (d) two straight lines if $\Delta = 0$, where we define $\Phi = H^2 - AB$, $\theta = A + B$, and

$$\Delta = \begin{vmatrix} A & H & F' \\ H & B & G' \\ F' & G' & C' \end{vmatrix}\,,$$

in which we abbreviate

$$F' = \tfrac{1}{2}(F - aA - bH)\,, G' = \tfrac{1}{2}(G - aH - bB)\,, C' = \tfrac{1}{2}(aF + bG)\,.$$

5. Show that if A's utility functions is

$$U = A\,x^p\,y^q,$$

then his bargaining locus is the equilateral hyperbola

$$(p + q)xy - bqx - apy = 0\,.$$

3. *The Bargaining Diagram*

In order to represent the bargaining between A and B it will be convenient to employ a graphical device which we may call the *bargaining diagram.* In this diagram the initial points of A and B are brought into coincidence and this point is chosen as the origin. A's and B's axes are then oriented with respect to this point as illustrated in Figure 27.

A's origin, O_1, is at a distance a units in the negative x-direction and b units in the positive y-direction from O. Similarly, B's origin, O_2, is a distance α units in the positive x-direction and β units in the negative y-direction from O. Hence, at any exchange point (x, y) A's holdings of either commodity added to B's holdings of the same commodity will equal the sum of the initial holdings of the two traders.

If $U(x, y)$ is A's utility function as defined in the preceding section, then

$$U'(x, y) = U(a - x, b + y) \tag{12}$$

is the same function referred to the new axes with origin at 0. The indifference lines are then obtained from $U'(x, y) = k$.

Similarly, if $V(x, y)$ is B's utility function as defined in the preceding section, then

$$V'(x, y) = V(\alpha + x, \beta - y) \tag{13}$$

is this function referred to the new axes.

Hence the initial utilities are those at the origin; that is to say, $U_0 = U'(0, 0)$ and $V_0 = V'(0, 0)$. Also, any point below the curve $U'(x, y) = U_0$ is a point of increased utility for A, while any point above the curve $V'(x, y) = V_0$ is a point of increased utility for B.

It will be observed that A's bargaining locus in terms of the new axes is given by

$$(14) \qquad xU'_x(x, y) + yU'_y(x, y) = 0 ,$$

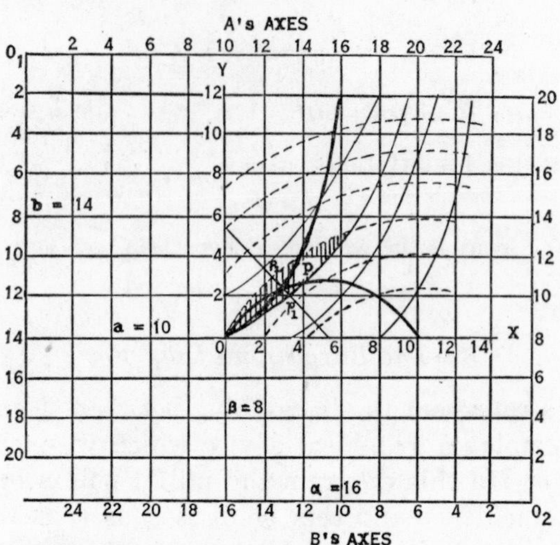

FIGURE 27.—THE BARGAINING DIAGRAM.

while B's bargaining locus is given by

$$(15) \qquad xV'_x(x, y) + yV'_y(x, y) = 0 .$$

The intersection of the two curves, that is to say, the point P, is the most advantageous position for both and is the point of ideal contract.

But the constant fluctuation of prices in actual trade indicates that the ideal point is not easily, nor exactly, attained. Hence the region about P is a region of bargaining.

Presumably a temporary bargain could be struck at any point where A's indifference curve touches an indifference curve of B within the region bounded by the two indifference curves

$$(16) \qquad U'(x, y) = U_0 , \qquad V'(x, y) = V_0 ;$$

that is to say, the shaded region of the bargaining diagram.

At such a point of contact the slopes of the tangents to the two indifference curves will be equal. Analytically this is expressed by the equation

$$\frac{U'_x(x,y)}{U'_y(x,y)} = \frac{V'_x(x,y)}{V'_y(x,y)} \, ;$$

or what is the same thing

$$(17) \qquad U'_x V'_y - U'_y V'_x = 0 \, .$$

The equation thus defined is called by A. L. Bowley the *contract curve*. It obviously passes through the point P. Acceptable points of temporary contract will be found upon the curve only between the bounding curves defined by the initial indifference lines. That is to say, a point of temporary contract must lie between p_1 and p_2.

Example. The example used in constructing the bargaining diagram shown in Figure 27 was taken from the example of the preceding section. Making the transformations indicated by equations (12) and (13), we obtain

$$U(x,y) = 664 + 20x - 12y - x^2 - y^2, \quad V(x,y) = (16 - x)(8 + y).$$

The initial indifference curves, that is to say, those defined by (16), are respectively

$$x^2 + y^2 - 20x + 12y = 0 \, , \quad xy + 8x - 16y = 0 \, .$$

The bargaining loci, obtained from equations (14) and (15), are given by

$$(x - 5)^2 + (y + 3)^2 = 34 \, , \quad y = \frac{4x}{8 - x} \, ,$$

and their intersection, the point P, is approximately (3.0, 2.4).

The contract curve, defined by (17), is found to be

$$2(x - 10)(16 - x) + 2(y + 6)(8 + y) = 0 \, ;$$

that is to say, the hyperbola

$$(x - 13)^2 - (y + 7)^2 = 8 \, .$$

Within the region of bargaining the graph of this hyperbola is nearly linear.

If we substitute the value of the point P in the two utility functions we obtain the numerical values: $U(P) = 680.4$ and $V(P) = 135.2$. These values, we observe, exceed the initial quantities: $U(0) = 664$ and $V(0) = 128$. Let us, however, consider the point (2, 2), which lies within the shaded region of the bargaining diagram. For this point we obtain $U(2,2) = 672$ and $V(2,2) = 140$. Hence, this would be a place of greater advantage to B than the point P, but of less advantage to A. Similarly the point (3, 2) gives the values $U(3,2) = 701$ and $V(3,2) = 130$, which shows that it is a place of more advantage to A than the point P, but of less advantage to B.

If, however, we take a point on the bargaining locus, for example, $P' = (3.0, 2.2)$, we then obtain $U(P') = 673.8$ and $V(P') = 132.6$. Neither utility is as great as at the point P and hence neither trader has an advantage over the other.

PROBLEMS

1. If the initial positions of A and B are respectively the points: $a = 9$, $b = 4$, and $\alpha = 8$, $\beta = 27$, and if their respective utility functions are

$$U = x^{\frac{1}{2}} y^{\frac{1}{2}}, \qquad V = x^{1/3} y^{1/3},$$

compute the bargaining loci and the contract curve. Determine the bargaining point and compute the respective utilities there.

2. Construct graphically the bargaining diagram corresponding to the following utility functions and initial positions:

$$U = 10xy, \qquad a = 12, b = 6;$$

$$V = 12x^2y^2, \qquad \alpha = 5, \beta = 10.$$

Compute and graph the bargaining loci and the contract curve.

3. Determine the point of contract for problem 2 and determine the respective utilities at this point. Compare these utilities with those at some other point within the bargaining area.

4. Find the contract curve corresponding to the following utility functions and initial positions:

$$U = 60x + 120y - 2x^2 - 3y^2, \qquad a = 10, b = 4;$$

$$V = 120x + 60y - 3x^2 - 2y^2, \qquad \alpha = 4, \beta = 10.$$

5. Form a bargaining diagram for the following:

$$U = 40x + 24y - 2x^2 - 3y^2, \qquad a = 10, b = 4;$$

$$V = 24x + 40y - 3x^2 - 2y^2, \qquad \alpha = 4, \beta = 10.$$

Compute and graph the bargaining loci and the contract curve.

4. Relationship with Curves of Demand and Supply

It will be instructive to trace the relationship between the bargaining loci discussed in Section 2 and the curves of demand and supply which were developed in Sections 7 and 8 of Chapter 4.

Let us return now to the variables of Section 2 and make a new derivation of B's bargaining locus, equation (11) of that section. If the point (x, y) represents B's position on the indifference map, then his budget equation is clearly given by

$$p_x x + p_y y = E = p_x \alpha + p_y \beta;$$

that is to say, by

$$p_x(x - \alpha) + p_y(y - \beta) = 0.$$

But from the fundamental equation (29) of Section 7, Chapter 3, we have the following relationship between the prices and the marginal utilities:

$$\text{(18)} \qquad \frac{\dfrac{\partial V}{\partial x}}{p_x} = \frac{\dfrac{\partial V}{\partial y}}{p_y} .$$

Hence the budget equation may be written

$$\frac{\partial V}{\partial x}(x - \alpha) + \frac{\partial V}{\partial y}(y - \beta) = 0 ,$$

which is the bargaining locus.

If we now examine equations (4) and (8) of Section 7, Chapter 4, we see that the demand curve is obtained by eliminating y' from the equations:

$$\text{(19)} \qquad y' = px' ,$$

$$\text{(20)} \qquad V'_x(x', y') + pV'_{y'}(x', y') = 0 ,$$

where $V'(x', y') = V(\alpha + x', \beta - y')$. The variables x and y of this section are related to x' and y' by the equations: $x = \alpha + x', y = \beta - y'$.

If we eliminate p from (20) and observe that

$$V_x = V'_{x'} , \qquad V_y = -V'_{y'}$$

then we can write (20) in the form

$$\text{(21)} \qquad V_x(x - \alpha) + V_y(y - \beta) = 0 .$$

That is to say, equation (20) is the bargaining locus translated into the variables x' and y'. If y is eliminated between equation (21) and the equation $(y - \beta) + p(x - \alpha) = 0$, then the resulting equation is the demand curve in the variables p and x.

Similar remarks apply also to A's bargaining locus from which the curve of supply is derived. Since the argument does not vary in any essential particular from that just given it will not be repeated here.

One may readily observe the significance in the theory of demand and supply of the contract curve. Bargaining between A and B depends primarily upon the respective judgments of the two traders about the ratio $p = p_x/p_y$. This judgment depends upon the ratio of marginal utilities, as we have seen above. Thus, in terms of the variables x and y, both A and B will have the same estimate of the price ratio provided

$$\frac{p_x}{p_y} = \frac{U_x}{U_y} = \frac{V_x}{V_y} .$$

Translated into the primed variables, this equation is identical with the contract curve.

PROBLEMS

1. Find the demand and supply curves corresponding to the specifications of problem 1 of Section 3.

2. Determine the demand and supply curves using the data of problem 2 of Section 3.

3. Using the initial positions and the utility functions of problem 4 of Section 3, find and graph the demand and supply curves.

5. *Generalization of the Bargaining Locus*

The theory which we have developed in preceding sections can be generalized so as to apply to n traders dealing in p different commodities. Thus, let us assume that we have n traders, $A, B, C, \cdots, N$, who have respectively utility functions designated by $U, V, W, \cdots, Z$. Let there be p commodities, $X_1, X_2, X_3, \cdots, X_p$, and let A have the initial amounts $a_1, a_2, a_3, \cdots, a_p$.

Then if A changes his amounts to $x_1, x_2, x_3, \cdots, x_p$, these quantities are subject to the restraint of the budget equation:

(22)
$$p_1(x_1 - a_1) + p_2(x_2 - a_2) + p_3(x_3 - a_3) + \cdots + p_p(x_p - a_p) = 0 ,$$

where $p_1, p_2, p_3, \cdots, p_p$ are the prices of the commodities $X_1, X_2, X_3, \cdots, X_p$.

But these prices, regarded from A's point of view, are subject to the following conditions:

(23)
$$\frac{U_{x_1}}{p_1} = \frac{U_{x_2}}{p_2} = \frac{U_{x_3}}{p} = \cdots = \frac{U_{x_p}}{p_p} .$$

Replacing the prices in (22) by their respective marginal utilities, we obtain (22) in the following form:

(24)
$$U_{x_1}(x_1 - a_1) + U_{x_2}(x_2 - a_2) + U_{x_3}(x_3 - a_3) + \cdots + U_{x_p}(x_p - a_p) = 0 .$$

This equation is A's *bargaining surface*, a functional relationship between the p variables: $x_1, x_2, x_3, \cdots, x_p$.

In a similar manner we may derive B's bargaining surface, which is explicitly given by the following:

(25)

$$V_{y_1}(y_1 - b_1) + V_{y_2}(y_2 - b_2) + V_{y_3}(y_3 - b_3) + \cdots + V_{y_p}(y_p - b_p) = 0 .$$

For the other traders we have similar equations depending upon the initial amounts of the commodities which they hold.

It is next interesting to inquire whether or not this complex situation leads in general to a solution of the final position of the traders and a determination of the price ratios. That is to say, do we have enough equations to determine the values of the pn variables of position: $x_1, x_2, \cdots, x_p; y_1, y_2, \cdots, y_p$, etc., and the p prices: $p_1, p_2, \cdots, p_p$, a total of $pn + p$ unknowns?

In order to decide this important question we observe that we have, first, a total of n *budget equations* like (22). In the second place we have $n(p - 1)$ equations in the system defined by (23). Finally, we note the p *equations of state*

$$(26) \qquad (x_i - a_i) + (y_i - b_i) + \cdots = 0 , \quad i = 1, 2, \cdots, p ,$$

which merely affirm that the sum of the final holdings of all the traders is equal to the sum of their initial holdings.

We now see that we have altogether $n(p - 1) + n + p = np + p$ equations for the determination of the $np + p$ unknown quantities. In general a solution would be expected.

When one first considers a system of equations of the degree of complexity exhibited by those of the general problem of exchange as set forth in this section, he must be led perforce to one interesting observation. *However complex the system of equations may be mathematically, and however difficult the attainment of a numerical solution may prove to be, nevertheless the system actually has a solution, which is given daily in the recorded transactions and the recorded prices of the board of trade, the stock market, and other agencies of exchange.*

It is obvious that no individual, or group of individuals, can solve numerically the system of equations which we have set up. But in some manner, guided perhaps by information about visible stocks of goods, or by the trend of production and business, or by the accumulation of inventories, traders actually exchange goods and the volume of this exchange both influences and is influenced by the level of prices in the market.

One of the primary goals of mathematics is to prove the *existence* of solutions of various equations and systems of equations as they arise in sciences devoted to the understanding of the natural world. Mathematics also seeks to determine the nature of the solutions when their existence has been proved. In the present instance, however, we know from empirical evidence that solutions exist. The problem of the mathematician thus becomes a kind of inverse one, namely, that of determining the nature of the essentially unknown marginal utilities from the observed solutions given to us daily in the actual markets of the world.

The unbelievable complexity of the general economic problem will become more evident to us when we examine the equations of the theory of equilibrium developed in Chapter 9. Our marvel grows when we realize that the empirical solution is attained daily in the process of making business transactions. But that this solution also maximizes the greatest number of individual utility functions is quite another matter.

6. Competitive Bargaining in Space Economics

A problem intimately associated with the subject of this chapter is found in competitive bargaining between two producers at varying distances from the consumer. This problem is called one in *space economics*.[1]

Let us assume, first, that a single manufacturer can produce goods at a place A, which he can sell in A at a price p per unit. But because of the cost of transportation, which is t dollars per unit of goods carried a unit distance, the manufacturer must sell his product at a point r units distant from A for

$$P = p + tr \,. \tag{27}$$

In this equation we have assumed that the cost of transportation is a linear function of the distance, a proposition which is not always true. For example, it might be possible to ship part of the distance by rail and the remainder by water. For simplicity, however, we shall assume the linear function.

But we now observe that, as the price increases, the demand for the goods will drop. Hence, if demand is given by the function

$$x = x(P) = x(p + tr), \tag{28}$$

there will exist a certain distance, designated by R, for which the demand will be essentially zero. It thus follows that the maximum area which the manufacturer can serve with his goods is a circle of radius

[1] See E. Schneider: "Bemerkungen zu einer Theorie der Raumwirtschaft," *Econometrica*, Vol. 3, 1935, pp. 79–105. W. Launhardt: *Mathematische Begründung der Volkswirtschaftslehre.* Leipzig, 1885, pp. 149 *et seq.* H. Hotelling: "Stability in Competition," *Economic Journal*, Vol. 41, 1929, pp. 41–57.

R. If the corresponding price of zero demand be designated by p', then we shall have from equation (27) the following definition of the radius:

$$R = \frac{p' - p}{t}. \tag{29}$$

One will then readily see that if ρ is a number which represents the density of population per unit area in the circle of radius R, the total demand for the manufacturers goods is given by the following integral:

$$X = 2\pi\rho \int_0^R x(p + tr)\, r\, dr. \tag{30}$$

Example. Let us assume that the demand is given by the linear function

$$\frac{p}{p_0} + \frac{x}{x_0} = 1.$$

Since the price of zero demand is p_0, we shall have for the demand radius

$$R = \frac{p_0 - p}{t}.$$

Substituting the proper values in equation (30), we obtain as the total demand the following:

$$X = 2\pi\rho \int_0^R \frac{x_0}{p_0} (p_0 - p - tr)\, r\, dr,$$

$$= 2\pi\rho \frac{x_0}{p_0} [\tfrac{1}{2}(p_0 - p)R^2 - tR^3/3],$$

$$= \frac{\pi\rho x_0 (p_0 - p)^3}{3p_0 t^2}.$$

We observe from this expression that X varies inversely as the square of the transportation rate, a result which one may show is true in the general case.

We next consider the case of two producers who are located respectively at the production centers A and B. We shall assume that these centers are at a distance $2a$ from one another, as indicated in Figure 28. Let us assume further that the price of production is the same at the two centers, but that the cost of transportation is t_1 per unit distance for the producer at A, and $t_2 < t_1$ for the producer at B. Let the consumer be located at the point (x, y).

We can then write

$$P_A = p + t_1 r_1, \quad P_B = p + t_2 r_2.$$

The boundary between the two areas of trade is then defined by the equation

$$P_A = P_B\,, \quad \text{that is,} \quad p + t_1 r_1 = p + t_2 r_2\,.$$

Expressing r_1 and r_2 in terms of x and y and substituting these values in the equation just written down, we obtain

$$t_1[(x-a)^2 + y^2]^{\frac{1}{2}} = t_2[(x+a)^2 + y^2]^{\frac{1}{2}}\,.$$

This equation may then be written in the following form

$$(x-b)^2 + y^2 = R^2\,, \tag{31}$$

where we use the abbreviations

$$b = \frac{t_1^2 + t_2^2}{t_1^2 - t_2^2}\,a\,, \quad R^2 = b^2 - a^2 = \frac{4t_1^2 t_2^2}{(t_1^2 - t_2^2)^2}\,a^2\,.$$

Equation (31) is, of course, a circle with center at the point $(b,0)$ and radius equal to R. In case $t_1 = t_2$, the circle degenerates into the straight line $x = 0$.

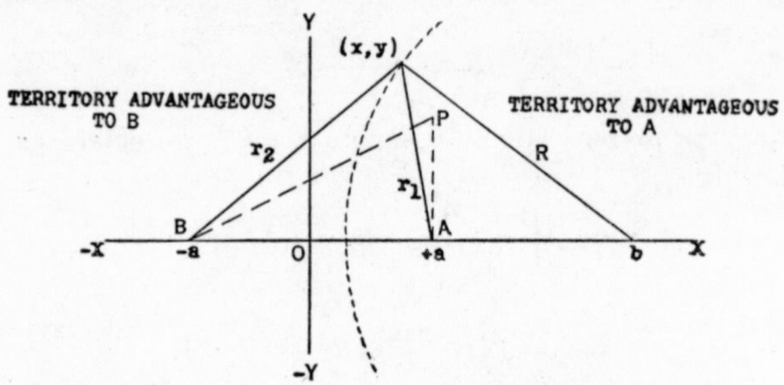

FIGURE 28.—REGIONS OF COMPETITIVE BARGAINING.

This problem has considerably more than a theoretical interest since it finds immediate application in what is called *the basing point method* for quoting prices in industries where freight is an important item. An example of such an industry is the production of steel and steel products. The basis of the method is the practice by competing mills of quoting a delivery price equal to that realized by the nearest mill designated as a basing point.

For example in constructing Figure 28 we have assumed that $a = 20$ distance units, and that A pays a freight rate of \$3 per unit distance, while B pays a freight rate of \$2 per unit distance. If B wishes to compete with A within the circular region which represents his territorial advantage, then he must be able to operate on a smaller mill net price than that actually quoted by A. For example, if the base price at both centers is \$500 per unit, and if P has the coordinate values (20, 20), then A's delivery price at P will be \$500 + \$60 =

\$560, while B's price will be $\$500 + \$2 \cdot 20\sqrt{5} = \$589.44$. Hence, in order to compete at P, B must be able to operate at a net mill price of $\$500 - (89.44 - 60) = \$470.56$.

PROBLEMS

1. Prove that if R_0 is the value for which demand, defined by the function

$$p = \frac{a}{b + cx},$$

may be regarded as being essentially zero, then total demand will be given by

$$X = \frac{2\pi\rho}{ct^2}\left[atR_0 - \tfrac{1}{2}b(tR_0)^2 + ap\log\left(\frac{p}{p + tR_0}\right)\right].$$

2. If demand is defined by the function $p = (x - a)^2$, show that total demand will be given by

$$X = \frac{2\pi\rho}{t^2}\left[\frac{a(a-p)^2}{2} + \frac{2(a^{5/2} - p^{7/2})}{5} - \frac{2(a^{3/2} - p^{5/2})}{3}\right].$$

3. Discuss the regions of influence of two mills if the basic prices are different, but if transportation rates are the same. In other words, discuss the locus defined by

$$p_1 + t\,d_1 = p_2 + t\,d_2\,.$$

4. Discuss the regions of influence for three mills A, B, and C, whose transportation rates are respectively $t_1 < t_2 < t_3$, but whose basic prices are the same.

5. If a factory plans to use equal amounts of steel from three mills, which charge identical prices and for which rates of transportation are the same, find the best place to locate the factory. That is, find the point such that $d_1 + d_2 + d_3$ is a minimum. Prove that if the mills are located at the vertices of the triangle ABC, then the factory should be located at a point P, which subtends angles of 120° with the three sides of the triangle. [See Goursat-Hedrick: *Mathematical Analysis*, Vol. 1, 1904, pp. 130–131].

6. A chain store dealing in a certain group of commodities has 96 branch stores in eight cities along a certain highway. Using city X with 9 branch stores as a reference point, the other seven cities with their branch stores are located as follows:

City	Number of Branch Stores	Distance from X (in miles)
A	10	60
B	12	33
C	5	15
D	6	—20
E	15	—65
F	20	—85
G	19	—102

The company wishes to establish a main office for this group of stores and is confronted with the most convenient location. Show that they should locate their branch at the median distance from X.

SELECTED BIBLIOGRAPHY ON PURE EXCHANGE

BOWLEY, A. L. *The Mathematical Groundwork of Economics.* Oxford, 1924, viii + 98 pp. In particular, Chapters 1 and 2.

EDGEWORTH, F. Y. *Mathematical Psychics.* London, 1881, viii + 150 pp. In particular, p. 39 et seq.

HOTELLING. H. "Stability in Competition," *Economic Journal,* Vol. 41, 1929, pp. 41–57.

LAUNHARDT, W. *Mathematische Begründung der Volkswirtschaftslehre.* Leipzig, 1885, p. 149 et seq.

SCHNEIDER, E. "Bemerkungen zu einer Theorie der Raumwirtschaft." *Econometrica,* Vol. 3, 1935, pp. 79–105.

CHAPTER 6

The Theory of Monopoly and Duopoly

1. Total, Average, and Marginal Costs

The theory of monopoly begins necessarily with a consideration of the problem of costs. We shall start, therefore, by assuming that the total cost of manufacturing and marketing u units of a commodity is known, and that this cost is a function of u alone. We shall designate total cost (T.C.) by $Q(u)$.

Then, if $Q(u)$ is the total cost of manufacturing and marketing u units, the quantity

$$(1) \qquad q(u) = \frac{Q(u)}{u}$$

will be the average cost (A. C.). In most manufacturing enterprises the function $q(u)$ will tend to diminish for certain ranges of the variable u, since overhead costs remain nearly constant, while the cost of materials, labor, and similar concomitants of actual production tend to increase linearly; that is to say, they increase proportionally to u.

It will be convenient to assume, for the sake of mathematical illustration and without subjecting the problem at this time to statistical verification, that $Q(u)$ may be represented approximately by a quadratic function; that is, we shall write

$$(2) \qquad Q(u) = au^2 + bu + c\,.$$

Hence average cost has the form

$$(3) \qquad q(u) = au + b + \frac{c}{u}\,.$$

Since c in (2) is the overhead constant, which exists no matter what u may be, any increase in u would tend to reduce the third term in the right member of (3) and a large increase in u would make it negligibly small with respect to the other two terms. Hence average cost becomes essentially a linear function of u. Such data as exist on the cost function show that (2) and (3) are essentially correct representations of total and average cost functions.

By the marginal cost (M.C.), which we shall designate by $M(u)$, we shall mean the derivatives of $Q(u)$; that is to say,

$$(4) \qquad M(u) = \frac{dQ}{du} = Q'(u) \;,$$
$$= q(u) + u\,q'(u) \;.$$

If we represent $M(u)$ as the ratio of increments, that is, $\Delta Q/\Delta u$, we see that marginal cost is the rate at which total cost changes when an increment is added to the number of units manufactured.

The rate of change of marginal cost is given by

$$(5) \qquad \frac{dM}{du} = \frac{d^2Q}{du^2} = Q''(u)$$
$$= 2q'(u) + u\,q''(u) \;.$$

The area under the marginal cost curve, $A(u)$, is equal to total cost, as one observes from the integral

$$A(u) = \int_0^u M(u)\,du = Q(u) = u\,q(u).$$

As in the previous discussion of supply and demand, the elasticities of total cost, average cost, and marginal cost can be computed. The formulas for these elasticities in terms of the variables defined above are given below as follows:

$$\textit{Total Cost:} \qquad \eta_Q = \frac{u\,Q'}{Q} = \frac{q + u\,q'}{q} = \frac{u\,M(u)}{A(u)} \;;$$

$$\textit{Average Cost:} \qquad \eta_q = \frac{u\,q'}{q} = \frac{u\,Q' - Q}{Q} = \frac{u\,M - A}{A} \;;$$

$$\textit{Marginal Cost:} \qquad \eta_M = \frac{u\,M'}{M} = \frac{u\,Q''}{Q'} = \frac{u(2q' + u\,q'')}{q + u\,q'} \;.$$

One may readily verify from these formulas that η_Q and η_q are connected by the equation

$$(6) \qquad \eta_Q = 1 + \eta_q \;.$$

If the total cost function is assumed to be quadratic, as stated in equation (2), then the elasticities have the following explicit values:

$$\eta_Q = \frac{2au^2 + bu}{au^2 + bu + c} \sim 2 + \frac{k}{u} + \cdots \;;$$

$$\eta_q = \frac{au^2 - c}{au^2 + bu + c} \backsim 1 - \frac{k}{u} + \cdots ;$$

$$\eta_M = \frac{2au}{2au + b} \backsim 1 + \frac{k'}{u} + \cdots ,$$

where k and k' are constants. It is clear from the asymptotic expansions that the elasticities approach respectively the values 2, 1, and 1 as u increases.

2. *Some Geometrical Aspects of Cost*

In working with cost functions it is frequently useful to have in mind a geometrical picture of them. Thus let us consider the average and marginal cost curves as illustrated in Figure 29.

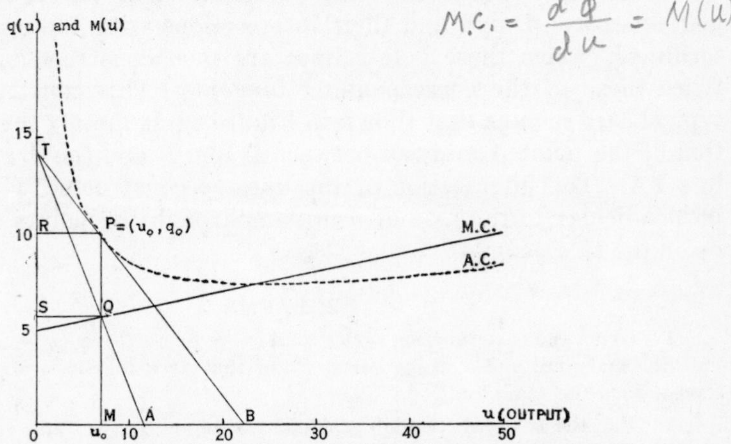

FIGURE 29.—AVERAGE COST AND MARGINAL COST CURVES.

In order to understand better the relationships which exist between the two curves, let us consider the point $P = (u_0, q_0)$ on the A. C. curve. Since the slope of the tangent TB at this point is $q'(u_0)$, the equation of the tangent is

$$q - q_0 = q'(u_0)(u - u_0).$$

Setting $u = 0$ in this equation, we find the length OT to be

$$OT = q_0 - u_0 q'(u_0).$$

Considering next the M. C. curve, we use equation (4) of Section 1 to compute

$$M(u_0) = q_0 + u_0 q'(u_0) = MQ = OS.$$

From these equations we are now able to compare the slope of the line TA with the slope of the tangent TB. Thus we compute

$$OT - OS = ST = -2u_0\, q'(u_0) = 2u_0 \frac{RT}{RP}.$$

The minus sign disappears in this equation since $q'(u_0)$ is essentially a negative number.

Dividing ST by $u_0 = RP = SQ$, we then obtain

$$\frac{ST}{RP} = 2\frac{RT}{RP};$$

that is to say, the slope of the line TA is equal to twice the slope of the line TB.

This relationship can be used to construct the M. C. curve if the A. C. curve is known. Thus, given the A. C. curve, a set of tangent lines are drawn and their intersections with the q-axis are determined. From these points lines are then constructed with slopes twice those of the corresponding tangents. This construction, in a typical case such as that shown in Figure 29, is merely the determination of the point A midway between O and B and the drawing of the line TA. The intersection of the lines so constructed with the lines perpendicular to the axis of u drawn through the points of tangency lie on the M. C. curve.

PROBLEMS

1. Given the cost function $Q(u) = A(u + c) + B \log(u + c) + C$, compute the marginal and average costs. Show that as u increases $M.\ C.$ and $A.\ C.$ tend toward the same limit.

2. For the cost function of problem 1, compue η_Q, η_q, and η_M. Verify directly that $\eta_Q = 1 + \eta_q$.

3. Represent graphically total, marginal, and average costs for the cost function

$$Q(u) = (u + 10) - 20 \log(u + 10) + 20.$$

4. Compute the three elasticities for the cost function of problem 3.

5. Given $M(u) = (au + b)^m$, compute $Q(u)$ and $q(u)$.

6. Given the marginal cost function

$$M(u) = \frac{a}{b - cu},$$

show that total cost is given by

$$Q(u) = -\frac{a}{c}\log(b - cu) + d,$$

where d is an arbitrary constant.

7. If $q(u) = au^{-1} + bu^{-1}e^{cu}$, compute $M(u)$ and $Q(u)$.

8. Represent graphically the average cost curve

$$q(u) = \frac{50}{u(1 - 0.01u)} .$$

Then, using the geometrical construction given in Section 2, construct graphically the curve of marginal cost.

9. Given the average cost curve

$$q(u) = 8u - 3 + \frac{2}{u} ,$$

show by the graphical method given in Section 2 that the marginal cost curve is a straight line.

10. Draw at random some curve which might represent average cost. Then construct geometrically the corresponding marginal cost curve.

3. *Total, Average, and Marginal Revenue*

In Section 6 of Chapter 4 we considered total revenue, which is defined as the area of the rectangle $OAPB$ under the demand curve $p = p(x)$, where x is the amount demanded (see Figure 30). As the

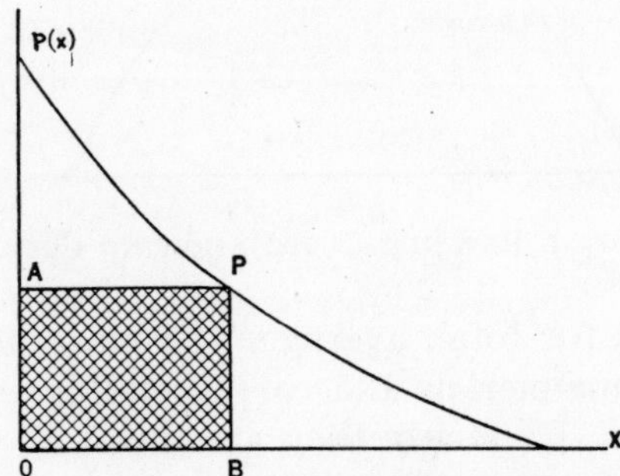

FIGURE 30.—DEMAND CURVE SHOWING TOTAL REVENUE.

point P moves along the curve of demand, the area of the rectangle will change. The graph of this value, as a function of x, is called the curve of total revenue (T. R.). We shall represent it by the equation

$$R = px , \tag{7}$$

which is graphically shown in Figure 31.

Average revenue (A.R.) is consequently R divided by x, that is to say, p. If we represent average revenue by r, we have

$$r = \frac{R}{x} = p(x) . \tag{8}$$

From this we conclude that the curve of average revenue is identical with the curve of demand.

Marginal revenue (M. R.) is then defined to be the derivative with respect to x of the total revenue, R. If we represent marginal revenue by $m(x)$, we then have

$$(9) \qquad m(x) = \frac{dR}{dx} = p + x\,p'(x) = r + x\,r'(x).$$

From this equation it will be seen that $m(x)$ is related to $r(x) = p(x)$ in the same manner as the marginal cost, $M(u)$, is related to the average cost, $q(u)$. Hence the curve of marginal revenue can be constructed from a given demand curve by the same geometrical method described in Section 2 by means of which $M(u)$ was obtained from the curve of average cost. Typical A. R. and M. R. curves are shown in Figure 32.

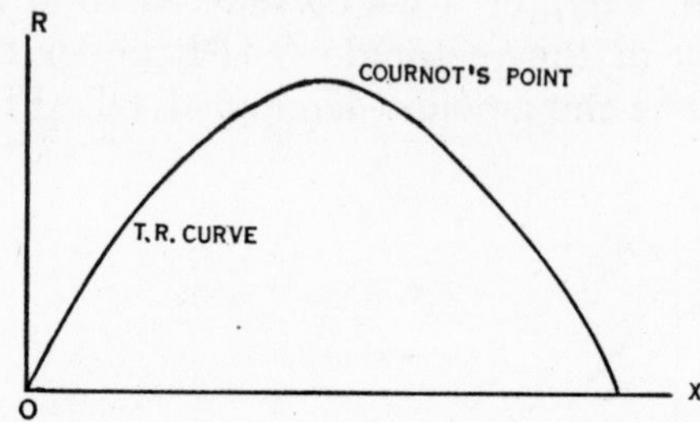

FIGURE 31.—TOTAL REVENUE CURVE SHOWING COURNOT'S POINT.

The elasticities for total, average, and marginal revenue are defined in the same manner as the corresponding elasticities for the three cost functions. Explicitly they are given by the following formulas:

Total Revenue: $$\eta_R = \frac{x\,R'}{R} = \frac{p + x\,p'(x)}{p};$$

Average Revenue: $$\eta_r = \eta_p = \frac{x\,p'}{p} = \frac{x\,R' - R}{R};$$

Marginal Revenue: $$\eta_m = \frac{x\,m'}{m} = \frac{x\,R''}{R'} = \frac{x(2p' + x\,p'')}{p + x\,p'}.$$

It is at once seen from these equations that η_R and η_p are connected by the equation

$$(10) \qquad \eta_R = 1 + \eta_p.$$

Since Cournot's point, from Section 6 of Chapter 4, is characterized by the value $\eta_p = -1$, it follows that $\eta_R = 0$ at the maximum of the total revenue curve. This is also evident immediately from the fact that $R' = 0$ at the Cournot point, and hence $\eta_R = xR'/R = 0$.

If the demand function is given by the value

$$p = \frac{m\,\beta}{n\,\alpha + (m+n)\,x},$$

then we have the following values for the elasticities:

$$\eta_R = \frac{n\,\alpha}{n\,\alpha + (m+n)\,x};$$

$$\eta_r = \eta_p = -\frac{(m+n)\,x}{n\,\alpha + (m+n)\,x} = \eta_R - 1;$$

$$\eta_m = -\frac{2\,(m+n)\,x}{n\,\alpha + (m+n)\,x} 2\,\eta_r.$$

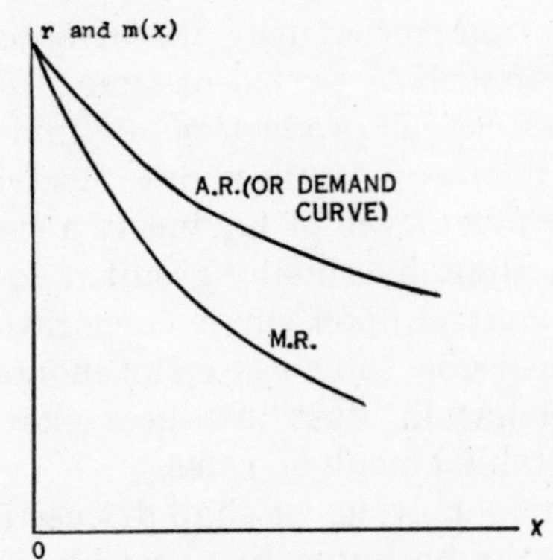

FIGURE 32.—CURVES OF AVERAGE REVENUE, OR DEMAND, AND OF MARGINAL REVENUE.

PROBLEMS

1. Given the total revenue function, $R(x) = ax - bx^2$, compute average and marginal revenue. If $a = 10$ and $b = 0.1$, represent these curves graphically.

2. Compute the elasticities η_R, η_r, and η_m corresponding to the total revenue curve of problem 1. Also compute the coordinates of Cournot's point.

3. Given the total revenue function

$$R = \frac{x}{x+b} - c,$$

compute η_R. Show that $x = \sqrt{(b/c)} - b$ is the abscissa of Cournot's point.

4. If the demand curve is given by

$$p = (10 - 0.1x)^2,$$

construct the marginal revenue curve graphically by the method of Section 2.

5. Given $m(x) = a \log(b/x) - a$, compute $R(x)$.

6. If the marginal revenue function is given by $m(x) = a - 3bx^2$, compute the demand function.

7. Show that if marginal revenue is defined by

$$m(x) = \frac{ac}{(bx + c)^2},$$

then the demand curve is given by: $p = a/(bx + c)$.

8. Compute the coordinates of Cournot's point for the demand function

$$p = a(x - c)^{-m}.$$

Show that at this point $\eta_p = -1$.

4. *The Problem of Monopoly*

By a monopolist we mean a producer of goods who has such control of the market that he may fix the price at which his goods are to be sold. It is probable that few real monopolies exist in an economy, but there are many approximations to monopoly. For example, patent rights to an invention confer upon the inventor monopolistic control of production over a fixed period of time. During early days in the development of electrical production we find many instances of competition for the business of supplying electrical power to communities. But the inconvenience of having two systems of wires, two power plants, and the like, has finally resulted in most cities in conferring monopolistic control upon single corporations. But these corporations have not been able to exercise full monopolistic rights since governmental control has in most instances exercised a restraining influence upon the establishment of rates.

The problem of monopoly, as we shall discuss it, is concerned with the determination of the optimum price which a corporation should set if this corporation has full monopolistic control of its production. In order to simplify the analysis we shall assume that the corporation manufactures one article for which both the demand and cost functions are known. It will also be assumed that all units manufactured are sold.

Employing the symbols of the preceding sections, we shall then obtain as the net return, or profit, $\pi(u)$, for the manufacturing and distribution of u units of the goods, the following expression:

$$\begin{aligned} \pi(u) &= R(u) - Q(u) \\ &= pu - Q(u), \end{aligned} \tag{11}$$

where $R(u)$ is total revenue and $Q(u)$ is total cost.

It may be assumed, as a plausible postulate, that the entrepreneur will attempt to adjust either the price or the production so that $\pi(u)$ will be a maximum. But since we have assumed the existence of a demand function for the goods, the adjustment of price is functionally controlled by the adjustment of production. In this case, taking the derivative of (11) with respect to u, we have, as the condition for maximum profits, the following equation:

$$\frac{d\pi}{du} = \frac{dR}{du} - \frac{dQ}{du} = 0 \,. \tag{12}$$

That is to say, *maximum profit is obtained when marginal revenue equals marginal cost.* This is the first principle of monopolistic production.

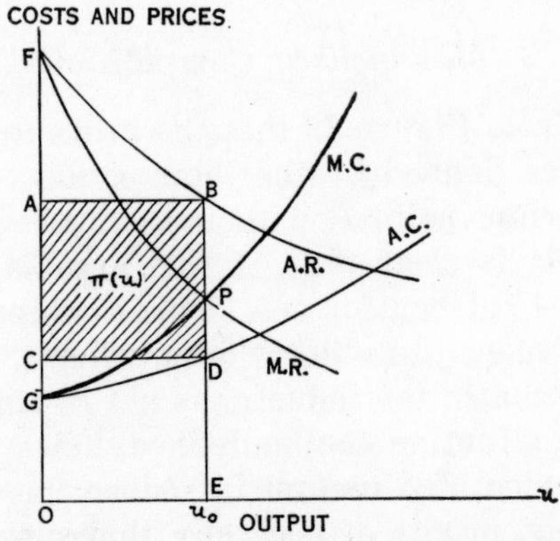

FIGURE 33.—CURVES OF MARGINAL AND AVERAGE COSTS AND OF MARGINAL AND AVERAGE REVENUE. PROFITS ARE INDICATED BY THE AREA *ABDC*.

In order to be sure that profit is maximized, we must impose the condition that the second derivative of π with respect to u is negative; that is to say,

$$\frac{d^2\pi}{du^2} = \frac{d^2R}{du^2} - \frac{d^2Q}{du^2} < 0 \,. \tag{13}$$

If we examine Figure 33 we see that the point P is the intersection of the marginal cost and the marginal revenue curves and hence, by equation (12), defines the output, u_0, which maximizes the profit function $\pi(u)$.

The area of the rectangle $ABDC$ is seen to equal profits since $u \times A.R. = R(u)$ and $u \times A.C. = Q(u)$ and the difference between these areas is equal to $\pi(u)$. In the figure it will be observed that the

M. C. and *A. C.* curves intersect on the vertical axis. This would be the case only on the assumption that $Q(0) = 0$. But with this assumption we observe that $\pi(u)$ is also equal to the area FPG. Thus we have for the area under the curve FP, the integral

$$\text{Area } FPEO = \int_0^{u_0} \frac{dR(u)}{du}\, du = R(u_0) - R(0) = R(u_0) \, ,$$

and for the area under the curve GP, namely, the area $GPEO$, the integral

$$\text{Area } GPEO = \int_0^{u_0} \frac{dQ(u)}{du}\, du = Q(u_0) - Q(0) = Q(u_0) \, .$$

The difference between these two areas, namely, the area FPG, is thus equal to $R(u_0) - Q(u_0) = \pi(u_0)$.

5. *Monopolistic Competition*

We have seen from Figure 33 that the profit $\pi(u)$ is given by the area $ABDC$, an area defined by the intersection of the vertical line through the equilibrium point P with the curves of average revenue and average cost. It is clear that, if this area is sufficiently large, then there will be a tendency for new firms to enter the industry and competition will increase. In other words, when profits are observed to be large, competition in the industry is not in equilibrium.

An equilibrium situation can be defined, however, by means of a simple analytical device. Let us first introduce the concept of *normal profits,* that is to say, profits of such size that new firms will not be induced to enter the industry under consideration, nor old firms to disappear from it. Whether the firms in an industry are earning normal profits or not might be determined statistically by observing whether the capitalization of the industry is stable, that is to say, whether it is increasing only as fast as the growth of population would warrant. Thus, we might compare the new capital entering an industry with the loss of old capital through business failures.

In order to obtain a theoretical criterion for the determination of monopolistic equilibrium we shall assume that normal profits are distributed over the average cost curve, so that the function $q(u)$ includes both average manufacturing and distributing costs plus average normal profits. Under this assumption an industry will be said to be in monopolistic equilibrium provided $\pi(u) = 0$. If $\pi(u) > 0$, then more than normal profits are being earned and the industry will expand; if $\pi(u) < 0$, then less than normal profits are being earned and the industry will decline. An example of the former is the automobile industry during the years from 1920 to 1930, and an example of the latter is furnished by the railroads since 1914. One industry has expanded rapidly, while the other has declined.

Let us now assume that an industry is in monopolistic equilibrium when $\pi(u) = 0$, provided normal profits are included in average costs. This would mean that $ED = EB$ in Figure 33.

If we represent by p_x the equilibrium price as determined by the demand curve, in other words, $p_x = EB$, and by p_u the equilibrium price as determined by the curve of average cost, in other words, $p_u = ED$, then the condition for monopolistic equilibrium becomes

$$p_x = p_u . \tag{14}$$

But from the conditions established in the preceding section that marginal revenue = marginal cost, we have

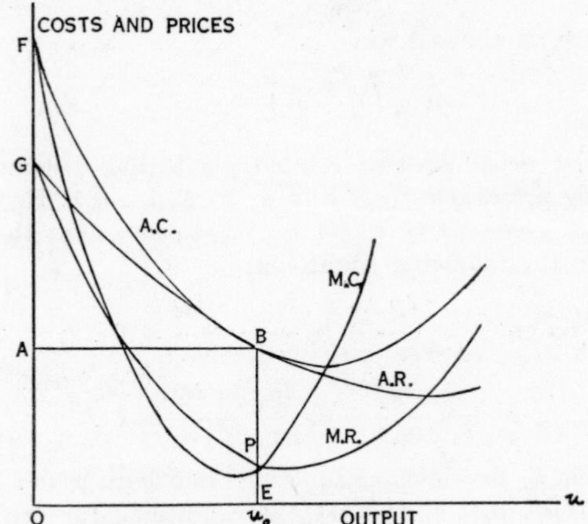

FIGURE 34.—COST AND REVENUE CURVES IN THE CASE OF COMPETITIVE EQUILIBRIUM.

$$\frac{d}{du}(up_x) = \frac{d}{du}(up_u) ,$$

or in expanded form,

$$p_x + u\frac{dp_x}{du} = p_u + u\frac{dp_u}{du} .$$

Making use of (14) we obtain finally the desired relationship,

$$\frac{dp_x}{du} = \frac{dp_u}{du} , \tag{15}$$

which states that *the demand curve and the average cost curve are tangent at the point of equilibrium.* This situation is shown graphically in Figure 34.

Contrasted with monopolistic equilibrium is *competitive equilibrium,* in which the demand curve is supposed to be horizontal on the assumption that no single firm can influence the price of the product. The theory of competitive equilibrium has been developed by E. H. Chamberlin, Joan Robinson, and others (see *Bibliography*).

PROBLEMS

1. Given $R(u) = au - bu^2$, and $Q(u) = cu^2 + du + e$, prove that profits are maximized when u is given by

$$u = \tfrac{1}{2}\left(\frac{d-a}{b+c}\right).$$

2. If total revenue and total cost are represented respectively by the functions

$$R(u) = \frac{u}{u+b} - cu\,, \quad Q(u) = au + d\,,$$

prove that profits are maximized when

$$u = \left(\frac{b}{a+b}\right)^{\frac{1}{2}} - b\,.$$

3. A monopolist produces two related goods the demands for which are given respectively by $p_1 = f(u_1, u_2)$ and $p_2 = g(u_1, u_2)$. If, then, the monopolist's cost function is given by $Q = Q(u_1, u_2)$, prove that the monopoly prices are determined from the following equations:

$$p_1 + u_1\frac{\partial p_1}{\partial u_1} + u_2\frac{\partial p_2}{\partial u_2} - \frac{\partial Q}{\partial u_1} = 0\,,$$

$$p_2 + u_2\frac{\partial p_2}{\partial u_2} + u_1\frac{\partial p_1}{\partial u_2} - \frac{\partial Q}{\partial u_2} = 0\,.$$

4. If in problem 3, the demand functions had been given in the form $u_1 = F(p_1, p_2)$, $u_2 = G(p_1, p_2)$, show that the conditions for the determination of monopoly prices are then written in the form

$$u_1 + \left(p_1 - \frac{\partial Q}{\partial u_1}\right)\frac{\partial u_1}{\partial p_1} + \left(p_2 - \frac{\partial Q}{\partial u_2}\right)\frac{\partial u_2}{\partial p_1} = 0\,,$$

$$u_2 + \left(p_1 - \frac{\partial Q}{\partial u_1}\right)\frac{\partial u_1}{\partial p_2} + \left(p_2 - \frac{\partial Q}{\partial u_2}\right)\frac{\partial u_2}{\partial p_2} = 0\,.$$

5. Suppose that a business, which has monopolistic control of the production and sale of two goods, finds that the demands are given by the functions

$$p_1 = 76 - 3u_1 - 5u_2\,, \quad p_2 = 100 - 4u_1 - 6u_2\,.$$

If, then, the cost is given by the function

$$Q = 10 + u_1u_2 + u_1^2 + u_2^2\,,$$

show that the monopolistic prices are respectively $p_1 = 43.33$, $p_2 = 58.67$.

6. In calculus it is proved that the function

$$z = f(x,y)$$

has a maximum at the point (x_0, y_0) determined from the equation

$$\frac{\partial z}{\partial x} = 0\,, \quad \frac{\partial z}{\partial y} = 0\,,$$

provided at the point the following inequalities hold:

$$\frac{\partial^2 z}{\partial x^2}\frac{\partial^2 z}{\partial y^2} - \left(\frac{\partial^2 z}{\partial x\,\partial y}\right)^2 > 0\,, \quad \text{and either } \frac{\partial^2 z}{\partial x^2}\,, \text{ or } \frac{\partial^2 z}{\partial y^2} < 0\,.$$

Determine explicitly these conditions for the profit function defined by the conditions given in problem 3.

7. Prove that the values determined in problem 5 make the profit function a maximum.

8. If $R(u) = au - bu^2$ and if $Q(u) = cu + d$, prove that the condition for monopolistic equilibrium reduces to

$$(c - a)^2 = 4bd\,.$$

9. If $R(u) = u(a - bu)^2$ and if $Q(u) = cu^2 + du$, determine the conditions for monopolistic equilibrium.

10. Graph the average revenue and average cost curves corresponding to the following total revenue and total cost curves: $R(u) = u(10 - u)^2$, $Q(u) = 51u - 6u^2$. Show that the conditions for monopolistic equilibrium are satisfied.

6. An Economic Example

What does a cost curve actually look like? This question has recently been answered by the U. S. Steel Corporation in an extensive report of its activities which was submitted to the Temporary National Economic Committee during the course of the hearings on the steel industry held in Washington, D. C., in November, 1939 and January, 1940.[1]

TOTAL COSTS AND VOLUME OF BUSINESS—1938 CONDITIONS*

Millions of Weighted Tons of Products Shipped	Costs—1938 Conditions (Millions of dollars)	Year on which Estimate is Based
4.4	436.0	1932
6.1	510.0	1934
6.2	512.0	1933
7.6	610.3	1935
7.8	614.3	1938
8.1	628.9	1931
11.0	818.2	1936
11.9	838.8	1930
13.0	954.5	1927
13.2	916.2	1937
14.0	966.2	1928
15.1	979.0	1929

* Total costs are adjusted to 1938 interest, pension, wage and tax rates, to 1938 price level, and to 1938 efficiency.

[1] See *United States Steel Corporation T. N. E. C. Papers*, 1940, Vol. 1 pp. 223–323. The analysis in these pages was done under the supervision of T. O. Yntema.

The table on page 137 gives the data on the total costs and the volume of business of the U. S. Steel Corporation and all of its subsidiaries, the data for the years other than 1938 being adjusted to the conditions of 1938.

The data given in this table are graphically represented in Figure 35. It will be observed that the costs are strictly linear over the range of business given. Hence, we have for the equation of total cost the function

$$Q(u) = 182.1 + 55.73u \,, \tag{16}$$

where $Q(u)$ is measured in millions of dollars, and u in millions of tons.

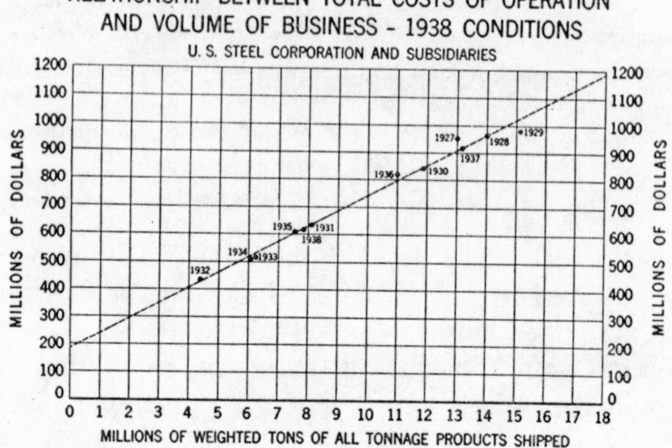

FIGURE 35.—FROM THE TNEC REPORT OF THE U. S. STEEL CORPORATION. Total costs are adjusted to 1938 interest, tax, pension, and wage rates; to 1938 price levels; and to 1938 efficiency.

The distribution of the total costs into their various categories is interesting in itself, and is reproduced in the table on page 139. One will observe that the column totals, expressed in proper units, furnish the constants in the total cost function given above in (16). The graphical representation of these data is shown in Figure 36.

Referring now to equation (16) we see that the average cost curve (A.C.) is given by the function

$$q(u) = \frac{182.1}{u} + 55.73 \,. \tag{17}$$

Similarly marginal cost (M.C.) is the constant $M(u) = 55.73$.

Turning next to revenues, we find that the Corporation realized an average sales return, in terms of 1938 prices, of $71.86 per ton of

COMPOSITION OF TOTAL COSTS OF OPERATION IN RELATION TO VOLUME OF BUSINESS

Items	Costs that Must be Met Regardless of Operating Rate	Additional Costs for Each Additional Weighted Ton* of Product Shipped
Interest	$ 8,300,000	$ 0.00
Pensions	7,700,000	0.00
Depreciation and Depletion	29,500,000	2.37
Taxes Other than Social Security and Federal Income	24,200,000	1.43
Payrolls	62,100,000	29.10
Social Security Taxes	2,500,000	1.16
Goods and Services Purchased	47,800,000	21.67
Total Costs	$182,100,000	$55.73

* Weighted tonnages are actual tonnages, adjusted for change in proportions of high and low cost products, and for the equivalent tonnage of average cost rolled and finished steel products represented by products other than steel.

products shipped, and an additional return of $5.80 per ton from transportation and miscellaneous revenues. This makes a total of $77.66 per ton.

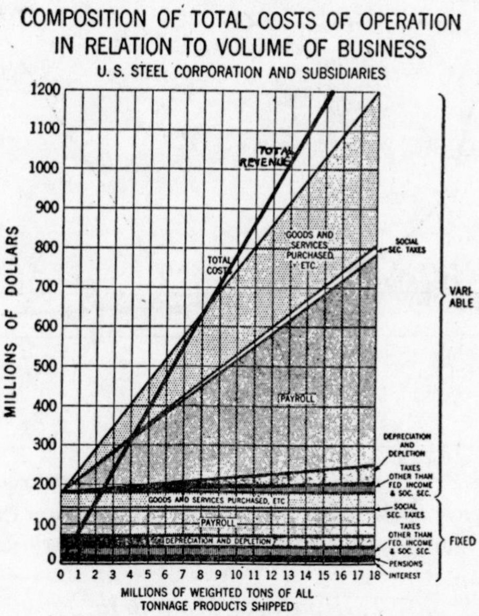

FIGURE 36.—FROM THE TNEC REPORT OF THE U. S. STEEL CORPORATION. The experience from 1927 to 1938 is adjusted to the conditions of 1938.

From this we see that the total revenue function would be given by

$$R(u) = 77.66u, \tag{18}$$

where u is measured in tons. Since the demand for steel appears to be almost completely inelastic, the average and marginal revenues would be equal to the same constant; that is,

$$M.R. = A.R. = 77.66 . \tag{19}$$

We would thus conclude that there is no point of maximum profit since the marginal revenue curve never intersects the curve of marginal cost. As a matter of fact, within the range of the data, the profit function is strictly linear and equal to

$$\pi(u) = -182.1 + 21.93u . \tag{20}$$

The situation is graphically portrayed in Figure 37, which shows that the steel corporation is more interested in keeping its operations above the "break even point", than it is in the attainment of a position of maximum profit.

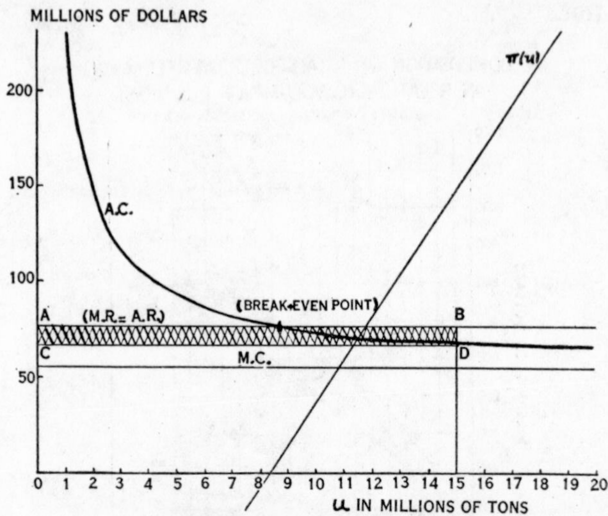

FIGURE 37.—GRAPHICAL REPRESENTATION OF THE VARIOUS COST AND REVENUE CURVES FOR THE U. S. STEEL CORPORATION.

7. *Bilateral Monopoly*

In the problem of bilateral monopoly we consider the situation where a monopolist A sells raw materials to a manufacturer B, also a monopolist, who must then dispose of his manufactured goods in a market independent of A.[2]

[2] In this section the author is indebted to A. L. Bowley: "Bilateral Monopoly," *Economic Journal*, Vol. 38, 1928, pp. 651–657.

In Figure 38 we have represented B's demand curve for A's raw materials by aa'. This is the average revenue curve for A. We have also represented A's marginal cost curve by bb', and his marginal revenue curve, based upon B's demand, by cc'. It is clear that the intersection of bb' with cc', namely the point P, determines the maximum profit for A. His optimum production is then the quantity represented by OP'.

Since bb' is A's supply curve, B's marginal cost curve, represented in the figure by dd', is based upon it. The intersection of dd' with aa', namely the point Q, determines the maximum profit for B. Since a unique equilibrium point is thus not established by this analysis, it follows that the final bargaining point must lie somewhere within or upon the boundary of the shaded area $PRQS$. It will be shown later

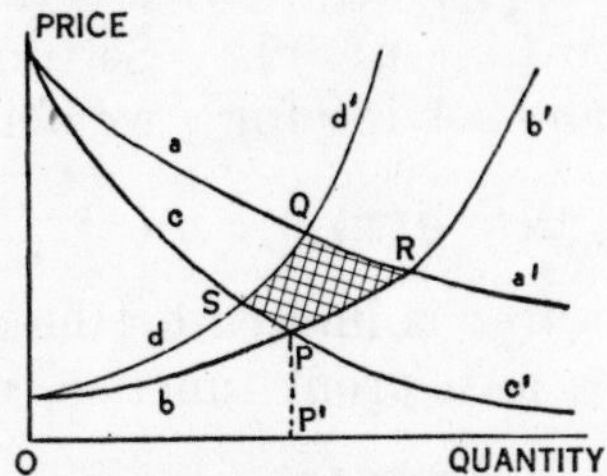

FIGURE 38.—AREA OF INDETERMINACY IN BILATERAL MONOPOLY.

that the point R might be a possible compromise between A and B since that is the point at which their joint gain is maximized.

In order to make the problem more precise, let us assume that the consumer's demand curve is given by the function $p = p(x)$. Hence, since B's demand for A's raw materials is determined by the marginal revenue based upon the consumer's demand, this curve, represented in Figure 38 by aa' is the graph of the function $p + xp'$. Moreover, since cc' is the marginal curve derived from B's demand aa', this marginal curve is the graphical representation of the function

$$\frac{d}{dx}[x(p + xp')] = p + 3xp' + x^2p'' .$$

Similarly, if we represent A's costs by the function $q = q(x)$, then bb', the curve of marginal costs, is the graph of the function $q + xq'$. The curve marginal to this, namely, dd', is then the graph of the function

$$q + 3xq' + x^2q'' .$$

The point Q is then determined from the equation

$$(21) \qquad p + xp' = q + 3xq' + x^2q'' ,$$

and the point P is determined from the equation

$$(22) \qquad q + xq' = p + 3xp' + x^2p'' .$$

The compromise point R is the intersection of aa' with bb', and hence is found from the solution of the equation

$$(23) \qquad p + xp' = q + xq' .$$

If equation (21) prevails for the determination of the point of contract, then this implies that the manufacturer B is able to dictate the price which he is willing to pay the monopolist A. In order to see this, let us assume that B dictates the price π to A, who is then willing to supply x units of his goods, where x is the quantity which maximizes his profit function $[\pi - q(x)]x$. Setting the derivative of this function equal to zero and solving for π we obtain the equation

$$\pi = q(x) + x\,q'(x).$$

Since the manufacturer is limited by the consumer's demand, he then must maximize his own profit function, namely,

$$(p - \pi)x = (p - q - xq')x .$$

Setting the derivative of this function equal to zero, we obtain equation (21).

On the other hand, if equation (22) prevails for the determination of the point of contract, then A is able to dictate the price at which he is willing to supply B. In order to prove this, let us assume that A dictates the price π. Then B must maximize $(p - \pi)x$, which leads to the condition $\pi = p + xp'$. A then maximizes his profit function

$$[\pi - q(x)]x = [p + xp' - q(x)]x .$$

Setting the derivative of this equation equal to zero, we obtain equation (22).

But if neither A nor B can dictate the price, then they may compromise and decide to maximize their joint profit, namely, the function

$$[\pi - q(x)]\,x + [p(x) - \pi]\,x = [p(x) - q(x)]\,x .$$

Setting the derivative of this equation equal to zero, we obtain equation (23).

The fact that these various solutions exist to the problem of bilateral monopoly has led to the conclusion that the realistic solution is indeterminate, although it will lie within or upon the boundary of the area $PRQS$. In commenting upon this situation J. R. Hicks says: " . . . this indeterminateness does not mean that the law of causality is suspended; it only means that the static assumptions of fixed demand and cost curves do not suffice to determine the price."[3]

8. *The Problem of Duopoly*

Since the theory of duopoly has had a long history, and since the solutions remain for the most part in the realm of conjecture because of a lack of statistical data, it will be sufficient for the purposes of this volume to give merely an outline of the problems which are involved in this intricate subject.

In duopoly we assume that there exist two entrepreneurs, who produce respectively amounts u_1 and u_2 of a certain goods. The sum, $u = u_1 + u_2$, is assumed to be equal to the demand, which is defined by the curve $p = p(u)$. The problem of duopoly is to determine the ratio of u_1 to u_2, under the assumption of known costs for the two entrepreneurs.

We shall assume that each duopolist equates his own marginal revenue to his marginal cost. That is to say, if $Q_1(u)$ and $Q_2(u)$ are the respective cost functions of the two entrepreneurs, we obtain the two equations

$$p(u) + u_1 p'(u) = Q'_1(u_1) , \tag{24}$$

$$p(u) + u_2 p'(u) = Q'_2(u_2) , \tag{25}$$

where $u = u_1 + u_2$.

In deriving these equations it will be observed that we have made the assumption that neither duopolist expects the other to change his output. Thus, in the case of the first equation, the first entrepreneur seeks to maximize his profit $u_1 p(u) - Q_1(u_1)$. Setting the derivative with respect to u_1 equal to zero, we obtain

$$p(u) + u_1 p'(u) \frac{du}{du_1} = Q'_1(u_1) .$$

It will be clear that du/du_1 reduces to unity only if u_2 is assumed to be independent of u_1.

One now observes that equations (24) and (25) define functions between the variables u_1 and u_2. The graphical representations of these functions are called *reaction curves,* and their simultaneous so-

[3] "Annual Survey of Economic Theory: The Theory of Monopoly," *Econometrica,* Vol. 3, 1935, p. 18.

lution determines the respective amounts which will be manufactured. From this solution we can determine the ratio $r = u_1/u_2$.

If we differentiate (24) with respect to u_1, and then solve for du_2/du_1, we shall obtain

$$\frac{du_2}{du_1} = -1 + \frac{Q''_1(u_1) - p'(u)}{p'(u) + u_1 p''(u)} = -1 + \rho_1 , \tag{26}$$

where we employ the abbreviation

$$\rho_1 = \frac{Q''_1(u_1) - p'(u)}{p'(u) + u_1 p''(u)} . \tag{27}$$

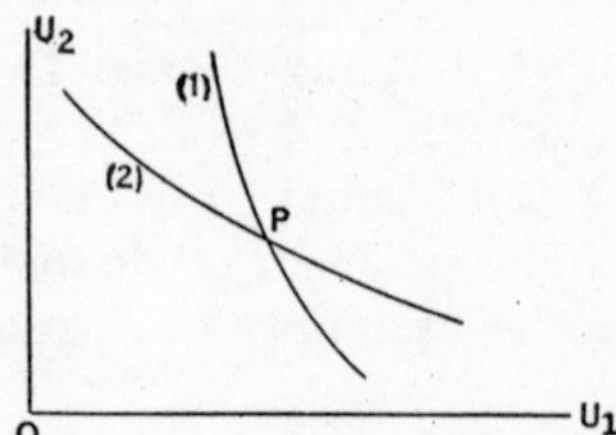

FIGURE 39.—REACTION CURVES.

It should be observed here that, although u_2 was assumed to be independent of u_1 in the derivation of equation (24), once the functional relationship between the two variables has been established, then the derivative of one variable with respect to the other is no longer zero, but is determined from the function.

Similarly, if we differentiate (25) with respect to u_2 and solve for du_2/du_1, we shall obtain

$$\frac{du_2}{du_1} = \frac{1}{-1 + \rho_2} , \tag{28}$$

where we employ the abbreviation

$$\rho_2 = \frac{Q''_2(u_2) - p'(u)}{p'(u) + u_2 p''(u)} . \tag{29}$$

If, now, we examine ρ_1 as defined by (27) we see that in the usual case the numerator of the fraction is positive, since $p(u)$ is a decreasing function and marginal cost is a non-decreasing function of the variables under normal conditions. This same remark applies also to ρ_2. Consequently, if we assume that the denominators of both fractions are negative, that is, if

$$p'(u) + u_1 p''(u) < 0 \, ,$$

(30)

$$p'(u) + u_2 p''(u) < 0 \, ,$$

then it follows that both ρ_1 and ρ_2 are negative.

Under these conditions we see that the slopes of both curves are negative, but in the case of (26) the slope is numerically greater than 1, whereas in the case of (28) the slope is numerically less than 1. We thus conclude that the two curves will intersect at some point P, as shown in Figure 39, which determines the desired ratio r.

In case p is a function of the form

$$p = \frac{a}{b + cu} \, ,$$

it may readily be shown that conditions (30) lead to the inequality

$$u_1 - u_2 < b/c \, .$$

9. Conjectural Variation

In this section we shall remove the restriction assumed in Section 8 that the adjustment of the production of one duopolist does not affect the production of the second. Under this condition equation (24) of Section 8 must be replaced by the more general equation

$$p(u) + u_1 p'(u) \left(1 + \frac{du_2}{du_1}\right) = Q'_1(u_1) \, , \tag{31}$$

where the added term takes account of the reaction of the second duopolist to the altered production of his competitor.

The derivative du_2/du_1 has been called by R. Frisch the *conjectural variation* of the second duopolist with respect to the first, an estimate made, of course, by the first duopolist.[4] We may assume that this variation is determined by a known function, which we may write in the form

$$u_2 = f(u_1).$$

Introducing this function into equation (31) we then have

$$p(u) + u_1 p'(u) [1 + f'(u_1)] = Q'(u_1) \, . \tag{32}$$

A similar equation would also apply to the second duopolist, if he took account of the reaction of his competitor to his own changing output.

[4] See Frisch: "Monopole-Polypole, etc." mentioned in the *Bibliography*.

Allen calls attention to the fact that if $f'(u_1)$ is negative, then the left hand member of equation (32) is increased since $p'(u)$ is normally a negative function.[5] Consequently the value of u_1 which satisfies equation (32) will be greater than the one which satisfies equation (24) of Section 8 where the conjectural variation term is absent, since marginal cost, given by $Q'(u_1)$, is normally an increasing function. We thus reach the conclusion *that the reaction curve in the case of a decreasing conjectural variation tends to shift to the right of the one computed without this variation term.*

As an application of this proposition we shall assume that the second duopolist acts as though his own change in output has no effect upon that of his competitor, while the first duopolist is able to make a correct forecast of the conjectural variation of the second. In this case the point of equilibrium which determines the ratio r shifts from P to P' as shown in Figure 40. The value of u_2 decreases while the value of u_1 increases and, to cite Allen, the "duopolist gains by being 'alive' to his rival's reactions." The situation is graphically shown in

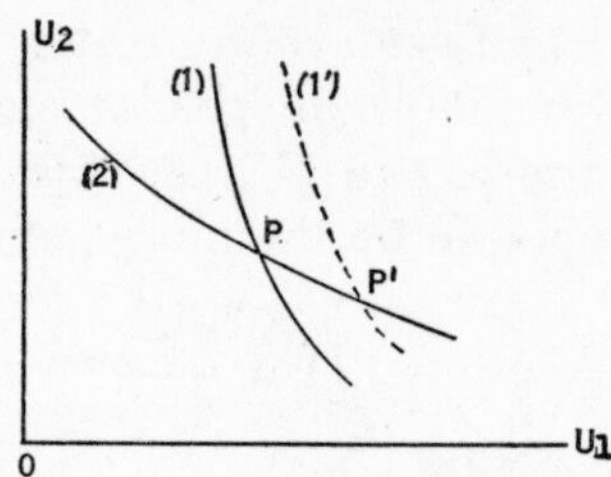

FIGURE 40.—REACTION CURVES SHOWING THE INFLUENCE OF CONJECTURAL VARIATION.

Figure 40, where the curve (1') is the reaction curve (1) after the conjectural variation has been introduced.

In order to see whether the first duopolist has actually made a gain in profits by his increased production, it would be necessary to compute the value of the profit function, which depends, of course, upon the joint output u of the two duopolists.

It is clear that the situation shown by this comparatively simple analysis of duopoly can be greatly generalized and extended. Some indication of the nature of these more general problems is given by J. R. Hicks in his review of the theory of monopoly published in *Econometrica* in 1935. (See *Bibliography*).

[5] See Allen in the reference given in the *Bibliography*, pp. 346–347.

PROBLEMS

1. Let us suppose that the consumer's demand for an article is given by $p = 100 - 4x$, and that the manufacturer, B, must buy from a monopolist A, whose cost curve is given, by $q = 10 + 2x$. Compare B's maximum profit if he can dictate the price, with his maximum profit if A can dictate the price.

2. Using the data of problem 1, determine the profits of both A and B if they compromise on a price which maximizes their joint profits.

3. Assume that the cost functions for two duopolists are respectively $Q_1 = 15 + 3u_1$, $Q_2 = 10 + 4u_2$, and that the demand is given by $p(u) = 100 - 5u$. Determine the ratio $r = u_1/u_2$.

4. If the cost functions for two duopolists are respectively, $Q_1 = 15 + 3u_1^2$ and $Q_2 = 10 + 4u_2^2$, and if the demand function is $p(u) = 100 - 5u$, compute the value of $r = u_1/u_2$.

5. Using the specifications of problem 4, let us assume that the second duopolist makes a conjectural change in his production with respect to the first duopolist. If his production is related to the first by the equation

$$u_2 = 5 + 2u_1 ,$$

show that the ratio $r = u_1/u_2$ is changed from 9/11 to 3/7.

6. Show that the profits under the conditions of problem 4 are respectively: $\pi_1 = 148.62$, $\pi_2 = 142.76$.

7. Show that by his conjectural change, the second duopolist of problem 5 increased his profits to 181.89, while the profits of his competitor dropped to 111.88.

8. If equations (21) and (23) yield the same answer, prove that the supply curve has a horizontal tangent at the maximum point and that supply and demand curves intersect there. (Tintner).

10. Concluding Summary

The theory of monopoly has come in recent times to occupy a central place in the mathematical development of economic statics. Founded originally by A. A. Cournot in his *Theory of Riches,* this domain of theoretical economics has been greatly extended and enriched by modern writers. The concepts of average and marginal revenue and of average and marginal costs tie together the theories of demand and supply through the primary concept of the profit function.

As the reader has observed, the main postulate invoked in attaining conditions of equilibrium has been that of maximizing profits. It has been assumed that manufacturers are guided in their decisions by the profit motive. Eliminate this, and the analysis of preceding sections becomes invalid. This is not the place to argue the validity of this proposition, which has been assumed generally to dominate the working of the capitalistic system, but one should observe that the picture which we have sketched of the operation of the system, depends primarily upon the postulate of maximizing profits.

But were this not the case, the concepts of average and marginal revenue and of average and marginal costs would still furnish a useful guide in appraising the operation of monopolists, duopolists, and other similar factors in the economic system.

SELECTED BIBLIOGRAPHY ON MONOPOLY AND DUOPOLY

ALLEN, R. G. D. *Mathematical Analysis for Economists.* London, 1938; New York, 1939. vi + 548 pp. In particular: *Monopoly problems*: pp. 196–200, 359–364, 381, 518, 519, 522, 533–536. *Duopoly problems*: pp. 200–204; 345–347.

BOWLEY, A. L. (1) *The Mathematical Groundwork of Economics.* Oxford, 1924, viii + 98 pp.

(2) "Bilateral Monopoly," *Economic Journal*, Vol. 38, 1928, pp. 651–657.

CHAMBERLIN, E. H. *Theory of Monopolistic Competition.* Cambridge, Mass., 1933, x + 225 pp.

COURNOT, A. A. *Recherches sur les principes mathématiques de la théorie des richesses.* Paris, 1938, xi + 198 pp. English translation by N. T. Bacon, New York, 1897, xxiv + 213 pp. In particular, Chapter 7.

DEAN, J. "Alternative Statistical Methods for Estimating Marginal Cost Functions," *Report of the Sixth Annual Conference of the Cowles Commission*, 1940, pp. 24–26.

EDGEWORTH, F. Y. "The Pure Theory of Monopoly." *Collected Papers*, II, pp. 122–126.

FRISCH, R. "Monopole-Polypole—la notion de force dans l'économie," *Nationaløkonomisk Tidsskrift*, 1933, 71: 241.

HICKS, J. R. "The Theory of Monopoly." *Econometrica*, Vol. 3, 1935, pp. 1–20.

HOTELLING, H. "Stability in Competition." *Economic Journal*, Vol. 39, 1929, pp. 41–57.

ROBINSON, JOAN. *The Economics of Imperfect Competition.* London, 1933, xii + 352 pp.

SCHNEIDER, E. (1) *Reine Theorie monopolistischer Wirtschaftsformen.* Tübingen, 1932.

(2) "Bemerkungen zu einer Theorie der Raumwirtschaft." *Econometrica*, Vol. 3, 1935, pp. 79–105.

STACKELBERG, H. VON. *Marktform und Gleichgewicht.* Vienna, 1934, 138 pp.

STIGLER, G. "Production and Distribution in the Short Run," *Journal of Political Economy*, Vol. 47, 1939, pp. 305–327.

TINTNER, G. "Note on the Problem of Bilateral Monopoly." *Journal of Political Economy*, Vol. 47, 1939, pp. 261–270.

ZEUTHEN, F. *Theory of Monopoly and Economic Warfare.* London, 1930.

CHAPTER 7.

Production and Allied Functions

1. *Factors of Production*

As will be observed by the most casual inspection of any modern factory, the process of creating material goods is a complicated matter. The manufacture of an automobile requires a variety of materials, the use of numerous machines, the employment of capital, the services of a varying quantity and quality of labor. We shall call these different elements the *factors of production,* and we shall designate them by $a_1, a_2, \cdots, a_n$.

It is clear that these factors depend in part upon the number of units, u, of the good which is produced. A simple, but scarcely realistic assumption, would be that all the factors are functions of u, that is,

$$(1) \qquad a_1 = a_1(u), \quad a_2 = a_2(u), \cdots, \quad a_n = a_n(u),$$

and hence u could be determined as the inverse of any one of the factors of production. Thus, the number of automobiles manufactured by a given company could be determined from a knowledge of the amount of rubber used in making the tires, or the volume of manufactured clothing could be estimated from data on the manufacture of thread. But it is also clear, that very uncertain estimates of the volume of production of a good could be obtained from overhead costs, which may vary slightly during wide fluctuations of actual manufacturing.

A more general formulation of the problem would be to assume that the production of u units of a certain good may be represented as a function of the factors of production; that is to say,

$$(2) \qquad u = f(a_1, a_2, \cdots, a_n).[1]$$

[1] A more inclusive formulation might assume that the factors of production and the number of units manufactured were connected by several functions; that is,

$$f_i(u; a_1, a_2, \cdots, a_n) = 0, \quad i = 1, 2, \cdots, m.$$

But the fact that statistical data relating to the actual form of production functions are very limited at the present time fails to justify the mathematical exploration of too complicated systems.

2. *Production as a Linear Homogeneous Function of the Factors of Production*

One of the most vigorously debated propositions in economics is the hypothesis that the production function defined by equation (2) is a *linear homogeneous function.* By this we mean that if each one of the variables $a_1, a_2, \cdots, a_n$ is multiplied by a constant factor λ, then the production function of these new variables is the production function of the old variables multiplied by λ. That is to say

$$(3) \qquad U = f(\lambda a_1, \lambda a_2, \cdots, \lambda a_n) = \lambda f(a_1, a_2, \cdots, a_n) = \lambda u .$$

Such homogeneous functions are easily constructed. For example, the functions

$$u = Ax^k y^{1-k}, \quad u = (ax^2 + bxy + cy^2)^{\frac{1}{2}}, \quad u = (x + y) \log (x/y) ,$$

are linear homogeneous functions. It should be pointed out that homogeneous functions of degree n may be similarly defined by assuming that the multiplier of the factors appears to the nth degree as a multiplier of the original function. For example, $\log (x/y)$ and $x^2 + y^2$ are homogeneous functions of degrees 0 and 2 respectively.

Linear homogeneous functions have a very useful property which is called *Euler's Theorem,* after the famous Swiss mathematician Leonhard Euler (1707-1783), who first stated it. This theorem says that if the function defined by (2) is linear homogeneous, then u can be written in the form

$$(4) \qquad u = a_1 f_{a_1} + a_2 f_{a_2} + \cdots + a_n f_{a_n} ;$$

where we employ the abbreviation

$$f_{a_i} = \frac{\partial f}{\partial a_i} .$$

In order to prove this result let us take the derivative with respect to λ of both sides of the identity

$$(5) \qquad \lambda f(a_1, a_2, \cdots, a_n) \equiv f(\lambda a_1, \lambda a_2, \cdots, \lambda a_n) .$$

It is clear that, after the differentiation, the left side is u. Moreover, the right side is equal to the right side of equation (4), except that the functions are all evaluated at $\lambda a_1, \lambda a_2, \cdots, \lambda a_n$. But since, after differentiation, the left member of the identity (5) is independent of λ so also must be the right member. Hence λ may be replaced by any value, and in particular, by the value 1. This establishes Euler's theorem.

PROBLEMS

1. Determine which of the following functions are homogeneous and of what order: (a) $(x^2 + y^2)^n \log(\frac{x^2+y^2}{xy})$; (b) e^{x+y}; (c) $\log(x^2 + y^2)$; (d) $w^p x^q y^r z^s$, where $p + q + r + s = 2$; (e) $\sin(\frac{u+v}{w}) \cos(\frac{w}{u+v})$; (f) $2x + \frac{y^2 + 2yz + z^2}{y+z}$.

2. Prove that the standard deviation

$$\sigma = \left[\frac{1}{N}\Sigma f_i(x_i - A)^2\right]^{\frac{1}{2}}.$$

is a linear homogeneous function of the class marks x_i.

3. Demonstrate directly the truth of Euler's theorem for the function

$$u = A x^k y^{1-k}.$$

4. Demonstrate Euler's theorem for the function

$$u = (x + y) \log(x/y).$$

5. Prove that if $u = f(a_1, a_2, \cdots, a_n)$ is a homogeneous function of degree n, then we have

$$n(n-1)u = a_1^2 \frac{\partial^2 u}{\partial a_1^2} + a_2^2 \frac{\partial^2 u}{\partial a_2^2} + \cdots + 2a_1 a_2 \frac{\partial^2 u}{\partial a_1 \partial a_2} + \cdots.$$

6. Prove that if $u = f(a_1, a_2, \cdots, a_n)$ is a linear homogeneous function, then we have

$$\frac{\partial^2 u}{\partial a_1^2} = -\frac{1}{a_1}\left[a_1 \frac{\partial^2 u}{\partial a_1 \partial a_2} + a_3 \frac{\partial^2 u}{\partial a_1 \partial a_3} + \cdots + a_n \frac{\partial^2 u}{\partial a_1 \partial a_n}\right].$$

7. Demonstrate the proposition of problem 5 for the function $u = x^2 + 3xy + 5y^2$.

8. Compute the second partial derivative with respect to x of the function $u = ax^k y^{1-k}$ by means of the proposition of problem 6.

3. The Economic Significance of the Assumption of a Linear Homogeneous Production Function.

If we assume that the production function has the property discussed in Section 2, then we have admitted the debatable proposition that if all the factors are doubled, the production will be doubled.

The problem involved here is one well known to engineers. It is, in fact, the old problem of the ant and the elephant. If the ant, which is reputed to be one of the strongest of living creatures for its size, were enlarged to the size of an elephant, would it preserve its relative strength? The answer to this question is in the negative, since it is well known in mechanics that a linear increase in dimensions does not yield a linear increase in strength. Some factors may increase logarithmically, some as the second power, some as the third, etc. This problem is one of great importance in aviation, where experiments must be conducted in wind tunnels with models. In interpreting these experiments for full-sized airplanes, the question of dimensional changes is obviously a fundamental one.[2]

It seems quite clear that the assumption of a linear homogeneous production function is probably not realistic in general for individual manufacturers. But the proposition, when applied to the production of a large economy, is probably sufficiently realistic so that it can serve as the basis for statistical and theoretical arguments. Pareto, however, was critical of the theory which has been constructed from this assumption, and we quote him upon this point as follows:[3]

> Some authors assume that if *all* the factors of production are doubled the product will also double. This may be true approximately, in a certain case, but not rigorously and in general. Some expenses vary with the importance of the business (*entreprise*). It is certain that if we could assume another business under conditions exactly resembling those of the first, we might double all the factors and the product. But this assumption is not, in general admissible. If, for example, one were engaged in the transportation business in Paris, it would be necessary to assume another business and another Paris. But, as this other Paris does not exist, we must consider two businesses in the same Paris, and then, we cannot assume that, when the quantities of the factors of production are doubled, the product will also double.
>
> We must observe that if one cannot assume that all the coefficients of production are constant, neither can we assume that they are all variable. From a certain quantity of iron ore, for example, it is impossible to extract more metallic iron than is contained in this mineral. A certain state of technical knowledge being given, the quantity of metallic iron which may be obtained from a ton of a certain ore is a fixed quantity. In other words, the quantity of ore to be employed is proportional to the quantity of iron which we wish to produce.

In the last analysis, of course, this question must be answered by the statistical evidence, which is as yet quite incomplete and unsatisfactory. We shall turn next, however, to an example provided by P. H. Douglas and C. W. Cobb, which throws some light on the situation.

---

[2] An excellent summary of this subject will be found in *The Handbook of Engineering Fundamentals*, edited by O. W. Eshbach, New York, 1936, Section 3, pp. 41–45. See also P. W. Bridgman, *Dimensional Analysis*, Yale University Press, 1922. The question of dimensions from the point of view of economic variables has been discussed by G. C. Evans, *Mathematical Introduction to Economics*, New York, 1930, Chapter 2.

[3] From V. Pareto, *Cours d'économie politique*, Vol. 2, 1897, pp. 82–83. The translation is from the notable article of H. Schultz, "Marginal Productivity and the General Pricing Process," *The Journal of Political Economy*, Vol. 37, 1929, pp. 505–551.

4. The Factors of Labor and Capital in Production

It is self evident that two of the greatest factors in the production of manufactured goods are labor and capital. Carl Snyder in his work *Capitalism the Creator* reaches the conclusions that (1) "real wages are determined by the product per worker, and are a fairly fixed share of the value of the product . . . (2) The product per worker is determined in the long run by the capital investment per worker . . . (3) an increase in product is dependent on the provision of additional capital . . . (4) The rate of growth of total wages and of total product has been nearly the same, so that over long periods the share of the product going to labor has remained nearly constant."[4]

From these propositions we may then readily surmise that industrial production may be represented by a linear homogeneous function in terms of the two factors labor and capital. P. H. Douglas and C. W. Cobb in 1928 proposed to test the function

$$P = kL^{\alpha}C^{1-\alpha}, \quad 0 < \alpha < 1, \tag{6}$$

where P is a measure of production, L a measure of labor, and C a measure of capital.[5]

The data used were Day's index of physical volume of manufacturing for P, an index of the average number of wage-earners in manufacture for L, and an index of fixed capital in manufacture for C. These data are given in the following table:

Indexes of Production (P), Labor (L), and Capital (C)
1899 = 100

Year	P	L	C	Year	P	L	C	Year	P	L	C
1900	101	105	107	1908	126	121	185	1916	225	182	298
1901	112	110	114	1909	155	140	198	1917	227	196	335
1902	122	118	122	1910	159	144	208	1918	223	200	366
1903	124	123	131	1911	153	145	216	1919	218	193	387
1904	122	116	138	1912	177	152	226	1920	231	193	407
1905	143	125	149	1913	184	154	236	1921	179	147	417
1906	152	133	163	1914	169	149	244	1922	240	161	431
1907	151	138	176	1915	189	154	266				

An evaluation of the parameters in (6) yields the interesting equation

$$P = 1.01\, L^{0.75}\, C^{0.25},$$

which correlates highly with the actual production figures.

Considerable criticism has been directed to the statistical pro-

[4] New York, 1940, xii + 473 pp. See, in particular, pp. 171–172.

[5] "A Theory of Production," *American Economic Review*, Vol. 18 (Supplement), 1928, pp. 139–165.

cedures by which this equation was attained. It will be observed, for example, that the period from 1900 to 1922 was one of uniform industrial development and all three series of data were affected by the same secular trend. No attempt was made to eliminate the effect of this common element in the three series. A spurious correlation is thus almost inevitably introduced into the statistical evaluation of the parameters. The nature of the indexes used has also been questioned, particularly that relating to the capital, which is admittedly a very difficult variable to measure.[6]

But in spite of these criticisms, and the obviously tentative character of the equation, it must be admitted that the attempt to give numerical expression to a production function of this basic character is interesting and instructive.

PROBLEMS

1. Given the production function

$$P = A\, L^p\, C^q,$$

prove that the ratio increase of P is given by the formula

$$\frac{dP}{P} = p\frac{dL}{L} + q\frac{dC}{C}\,.$$

If $p = 0.75$ and $q = 0.25$, by what per cent will production be increased if capital is increased by 10 per cent, while labor remains unchanged? By what device could this be accomplished?

If labor is increased by 10 per cent while capital remains unchanged, by what per cent will production be increased? In what manner could this increase be effected?

2. The graph of the function $u = f(a,b)$, where the factors of production, a and b, are varied but u is held constant, are called *iso-quants*. A set of iso-quants computed for various levels of production form a map. In general, iso-quants are assumed to be convex toward the origin, but they do not necessarily satisfy the convexity conditions given in Section 5 of Chapter 3. Given the production function,

$$u = 32ab - 7a^2 - 16b^2,$$

graph the lines along which production is zero. Also, represent graphically the iso-quant corresponding to $u = 500$.

3. Form a map of iso-quants for the production function

$$u = 100\, a^{\frac{1}{2}}\, b^{\frac{1}{2}}.$$

[6] An excellent résumé of the arguments both for and against the linear homogeneous production function, and a summary of the criticism of the Douglas-Cobb experiment, have been made by V. E. Smith in his doctor's dissertation, "An Application and Critique of Certain Methods for the Determination of a Statistical Production Function for the Canadian Automobile Industry, 1917–1930," Northwestern University, 1940. See also Douglas (6) in the *Bibliography*.

4. Given the production function

$$P = 1.01\, L^{0.75}\, C^{0.25},$$

form the iso-quants corresponding to $P = 101, 151.5, 202$, and 252.5. On the graph of these functions locate the points corresponding to the values of L and C given in the table of this section. What conclusions do you draw?

5. In the production function of problem 2, assume that the factor a equals 10 and represent graphically the resulting function in u and b. For what value of b is u a maximum?

6. Assuming in problem 4 that $L = 150$, represent graphically the resulting function in P and C.

7. Under the assumption that L and C are connected by the equation $L + C = 450$, determine maximum production.

8. By an *expansion path* associated with a production function

$$u = f(a, b, c, \cdots),$$

we shall mean any solution of the following set of equations:

$$\frac{da}{f_a} = \frac{db}{f_b} = \frac{dc}{f_c} = \cdots .$$

Show that the expansion paths for the function

$$u = f(a,b) = A\, a^p\, b^q, \qquad p > q\,,$$

are rectangular hyperbolas with excentricities given by

$$e = \left(\frac{p+q}{p}\right)^{\frac{1}{2}}.$$

9. Graph the expansion paths for the production function of problem 4.

10. A manufacturer finds that his costs are given by the function $Q = a + 8b$. Under the assumption that he keeps his cost fixed at the value $Q = 50$, and that his production function is defined by

$$u = 32ab - 7a^2 - 16b^2,$$

prove that his maximum production is $u = 500$.

5. *Marginal Productivity*

The theory of marginal productivity, depending as it does upon the assumption of a linear homogeneous production function, has been vigorously debated by economists. Since adequate statistical data are lacking to confirm the theory, it remains at present a part of theoretical economics.

Let us begin by assuming the existence of a linear homogeneous production function of the form

$$u = f(a_1, a_2, \cdots, a_n)\,, \tag{7}$$

where $a_1, a_2, \cdots, a_n$ are the factors of production.

If we assume further that the prices of the factors are fixed and equal to $p_1, p_2, \cdots, p_n$, then the total cost is given by

(8) $$Q = a_1 p_1 + a_2 p_2 + \cdots + a_n p_n \,.$$

It follows then, that if p is the selling price of the manufactured goods, the profit to the manufacturer will be given by the function

(9) $$\pi = pu - Q$$

A producer, wishing to maximize his profits, may make either of two assumptions. First, he may wish to maximize his production, while keeping his costs fixed, or, second, he may keep his production constant and minimize his costs. Since either assumption leads to the same analytical conditions, we shall adopt the first position.

Hence we are led to the problem of maximizing u, under the restraint condition that Q is constant. Adopting the procedure discussed in Section 7 of Chapter 3, we must maximize the function

(10) $$f + \lambda Q \,,$$

where λ is the Lagrangian multiplier introduced in the section to which reference has just been made.

Setting the derivatives of (10) with respect to the factors equal to zero, we obtain the following necessary conditions:

(11) $$f_{a_i} + \lambda p_i = 0 \,, \quad i = 1, 2, 3, \cdots, n \,,$$

where we adopt the notation

$$f_{a_i} = \frac{\partial f}{\partial a_i} \,.$$

Taking note next of the assumption that $f(a_1, a_2, \cdots, a_n)$ is a linear homogeneous function, we can determine the value of the multiplier in the following manner. Let us first multiply (11) by a_i and sum with respect to i. We thus obtain

(12) $$\sum_{i=1}^{n} a_i f_{a_i} + \lambda \sum_{i=1}^{n} a_i p_i = 0 \,.$$

We now observe from equation (4) of Section 2 that the first term is f. Moreover, the multiplier of λ is Q by equation (8). Hence, for the determination of λ we have

$$f + \lambda Q = 0;$$

from which it follows that $\lambda = - f/Q$.

Introducing this value into system (11), we obtain the following set of equations:

$$(13)\qquad f_{a_i} - \frac{f}{Q} p_i = 0 \ , \quad i = 1, 2, 3, \cdots, n \, .$$

We now make the final assumption that total revenue just equals total cost, that is to say, $Q = pf$. This we observe from Section 5 of Chapter 6 is the condition for monopolistic equilibrium if normal profits have been introduced as part of the original cost. Under this assumption we can replace Q in (13) by its equivalent and hence obtain the following system of equations:

$$(14)\qquad f_{a_1} = \frac{p_1}{p} \ , \quad f_{a_2} = \frac{p_2}{p} \ , \ \cdots , \ f_{a_n} = \frac{p_n}{p} \, .$$

In other words, we have shown that *for maximum production under a schedule of constant costs, the ratios of the prices of the factors of production to the selling price of the product must equal the marginal degree of productivity of the factors.* This statement as expressed in equations (14) is called the *law of marginal productivity.*

If the law of demand for the product is known as a function of the price, that is to say, if $u = \phi(p)$, then we may add to the system (14) the equation

$$(15)\qquad \phi(p) = f(a_1 \, , a_2 \, , \cdots , a_n) \, .$$

Hence in general equations (14) and (15) together are sufficient to determine the values of the factors $a_1 \, , a_2 \, , \cdots , a_n$ and the selling price p.

Example. As an example let us determine the selling price, p, and the factors a_1 and a_2 under the assumption that the demand function is given by

$$(16)\qquad p = \frac{a}{b + cu} \, ,$$

and production is defined by the linear homogeneous function

$$(17)\qquad u = A \, a_1^{\alpha} \, a_2^{1-\alpha} \, .$$

Solution. Assuming the law of marginal productivity, we obtain from (14) the conditions

$$(18)\qquad p_1 = \frac{p \, \alpha \, u}{a_1} \, , \quad p_2 = \frac{p(1 - \alpha) u}{a_2} \, .$$

If we raise both sides of the first equation to the power α and both sides of the second to the power $1 - \alpha$, and then multiply one by the other, we obtain

$$p_1^{\alpha} \, p_2^{1-\alpha} = \frac{pu \, \alpha^{\alpha} (1 - \alpha)^{1-\alpha}}{a_1^{\alpha} \, a_2^{1-\alpha}} \, .$$

Taking account of (17), we then get

$$p_1{}^a\, p_2{}^{1-a} = Ap\, \alpha^a (1-\alpha)^{1-a},$$

from which it follows that

$$p = \frac{p_1{}^a\, p_2{}^{1-a}}{A\, \alpha^a (1-\alpha)^{1-a}} = \frac{p_2}{A(1-\alpha)} \left(\frac{p_1}{p_2}\right)^a \left(\frac{1-\alpha}{\alpha}\right)^a, \tag{19}$$

which is the desired value of the selling price in terms of the known parameters.

We next divide the second equation of (18) by the first and solve for a_1/a_2. We thus obtain

$$\frac{a_1}{a_2} = \frac{p_2}{p_1} \frac{\alpha}{1-\alpha}. \tag{20}$$

Introducing this ratio into (17), we get

$$u = A \left(\frac{a}{a_2}\right)^a a_2 = A\, a_2 \left(\frac{p_2}{p_1} \cdot \frac{\alpha}{1-\alpha}\right)^a.$$

When this value is equated to u as computed from the demand function (16), we then readily obtain the desired value of a_2 as follows:

$$a_2 = \left(\frac{p_1}{p_2}\right)^a \left(\frac{1-\alpha}{\alpha}\right)^a \frac{(a-pb)}{Acp} = \frac{(a-pb)(1-\alpha)}{cp_2},$$

where p is given by (19).

The value of a_1 is then readily found from (20) to be

$$a_1 = \frac{a_2 \alpha p_2}{p_1(1-\alpha)} = \frac{(a-pb)\alpha}{cp_1}.$$

PROBLEMS

1. Referring to the illustrative example of this section, show that if $p = a - bu$, then the factors of production are explicitly the following:

$$a_1 = \frac{a}{Ab}\sqrt{\frac{p_2}{p_1}} - \frac{2p_2}{bA^2}, \qquad a_2 = \frac{a}{Ab}\sqrt{\frac{p_1}{p_2}} - \frac{2p_1}{bA^2}.$$

Show also that the demand price is given by

$$p = \frac{2\sqrt{p_1 p_2}}{A}.$$

2. Given the demand function $p = 100 - 5u$, the cost function $Q = 16a_1 + 9a_2$, and the production function

$$u = 2(a_1\, a_2)^{\frac{1}{4}},$$

determine p, u, a_1, and a_2.

3. Show that the condition

$$\frac{p_1}{f_a} = \frac{p_2}{f_b} = \frac{p_3}{f_c} = \cdots$$

defines lines perpendicular to the hyperplanes

$$Q = p_1 a + p_2 b + p_3 c + \cdots, \qquad Q \text{ variable},$$

at their points of tangency with the hypersurfaces

$$u = f(a, b, c, \cdots), \qquad u \text{ variable.}$$

4. Making use of the theorem stated in problem 3, determine the line which is perpendicular to the cost lines

$$Q = a + 8b, \qquad Q \text{ variable,}$$

at their points of tangency with the production curves

$$u = 32ab - 7a^2 - 16b^2, \qquad u \text{ variable.}$$

Illustrate this problem graphically.

SELECTED BIBLIOGRAPHY ON THE PRODUCTION FUNCTION

BRONFENBRENNER, M. "The Cobb-Douglas Function and Trade-Union Policy," *American Economic Review*, Vol. 29, 1939, pp. 793–796.

CLARK, J. M. "Inductive Evidence of Marginal Productivity," *American Economic Review*, Vol. 18, 1928, pp. 449–467.

COBB, C. W. (1) [see Douglas, P. H. (1)].

(2) "Contour Lines in Economics," *Journal of Political Economy*, Vol. 37, 1929, pp. 225–229.

(3) "Production in Massachusetts Manufacturing, 1890–1928," *Journal of Political Economy*, Vol. 38, 1930, pp. 705–707.

DOUGLAS, P. H. (1) (with C. W. COBB), "A Theory of Production," *American Economic Review*, Vol. 18 (Supplement), 1928, pp. 139–165.

(2) *The Theory of Wages*. New York, 1934, xx + 639 pp.

(3) (with M. L. HANDSAKER), "Theory of Marginal Productivity Tested by Data for Manufacturing in Victoria," *Quarterly Journal of Economics*, Vol. 52, 1937–38, pp. 1–36, 215–254.

(4) "The Effect of Wage Increases upon Employment," *American Economic Review*, Vol. 29 (Supplement), 1939, pp. 138–157.

(5) (with GRACE GUNN), "Further Measurements of Marginal Productivity," *Quarterly Journal of Economics*, Vol. 54, 1940, pp. 399–428.

(6) (with GRACE GUNN), "The Production Function for American Manufacturing in 1919," *American Economic Review*, 1941.

DURAND, D. "Some Thoughts on Marginal Productivity with Special Reference to Professor Douglas' Analysis," *Journal of Political Economy*, Vol. 45, 1937, pp. 740–758.

GUNN, GRACE [see Douglas, P. H. (5)].

HANDSAKER, M. L. [see Douglas, P. H. (3)].

MENDERSHAUSEN, H. "On the Significance of Professor Douglas' Production Function," *Econometrica*, Vol. 6, 1938, pp. 143–153. "A Correction," Vol. 7, 1939, p. 362.

MOSAK, J. L. "Interrelations of Production, Price, and Derived Demand," *Journal of Political Economy*, Vol. 46, 1938, pp. 761–787.

ROBINSON, JOAN. "Euler's Theorem and the Problem of Distribution," *Economic Journal*, Vol. 44, 1934, pp. 398–414.

SCHNEIDER, E. *Theorie der Produktion*. Vienna, 1934, iv + 92 pp.

SCHULTZ, H. (1) "Marginal Productivity and the General Pricing Process," *Journal of Political Economy*, Vol. 37, 1929, pp. 505–551.

(2) *The Theory and Measurement of Demand*. Chicago, 1938, xxxi + 817 pp.

SMITH, V. E. "An Application and Critique of Certain Methods for the Determination of a Statistical Production Function for the Canadian Automobile Industry, 1917–1930," Doctor's Dissertation, Northwestern University, 1940.

CHAPTER 8

BUDGETS

1. *The Problem of Budgets*

In problems connected with the maximization of the utility function, which were considered earlier in the book, we have had occasion to consider the budget equation

$$(1) \qquad \sum_{i=1}^{n} p_i x_i = E,$$

where E is, let us say, family expenditure, x_i the items purchased during a specified period of time, and p_i the corresponding prices.

It is our purpose in this chapter to subject this equation to more careful scrutiny. It will be instructive to ascertain how certain necessary items in any budget, such, for example, as rent, food, clothing, and the like, depend upon levels of income. We shall contrast these with luxury items and with expenditures for gifts, that is to say, with those parts of the budget which are found only when the income is above the level of subsistence. We shall use I to designate family income as distinct from family expenditure.

2. *Engel Curves*

We shall first assume that the quantities in the budget equation are purchased at some one point in time so that prices are constant, or, perhaps, more realistically, that the purchases are made over a period of time within which the level of prices has remained essentially constant. We shall also assume, in the second place, that the individual quantities purchased depend entirely upon the level of income. That is to say, we shall assume the following relationships:

$$(2) \qquad x_1 = x_1(I), \quad x_2 = x_2(I), \cdots, x_n = x_n(I).$$

If, now, we regard I as a parameter, then these functions will vary as I assumes different values, and we shall trace a curve in the n-dimensional quantity space $(x_1, x_2, \cdots, x_n)$. This curve is called an *Engel curve* after Ernst Engel, (1821–1896), a German economist of the nineteenth century who devoted considerable attention to the problem of budgets and the cost of living.

In recent years considerable information has been obtained about family budgets, the most elaborate study being one carried out under the direction of the U. S. Bureau of Labor Statistics. From similar, but much less elaborate investigations in other countries, it has been assumed that the functions given in equations (2) are linear. To a first approximation this is true if the commodity in question belongs to the class of necessities, such as food, clothing, housing, etc., and if income is not too large, that is to say, less than \$5,000.

But apparently the assumption of strict linearity, which in the literature of budgets is generally referred to as *Engel's law,* that is to say, the assumption that between the amount of goods purchased, x_i, and the income, I, there exists the linear relationship

$$x_i = A_i + B_i I , \tag{3}$$

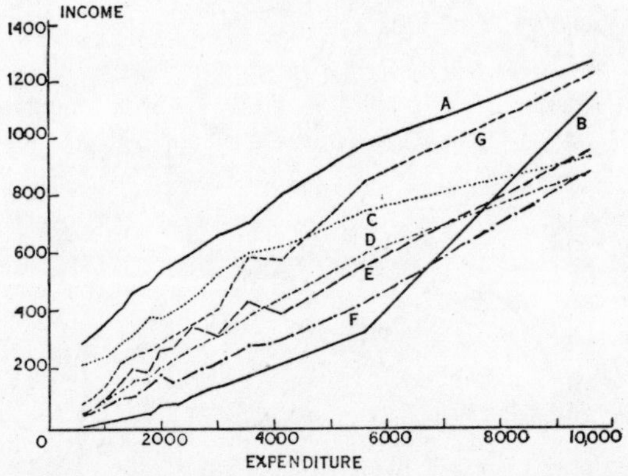

FIGURE 41.—EXPENDITURE PATTERNS OF DENVER FAMILIES, 1935–1936. A = Food; B = Gifts, Taxes; C = Housing; D = Clothing; E = Automobile and other transportation; F = Household operation, furnishings, equipment; G = All other items.

fails to hold when I is large, or when x_i belongs to the class of luxury goods. However, it will be seen from the graphical representation of Engel curves given in Figures 41 and 42 that for a sufficiently restricted range of income the assumption of linearity is a satisfactory approximation.

It is probable that a function of the form

$$x = a - b\, e^{-\mu I} , \tag{4}$$

where a, b, and μ are positive numbers and where b is less than a, would furnish in general a better approximation to Engel curves within the class of necessities than does the straight line given by (3).

In fact, if I is sufficiently small, then (4) is approximately given by the straight line

$$x = (a - b) + \mu b I .$$

If I is large, then x approaches the asymptotic limit $x = a$. This conclusion seems realistic when one reflects that there is a limit to the amount of food that can be consumed, and presumably, also, for the use of other necessities.

On the other hand, there is no limit to the amount of money that one can expend in gifts. Consequently, when one's income exceeds the point at which all necessities are amply provided for, then the expenditure for gifts should rise sharply as is indicated in Figures 41 and 42. Recognizing the existence of such a *Midas point* in income,

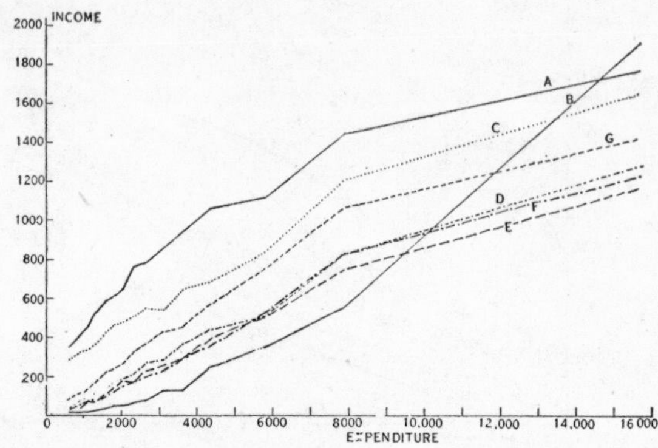

FIGURE 42.—EXPENDITURE PATTERNS OF CHICAGO FAMILIES, 1935–1936.
A = Food; B = Gifts, Taxes; C = Housing; D = Clothing; E = Automobile and other transportation; F = Household operation, furnishings, equipment; G = All other items.

the government has imposed income taxes of graduated schedule in order to divert private charitable expenditures into governmental expenditures. Since data do not appear to be available at the present time concerning the relationship between income and the value of gifts for a range extending into high income groups it would be rash to suggest a mathematical form for this important Engel curve.

3. The Data

The data on expenditure patterns are obtained from the comprehensive studies of the U. S. Bureau of Labor Statistics, which we have mentioned above. But expenditure patterns are obviously related to prevailing prices, and shifts in the slope of the linear Engel curves would certainly be observed in periods where there was an essential difference between the prevailing "standards of living."

In order to have a statistical interpretation of this somewhat general term, "standards of living," a study was instituted to ascertain the differences in costs of living in 59 cities of the United States during the month of March, 1935. This report, published under the direction of Margaret L. Stecker (see *Bibliography*), is illuminating in connection with the budget study of the Bureau of Labor Statistics.

Quoting from the report, we find that two levels of living in the year 1935 were established for a 4-person manual worker's family, one a *maintenance* level (*M*-level) representing "normal or average minimum requirements for industrial, service, and other manual workers," and the other an *emergency* level (*E*-level), which "allows more exclusively, though not entirely, for material wants," but which "might be questioned on grounds of health hazards if families had to live at this level for a considerable period of time."

Expenditure Levels in American Cities, March, 1935

Maintenance Level

Cities	Total	Food	Clothing	Housing	Household Operation	Miscellaneous, including recreations, taxes, etc.			
						Total	Life Ins.	Medical	Recreation
59 Cities	$1,260.62	448.18	184.35	221.89	153.54	252.62	46.40	52.32	75.18
Washington	1,414.54	476.34	179.23	342.00	146.62	270.34	46.40	58.91	76.84
Chicago	1,356.11	462.08	193.45	240.00	162.36	298.21	46.40	57.42	80.84
New York	1,375.13	477.22	172.67	300.00	155.87	269.38	46.40	56.29	78.41
Denver	1,246.67	434.93	182.40	204.00	142.54	282.20	46.40	56.52	81.26
Wichita	1,131.30	426.97	174.32	165.00	146.53	218.49	46.40	50.08	65.86
Mobile	1,129.81	433.40	165.00	163.44	142.22	225.75	46.40	51.84	67.22

Emergency Level

Cities	Total	Food	Clothing	ing Hous-	House-hold tion Opera-	Miscellaneous, including recreations, taxes, etc.			
						Total	Life Ins.	Medical	Recreation
59 Cities	$ 903.27	340.30	128.05	167.79	121.84	145.30	20.80	47.08	12.63
Washington	1,013.98	356.94	124.24	258.00	115.98	158.83	20.80	53.02	13.72
Chicago	972.59	349.16	134.17	180.00	129.98	179.28	20.80	51.67	13.80
New York	982.11	359.24	120.06	222.00	124.14	156.68	20.80	50.66	13.84
Denver	885.24	331.04	127.64	150.00	110.81	165.75	20.80	50.86	13.54
Wichita	809.64	323.17	122.46	123.00	117.18	123.83	20.80	45.07	11.18
Mobile	814.92	330.35	113.50	127.44	113.47	130.16	20.80	46.66	10.90

The base family "consists of a moderately active man, a moderately active woman, a boy age 13, and a girl age 8," the size and composition of this family having been selected "as the nearest approach to the average census private family, which consists of 4.01 persons." The range for the M-level was from $1,129.81 in Mobile to $1,414.54 in Washington; the range of the E-level was from $809.64 in Wichita to $1,013.98 in Washington. We may observe with some interest that if the Wichita E-level figure be divided by 4, then the per capita figure of $202.82 is only slightly greater than the wolf point of $196, which we computed for the year 1918 in Chapter 2. Some correction must be made, however, for the level of prices, the general price index being 157 in 1918 and 145 in 1935. But one may also presume that the *E*-level is not actually the value of the wolf point, although it is not far above it.

A partial summary of the two levels for the average of the 59 cities studied in the report and for several individual cities, including the lowest and the highest, is given in the accompanying table.

With these estimates before us we next proceed to an examination of the individual items of spending as reported in the study of the United States Bureau of Labor. For this purpose we have selected the expenditure patterns for Denver families and for Chicago families. The data, somewhat abbreviated, are given in the accompanying tables. A few of the columns are graphically represented in Figures 41 and 42.

EXPENDITURE PATTERNS OF DENVER FAMILIES BY INCOME GROUPS, 1935–1936

Income Range	Aver. Income	Number in Report	Total Expenditure	Food	Clothing	Housing	Household Oper. and Equipment	Transportation	Gifts, Taxes, etc.	Other Items	Savings
$500– 750	$ 615	19	$748	$295	$46	$220	$46	$51	$ 9	$ 81	$–133
750–1000	830	58	903	328	73	235	61	77	17	112	– 73
1000–1250	1076	81	1117	388	105	254	80	106	26	158	– 41
1250–1500	1327	132	1384	419	135	300	102	163	38	227	– 57
1500–1750	1557	144	1591	476	166	330	119	201	43	256	– 34
1750–2000	1804	166	1739	499	177	388	149	196	58	272	65
2000–2250	2011	141	1969	547	209	384	193	264	81	291	42
2250–2500	2237	147	2068	571	234	405	163	282	91	322	169
2500–3000	2587	170	2362	611	279	456	197	343	118	358	225
3000–3500	3040	77	2656	669	320	541	238	322	156	410	384
3500–4000	3591	54	3218	712	389	607	288	439	188	595	373
4000–5000	4194	81	3406	813	452	632	307	395	224	583	788
5000–7500	5631	51	4527	972	604	754	439	561	344	853	1104
over 7500	9617	25	7169	1264	884	935	888	832	1144	1222	2448

EXPENDITURE PATTERNS OF CHICAGO FAMILIES BY INCOME GROUPS, 1935–1936

Income Range	Aver. Income	Number in Report	Total Expenditure	Food	Clothing	Housing	Household Oper. and Equipment	Transportation	Gifts, Taxes, etc.	Other Items	Savings
\$500– 750	\$ 626	50	\$ 830	\$348	\$ 46	\$286	\$ 32	\$ 26	\$ 10	\$ 82	\$-204
750– 1000	903	110	1016	405	74	325	47	39	10	116	-113
1000– 1250	1103	139	1165	457	93	335	66	65	17	132	- 62
1250– 1500	1324	238	1353	529	109	366	78	75	24	172	- 29
1500– 1750	1602	217	1605	589	136	428	95	103	33	221	- 3
1750– 2000	1841	264	1799	619	164	465	126	141	43	241	42
2000– 2250	2073	256	1986	660	192	481	148	175	56	274	87
2250– 2500	2320	269	2222	761	212	517	173	168	63	328	98
2500– 3000	2664	295	2479	786	262	554	200	229	82	366	185
3000– 3500	3112	226	2741	863	287	545	232	258	126	430	371
3500– 4000	3635	206	3144	945	371	651	296	292	132	457	491
4000– 5000	4349	197	3760	1064	440	688	357	399	246	566	589
5000– 7500	5800	102	4619	1125	513	842	529	508	346	756	1181
7500–10000	7881	37	6695	1449	836	1212	835	743	555	1065	1186
over 10000	15692	29	10358	1781	1289	1663	1235	1041	1923	1426	5334

PROBLEMS

1. Fit the straight line, $x = A + BI$, to the item of food in the budget for Denver families.

2. Solve problem 1 using the item of food in the budget of Chicago families.

3. Assuming the equation

$$x = a - b\,e^{-\mu I},$$

estimate a, b, and μ for the item of food in the budget of Denver families. *Hint*: First write the approximation $x = (a - b) + \mu b I$, and identify $(a - b)$ and μb respectively with the values of A and B determined in problem 1. Then estimate a from the graph.

4. Solve problem 3 for the item of food in the budget of Chicago families.

5. Compare the costs of living in Denver and Chicago by comparing the total expenditures for the same income classes. Does the relative cost of living appear to remain the same from one income class to another?

4. Engel Curves and the Utility Function

It will be clear, from a re-examination of Section 6 of Chapter 3, that a knowledge of the actual form of Engel curves will give us considerable information about the shape of the utility surface itself, since the path described by equation (2) of Section 2 of this chapter is nothing but a preference line expressed in terms of the parameter I.

For simplicity let us consider the situation in two variables x_1 and x_2, although the argument to be advanced is entirely general. The Engel curve

$$x_1 = x_1(I)\,, \qquad x_2 = x_2(I) \tag{3}$$

determines the preference path as indicated in Figure 43. The preference path is perpendicular to the budget lines

$$p_1 x_1 + p_2 x_2 = E \, , \tag{4}$$

where E is a variable parameter, but where the prices are fixed. Hence the budget lines are parallel and tangent, of course, to the indifference curves at their points of intersection with the preference path.

Let us now recall from Section 6 of Chapter 3 that the preference paths, that is to say, the Engel curves, are solutions of the following equation:

$$\frac{dx_1}{U_1} = \frac{dx_2}{U_2} \, , \tag{5}$$

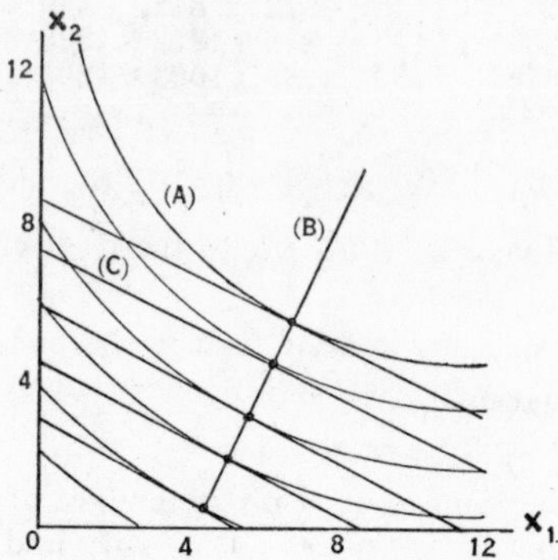

FIGURE 43.—INDIFFERENCE MAP SHOWING INDIFFERENCE CURVES (A), PREFERENCE PATH (B), AND BUDGET LINES AT CONSTANT PRICES (C).

where U_1 and U_2 are the marginal utilities corresponding to the two variables x_1 and x_2.

Since, as we have just observed, the indifference curve is orthogonal to the preference line at their point of intersection, it is clear that the knowledge of a set of preference lines gives us a solution *im kleinen* of the indifference lines, and consequently a determination of the utility function itself. In general, however, our knowledge is limited to two or three Engel curves at most, since the accumulation of budgetary data is arduous. It is thus important to be able to obtain maximum information from a study of one or two such curves.

One particular case is important, however, and this is the one where the utility function, $U(x_1, x_2)$, is a quadratic function in the two variables. In this case equation (5) has the explicit form

$$\frac{dx_1}{a_1x_1 + b_1x_2 + c_1} = \frac{dx_2}{a_2x_1 + b_2x_2 + c_2} \, . \tag{6}$$

This differential equation can be integrated by the following device. Denoting the denominators of (6) respectively by U_1 and U_2, let us introduce the new term dt/t and write equation (6) in the form

$$(7)\quad \frac{dt}{t}=\frac{dx_1}{U_1}=\frac{dx_2}{U_2}=\frac{l\,dx_1+m\,dx_2}{l\,U_1+m\,U_2}=\frac{l\,dx_1+m\,dx_2}{\rho(l\,x_1+m\,x_2)+r}.$$

For the determination of the constants l and m we have the following equations:

$$(8)\quad \begin{aligned} l\,a_1+m\,a_2&=\rho l\,,\\ l\,b_1+m\,b_2&=\rho m\,. \end{aligned}$$

In terms of them we can then write

$$(9)\quad r=l\,c_1+m\,c_2\,.$$

Since (8) is a homogeneous system in l and m, non-trivial solutions will exist for values of ρ which satisfy the equation

$$(10)\quad \begin{vmatrix} a_1-\rho & a_2 \\ b_1 & b_2-\rho \end{vmatrix}=(a_1b_2-a_2b_1)-(a_1+b_2)\rho+\rho^2=0\,.$$

Returning now to (7) we integrate the equation formed from the first term and the last, and thus obtain

$$(11)\quad \begin{aligned} t&=k_1[\rho_1(l_1\,x_1+m_1\,x_2)+r_1]^{1/\rho_1}\,,\\ t&=k_2[\rho_2(l_2\,x_1+m_2\,x_2)+r_2]^{1/\rho_2}\,, \end{aligned}$$

where l_i, m_i, r_i are the values obtained from (8) and (9) corresponding to the roots ρ_i of (10). The quantities k_1 and k_2 are arbitrary constants.

Finally, upon eliminating t from (11), we obtain as the corresponding preference lines associated with the original quadratic utility function, the one-parameter family of curves defined by the function

$$(12)\quad \rho_1(l_1\,x_1+m_1\,x_2)+r_1=K[\rho_2(l_2\,x_1+m_2\,x_2)+r_2]^{\rho_1/\rho_2}.$$

It is clear that the preference curves become straight lines only when $\rho_1=\rho_2$. In this case equation (12) reduces to the following form:

$$(13)\quad \rho\,x_1+c_1=K(\rho\,x_2+c_2)\,.$$

It will be readily seen that the argument which we have just given is not limited to two variables, but can be extended to any number.

The significance of the problem which we have studied above is found in the fact that Engel curves appear to be approximated closely by straight lines. Moreover a quadratic function is suitable as a representation of utility since it can meet the convexity conditions imposed by the theory as it was developed in Section 5 of Chapter 3.

In an analysis of more complexity than the one which we have just given A. Wald has shown (see *Bibliography*) how a utility function (or preference indicator) of second degree in $2k-1$ variables can be determined, apart from an arbitrary proportionality factor and an arbitrary additive constant, from the knowledge of k linear Engel curves. It will be instructive for us to see how the present analysis also enables us to construct the utility function. The method may be best illustrated by the following example:

Example. Let us assume the existence of two Engel curves

$$y = 3x - 20 \,, \quad y = 5x - 44 \,, \tag{14}$$

between the amounts x and y demanded of two commodities under two different price schedules. Let us also assume that the utility function has the form

$$U = ax^2 + 2bxy + cy^2 + 2dx + 2ey + f \,.$$

Under these assumptions we now inquire into the degree of determinateness of the utility function.

Solution. From the linear character of the Engel curves we first require that equation (10), which now has the form

$$\rho^2 - (a+c)\,\rho + ac - b^2 = 0 \,, \tag{15}$$

shall have equal roots. The condition for this is given by the equation

$$(a-c)^2 = -4b^2 \,,$$

from which we derive the relationships $a = c$, $b = 0$. We thus observe that *the indifference lines are arcs of circles.*

Under the conditions just imposed equation (15) becomes

$$\rho^2 - 2a\rho + a^2 = 0 \,,$$

from which it follows that $\rho = a$.

Equation (13) then takes the form

$$ax + d = K(ay + e) \,,$$

which we can rewrite in the form

$$y = \frac{1}{K}x - \frac{e}{a} + \frac{d}{aK} \,.$$

Identifying these coefficients with those of the two Engel curves given in (14), noting also that K in the first instance is equal to 1/3 and in the second instance is equal to 1/5, we obtain the following equations for the evaluation of the ratios e/a and d/a:

$$\frac{e}{a} - 3\frac{d}{a} = 20\,, \quad \frac{e}{a} - 5\frac{d}{a} = 44\,.$$

From these equations we then obtain the solutions $d = -12a$, $e = -16a$. The utility function may then be written in the form

$$U(x,y) = a(x^2 + y^2 - 24x - 32y) + f\,;$$

that is to say, we have determined it to within an arbitrary multiplier and an arbitrary additive constant. Applying the test of convexity to the function we immediately find that a must be a negative number.

If the reader will now examine the illustrative example of Section 7, Chapter 3 he will see that we have started with two special preference lines of that example and from them have made a partial reconstruction of the utility function.

PROBLEMS

1. Using the method of this section integrate the following equation:

$$\frac{dx_1}{3x_1 + 6x_2 + 4} = \frac{dx_2}{2x_1 - 3x_2 + 5}\,.$$

2. Find the solution of the following equation:

$$\frac{dx_1}{10x_1 - 3x_2 + 2} = \frac{dx_2}{6x_1 + 7x_2 + 3}\,.$$

3. Determine as far as possible the character of the utility function if two of the Engel curves are the following:

$$y = 2x + 2, \qquad y = 7x - 48\,.$$

4. Assuming that two Engel curves are given by

$$y = \frac{3}{2x - 1} \quad \text{and} \quad y = \frac{5}{2x - 1}$$

determine the utility function as far as possible under the assumption that it is quadratic.

5. Discuss the integration of the following system of equations:

$$\frac{dx_1}{a_1x_1 + b_1x_2 + c_1x_3 + d_1} = \frac{dx_2}{a_2x_1 + b_2x_2 + c_2x_3 + d_2} = \frac{dx_3}{a_3x_1 + b_3x_2 + c_3x_3 + d_3}\,.$$

6. Under what conditions do the solutions of problem 5 become linear?

7. Solve the following system of equations:

$$\frac{dx_1}{4x_1 + 5x_2 + 8x_3 - 3} = \frac{dx_2}{3x_1 + 8x_2 + 9x_3 + 2} = \frac{dx_3}{4x_1 + 7x_2 + 12x_3 - 4}\,.$$

8. Let us assume that an individual spends all his income so that the conditions of equilibrium can be written

$$\Sigma p_i x_i = I\,, \quad U_i = \lambda pi\,, \quad i = 1, 2, \cdots, n\,.$$

Now under the assumption that prices are independent of I, but that λ is a function of I, prove that

$$\frac{\partial x_r}{\partial \mathrm{I}} = \frac{\lambda U^{(r)}}{U_0}\,,$$

where we use the abbreviation

$$U_0 = \begin{vmatrix} 0 & U_1 & U_2 & \cdots & U_n \\ U_1 & U_{11} & U_{12} & \cdots & U_{1n} \\ U_2 & U_{21} & U_{22} & \cdots & U_{2n} \\ \cdot & \cdot & \cdot & \cdot & \cdot \\ U_n & U_{n1} & U_{n2} & \cdots & U_{nn} \end{vmatrix}\,,$$

and where $U^{(r)}$ is the cofactor of the element U_r in the first row. We also use the customary notation, U_{ij}, to designate the partial derivative of U with respect to x_i and x_j. (For a discussion of this problem see J. R. Hicks: *Théorie mathématique de la valeur en régime de libre concurrence,* Paris, 1937, pp. 11–13).

9. Let us now assume that I in the equations of problem 8 is constant and that all the prices, except the price p_r, are independent of I. Then, if p_r and all the x's are functions of I, prove that

$$\frac{\partial x_s}{\partial p_r} = \frac{1}{U_0}\left[-x_r \lambda U^{(s)} + \lambda U^{(rs)}\right]\,,$$

where $U^{(rs)}$ is the cofactor of the element U_{rs} in the determinant U_0.

Now taking account of the result obtained in problem 8, prove the following:

$$\left(\frac{\partial x}{\partial p_r}\right)_{I\ \text{const.}} = -x_r\left(\frac{\partial x_s}{\partial I}\right)_{\text{Prices const.}} + \lambda\frac{U^{(rs)}}{U_0}\,.$$

This result is due to E. Slutsky. (See J. R. Hicks: *loc. cit.,* p. 13).

10. Given the utility function $U = x_1{}^a x_2{}^b$, solve for the derivatives of x_1 and x_2 with respect to I under the conditions of problem 8.

11. Given the utility function of problem 10 and the conditions of problem 9, where p_1 varies with I, solve for the derivatives of x_1 and x_2 with respect to p_1.

5. *The Functional Concept in the Theory of Budgets*

Since, as we have seen earlier, our information about budgets and their associated Engel curves is limited at the present time to data collected essentially from a single year, it may seem an unwarranted extension of theory to introduce the concept of functionals into a subject so completely analyzed. But the authority of Pareto may be invoked for this, as we have already remarked in Section 10 of Chapter 3, where that economist states his concept of closed and open cycles in connection with the integral

$$U = \int_c U_1\,dx_1 + U_2\,dx_2 + \cdots + U_n\,dx_n\,. \tag{16}$$

Pareto goes on to say in his *Manuel d'économie politique* (p. 543) with reference to integral (16):

> It would appear, then, in order to abridge the discussion, that one should give some name to the quantity U; thus in mechanics it has been thought appropriate to give the name of *potential energy* to a certain integral, and in thermodynamics the name of *entropy* to another.

Now the concepts of *potential energy* and *entropy* are related in the field of physical phenomena by one common property; their integrals, taken over a path of variation in the variables of state, are *exact* in the sense in which this word was defined in Section 10 of Chapter 3. The recognition of the existence of such functional relationships between physical variables marked one of the major advances in science. It is conceivable that a similar recognition may be given to economic concepts other than that of utility, where it has already been applied with such conspicuous success. The place where such recognition may be expected is in the domain of budgets.

It is our purpose in this section to make certain tentative suggestions about economic variables which look toward the discovery of functional relationships comparable to that of utility. If the reader is familiar with the theory of thermodynamics he will recognize an isomorphism between the theory about to be set forth and the postulates of that profound subject in the physical sciences. In particular, the theory recognizes an isomorphism between money utility on the one hand and entropy on the other.

In this discussion we shall distinguish between expenditure, E, income, I, and savings, S. From the budgets given in Section 3 of this chapter, we observe that between these three quantities there exists the identical relationship

$$I = S + E\,. \tag{17}$$

Since, however, we shall be concerned with the infinitesimal changes in these quantities, we shall consider the differential form

$$dI = dS + dE\,. \tag{18}$$

In the next place we shall recognize an equation of state

$$P \cdot Q = W\,, \tag{19}$$

where P is the average price at which the quantity of goods Q was purchased. More particularly, we might regard $P \cdot Q$ as the sum

$p_1q_1 + p_2q_2 + \cdots + p_nq_n$, although it will be more convenient in our analysis to assume that P and Q are average quantities whose product equals W. The variable W is the total wealth, or the *absolute expenditure* of the individual, whose budget is under examination.

Since an increment of wealth may be acquired either by a change in prices, as, for example, when real estate appreciates during a boom, or by the acquiring of new goods by current expenditure from income, we may write (19) in the differential form:

$$dW = Q\,dP + P\,dQ\,. \tag{20}$$

The quantities $Q\,dP$ and $P\,dQ$ are not unknown in economic literature, since they have been introduced by F. Divisia in connection with his theory of index numbers (see Chapter 15). It is clear that the second quantity can be identified with expenditure, that is to say,

$$dE = P\,dQ\,. \tag{21}$$

We shall now write savings in the form

$$dS = C_Q\,dW\,, \tag{22}$$

where C_Q is a quantity, which we identify with the rate of change of income with wealth if no additional goods are purchased. That is to say, we define

$$C_Q = \left(\frac{\partial I}{\partial W}\right)_Q, \tag{23}$$

where the subscript designates that Q does not vary. It is assumed that this coefficient is a measurable quantity and can be evaluated from sufficiently adequate budgetary data. It is probable that C_Q is a linear function of W, at least when W is restricted to moderate ranges.

Introducing (21), and (22) into (18) we then obtain the differential

$$dI = C_Q\,dW + P\,dQ\,. \tag{24}$$

If we now replace dW in this expression by its equivalent as given by (20), we get the equation

$$dI = (C_Q + 1)\,p\,dQ + C_Q\,QdP\,. \tag{25}$$

Let us return for a moment to our indifference map and the Engel curves as shown in Figure 44. In a complete map the Engel curves would be computed from equations of the form

$$x_1^{(m)} = x_1^{(m)}(I)\,, \qquad x_2^{(m)} = x_2^{(m)}(I)\,,$$

where the superscript (m) refers to different price situations. Consequently, in a complete map, we could compute *iso-income curves* by holding I fixed in these equations and letting m vary. Such a set of curves is shown in Figure 44.

In our more general pattern we can now obtain these iso-income curves in terms of the variation of P and Q by setting $dI = 0$ in (25). Dividing by PQ we thus obtain

$$(26) \qquad (C_Q + 1)\frac{dQ}{Q} + C_Q\frac{dP}{P} = 0 .$$

Assuming that C_Q is constant for small variations in W, we can integrate (26) and thus find for the iso-income curves the following equation:

$$(27) \qquad P = CQ^{-k} ,$$

where C is an arbitrary constant and $k = 1 + 1/C_Q$.

In the foregoing analysis we have made no assumptions regarding the exactness of the differentials which have been introduced. But if

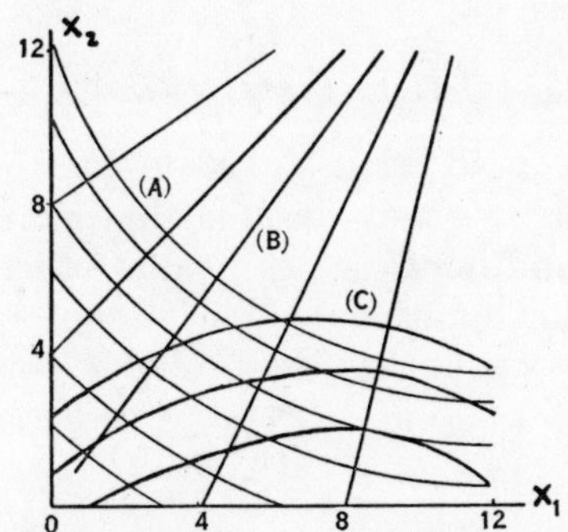

FIGURE 44.—INDIFFERENCE MAP SHOWING INDIFFERENCE CURVES (A), PREFERENCE PATHS (B), AND ISO-INCOME CURVES (C).

we now introduce such postulates, numerous interesting relationships may be derived. Let us begin by considering the marginal utility of money, discussed in Section 3 of Chapter 3, which we shall write for convenience in the form

$$(28) \qquad dU = \frac{dI}{\phi} ,$$

where ϕ is connected with the variables of Chapter 3 by the relationship

$$(29) \qquad \phi = \frac{1}{\mu F(W)} .$$

We now introduce the postulate that dU is an exact differential, that is to say, the function $1/\phi$ acts as an integrating factor for the differential of income, dI.

It will be convenient, also, to assume that savings play a role in economics similar to that of utility, or, in symbols, dS is itself an exact differential. By this assumption we have identified S as a kind of internal energy in the economic system.

Whether these postulates are realistic or not can be judged only by the consequences which may be derived from them. One of these consequences we shall now develop.

For this purpose we write the differential of income in the following two forms

$$(30) \qquad dI = \left(\frac{\partial I}{\partial W}\right)_P dW + \left(\frac{\partial I}{\partial P}\right)_W dP = C_P\, dW + l_P\, dP\,,$$

$$(31) \qquad dI = \left(\frac{\partial I}{\partial W}\right)_Q dW + \left(\frac{\partial I}{\partial Q}\right)_W dQ = C_Q\, dW + l_Q\, dQ\,.$$

Subtracting (31) from (30) and replacing dW by its equivalent from equation (20), we get

$$(C_P - C_Q)\,(Q\, dP + P\, dQ) = l_Q\, dQ - l_P\, dP\,.$$

Since no definite path of integration has been specified in the commodity space itself, we may assume that dP and dQ are independent of one another, and hence we can equate their coefficients. From this we then obtain the equations

$$(32) \qquad C_P - C_Q = \frac{l_Q}{P} = -\frac{l_P}{Q}\,.$$

It is with the first of these equations that we shall now be concerned. Our purpose is to connect l_Q with ϕ defined by (29).

Since by hypothesis both S and U are functions of state, that is to say, their differentials are exact, and since ϕ is itself explicitly a function of W, we conclude that the function

$$(33) \qquad f = S - \phi U$$

is also a function of state. We then write

$$(34) \qquad df = dS - \phi\, dU - U\, d\phi\,.$$

But from (18) and (21) we get

$$(35) \qquad dS = dI - dE = dI - P\, dQ\;;$$

and since $dI = \phi\, dU$ by (28), we can write

(36) $$dS = \phi\, dU - P\, dQ\,.$$

Substituting this in (34) we then obtain

(37) $$df = -P\, dQ - U\, d\phi\,.$$

But since this differential form is exact, we may equate the derivatives of the coefficients of dQ and $d\phi$ and thus obtain

(38) $$\left(\frac{\partial U}{\partial Q}\right)_\phi = \left(\frac{\partial P}{\partial \phi}\right)_Q.$$

Returning now to equation (31), we divide by ϕ and thus get

$$\frac{dI}{\phi} = dU = \frac{C_Q}{\phi}\, dW + \frac{l_Q}{\phi}\, dQ = \left(\frac{\partial U}{\partial W}\right)_Q dW + \left(\frac{\partial U}{\partial Q}\right)_W dQ\,.$$

Equating the coefficients of dQ, we get

(39) $$l_Q = \phi\left(\frac{\partial U}{\partial Q}\right)_W.$$

But since ϕ is an explicit function of W by assumption, it follows that when W is constant then also ϕ is constant. Consequently we have the equivalence

$$\left(\frac{\partial U}{\partial Q}\right)_\phi = \left(\frac{\partial U}{\partial Q}\right)_W$$

It follows then from (38) and (39), that we have

$$l_Q = \phi\left(\frac{\partial P}{\partial \phi}\right)_Q.$$

Substituting this value of l_Q in (32) we finally obtain the desired formula

(40) $$C_P - C_Q = \frac{\phi}{P}\left(\frac{\partial P}{\partial \phi}\right)_Q = \frac{\partial(\log P)}{\partial(\log \phi)} \ (Q \text{ constant}).$$

The significance of this result is found in the possibility which it offers for testing the various hypotheses regarding the form of ϕ, namely, those of Bernoulli, Jordan, and Frisch, which have been given in Section 3 of Chapter 3. Presumably C_Q and C_P are measurable from the data for Engel curves, combined with a wealth appraisal of the individuals whose budgets are examined. The right hand member is the partial elasticity of price with respect to ϕ, an elasticity which may be determined when ϕ is known. A comparison of the two sides of this equation, under various assumptions regarding the form of ϕ as a function of W, should throw some light upon the puzzling nature of the marginal utility of money. Unfortunately data do not appear to be available at the present time for making this comparison. However, the computations resulting from problem 5 below are quite instructive in showing that a certain measure of realism is contained in the postulates.

PROBLEMS

1. Establish the equation

$$C_P - C_Q = -\frac{F}{F'W}.$$

Hence, show that if $F = W^{-n}$, then

$$C_P - C_Q = \frac{1}{n}.$$

2. Making use of problem 1, prove that if $F = 1/\log W$, then

$$C_P - C_Q = \log W.$$

3. Prove that when the utility of money is constant, then the relationship between P and Q is given by the equation

$$P = CQ^{-\kappa},$$

where $\kappa = C_P/C_Q$.

4. Assuming that $\kappa = 1.7$, graph $P = CQ^{-\kappa}$, for $C = 80$, 100, and 120. Explain the significance of these curves.

5. In the following table there is recorded the production index, the price index, the value of wealth in billions of dollars, and the value of income in billions of dollars for the United States over the two year periods 1918 to 1920 inclusive and 1921 to 1923 inclusive.

Year	Production	Price	W	I	Year	Production	Price	W	I
1918	107	157	400.5	60.2	1921	76	163	317.2	52.6
1919	100	173	431.0	67.4	1922	94	158	320.8	61.7
1920	101	193	488.7	74.3	1923	109	165	339.9	69.8

In the first period we observe that production changed little, but prices increased greatly. In the second period, however, prices remained relatively constant, while production increased. For these two periods form the ratios

$$C = \left(\frac{\Delta I}{\Delta W}\right),$$

and hence estimate C_Q and C_P. Observe that the latter is considerably larger than the former. What conclusion can you draw?

SELECTED BIBLIOGRAPHY ON BUDGETS

ALLEN, R. G. D. (with A. L. BOWLEY), *Family Expenditure.* London, 1935, viii + 145 pp.

BOWLEY, A. L. (1) "The Action of Economic Forces in Producing Frequency Distributions of Income, Prices, and other Phenomena: A Suggestion for Study," *Econometrica,* Vol. 1, 1933, pp. 358–372.
(2) (see R. G. D. Allen).

HEIBERG, P. "Has Engel's Law its Limitation?" *Journal of the American Statistical Association,* Vol. 41, pp. 175–177.

KAPLAN, A. D. H. [with FAITH M. WILLIAMS and ERIKA H. WULFF (assistant)]. *Family Income and Expenditure in Chicago, 1935–36.* Bulletin No. 642, 1938, U. S. Dept. of Labor, x + 210 pp.

STAEHLE, H. "Family Budgets," *Econometrica,* Vol. 3, 1935, pp. 106–118.

STECKER, MARGARET L. *Intercity Differences in Costs of Living in March, 1935, 59 Cities.* Research Monograph XII, WPA, Division of Social Research, Washington, D. C., 1937, xxvi + 216 pp.

U. S. BUREAU OF LABOR STATISTICS. *Urban Study of Consumer Purchases.* 1937, Washington, D. C.

WALD, A. "The Approximate Determination of Indifference Surfaces by Means of Engel Curves," *Econometrica,* Vol. 8, 1940, pp. 144–175.

WILLIAMS, FAITH M. (See Kaplan, A. D. H.).

WULFF, ERIKA H. (see Kaplan, A. D. H.).

CHAPTER 9

The Theory of Equilibrium

1. *Introduction*

From the days when Plato in his *Republic* conceived of the Philosopher King and a social utopia there has persisted the ideal of establishing a regimented social order in which the maximum good could be attained by the largest number. This ideal has been at the heart of many social theories.

In this chapter we shall review some of the principal features of what has come to be called the theory of equilibrium economics. Probably the first general statement of the problem in a form acceptable to modern science was made by Leon Walras (1834–1910), professor at the University of Lausanne from 1870 to 1892 and founder of the "Lausanne School" of economic thought. Beginning with the concept of marginal utility he set up a theory of exchange for any number of commodities. He established conditions of equilibrium which assumed, first, the realization of maximum satisfaction for each individual, second, the balance of receipts and expenditures for each individual; third, the equivalence between the quantities of producer services offered and asked; and, fourth, the equality between net cost and sale price.

The ideas of Walras were later absorbed by Vilfredo Pareto (1848–1923), his successor in the chair of political economy at the University of Lausanne. His principal works in economics are *Cours d'économie politique,* published in 1896 at Lausanne, *Manuale di economia politica con una introduzione alla scienza sociale,* published in Milan in 1906 and *Manuel d'économie politique,* published in Paris in 1909. Pareto expanded and deepened the equilibrium theory of Walras and cast it into a satisfactory mathematical form. An excellent summary of his system will be found in his article in the French encyclopedia of mathematics.[1]

In this chapter we shall follow somewhat the presentation of the equilibrium theory as it was set forth by Enrico Barone in 1908 in

[1] See *Bibliography.*

an article on *The Ministry of Production in the Collectivist State.*[2] A translation of this article, which followed a suggestion of Pareto, was reprinted in 1935.

More recently in the work of J. R. Hicks, R. G. D. Allen, E. Slutsky, and others a theory of value has been developed in terms of a set of equilibrium conditions. These conditions include a theory of prices, based upon the concept of marginal utility, a theory of exchange, formulated in terms of elasticities of demand and supply, and a theory of production based upon a general formulation of the concept of factors of production. Since many of these ideas have already been presented in earlier chapters, the equilibrium equations to which they lead will be assumed as part of the general scheme. Through them the parameters of the functions of demand, and the technical coefficients associated with the factors of production, are assumed to be determined.

It should also be pointed out to the reader that the material in this chapter is not intended as an argument for or against the possibility of establishing a regimented economic order commonly regarded as the goal of many social theories. Although certain implications may be drawn from the complexity of the resulting system of equations, the development of the theory of general equilibrium belongs to the history of classical economics.

2. The Economic Variables

The difficulty in formulating an equilibrium theory of economics is inherent in the complexity of the system itself. Each individual is the center of a miniature economic system which is subject to many forces, and the total population of individuals is presumably governed by the sum of the influences which affect the individuals. If anyone will himself estimate the number of stimuli by which he is influenced during the course of a day, the numerous judgments that are entailed, and, in frequent instances, the chains of circumstances which follow from these judgments, he will recognize at once the complex character of the problem.

The proposition of formulating, and ultimately solving, a set of equations which contain all the elements of an economic system — prices, production, consumption, savings, and the like—is one that has intrigued the imagination of many. This is the hope of those who cherish the belief that society can be so regulated that maximum use

[2] Appendix A, pp. 245-290 in *Collectivist Economic Planning.* Edited by F. A. von Hayek. London, 1935, 293 pp.

may be made of the factors of production, and that the resulting income may be equitably and completely distributed. It is for this reason, more than for any other, that attempts have been made to formulate the general and exceedingly complex system of equations which constitutes the theoretical basis of the theory of *general equilibrium.* The number of these equations is probably in the millions. The task of reaching even an approximate solution is beyond present hope; although some attempts, heroic in nature, have been made to attain such a solution.[3]

But in spite of the statistical difficulties which bar the pathway to a practical solution, it is instructive indeed to survey the problem and to formulate the equations of the system. From these general studies one significant fact may be gleaned, namely, that total income is a dominating quantity. Production and consumption can never exceed the total value made possible by the factors of production. Prosperity attends the year when the value of the income exceeds an average norm determined both by the size of the population and the standard of living which it has established; depression follows a decline of income below this norm. The kernel of the problem is found in the task of attempting to distribute the creation of income among the factors of production, and then of distributing the created income equitably among the individual units of consumption.

Observing thus the intricacies of the situation, let us first attempt to define the general system of economic variables whose equilibrium is desired. These variables we may tabulate as follows:

Types	Symbols	Number of Variables
	The Elements of Production.	
1. Categories of things produced.	$A, B, C, \cdots$	m
2. Quantities produced.	$R_a, R_b, R_c, \cdots$	m
3. Costs of production.	$P_a, P_b, P_c, \cdots$	m
	Structure of Existing Capital.	
4. Categories of capital.	$S, T, U, \cdots$	n
5. Quantities of services required.	$R_s, R_t, R_u, \cdots$	n
6. Prices of services.	$P_s, P_t, P_u, \cdots$	n
7. Technical coefficients associated with categories of capital in the process of production.	$a_s, a_t, a_u, \cdots$ $b_s, b_t, b_u, \cdots$ $c_s, c_t, c_u, \cdots$ $\cdot \cdot \cdot \cdot \cdot \cdot \cdot$	mn

[3] See, for example, the computations of W. W. Leontief (*Bibliography*) who comments as follows about his task: "The total number of multiplications involved in the practical solution of our problem exceeds 450,000. This task alone would mean a two-year job, at 120 multiplications per hour." The system studied by Leontief contained ten primary variables.

Structure of New Capital.

8. Categories of new capital.	$H, K, L, \cdots$	r
9. Quantities of services required.	$R_h, R_k, R_l, \cdots$	r
10. Costs of production.	$P_h, P_k, P_l, \cdots$	r
11. Technical coefficients associated with the categories of capital in the process of production.	$h_s, k_s, l_s, \cdots$ $h_t, k_t, l_t, \cdots$ $h_u, k_u, l_u, \cdots$ $\cdots\cdots$	nr

Elements of Consumption.

12. Quantities of production consumed.	$Q_a, Q_b, Q_c, \cdots$	m
13. Prices of quantities consumed.	$p_a = 1, p_b, p_c, \cdots$	$m - 1$
14. Quantities of capital consumed.	$Q_s, Q_t, Q_u, \cdots$	n
15. Savings.	E	1

Of these symbolic quantities we shall assume that those under the following types are unknown and must be determined by equilibrium conditions: (2), (3), (5), (6), (9), (10), (13), and (15). If we sum the number of variables under these types we find that there is a total of $3m + 2n + 2r$ quantities. The one given price, $p_a = 1$, is the price of money and consequently may be assigned an arbitrary value. In the system of Walras the commodity in terms of which the prices of all the others are given is called the *numéraire.*

3. *Statistical Summary of the Variables*

With the rapid growth of statistical information in the past three decades, we are nearer the attainment of estimates of many of the magnitudes in the table of the variables than ever before. For example, the value of income, that is to say, the value of the total amount of goods produced in any year, is known to a satisfactory degree of approximation. We thus have an excellent estimate of the sum

$$R_a + R_b + R_c + \cdots.$$

Considerable information is also available for the individual terms of the sum, provided too fine a differentiation is not required.

For example, from the data on national income which were given

Industrial Origin	Per Cent of Total Income	Industrial Origin	Per Cent of Total Income
Agriculture	8.87	Communication	1.45
Mining and quarrying	2.06	Trade	14.46
Electric light, power, etc.	2.15	Finance	3.59
Manufacturing	20.63	Service	11.05
Construction	2.66	Government	11.37
Transportation	8.28	Miscellaneous	6.03
		Other income	7.45

in Section 2 of Chapter 2, we observe on page 181 the percentages allocated to each of 13 categories into which the national income may be divided.

Reasons have been given in Chapter 2 to show that these ratios tend to have stability through great fluctuations of the business cycle. Hence in any year the approximate share of national income which is to be attributed to these various factors may be obtained by multiplying the value of the total income by the per cents given in the table.

An interesting attempt has recently been made by the Industrial Committee of the National Resources Committee to estimate the proportional parts contributed to national income at different levels of the total income by some 81 segments of the economy. The data and the statistical techniques employed in the study are included in a report entitled *Patterns of Resource Use,* prepared under the direction of G. C. Means (see *Bibliography*). The estimates made in the report are concerned principally with manpower and the consumption of national production.

The following brief table gives a sample of what was attempted by the committee:

Items	Actual Values		Assumed Values					
	1929	1935						
1. Consumer Income in billions of 1936 dollars	65.3	56.9	50	60	70	80	90	100
2. Index of Industrial Production, 1923–25 = 100.	119	90	68	90	113	139	166	195
3. Passenger automobile sales. (Unit = 1,000).	3,850	3,480	1,300	2,390	3,640	5,270	7,280	10,350
4. Consumption of iron and steel. Unit = 1,000,000 gross tons).	51.3	31.7	15.7	31.7	48.5	67.4	87.1	108.2
5. Employment in iron and steel. (Unit = 1,000).	420	375	163	282	398	515	630	748
6. Construction (consumption) in billions of 1929 dollars.	6.44	2.42	4.10	5.89	7.67	9.43	11.18	12.94
7. Electric light and power consumption in billions of kilowatt-hours.	97.4	99.4	116.0	123.5	131.2	139.1	147.1	155.4
8. Agricultural employment. (Unit = 1,000).	9,888	9,925	10,100	10,100	10,100	10,100	10,100	10,100
9. Total employment. (Unit = 1,000).[4]	46,624	41,409	39,461	43,388	47,234	51,258	55,534	60,084

[4] It is estimated that the total manpower for 1938 was 54,500,000.

The great difficulty which attends the making of such a schedule of estimates may readily be seen from an examination of one or two of the items. For example, in No. 7 a strong secular trend in the use of electrical power must be reckoned with. Society is not static and the estimates of a factor in an economy which produces 60 billions in income at one period may require revising in an economy of the same income at another period. In the case of electrical power, the time factor, involving as it does the unknown development of new scientific methods, must be accounted for.

A second example is found in a comparison of the estimates for the consumption of iron and steel on the one hand and the production of iron ore on the other. We see from No. 4 in the table that 15.7 millions of tons are estimated for an economy of 50 billion income and 108.2 millions of tons are estimated for an economy of 100 billion income, an increase of about 700 per cent. But if one examines the approximations for the production of iron ore, approximations contained in the report but not reproduced in our table, he will find that this production increases from 6.1 millions of tons to 149.7 millions of tons, that is to say, approximately 2450 per cent, as the economy grows from a production of 50 billions to 100 billions. The apparent discrepancy is accounted for by the relationship of the use of scrap iron to that produced from ore in the manufacturing of steel products. The report, commenting upon this, says "that during periods of depression scrap iron prices are low compared to the cost of making pig iron and hence a smaller proportion of steel is made from pig iron; on the other hand, during periods of prosperity scrap iron prices are high relative to the cost of pig iron and a larger proportion of pig iron is used in steel-making." This comment thus introduces another factor, namely that of the size of the population of the economy under consideration. An income of 50 billions would be a high economic level for a population of 100 million people, but a low one for a population of 130 million people. In the first case prices would probably be high and in the second prices would be low. We thus see that the estimates given in the table are not unrelated to the schedules of prices and hence are meaningless without information upon this vital point. The equilibrium conditions introduced in the next section will show how significant a role is played by prices in making estimates of national production.

In order to avoid this troublesome question of fluctuating prices the committee studied the variations in the elements of the segments with which they were concerned over periods of time which included in most instances the boom period around 1929 and the depression period around 1932. National income and prices fluctuated greatly while population remained reasonably constant. The method of analysis may be illustrated by the formula employed in the calculation of industrial production. Employing data for both industrial production (P) and consumer income (I), the latter measured in terms of the price level of 1936, it was found empirically that a formula of the type

$$P = A\, a^t\, I^k, \tag{1}$$

would fit the data over the period from 1919 to 1936. In this formula t is time, measured from 1927 as origin, while A, a, and k are parameters to be determined by the method of least squares from the observed data. The values of these parameters were thus found to be: $A = 0.2004$, $a = 0.9837$, $k = 1.5284$. Hence, using 1938 as the year of estimate, that is, $t = 11$, the production can be computed for the assumed ranges of income from $I = 50$ to $I = 100$.

A device of this sort is thus seen to be an ingenious method for surmounting the difficulties involved in the calculation of the unknowns in the equations of general equilibrium. The weakness is found obviously in the difficulties which attend the determination of the proper relationship between the variables.

4. The Equations of Economic Equilibrium

Returning now to the system of variables tabulated in Section 2, we shall formulate the equations, called the *equations of economic equilibrium,* which must be solved in order to determine the values of the variables. We assume in this a static equilibrium.

We observe in the first place the following relationships:

$$\begin{aligned} Q_s &= R_s + a_s R_a + b_s R_b + \cdots + h_s R_h + k_s R_k + \cdots, \\ Q_t &= R_t + a_t R_a + b_t R_b + \cdots + h_t R_h + k_t R_h + \cdots, \\ &\cdots\cdots\cdots\cdots\cdots \end{aligned} \tag{A}$$

This system contains a total of n equations between the $m + n$ unknown quantities $R_s, R_t, \cdots, R_h, R_k, \cdots$. These equations merely assert that the quantities of capital consumed are equal to the sums of the individual productive parts.

The next equation states that E, that is to say, total savings, is equal to the new capital created. We thus obtain the single equation

$$E = P_h R_h + P_k R_k + \cdots, \tag{B}$$

in the $2r + 1$ unknown quantities, $E, R_h, R_k, \cdots, P_h, P_k, \cdots$.

The next system of equations connects prices as follows:

$$\text{(C)} \qquad \begin{aligned} P_a &= a_s p_s + a_t p_t + \cdots ; \quad & P_h &= h_s p_s + h_t p_t + \cdots ; \\ P_b &= b_s p_s + b_t p_t + \cdots ; \quad & P_k &= k_s p_s + k_t p_t + \cdots ; \\ &\cdots & &\cdots \end{aligned}$$

These equations merely state that the cost of production of finished goods, and of new capital, is equal to the sum of the partial costs. We observe that in this system we have $m + r$ equations in the unknowns $P_a, P_b, \cdots, P_h, P_k, \cdots$.

The next system is given by the following price relationships:

$$\text{(D)} \qquad \begin{aligned} P_a &= 1 ; \quad & P_h p_e &= p_h ; \\ P_b &= p_b ; \quad & P_k p_e &= p_k ; \\ &\cdots & &\cdots \end{aligned}$$

The first of these equations state that the selling price of goods is equal to the cost of production, the price of the first good being chosen as the *numéraire*. The second set assumes that the cost of production of new capital, multiplied by the price of new capital, p_e, is equal to the price of the final service. We see that we have $m + r - 1$ equations in the unknowns $P_a, P_b, \cdots, P_h, P_k, \cdots$.

Some comments, however, should be made about system (D). In a regimented economy, the goal, perhaps, of the equilibrium theory, final costs would be set equal to final consumers' prices, and equations (D) would certainly *prevail.* But in a free economy under competition, this would not be the case as we have already indicated in previous chapters. By his control of a monopoly, and consequently of prices, the entrepreneur would seek to maximize his profits given by $(P_b - p_b)R_b$. Under this assumption, the first equations in (D) would be replaced by others of the form

$$\text{(2)} \qquad P_b = p_b - R_b \frac{\partial p_b}{\partial R_b} .$$

We now have a total of $2m + n + 2r$ equations in the $3m + 2n + 2r$ unknown quantities which we have introduced. Another equation might appear to be found in the following relationship:

(3)

$$P_a R_a + P_b R_b + \cdots + P_h R_h + P_k R_k + \cdots + E = Q_s p_s + Q_t p_t + \cdots .$$

But this equation is not independent of the systems already established. Thus from (A) we get

$$\sum Q_s p_s = \sum p_s R_s + (\sum p_s a_s) R_a + (\sum p_s b_s) R_b + \cdots + (\sum p_s h_s) R_h + (\sum p_s k_s) R_k + \cdots .$$

Then, from system (C), we have

$$\sum Q_s\, p_s = \sum p_s\, R_s + \sum P_a\, R_a + \sum P_h\, R_h \; ;$$

and finally, introducing the equations from (B) and (D), we obtain

$$\sum Q_s\, p_s = \sum P_a\, R_a + \sum P_h\, R_h + E \; ,$$

which is observed to be identical with equation (3).

So far, in the system which has been constructed, we have not introduced the demand relationships, which must exist in any economic system, whether it be regimented or free. We thus add the final equations, expressed as generalized curves of demand between the quantities consumed and their prices. That is to say, we have the following system:

$$\text{(E)} \qquad F_i(R_a\,, R_b\,, \cdots ; R_s\,, R_t\,, \cdots ; P_a\,, P_b\,, \cdots ; p_s\,, p_t\,, \cdots ; E) = 0\,,$$

where i runs from 1 to $m + n$.

Adjoining this demand system to the systems (A), (B), (C), and (D), we obtain a complete system of $3n + 2n + 2r$ equations in the same number of variables. Presumably a mathematical solution exists for the unknown quantities. Looking about us, we observe that a solution is empirically attained in the actual economic activities of the economy itself.

A final remark should be made about the values of the technical coefficients, which, throughout our analysis, have been assumed to be known. From the discussion of Chapter 7, however, we observe that they also depend in their turn upon the solution of a system of equations of the form

$$Q_a = f_q(a_s\,, a_t\,, \cdots) \; ,$$

where q runs from 1 to k.

5. *Concluding Remarks*

What Hercules will attempt to solve the system of equations which we have established above for the determination of general equilibrium! It will be observed that the system is not linear in character, since the relationship (B) is a bilinear form in the unknown quantities. It is also difficult to believe that the system of demand functions given by (E) is essentially linear, although this assumption is not entirely realistic and could be assumed as a first approximation. Why, then, should we make the effort to formulate the system of general equilibrium?

The value in the scrutiny of such a complex of variables is found principally in the concept which we thus attain of the essential nature of the interaction of economic quantities. It is worth our effort to see the system as a whole; there is certainly gain in discovering the quadratic, as contrasted with the linear, character of the equations which must be solved. W. W. Leontief has given a reasonable appraisal of the matter as follows:[5]

> The principal merit of the general equilibrium theory lies in the fact that it enables us to take account of the highly complex network of mutual relationships which transmits the impulses of any local primary change into the remotest corners of the existing economic system. While in the case of partial analysis, which operates simultaneously with only two or three variables, the interrelation among these few elements can often be perceived directly, such intuitive inference becomes practically impossible as soon as the number of variables increases up to four or five, not to mention ten or twenty.

Leontief, himself, making use of ten categories of production, has actually attempted to solve the system for certain output and price variations with respect to increases in the productivity coefficients. We have already commented upon the numerical magnitude of his undertaking.

A partial existence theorem has also been given for the mathematical problem by A. Wald (see *Bibliography*), who considered a system of the Walrasian form. He enumerated a set of conditions both upon the demand functions and the technical coefficients, which would assure the existence of a mathematical solution of the equations. The complex character of the problem makes it impossible to summarize the analysis here.

PROBLEMS

1. Using the data from the table of Section 3, graph the values of industrial production, passenger car sales, consumption of iron and steel, construction, and electric light and power consumption as functions of the assumed income. Are these true Engel curves?

2. Using formula (1) compute P over the period from 1919 to 1938 employing the data for I as given in Section 2 of Chapter 2. Graph your values and compare with the data for industrial production given in Section 8 of Chapter 11.

3. Estimate the correlation between the two series of problem 2.

4. Solve the following simplified system for the values of R_a, R_s, R_h, R_k, P_h, P_k, E, and p_s:

[5] See page 110 of the article cited in the *Bibliography*.

$$Q_s = 22 = R_s + R_a + 2R_h + 2R_k\,, \quad E = P_h R_h + P_k R_k\,,$$
$$P_a = 1 = 2p_s\,, \quad P_h = 6p_s\,, \quad P_k = 8p_s\,, \quad P_h p_k = P_k p_h\,, \quad p_k = 1/4\,, \quad p_k = 1/3\,,$$
$$P_a = -R_a - 2R_s - 0.2\,E + 16\,,$$
$$p_s = -\tfrac{1}{2}R_a - R_s - 0.3\,E + 12\,.$$

5. In the development of an armament program, such as that being inaugurated by the United States at the time this is written, would an equilibrium system comparable to the one discussed in this chapter be necessary? What variables would be under the control of the government?

6. In the simplified system given in problem 4 the values of the factors of production were assumed known. Would this be true in the establishment of a war armament program? Which of the quantities in the general equations of equilibrium would be accurately known, and which must be determined from the equations?

7. Would you say that prices are controllable under an armament program? Can the magnitude of their change be estimated from the equilibrium equations of the armament program itself, or must other factors be considered?

SELECTED BIBLIOGRAPHY ON THE THEORY OF EQUILIBRIUM

BARONE, E. "The Ministry of Production in the Collectivist State," (1908). Translated in *Collectivist Economic Planning*. Edited by F. A. von Hayek, London, 1935, 293 pp. In particular, pp. 245–290.

HICKS, J. R. (1) *Théorie mathématique de la valeur en régime de libre concurrence*. Paris, 1937, 55 pp.

(2) *Value and Capital: An Inquiry into some Fundamental Principles of Economic Theory*. Oxford, 1939, xi + 331 pp.

LEONTIEF, W. W. "Interrelation of Prices, Output, Savings, and Investment," *The Review of Economic Statistics*, Vol. 19, 1939, pp. 109–132.

MEANS, G. C. *Patterns of Resource Use*. Issued by the Industrial Committee of the National Resources Committee, 1939, v + 149 pp.

PARETO, V. (1) *Cours d'économie politique*. Vol. 2, Lausanne, 1897, pp. 364 et seq.

(2) *Manuel d'économie politique*. Paris, 1909; 2nd ed., 1927, 694 pp.

(3) "Economie mathématique," *Encyclopédie des Sciences Mathématiques*, Paris, 1911, Tome I, Volume 4, Fascicule 4, I 26, pp. 591–640. In particular, pp. 626 et seq.

TINBERGEN, J. *An Econometric Approach to Business Cycle Problems*. Paris, 1937, 75 pp.

WALD, A. "Über einige Gleichungssysteme der mathematischen Ökonomie," *Zeitschrift für Nationalökonomie*, Vol. 7, 1936, pp. 637–670.

WALRAS, L. *Elements d'économie politique pure*. 1874; 5th ed., Paris and Lausanne, 1926, xx + 487 pp.

CHAPTER 10

TAXATION

1. The General Problem

The old statement that "nothing is certain except death and taxes" exhibits the fundamental nature of taxes in an economy. By a tax we shall mean a charge, usually pecuniary, laid upon persons or property for public use. Taxes are generically of two kinds, direct and indirect. The first tax is made directly to each person, such as property and income taxes; the second tax includes such charges as are levied upon goods before they become the property of the consumer, such, for example, as export, import, or excise duties. Taxes are of many forms and kinds. The most common kind of tax is that levied upon property values. This tax is apportioned between city, county, and state governments for the maintenance of these governments, for fire and police protection, for schools, etc. The federal government and many states have also adopted an income tax, which is a graduated assessment against net income from which certain deductions are generally allowed.

In the expenditure of money, as we have stated earlier in this work, the individual usually obtains an equivalent utility, and his expenditure is guided by his estimates of this utility. We have stated elsewhere that the fundamental law of economics is probably the proposition that *marginal utility is proportional to price.* But it will be seen that in the case of taxes this law is generally violated. Special taxes, such as those paid by motorists for the building and maintenance of roads, probably purchase a utility directly proportional to the money expended; but general taxes usually fail in most cases to purchase an equivalent utility. Thus two men may pay equal taxes, but one of these may have no child who will benefit by the schools maintained by the tax, while the other may have a large family. One derives only a share of the general benefit of living in a community which supports education, while the other has the direct benefit of having his children educated at comparatively small cost to himself.

We may thus say that in the general case the money paid by individuals purchases either a greater or a less utility than the money otherwise spent would purchase. This is because the taxpayer deals with a very special kind of a monopoly, which not only forces him to pay a monopoly price, but also to purchase things for which he has no special need.

This is especially true in the case of corporations. J. B. Williams in his comprehensive treatise on *The Theory of Investment Value* (1938) makes the startling statement that "an increase in the property-tax rate of \$10 a thousand, for instance, say from \$15 to \$25 a thousand, such as has occurred during the past generation, is as burdensome, in a typical case, as the grant of a first mortgage equal to 25 per cent of a corporation's assets." His argument is given simply as follows: Let A represent the total assets of the corporation, $i = 0.015$ the initial tax rate, and $i' = 0.025$ the increased tax rate. Then, if money may be borrowed at $r = 0.04$, the bond issue, B, equivalent to the increased tax rate is given by

$$rB = i'A - iA \, .$$

Substituting the numerical values, we obtain $B = \frac{1}{4}A$, a value which we observe is independent of the earnings of the company.

In the following sections we shall consider a few of the special influences exerted by taxation upon the ordinary economic variables which we have considered in previous chapters. We shall first examine the effects of taxation in connection with a static economy of fixed demand and supply curves. We shall assume the existence of a utility surface and we shall attempt to describe the effects of taxation upon measures determined from this psychic function. But in this connection it will be observed also that the effects of taxation are often dynamic rather than static. Indications will be given as to the mechanism through which the effects of excessive taxation are sometimes translated into political action.

2. Taxation and the Problem of Demand

In order to obtain some elementary concepts regarding the effect upon demand of the imposing of an excise tax upon the sale of goods, let us begin with an argument given by J. Dupuit prior to 1850, but recently extended by H. Hotelling (see *Bibliography*).[1]

In Figure 45 DB is the curve of demand, $p = f(q)$, and SB is the curve of supply, $p = g(q)$, identified, as in Chapter 6, with the curve of marginal cost.

[1] The material in this and the following two sections is based upon the extremely penetrating analysis of Hotelling, which brings into clear relief the essential problem of taxation.

Using a customary nomenclature, we shall designate as *consumers' surplus* (C. S.) the area ABD. This we observe is the area from O to q under the demand curve diminished by the total revenue, $R(q) = ABCO$. That is to say.

$$(1) \qquad C.S. = \int_0^q f(q)\,dq - R(q).$$

In a similar manner we define producers' surplus (P. S.) to be the area SBA, which is seen to equal total revenue diminished by the area under the marginal cost curve. That is to say,

$$(2) \qquad P.S. = R(q) - \int_0^q g(q)\,dq.$$

If a tax equal to $t = RS$ is imposed upon the goods, the demand will be reduced to the point represented by L. In this case the consumers' surplus and the producers' surplus are equal respectively to

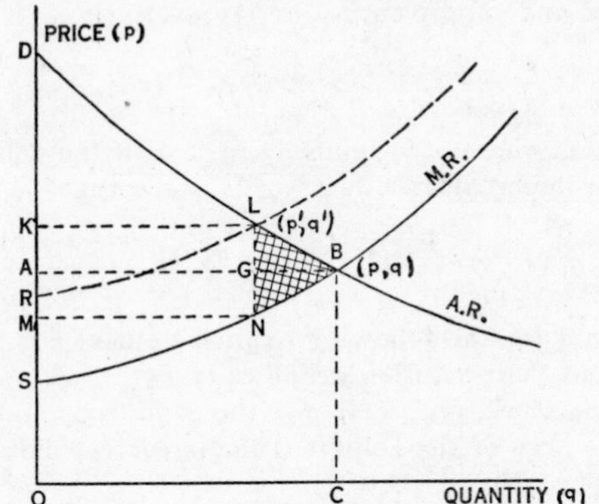

FIGURE 45.—MARGINAL AND AVERAGE REVENUE CURVES SHOWING THE EFFECT OF TAXATION.

the areas KLD and $RLK = SNM$. The government revenue (G. R.) is equal to $MN \times NL$, that is to say

$$(3) \qquad \text{G. R.} = MNLK.$$

If now we replace q by q' in (1) and (2), and add the resulting values to G. R. defined by (3), we shall obtain

$$C.S. + P.S. + G.R. = \int_0^{q'} [f(q) - g(q)]\,dq + MNLK = SBD - LNB$$

$$= \int_0^q [f(q) - g(q)]\,dq - LNB.$$

Hence the net result of the addition of the tax to the cost of the goods has been to reduce the net surplus by the area LNB. Dupuit called this the amount of *social loss* occasioned by the tax.

If we neglect the curvatures of the curves of demand and marginal cost, then we can write approximately

$$\text{Area } LNB = \tfrac{1}{2}\, GB \times NL \,.$$

Since for small taxes the decrement in quantity purchased, namely GB, is usually proportional to the tax rate, it follows that

$$\text{Area } LNB = k(NL)^2,$$

where k is the factor of proportionality. We thus reach the conclusion (Dupuit's theorem), that *the net loss in social benefit resulting from an excise tax varies as the square of the tax rate.*

PROBLEMS

1. If the demand and supply curves are respectively

$$\frac{p}{a} + \frac{q}{b} = 1\,, \quad \text{and} \quad \frac{p}{c} - \frac{q}{d} = 1\,,$$

compare the equilibrium value of q, namely, q_0, with the equilibrium value, q_1, after a tax t has been imposed. In other words, show that

$$q_1 = q_0\left(1 - \frac{t}{a-c}\right), \quad \text{where} \quad q_0 = \frac{bd(a-c)}{bc+ad}\,.$$

2. Solve problem 1 for the following explicit values: $a = 10$, $b = 20$, $c = 5$, $d = 10$, $t = 1$. Present your solution graphically.

3. Compute *C. S.*, *P. S.*, and *G. R.* for the conditions stated in problem 2.

4. Show that the area of the Dupuit triangle corresponding to the conditions of problem 1 is given by

$$A = \frac{bdt^2}{2(ad+bc)}\,.$$

5. If the demand and supply curves are respectively

$$p = \frac{a}{b+cq} \quad \text{and} \quad p = \frac{d}{e-fq}\,,$$

compare the equilibrium value of q, namely q_0, with the equilibrium value, q_1, after a tax t has been imposed.

6. Solve problem 5 for the following explicit values: $a = 100$, $b = 6$, $c = 1$, $d = 50$, $e = 10$, $f = 1$, $t = 1$. Present your solution graphically.

7. Prove that the area of the Dupuit triangle for problem 4 is given by the following:

$$A = \log\left[\left(\frac{b+cq_0}{b+cq_1}\right)^{a/c}\left(\frac{e-fq_0}{e-fq_1}\right)^{d/f}\right].$$

8. Show that the area of the Dupuit triangle for problem 6 is equal to 0.2026.

9. Compute *C. S.*, *P. S.*, and *G. R.* for problem 6.

10. If a monopolist is taxed t per unit of good produced, and if this tax is added to cost, show that the addition in price charged is less than t, provided the demand curve is linear and the cost function is quadratic.

11. Compute the increase in price caused by a manufacturing tax of 1 per unit of goods produced, if the demand function is given by $p = 20 - u$, and the cost function is given by $Q(u) = 5 - u + 0.1\, u^2$. Present your results graphically.

12. The following data give the ratio of dividends to earnings as reported by F. McIntyre in "The Effect of the Undistributed Profits Tax upon the Distribution of Corporate Earnings—A Statistical Appraisal," *Econometrica*, Vol. 7, 1939, pp. 336–348:

Year Ratio of Dividends	1928	1929	1930	1931	1932	1933	1934	1935	1936	1937
to Earnings	52.8	52.2	62.4	71.7	69.8	56.2	64.6	54.3	65.7	66.8

What conclusions would you reach from these data as to the effect upon the distribution of corporate profits of the Undistributed Profits Tax of the Revenue Act of 1936? What effect does the business cycle appear to exert?

3. *Comparison of Income with Excise Taxes*

The ideas of the preceding section have been extended by Hotelling to a more general situation. By his analysis he reaches the following conclusion: "*If a person must pay a certain sum of money in taxes, his satisfaction will be greater if the levy is made directly on him as a fixed amount than if it is made through a system of excise taxes which he can to some extent avoid by rearranging his production and consumption.*"[2]

Let us review the argument by which this conclusion is reached. We shall assume that E is a man's money income after he has paid his fixed tax. His budget will then be

$$(5) \qquad \sum p_i\, q_i = E\,,$$

where the q_i are purchased in such a manner that the utility function

$$(6) \qquad U = U(q_1, q_2, \cdots, q_n)$$

is maximized as shown in Section 7 of Chapter 3.

Let us now consider another set of quantities, $q'_i = q_i + \delta q_i$, which also satisfy the budget equation. Substituting them in (5), we

[2] See *Bibliography*: Hotelling (2), p. 252.

see that the increments also satisfy the following condition:

$$\sum p_i \, \delta q_i = 0 \,. \tag{7}$$

If the utility function has the properties postulated in Chapter 3, then there will exist a unique maximum subject to the budgetary restraint imposed by (5), and consequently the utility, evaluated at the point defined by the quantities q'_i will be smaller than that defined by (6). This is certainly the case for any point defined by adding to q_i a set of increments which satisfy condition (7).

Let us now assume that the income tax is diminished and that an excise tax is then imposed. The individual will then purchase a new set of quantities, $q'_i = q_i + \delta q_i$, at new prices $p'_i = p_i + \delta p_i$. The government's revenue is then equal to

$$r = \sum q'_i \, \delta p_i - \delta E \,, \tag{8}$$

where the summation is taken over both buyers and sellers. That this assumption is necessary is readily seen by referring to Figure 45, where the government's revenue, $MNLK$, is made up of the rectangles $AGLK = q' \times GL$ (change in buyer's price) and $AGNM = q' \times GN$ (change in seller's price).

In (8) we now replace δE by its equivalent

$$\delta E = \sum q'_i \, \delta p_i + \sum p_i \, \delta q_i \,, \tag{9}$$

which gives the equation

$$\delta r = - \sum p_i \, \delta q_i \,. \tag{10}$$

If now we assume that the increase in the government's revenue from the excise tax is just equal to the reduction caused by diminishing the income tax, that is to say, if $\delta r = 0$, then equation (10) reduces to equation (7). Hence the value of the utility declines and the statement of the theorem follows as a consequence.

It is instructive to evaluate the utility function in terms of δr. For this purpose let us designate by $U(q')$ the utility at the point $q' = (q'_1, q'_2, \cdots, q'_n)$, and by $U(q)$ the utility at the point $q = (q_1, q_2, \cdots, q_n)$. Employing Taylor's theorem, we have the expansion

$$U(q') = U(q) + \sum U_i \, \delta q_i + \tfrac{1}{2} \sum U_{ij} \, \delta q_i \, \delta q_j \,, \tag{11}$$

where we use the abbreviations

$$U_i = \frac{\partial U}{\partial q_i} \,, \quad U_{ij} = \frac{\partial U}{\partial q_i \, \partial q_j} \,.$$

If q is now assumed to be a maximum point for U subject to the restraint of the budget equation, then we see from Section 7, Chapter 3 that $U_i = \lambda p_i$. Differentiating this with respect to q_j we then obtain

$$(12) \qquad U_{ij} = \lambda \frac{\partial p_i}{\partial q_j} + p_i \frac{\partial \lambda}{\partial q_j} .$$

Substituting these values in (11), we get the equation

$$(13) \qquad U(q') = U(q) + \lambda \sum p_i \, \delta q_i + \tfrac{1}{2} \sum_i \lambda \Big(\sum_j \frac{\partial p_i}{\partial q_j} \delta q_i\Big) \delta q_j + \tfrac{1}{2} \sum_i p_i \Big(\sum_j \frac{\partial \lambda}{\partial q_j} \delta q_j\Big) \delta q_i .$$

If the sum in the first parenthesis is now replaced by δp_i and the sum in the second parenthesis by $\delta \lambda$, then equation (13) can be written in the form

$$(14) \quad U(q') = U(q) + \lambda \sum p_i \, \delta q_i + \tfrac{1}{2} \lambda \sum \delta p_i \, \delta q_i + \tfrac{1}{2} \delta \lambda \sum p_i \, \delta q_i .$$

We now introduce the value for δr given by equation (10) and thus obtain

$$(15) \qquad U(q') = U(q) - \lambda \, \delta r + \tfrac{1}{2} \lambda \sum \delta p_i \, \delta q_i - \tfrac{1}{2} \delta \lambda \, \delta r .$$

Suppose now that we assume as before that $\delta r = 0$. Then the difference in utility may be written in the form

$$(16) \qquad U(q') - U(q) = \tfrac{1}{2} \lambda \sum \delta p_i \, \delta q_i .$$

In order to give an interpretation to the right hand member, let us now ask what tax would leave the utility unchanged. To answer this we set the difference $U(q') - U(q)$ equal to zero, and then compute δr from (15). We thus obtain

$$\delta r = \tfrac{1}{2} \sum \delta p_i \, \delta q_i .$$

Hence the difference in utility as given by (16) is equal to δr multiplied by the marginal utility of money. The expression for δr can, of course, be identified in Figure 45 as the area of the Dupuit triangle LNB. Consequently there is a net loss in social benefit even though there is no change in utility.

4. The Edgeworth Paradox

In the course of a discussion of taxation from the point of view of monopoly, F. Y. Edgeworth reached the curious conclusion that there exist circumstances under which the actual levying of a tax may result in reduced prices on the articles so taxed. This proposition, called the *Edgeworth paradox,* has been the subject of much controversy since it was first announced. It was considered by Edgeworth himself to be a "mere *curiosum,*" not likely to occur in actual trade.

Since the paradox is related to some extent to the discussion given in the preceding section, we shall review the argument by which such a strange phenomenon may be reproduced. Let us represent a general system of demand functions by

$$p_i = f_i(q_1, q_2, \cdots, q_n), \quad i = 1, 2, \cdots, n;$$

and a general system of supply, or marginal cost, functions by

$$p_i = g_i(q_1, q_2, \cdots, q_n), \quad i = 1, 2, \cdots, n.$$

If we designate by h_i the difference between these functions, that is,

$$h_i = f_i - g_i,$$

then the sum of consumers' and producers' surpluses, as defined in Section 2, is given by the line integral

$$I = \int \sum h_i \, dq_i \tag{17}$$

taken from the origin to the equilibrium point B. It is clear that at B (Figure 45) we shall have

$$h_i = 0. \tag{18}$$

But if a system of taxes, $t_1, t_2, \cdots, t_n$, is now imposed upon the variables, equation (18) is then replaced by the conditions

$$h_i(q'_1, q'_2, \cdots, q'_n) = t_i, \tag{19}$$

We now expand the left hand members of (19) about the point $q_1, q_2, \cdots, q_n$ by means of Taylor's theorem and take account of (18). Neglecting variations of higher order than the first, we obtain the following system of equations for the determination of the unknown increments δq_i:

$$h_{i1}\,\delta q_1 + h_{i2}\,\delta q_2 + \cdots + h_{in}\,\delta q_n = t_i. \tag{20}$$

In these equations we employ the abbreviation $h_{ij} = \partial h_i / \partial q_j$.

The system of equations (20) can now be solved for δq_j. We can write the solution symbolically in the form

$$\delta q_j = \frac{D_{ij}}{D}, \tag{21}$$

where D is the determinant of the h_{ij} and D_{ij} is the determinant D in which the jth column has been replaced by $t_1, t_2, \cdots, t_n$.

The price changes to the buyers resulting from the taxes are given by the expressions

$$\delta p_i = \sum_j f_{ij}\, \delta q_j \,, \tag{22}$$

which are merely the variations of the demand functions.

If in these expressions we replace δq_j by (21), then the price variations have the simple form

$$\delta p_i = -\frac{B_i}{D} \,, \tag{23}$$

where B_i is the determinant

$$B_i = \begin{vmatrix} 0 & f_{i1} & \cdots & f_{in} \\ t_1 & h_{11} & \cdots & h_{1n} \\ t_2 & h_{21} & \cdots & h_{2n} \\ \cdot & \cdot & \cdot & \cdot \\ t_n & h_{n1} & \cdots & h_{nn} \end{vmatrix} .$$

In these expressions we have used the abbreviation $f_{ij} = \partial f_i / \partial q_j$.

The following example has been constructed by Hotelling to illustrate the Edgeworth paradox:

Example. Let the demand functions for wheat and rye be respectively

$$p_1 = 41 - 5q_1 - 7q_2 \,,$$

$$p_2 = 58 - 7q_1 - 10q_2 \,,$$

and let the supply functions for the two commodities be respectively

$$p_1 = 13 + 2q_1 + 2q_2 \,,$$

$$p_2 = 20 + q_1 + q_2 \,.$$

Determine the effect upon the buyers' prices if taxes t_1 and t_2 are imposed respectively upon the commodities.

Solution: Employing equation (23) we immediately obtain

$$\delta p_1 = \frac{-t_1 + 9t_2}{13} \,, \quad \delta p_2 = \frac{-3t_1 + 14t_2}{13} \,.$$

If in these variations we substitute $t_1 = 13$, $t_2 = 0$, we obtain $\delta p_1 = -1$ and $\delta p_2 = -3$. This means that if a tax of 13 cents a bushel is put on wheat, while rye remains untaxed, there will result a lowering of the price on wheat by 1 cent and on rye by 3 cents. It is possible, of course, that the high tax on wheat may stop the production of that cereal entirely. On the other hand, if we set $t_1 = 0$, both prices will be increased, since, in this case, we have $\delta p_1 = 9t_2/13$, and $\delta p_2 = 14t_2/13$.

One may question, as did Edgeworth, whether or not the phenomenon described above will ever be found in a real economy. The most illuminating remark on this question is the following statement by Hotelling:[3]

There is no basis known at present for denying that Edgeworth's phenomenon may pertain to a large proportion of ordinary situations, or for affirming that it is, in his language, a mere *curiosum*. It is quite possible so far as the evidence now goes, that in many practical questions of governmental policy the best expert advice has gone astray because of reliance on the simplified cases treated in textbooks, in which the correlation of demand for different commodities is neglected. Factual investigations of particular sets of commodities may some day produce more definite knowledge of the effects of taxes upon prices. For a random case, the purely deductive reasoning now available fails to tell us definitely whether it is more probable that a tax will increase or decrease the price paid by buyers.

PROBLEMS

1. If the demand curves for two related commodities are given by the functions

$$p_1 = a_1 - b_1 q_1 - c_1 c_2 , \qquad p_2 = a_2 - b_2 q_1 - c_2 q_2 ,$$

and if the corresponding supply curves are respectively

$$p_1 = A_1 + B_1 q_1 + C_1 q_2 , \qquad p_2 = A_2 + B_2 q_1 + C_2 q_2 ,$$

compute explicitly the changes in the prices, namely, the values δp_1 and δp_2, which correspond to taxes t_1 and t_2 imposed upon the supply.

2. If the demand curves of two related commodities are explicitly

$$p_1 = 80 - 2q_1 - 3q_2 , \qquad p_2 = 95 - 5q_1 - 4q_2 ,$$

and if the corresponding supply curves are respectively

$$p_1 = 15 + 5q_1 + 7q_2 , \qquad p_2 = 10 + 6q_1 + 10q_2 ,$$

show that, corresponding to taxes of t_1 and t_2 imposed upon supply, the change in demand prices will be given explicitly as follows:

$$\delta p_1 = -\frac{5}{12} t_1 + \frac{1}{12} t_2 , \qquad \delta p_2 = \frac{26}{12} t_1 - \frac{22}{12} t_2 .$$

What conclusions do you draw from these results?

3. The following example is taken from H. Hotelling [see *Bibliography*, Hotelling (1)]: "A railway company supplies first- and second-class transportation between two points and has the following potential customers:

"Group A, consisting of 450 persons who will ride first class if this does not cost as much as \$5.00 above the second-class fare, or second class if the difference is \$5.00 or more, but who will not pay more than \$12.00 for a first-class or \$7.00 for a second-class ticket.

---

[3] See *Bibliography*, Hotelling (1), p. 583.

"Group B, 40 persons who will ride first class if the fare is $11.00 or less, but whose distaste for the second class is so profound that they will not use it at any price.

"Group C, a mass of 900 who will ride second class if this fare is $8.00 or less, but who will not pay appreciably more for a first-class than for a second-class ticket.

"Group D, 200 persons who will travel second class if the fare is not more than $6.00, and who will not pay more even for first class tickets."

Neglecting the cost of production, first prove that the maximum revenue is obtained by establishing a rate of $12.00 for first-class and $8.00 for second-class fares. Now prove that if a tax of $7.00 is imposed on each first-class ticket, but none on the second-class ticket, then the revenue of the company will be less seriously affected if the first-class fare is lowered to $11.00 and the second-class fare is lowered to $6.00.

5. *Critique of the Theory of Taxation*

The arguments advanced in Section 3 appear to show that utility declines less under a schedule of income taxes than under a schedule of excise taxes. This conclusion, however, is subject to a restrictive set of postulates, which imply, first, that static equilibrium prevails; second, that static demand and supply functions exist; third, that prices in the absence of the excise tax are equal to marginal costs; and, fourth, that utility is a function of the quantities involved and not a functional dependent upon some path of integration in the commodity space.

Since the conclusions stated in Hotelling's theorem, if assumed to be realistic, might have wide application in the formulation of governmental policies of taxation, it is important to have a critical survey of the situation. Weakness must be sought for in the postulates rather than in the mathematical argument which follows from them. R. Frisch in two notes has reviewed the system and, among other things, has taken exception to the third postulate as stated above. Thus he says: "When it comes to *application* to a modern society where all sorts of monopolies and quasi-monopolies exist, the equality between prices and marginal cost cannot be taken as a criterion for the absence of excise taxes."

Perhaps, also, some trouble may be experienced in establishing the proposition that the expression (17) of Section 4, namely

$$I = \int \Sigma\, h_i\, dq_i\,,$$

which we have seen above is the sum of consumers' and producers' surpluses, is independent of the commodity path over which the integral is taken. Especially might one doubt that this is an invariant integral if the element of time is introduced. We know, in fact, from actual observation that in a time situation some demand functions remain stable, while supply functions vary; in other situations the demand varies and supply remains fixed. Under these conditions the effects of taxation would be greater at one time than at another, and the utility differences would change. Such a situation requires analysis beyond that given in previous sections.

Few if any studies have been made on the dynamics of taxation, but there is reason to believe that variations in basic time series may at times be traced to the effects of excessive taxation. There are instances of dramatic events which were associated closely with both high excise and high income taxes. Thus we find among the fundamental causes of the American Revolution the enforcement of an odious Stamp Act upon the American colonists. In the next section we shall consider the effect of high income taxes upon an economic system which is nearing political instability.

6. Political Effects of High Income Taxes

As one may readily surmise, the problem of taxation plays an essential role in determining the distribution of income in an economy, and this, in turn, has its effect upon political events. If very high income taxes are imposed upon the rich, taxes graduated to a scale increasing too rapidly with the level of income, it would be possible, in theory at least, to lower materially the value of the concentration ratio which we defined in Section 7 of Chapter 2. On the other hand, a modification of existing laws, and a lowering of surtax schedules on the incomes of the rich, would presumably raise the value of the concentration ratio. Our inquiry concerns the possible political effects which would attend a substantial change in the concentration ratio.

It will be recalled from Section 7 of Chapter 2 that the concentration ratio, ρ, was defined by the formula

$$\rho = \frac{\delta - 1}{\delta + 1} = \frac{1}{2\nu - 1}, \quad \delta = \frac{\nu}{\nu - 1},$$

where ν is the Pareto constant with an empirical value of 1.5.

In the United States we have observed a variation in ν from 1.34 in 1916 to 1.90 in 1921 (Johnson's estimates). This means that the concentration ratio has varied from 0.5952 in the first instance to 0.3571 in the second. It will be observed, however, that the concentration ratio has never remained long at these extreme levels, but has oscillated regularly around the Pareto value of 0.50. That is to say, there has never been in the United States a trend in the concentration ratio toward a higher or a lower level caused by the undue increase of income tax schedules or by the relaxing of such taxation.

It is interesting to speculate, however, as to the possible political effects of an abnormal and sustained deviation of the concentration ratio from its Pareto value. For example, we observe in the critical years 1920 and 1921, when one of the most spectacular price declines in economic history occurred, and again in the depression years 1931 and 1932, that the concentration ratio was far below normal. Again, in the highly inflationary years 1928 and 1929, the concentration ratio was substantially above normal. The decade of depression since the collapse of the great bull market in 1929 has witnessed a persistent decline in the concentration ratio. From the great sensitivity of the income of the upper classes to fluctuations in the business cycle, as described in Section 4 of Chapter 19, it is not unreasonable to suppose that disturbances in the concentration ratio may be accompanied by economic and political dislocations.

Unfortunately for the statistical verification of this thesis, data are lacking from those political economies which have been disrupted by revolution and civil war. It is quite plausible, however, to infer from historical sources that the French Revolution and the more recent Russian Revolution were both aggravated, if not actually caused, by an undue concentration of wealth and income. Similarly, the socialistic trends of the Spanish government after the overthrow of the monarchy must certainly have lowered greatly the ratio of concentration from its Pareto norm. The civil war may thus have been a consequence of this disruption. The American Civil War was largely a result of the question of slavery in the Southern states. The distribution of slave holdings in this region was approximately Paretean and hence a large disturbance was caused in the concentration ratio when the slaves were freed. It is not unreasonable to suppose that the slow economic recovery of the South, when compared with that of the North, was not due so much to the fact that the North was victorious as to the dislocation of the concentration parameter.

We shall advance the tentative hypothesis that revolution is likely in any economy where the concentration ratio exceeds a certain critical value, $\rho_0 > 0.5$, and that a civil war is likely in any economy where the concentration ratio falls below a certain critical value, $\rho_1 < 0.5$. Since the mass of the people is affected adversely in the first instance, the revolution will be rapid and overwhelming. In the second instance, the upper economic classes, numerically small, but powerful in resources, are effected. Hence the civil war is slow to start and must be long in duration, since it must be waged to a considerable extent by mercenary means.

What these critical values are we have at present no way of estimating. In the United States, if we exclude the period of the World War, the concentration ratio has varied from approximately 0.40 to approximately 0.60 without an undue amount of political unrest. Hence we may assume that any values within these limits are not politically dangerous.

An instructive example is furnished by France during the past few years, where political unrest was followed by the dramatic events of the German occupation. Unfortunately adequate data are not available as to the value of the concentration ratio over these years, but the following figures on the French declaration of estates in the year 1935 may throw some light on the matter:

French Declaration of Estates in 1935

Range of net value in francs (x)	Number	Accumulated Frequency (y)	log x	log y
1 to 500	26,382	370,150	0.00000	5.56838
501 to 2,000	46,103	343,768	2.69984	5.53627
2,001 to 10,000	121,581	297,665	3.30125	5.47373
10,001 to 50,000	127,694	176,084	4.00000	5.24571
50,001 to 100,000	25,529	48,390	4.69898	4.68476
100,001 to 250,000	14,789	22,861	5.00000	4.35910
250,001 to 500,000	4,637	8,072	5.39794	3.90698
500,001 to 1,000,000	2,004	3,435	5.69897	3.53593
1 million to 2 millions	891	1,431	6.00000	3.15564
2 millions to 5 millions	418	540	6.30103	2.73239
5 millions to 10 millions	83	122	6.69897	2.08636
10 millions to 50 millions	37	39	7.00000	1.59106
over 50 millions	2	2	7.69897	0.30103

Since the average value of these estates is found to equal 45,579 francs we see that these data do not carry us a long way into the Pareto tail. Hence the slope of the distribution must be approximated from the last items of the data rather than from the data as a whole. Thus, employing the last three items only in our calculation, we obtain as estimates of the Pareto index the numbers 1.62, 1.65, and 1.85. The latter corresponds to a concentration ratio of 0.3704. The obvious socialistic tendency of the French economy is thus apparent and there are reasons to believe that it progressed in this direction during the years after 1935 to which the above data pertain. Thus we find that the Chamber of Deputies had 100 socialists in 1928, 131 in 1932, and

149 in 1936. Political and social disturbances might be expected to follow from this downward trend of the concentration ratio.

Can the disruptive events of 1940 be attributed in part to the observed decline in the concentration of income in France? The swift and easy victory of the German army over that of the French was phenomenal. The great fortresses of the Maginot line were taken with scarcely a blow. Why this curious weakness? It seems to be the conclusion of careful political observers that the French collapse was internal. Industry was inefficient and a lack of unity was evident in the government. It is not difficult to infer that the industrial dislocations, inevitable when there prevails a low index of the concentration of wealth, furnish a partial if not a major interpretation of the situation.

The a priori reason for these deductions is found in the general assumption that a concentration of wealth and income of approximately the Pareto concentration is essential in supplying the necessary capital to provide employment for the optimum number of workers. A drop in income concentration is symptomatic of a drop in capital concentration and this reacts upon employment. Those affected then assume that the concentration of wealth is responsible for their difficulties and the urge toward socialism is accelerated.

If these conclusions are valid, then it is clear that one of the first concerns of a government should be an analysis of the concentration ratio. If this is observed to be too high, income tax schedules should be raised and labor laws relaxed until a proper balance is achieved. On the other hand, if the concentration ratio is too low, income tax laws should be modified and labor laws strengthened. This appears to be the torque, available to governments, to keep their economic systems in efficient balance.

Because of the sweeping generalization of this section, made as one observes on the basis of very limited data and without adequate theoretical justification, the reader should be warned again that the propositions stated are very tentative. They do not rest upon the same solid foundation of fact and theory as many of the other portions of the book. But one must admit that there are powerful causes which underlie great political disturbances, and these causes are usually rooted deeply in economic patterns. It is a proper function of this science, then, to inquire into the nature of these causes; and if more adequate data and a better understanding of theoretical economics shall show the errors in the interpretation, then, in the language of a great mathematician, who had suddenly seen the flaw in his argument, "we must think again."

PROBLEMS

(The following problems are designed to show why changes in the concentration of wealth as measured by the ratio, ρ, described in Section 7, Chapter 2, should cause political unrest).

1. In Section 4, Chapter 19 there will be found values of the concentration ratio, ρ, computed from the Johnson estimates of ν given in Section 6, Chapter 2. Graph on the same chart these values and the values of some other index measuring business. What inference do you draw about the relationship between ρ and the business cycle?

2. Assuming that individual savings are given in terms of income by the Engel curve

$$S = A + B\,I^a,$$

and making use of the abbreviation

$$F(\mu, a) = \frac{\Gamma(\mu - a)\,\zeta(\mu - a)}{\Gamma(\mu)\,\zeta(\mu)},$$

show from the relationships established in Section 9, Chapter 2 that average savings per income receiver are given by the formula

$$S = A + B\,b\,\Gamma(\mu, a),$$

where b, assumed constant, is one of the parameters in the general distribution function.

3. Assuming a Pareto distribution, that is, $\mu = 2.5$, and assuming a linear Engel curve, that is, $a = 1$, show that average savings, S_0, for this case are given by

$$S_0 = A + 1.2983\,Bb.$$

4. Noting that μ is connected with the concentration ratio ρ by the equation

$$\mu = 1.5 + 0.5\,\rho^{-1},$$

show that when $\rho = 0.3$, average savings, designated in this case by S_1, are given by the formula

$$S_1 = A + 0.5807\,Bb.$$

In addition to the table given in Section 9, Chapter 2, the following values will be required: $\Gamma(3.2) = 2.42396$, $\zeta(3.2) = 1.16677$.

5. Noting the relationship given in problem 4, show that when $\rho = 0.7$, average savings, designated in this case by S_2, are given by the formula

$$S_2 = A + 3.1263\,Bb.$$

6. Forming the difference $\alpha_i = (S_i - A)$, we see that the defect, or increase, in savings referred to the savings of the Pareto distribution, is measured by

$$\Delta_i = \left(\frac{\alpha_i}{\alpha_0} - 1\right).$$

Show that when $\rho = 0.3$, $\Delta_1 = -0.5528$, and when $\rho = 0.7$, $\Delta_2 = 1.4079$.

7. Introducing the assumption that the defect, or increase, in capital supply as compared with that available in a Paratean economy, is equal to $\Delta_i\,C$, and

assuming the validity of the production function of Section 4, Chapter 7, namely

$$P = 1.01\, L^{0.75}\, C^{0.25},$$

derive the relationship

$$\frac{\Delta P}{P} = 0.75\, \frac{\Delta L}{L} + 0.25\, \Delta_i \,.$$

8. Making use of the results in problems 6 and 7, show that when $\rho = 0.3$, and $\Delta P = 0$, $\Delta L/L = 0.1843$. Show also that when $\rho = 0.7$ and $\Delta P = 0$, that $\Delta L/L = -0.4693$. What conclusions would you infer from these calculations about the relationship between capital and labor under wide swings of the concentration ratio?

SELECTED BIBLIOGRAPHY ON TAXATION

ALLEN, R. G. D. *Mathematical Analysis for Economists*, pp. 60 and 208.

DUPUIT, J. "De l'utilité et de sa mesure," reprinted in a collection of Dupuit's work of 1844 and later, edited by M. di Bernardi and L. Einaudi, *La Riforma Soziale*, Turin, 1932.

EDGEWORTH, F. Y. *Papers Relating to Political Economy*, London, 1925, Vol. 1, pp. 132, 143 et seq., and Vol. 2, p. 401.

EVANS, G. C. *Mathematical Introduction to Economics*, Chapter 5.

FRISCH, R. "The Dupuit Taxation Problem," *Econometrica*, Vol. 7, 1939, pp. 145–150. Also, pp. 156–157.

HOTELLING, H. (1) "Edgeworth's Taxation Paradox and the Nature of Demand and Supply Functions," *The Journal of Political Economy*, Vol. 40, 1932, pp. 577–616.

(2) "The General Welfare in Relation to Problems of Taxation and of Railway and Utility Rates," *Econometrica*, Vol. 6, 1938, pp. 242–269.

(3) "The Relation of Prices to Marginal Costs in an Optimum System," *Econometrica*, Vol. 7, 1939, pp. 151–155. Also, pp. 158–160.

WILLIAMS, J. B. *The Theory of Investment Value*, Cambridge, Mass., 1938, xxiii +613 pp. In particular, Chapter 17 "Taxes and Socialism."

ECONOMIC DYNAMICS

CHAPTER 11

The Growth of Population and Industry

1. The Phenomenon of Growth

It is inevitable in any discipline which anticipates applications to problems of economics, that there should be a theory of growth. Growth phenomena are dynamic in character and clearly must be considered as among the most fundamental constituents of economic dynamics.

We encounter on the threshold the problem of population growth, a problem which cannot be neglected in any attempt to anticipate the trend of economic series. This age of intensive scientific and industrial expansion is continually producing new industries and new enterprises, the growth of which profoundly affects the general economic pattern. As an example, we might consider the automobile industry, which started with an insignificant production about 1908 and had reached maturity, sometimes called *the saturation point,* by 1929. The growth of this great enterprise naturally had an enormous influence upon industrial production as a whole. The attainment of that position where apparently the productive mechanism was in equilibrium with, or perhaps had exceeded, the capacity of the population to employ its production, was certain to cause great economic readjustments. The critical years that followed 1929 give evidence of the dislocations that attend the attainment of a certain amount of economic maturity.

In the discussion of the phenomena of growth it will be convenient for us to employ the so-called *logistic,* or *curve of growth,* which has been extensively applied by Raymond Pearl, L. J. Reed, and others in the study of biological and population data.[1]

The curve itself is given by the formula

$$y = \frac{k}{1 + be^{-at}}, \tag{1}$$

[1] The use of this curve in population studies is to be found in numerous works, a selected few of which are cited in the *Bibliography* at the end of this chapter.

where a, b, and k are positive constants to be determined from the data. The characteristics of this curve will be discussed in the next section.

The logistic curve appears to have been employed in population studies as early as 1845 by P. F. Verhulst, but its application in economics is subsequent to the work of Pearl and Reed. The most extensive use of this curve as a trend for production data has been made by S. S. Kuznets, who fitted logistics to some 50 or more series such as the production of wheat, corn, potatoes, cotton, pig iron, Portland cement, coal, copper, lead, etc. He also studied by this means the growth of bank clearings in New York City, Boston, Chicago, and Philadelphia, the growth of railroads, and the tonnage cleared from various countries. Modern industrial development, which has grown so uniformly over the past century, has furnished series admirably adapted to graduation by means of the logistic curve.

The logistic curve seems to be especially well designed for the description of new industries, for population studies, and for production series which depend upon the growth of population itself. The curve has been subjected to some biological tests such as the growth of bacterial cultures[2] and the growth of a population of fruit flies (*drosophila melanogaster*) under controlled experimental conditions.[3] The unusual success of this curve in such varied fields of application has suggested that the basis of this success may be found in the fact that the law of formation of a chemical sustance by autocatalysis may be described in some instances by the logistic.[4] Whether this relationship is merely an analogy or a real connection between chemical processes and the progress of biological growth is still unknown. An excellent account of the problem as a whole has been given by A. J. Lotka and E. B. Wilson (see *Bibliography*).

The characteristics of the logistic curve which make it so attractive as a means of examining modern production data are revealed in Figure 46, which shows the logistic fitted to data for automobile production in the United States. As one sees from the figure, the logistic curve may be regarded as a transition trend line intermediate between a lower initial level and an upper stable level. In such a transition curve there must necessarily be a *point of inflection*, where the *rate* of *increase* of production begins to decline. In the example this point was midway between the years 1920 and 1921.

---

[2] H. G. Thorton. (See *Bibliography* at end of chapter).

[3] Raymond Pearl: *The Biology of Population Growth*. Chapter 2.

[4] T. B. Robertson: *The Chemical Basis of Growth and Senescence*. See also W. Ostwald. (*Bibliography*).

The existence of an upper asymptote, the line of complete maturity, is the distinguishing feature of the logistic which makes it superior to a purely exponential law of growth in applications to economic time series. In the example, the data used in fitting the logistic were taken for the years from 1913 to 1927, and the curve was then extrapolated to 1939. The range chosen, since it included the critical inflection point, was probably long enough to assure some validity to the extrapolation. A gross overproduction in 1929 was indicated by the trend and a gross underproduction was similarly shown for the

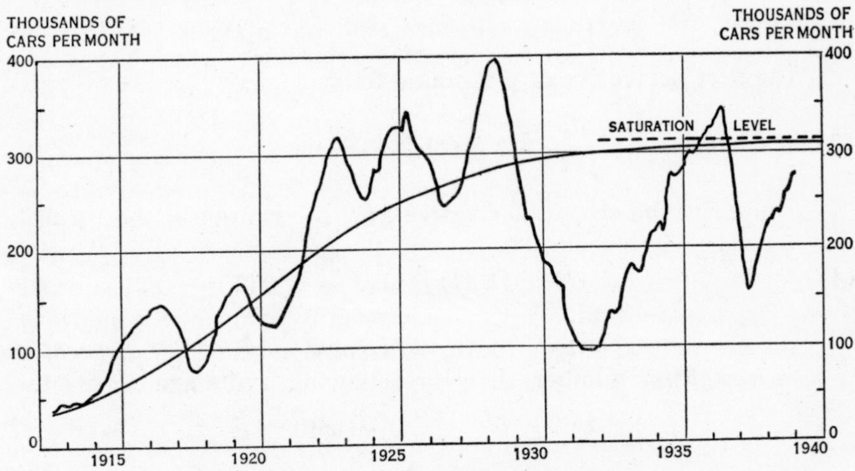

FIGURE 46.—THE PRODUCTION OF PASSENGER AUTOMOBILES IN THE UNITED STATES—MONTHLY AVERAGES—Unit = 1,000 Cars.

period from 1930 to 1936. Although an extrapolation over so long a period with so short a base is of doubtful statistical validity, it is a matter of considerable interest to observe that the forecasted *normal production* was again attained in 1937. But this penetration of the logistic norm again appeared to be too great and once more production fell off in the depression year of 1938.

It is quite clear that factors other than growth influence the purchase of automobiles and hence their production. It is for this reason that such wide fluctuations are to be observed in the production curve which we have just examined. But it is also quite evident that the trend of production is probably represented as well by the logistic as by any other curve that could be described by three statistical parameters. The logistic has entered in an essential manner into recent studies of the factors which influence automobile demand.[5]

2. *Mathematical Characteristics of the Logistic Curve*

It will be convenient for us to consider the following more general function:

$$y = \frac{k}{1 + e^{\phi(t)}}, \tag{2}$$

where k is a positive number and $\phi(t)$ is the following polynomial:

$$\phi(t) = a_0 + a_1 t + a_2 t^2 + \cdots + a_n t^n .$$

The first derivative of y is found to be

$$\frac{dy}{dt} = -\phi'(t)\, y\left(1 - \frac{y}{k}\right). \tag{3}$$

Similarly, the second derivative may be written in the form:

$$\frac{d^2y}{dt^2} = \left\{-\phi''(t) + [\phi'(t)]^2\left(1 - \frac{2y}{k}\right)\right\} y\left(1 - \frac{y}{k}\right). \tag{4}$$

We now observe that if $\phi(t)$ is a polynomial of *odd degree,* and if a_n is a *negative* number, then the following limits are obtained:

$$\lim_{t=+\infty} e^{\phi(t)} = 0 , \qquad \lim_{t=-\infty} e^{\phi(t)} = \infty .$$

Hence the variable y will approach the line $y = k$ as t approaches $+\infty$, and the axis of t as t approaches $-\infty$. Since $e^{\phi(t)}$ is never negative, the graph of equation (2) must lie between the two asymptotes $y = 0$ and $y = k$. The graph is thus represented by Figure 47.

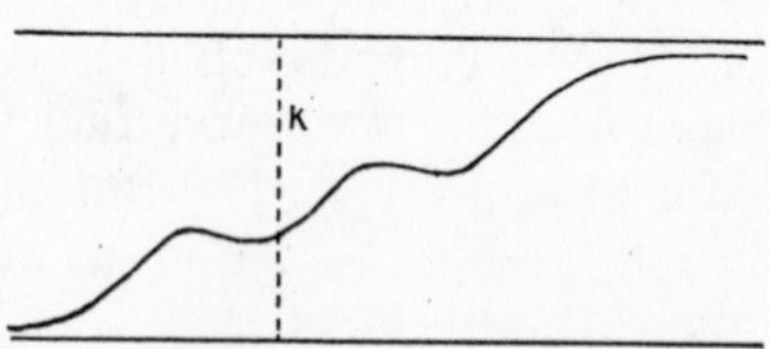

FIGURE 47.—GRAPH OF EQUATION (2), WHEN n IS ODD AND $a_n < 0$.

---

[5] See, for example, P. deWolff: "The Demand for Passenger Cars in the United States." *Econometrica,* Vol. 6, 1938, pp. 113–129. See also *The Dynamics of Automobile Demand,* New York, 1939, a symposium by S. L. Horner, C. F. Roos, V. von Szeliski, A. T. Court, and S. B. DuBrul. See also Section 9 of Chapter 17 in this book.

A second case should also be observed, namely, where $\phi(t)$ is a polynomial of *even degree* and a_n is a *positive* number. We then observe the following limits:

$$\lim_{t=+\infty} e^{\phi(t)} = \infty \;, \qquad \lim_{t=-\infty} e^{\phi(t)} = \infty \;.$$

Consequently the variable y will approach the axis of t asymptotically in either direction. Moreover, since $e^{\phi(t)}$ is never zero in the finite range, y will never be as large as k. It is thus clear that equation (2) will have the graphical representation given in Figure 48.

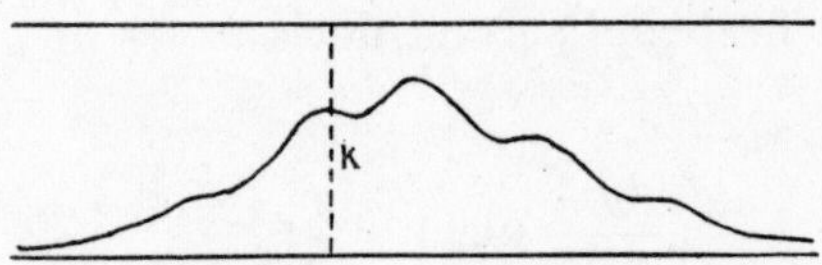

FIGURE 48.—GRAPH OF EQUATION (2), WHEN n IS EVEN AND $a_n > 0$.

In its application to economic data, we readily observe that the first case discussed above has more applications than the second, since we are concerned in general with problems of growth. But one should also observe that the second case might apply in the description of an industry from its beginning, through its growth, to its ultimate decline and extinction.

In the practical application of equation (2) to data it is frequently necessary to assume that y is replaced by $y - c$, since the variable whose growth is to be investigated may start from a lower asymptote given by the line $y = c$ instead of the axis of x as is assumed in equation (2). If c is already known, or if it may be determined before the logistic is actually fitted to the data, then in the application of equation (2) to the data it is advisable to begin by subtracting c from all the given values of y.

Maxima and minima of the general curve defined by (2), other than the asymptotic values which we have discussed above, are given for values of t which satisfy the equation

$$\phi'(t) = 0 \;. \tag{5}$$

Points of inflection are found for the values of t which satisfy the equation

$$k\phi''(t) + [\phi'(t)]^2(2y - k) = 0 \;. \tag{6}$$

This equation is found, of course, by setting the second derivative equal to zero. Moreover, if the value of y from (2) is substituted in (6), it becomes the following equation in the variable t:

$$\phi''(t) + [\phi'(t)]^2 + e^{\phi(t)}\{\phi''(t) - [\phi'(t)]^2\} = 0 . \tag{7}$$

The name *logistic*, as we have said in Section 1, is reserved primarily for the special case of (2) where $\phi(t) = \log b - at$, $a > 0$, that is to say, for the equation

$$y = \frac{k}{1 + be^{-at}} , \tag{8}$$

where a, b, and k are positive numbers.

In this case the first and second derivatives of y are found to be respectively

$$\frac{dy}{dt} = ay\left(1 - \frac{y}{k}\right) , \tag{9}$$

and

$$\frac{d^2y}{dt^2} = a^2 y\left(1 - \frac{y}{k}\right)\left(1 - \frac{2y}{k}\right) . \tag{10}$$

Equation (7) shows that the logistic has one point of inflection determined from the equation

$$e^{at} = b ,$$

which gives the following values as the coordinates of the point:

$$t = \frac{\log_e b}{a} = 2.302585 \frac{\log_{10} b}{a} , \quad y = \tfrac{1}{2}k . \tag{11}$$

This point of inflection is called the *critical point* of the logistic, since it defines the place where half the complete growth has been attained and the rate of growth has begun to decline.

PROBLEMS

1. Verify formulas (3) and (4) by the direct differentiation of equation (2).

2. Discuss the characteristics of the equation

$$y = \frac{100}{1 + e^{-t^2}} .$$

Represent this function graphically.

3. Discuss the characteristics of the function

$$y = \frac{100}{1 + e^{-t^3}}.$$

Make a graph of this function.

4. Graph the function

$$y = \frac{100}{1 + e^{-(t+t^3)}}.$$

In what manner does it differ from the function given in problem 3?

5. Represent the following function graphically:

$$y = 5 + \frac{100}{1 + 4e^{-0.2t}}.$$

Find the critical point and the two asymptotes.

3. Methods of Adjusting the Logistic Curve to Data

Because of the intrinsic significance of the logistic curve in all studies of production, it is important to have ready methods for the determination of the parameters of the curve. Although this problem belongs essentially to the theory of statistics, there is so intimate a connection between the interpretation of the significance of the curve and the assumptions used in the computation of the parameters that a survey of some of the methods proposed belongs to econometrics. The parameters determined by the different methods vary slightly from one another and this variation is attributable to the difference in the postulates used as the basis of the computation.

We shall survey two methods here. The first of these, which we shall call the *least square approximation,* was proposed by Raymond Pearl and L. J. Reed in the works to which reference has already been made. This method consists of a preliminary estimate of the parameters, which are then adjusted by the method of least squares.

The second method is due to H. Hotelling (see *Bibliography*), who adjusted the curve to the observed *rate of increase* (R. O. I.) defined by

$$R.\,O.\,I. = \frac{1}{y}\frac{dy}{dt}.$$

Since the rate of increase in the logistic is linear, this method assumes that the rate of increase as observed is also linear. Since y enters reciprocally in the formula, the greatest variation from this linearity is likely to be found at the lower end of the data. Because of this difficulty, caution must be employed in choosing the origin.

4. *The Pearl-Reed Method of Least Square Approximation*

The preliminary adjustment of the logistic to the given data is made as follows. Three equally spaced points are chosen which seem to be fairly characteristic of the data to which the curve is to be fitted. These may well be averages of several values at the beginning of the range, at the middle of the range, and at the end. Considerable judgment must be exercised in the selection of these values, since the final adjustment of the parameters is greatly aided if the first approximations are close to the adjusted values. Let us designate these points by $(0, y_0)$, (t_1, y_1), $(2t_1, y_2)$.

Writing the logistic of Section 2 in the form

$$y = \frac{k}{1 + e^{a_0 + a_1 t}}, \tag{12}$$

we now solve for $a_0 + a_1 t$ in terms of y and k, and, in the resulting expression, substitute the three points given in the preceding paragraph. We thus obtain the following equations:

$$\begin{aligned} a_0 + a_1 \cdot 0 &= \log_e[(k - y_0)/y_0], \\ a_0 + a_1 \cdot t_1 &= \log_e[(k - y_1)/y_1], \\ a_0 + a_1 \cdot 2t_1 &= \log_e[(k - y_2)/y_2], \end{aligned} \tag{13}$$

from which we are to determine k, a_0, and a_1.

It is at once seen that a_0 can be found from the first equation as soon as the value of k is known, since we have

$$a_0 = \log_e[(k - y_0) y_0] = 2.302585 \log_{10}[(k - y_0)/y_0]. \tag{14}$$

In order to find k we substitute this value of a_0 in the second equation of (13) and thus find

$$\begin{aligned} a_1 &= \frac{1}{t_1} \{\log_e[(k - y_1)/y_1] - \log_e[(k - y_0)/y_0]\} \\ &= \frac{1}{t_1} \left\{\log_e \left[\frac{y_0(k - y_1)}{y_1(k - y_0)}\right]\right\}. \end{aligned} \tag{15}$$

Similarly eliminating a_0 from the third equation of (13) we get

$$a_1 = \frac{1}{2t_1} \left\{\log_e \left[\frac{y_0(k - y_2)}{y_2(k - y_0)}\right]\right\} = \frac{1}{t_1} \left\{ \log_e \left[\frac{y_0(k - y_2)}{y_2(k - y_0)}\right]^{\frac{1}{2}}\right\}. \tag{16}$$

Equating these two values of a_1 and comparing logarithms, we obtain for the determination of k the equation

$$\frac{y_0(k-y_1)}{y_1(k-y_0)} = \left[\frac{y_0(k-y_2)}{y_2(k-y_0)}\right]^{\frac{1}{2}}.$$

Squaring both sides and collecting terms involving k on the right hand side of the equation, we get

$$(y_0y_2 - y_1^2)k = 2y_0y_1y_2 - y_1^2(y_0 + y_2),$$

from which we then obtain

$$k = \frac{2y_0y_1y_2 - y_1^2(y_0+y_2)}{y_0y_2 - y_1^2}. \tag{17}$$

When this determination of k is substituted in either the second or third equation of (13), the value of a_1 is readily obtained.[6]

The second step in the process of graduation is the correction of the preliminary estimate of the parameters by the following application of the method of least squares:

We first write equation (12) in the form

$$y = \frac{d}{e^{-(a+h)t} + c} = \frac{d}{e^{-at}\, e^{-ht} + c}, \tag{18}$$

where we use the abbreviation $a = -a_1$. The quantities h, c, and d are constants to be determined.

If our first approximation to a_1, that is to say, $-a$, has been

---

[6] The same preliminary adjustment can be made for the more general equation

$$y = \frac{k}{1 + e^{\phi(t)}},$$

where we write $\phi(t) = a_0 + a_1t + a_2t^2 + a_3t^3$.

Five equally spaced points $(0, y_0)$, (t_1, y_1), $(2t_1, y_2)$, $(3t_1, y_3)$, $(4t_1, y_4)$ are first determined. The value of k is then computed from the following equation:

$$y_1^4y_3^4(k-y_0)(k-y_2)^6(k-y_4) = y_0y_2^6y_4(k-y_1)^4(k-y_3)^4.$$

The coefficients a_0, a_1, a_2 and a_3 are then obtained from the formulas

$$a_0 = \log_e\left[\frac{(k-y_0)}{y_0}\right],\quad a_1 = (18\beta_1 - 9\beta_2 + 2\beta_3)/6t_1,$$
$$a_2 = (4\beta_2 - 5\beta_1 - \beta_3)/2t_1^2,\quad a_3 = (\beta_3 + 3\beta_1 - 3\beta_2)/6t_1^3,$$

where the following abbreviations are used:

$$\beta_1 = \log_e\left[\frac{y_0(k-y_1)}{y_1(k-y_0)}\right],\quad \beta_2 = \log_e\left[\frac{y_0(k-y_2)}{y_2(k-y_0)}\right],\quad \beta_3 = \log_e\left[\frac{y_0(k-y_3)}{y_3(k-y_0)}\right].$$

For an application of this to population data, see Raymond Pearl: *Studies in Human Biology*, p. 607.

properly made, then h will be sufficiently small so that we can replace e^{-ht} by $1 - ht$. Thus we shall have

$$(19) \qquad y = \frac{d}{e^{-at}(1 - ht) + c} .$$

Multiplying through by the denominator of the right hand side, we obtain a new equation with linear coefficients

$$(20) \qquad d - cy + ht\, y\, e^{-at} = y\, e^{-at} .$$

The parameters c, d, and h are now estimated in the usual manner by means of the method of least squares.

Example. As an example we shall apply this method of graduation to the data of a production series which has basic significance in economics, namely, that of the production of pig iron. We shall fit our logistic over the range from 1860 to 1920, and in a later section we shall discuss the economic significance of the example. The basic data are given in the accompanying table.

PRODUCTION OF PIG IRON

Year	Production in 1000 long tons	Per Capita Production in long tons	Year	Production in 1000 long tons	Per Capita Production in long tons	Year	Production in 1000 long tons	Per Capita Production in long tons
1855	700	0.0256	1884	4098	0.0740	1913	30966	0.3209
1856	789	0.0280	1885	4045	0.0714	1914	23332	0.2383
1857	713	0.0246	1886	5683	0.0981	1915	29916	0.3011
1858	630	0.0211	1887	6417	0.1084	1916	39435	0.3914
1859	751	0.0245	1888	6490	0.1073	1917	38621	0.3780
1860	821	0.0261	1889	7604	0.1231	1918	39055	0.3770
1861	653	0.0203	1890	9203	0.1459	1919	31015	0.2954
1862	703	0.0214	1891	8280	0.1286	1920	36926	0.3466
1863	846	0.0252	1892	9157	0.1394	1921	16688	0.1542
1864	1014	0.0295	1893	7125	0.1064	1922	27220	0.2477
1865	832	0.0237	1894	6657	0.0975	1923	40361	0.3619
1866	1206	0.0337	1895	9446	0.1358	1924	30406	0.2686
1867	1305	0.0358	1896	8623	0.1216	1925	36116	0.3144
1868	1431	0.0385	1897	9653	0.1337	1926	38698	0.3321
1869	1711	0.0451	1898	11774	0.1602	1927	35858	0.3215
1870	1665	0.0431	1899	13621	0.1821	1928	37402	0.3120
1871	1707	0.0429	1900	13789	0.1811	1929	41757	0.3436
1872	2549	0.0622	1901	15878	0.2042	1930	29905	0.2430
1873	2561	0.0608	1902	17821	0.2245	1931	17813	0.1435
1874	2401	0.0555	1903	18009	0.2224	1932	8550	0.0684
1875	2024	0.0455	1904	16497	0.1997	1933	13001	0.1034
1876	1869	0.0410	1905	22992	0.2730	1934	16139	0.1275
1877	2067	0.0442	1906	25307	0.2948	1935	21373	0.1676
1878	2301	0.0480	1907	25781	0.2948	1936	30712	0.2391
1879	2742	0.0559	1908	15936	0.1789	1937	36600	0.2830
1880	3835	0.0763	1909	25795	0.2844	1938	18763	0.1441
1881	4144	0.0804	1910	27304	0.2959	1939		
1882	4623	0.0875	1911	23650	0.2525	1940		
1883	4596	0.0850	1912	29727	0.3127			

Solution: Taking five year averages about each fifth year in the table, we obtain the following values for the determination of the logistic:

Year	t	y	Year	t	y	Year	t	y
1860	0	712	1880	20	3529	1900	40	14577
1865	5	1041	1885	25	4968	1905	45	21717
1870	10	1813	1890	30	8147	1910	50	24482
1875	15	2184	1895	35	8301	1915	55	32454
						1920	60	30181

To these data the foregoing theory is now applied. For the preliminary estimate of the parameters we select the values at $t_0 = 0$, $t_1 = 30$, and $t_2 = 2t_1 = 60$. Using equation (17) we at once compute $k = 37{,}882$.

From equations (14) and (15) we then obtain $a_0 = 3.9552$, and $a_1 = -a = -0.08868$. When these values are substituted in formula (12), we have the logistic

$$y = \frac{37{,}882}{1 + e^{3.9552 - 0.08868t}}. \tag{21}$$

We next make the adjustment of the parameters of the equation by means of a least square's determination of d, c, and h in equation (20). The pertinent calculations are given in the accompanying table.

t	y	y^2	e^{-at}	ye^{-at}	y^2e^{-at}	$ty\,e^{-at}$	ty^2e^{-at}
0	712	506,944	1.00000	712	506,944	0	0
5	1,041	1,083,681	.64211	668	695,839	3,340	3,479,195
10	1,813	3,286,969	.41189	747	1,353,868	7,470	13,538,680
15	2,184	4,769,856	.26448	578	1,261,519	8,670	18,922,785
20	3,529	12,453,841	.16965	599	2,112,831	11,980	42,256,620
25	4,968	24,681,024	.10894	541	2,688,637	13,525	67,215,925
30	8,147	66,373,609	.06988	569	4,638,074	17,070	139,142,220
35	8,301	68,906,601	.04487	372	3,091,798	13,020	108,212,930
40	14,577	212,488,929	.02881	420	6,121,997	16,800	244,879,880
45	21,717	471,628,089	.01848	401	8,716,253	18,045	392,231,385
50	24,482	599,368,324	.01187	291	7,112,644	13,095	355,632,200
55	32,454	1,053,262,116	.00761	247	8,017,642	13,585	440,970,310
60	30,181	910,892,761	.00489	148	4,452,353	8,880	267,141,180
	154,106	3,429,702,744		6,293	50,770,399	145,480	2,093,623,310

t	$t^2y^2\,e^{-2at}$	$ty^2\,e^{-2at}$	t	$t^2y^2e^{-2at}$	ty^2e^{-2at}
0	0	0			
5	11,155,600	2,231,120	35	169,520,400	4,843,440
10	55,800,900	5,580,090	40	282,240,000	7,056,000
15	75,168,900	5,011,260	45	325,622,025	7,236,045
20	143,520,400	7,176,020	50	171,479,025	3,810,645
25	182,925,625	7,317,025	55	184,552,225	3,355,495
30	291,384,900	9,712,830	60	78,854,400	1,314,240
				1,972,224,400	64,644,210

From the column totals we now form the following set of *normal equations*:[7]

$$\begin{aligned} 13d - 154{,}106c + 145{,}480h &= 6{,}293\,, \\ 154{,}106d - 3{,}429{,}702{,}744c + 2{,}093{,}623{,}310h &= 50{,}770{,}399\,, \\ 145{,}480d - 2{,}093{,}623{,}310c + 1{,}972{,}224{,}400h &= 64{,}644{,}210\,. \end{aligned}$$

Solving these equations, we obtain

$$d = 650.7476\,, \qquad c = 0.015126\,, \qquad h = 0.00112958\,.$$

When these values are substituted in equation (18) above, the desired logistic is obtained:

$$y = \frac{650.7476}{e^{-0.08981t} + 0.015126} = \frac{43{,}021}{1 + 66.1102e^{-0.08981t}}\,. \tag{22}$$

The graphical representations of both the data and the adjusted curve (22) are shown in Figure 49.

The actual values obtained from (22) are compared with the original averages in the following table:

Year	t	Observed	Computed	Year	t	Observed	Computed
1860	0	712	641	1895	35	8301	11169
1865	5	1041	996	1900	40	14577	15255
1870	10	1813	1540	1905	45	21717	19902
1875	15	2184	2365	1910	50	24482	24704
1880	20	3529	3594	1915	55	32454	29202
1885	25	4968	5377	1920	60	30181	33042
1890	30	8147	7867				

It has been pointed out by Henry Schultz that the adjustment of the parameters of the logistic as given above does not lead to the true least square's solution, which is obtained by minimizing the sum of the squares of the differences between the data and the functional values. He suggests the following alternative procedure:[8]

We first determine approximate values of the parameters, which we may designate by a_0, b_0, and k_0. The desired corrections may then be denoted by Δa, Δb, and Δk. The function

$$y = \frac{k_0 + \Delta k}{1 + (b_0 + \Delta b)\, e^{(a_0 + \Delta a)t}}$$

is then expanded to a first approximation in the corrections by means of Taylor's series. If we designate by y_0 the value of y when Δa, Δb, and Δk are zero, then it may be shown by a slight algebraic manipulation that the expansion assumes the following form:

[7] See Davis and Nelson: *Elements of Statistics,* 2nd edition, Bloomington, Indiana, 1937, p. 222.

[8] See *Bibliography* at the end of this chapter.

$$(23) \qquad y = y_0 + \frac{\Delta k}{b_0} + \left[\frac{y_0 - k_0 y_0}{k_0}\right]\frac{\Delta b}{b_0} + \left[\frac{y_0 - k_0 y_0}{k_0}\right] t\Delta a \,.$$

The computation of the corrections is then effected by the method of least squares.

The principal objection to this adjustment is found in the fact that Δk may be so large that differences of second order cannot be neglected. Hence the correction must be made successively several times before an approximation better than that of the Pearl-Reed method is attained.

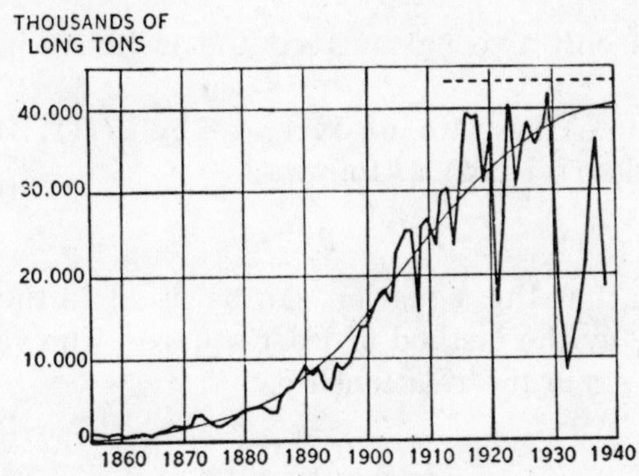

FIGURE 49.—THE LOGISTIC OF THE PRODUCTION OF PIG IRON.

PROBLEMS

1. Using the data for the production of wheat given in Section 8, select three characteristic points and obtain the preliminary adjustment of the logistic to the data.

2. From the results of problem 1 compute the critical point for the logistic of wheat production as determined from your curve. Also determine the saturation level. Compare your values with those given in Section 8.

3. Using the data for the production of corn given in Section 8, select three characteristic points and obtain a preliminary adjustment of the logistic to the data.

4. From the results of problem 3, determine the critical point of corn production and the saturation level. Compare your values with those given in Section 8.

5. Compute the critical point for the logistic of pig iron production. What conclusion would you draw from this? What is your forecast for industrial production? Compare Figure 55 (c) with Figure 49.

6. Derive equation (23).

7. From the differences in a, b, and k between the first and second approximation to the logistic of pig iron production, formulas (21) and (22), estimate

the magnitudes of Δa, Δb, and Δk. Using as y_0 the value given by (21) at $t = 40$, compute the magnitude of each correction term in (23). What conclusion do you draw?

5. *The Method of the Rate of Increase*

In his discussion of the logistic curve H. Hotelling has considered the rate of increase

$$\frac{1}{y}\frac{dy}{dt} = a - \frac{a}{k}y \,, \tag{24}$$

which contains only two parameters and is linear in its right hand member.

If we denote the rate of increase by $R(t)$, that is $R(t) = y'(t)/y(t)$, and write (24) as follows:

$$R = p + qy \,, \tag{25}$$

then it is clear that this equation can be fitted to the data by determining p and q by the method of least squares. The values of a and k are then found from the relationships:

$$a = p, \quad k = -\frac{p}{q} \,. \tag{26}$$

If d denotes the class interval of the data, and if we employ the abbreviation $F(t) = \log y(t)$, that is, if $R(t) = F'(t)$, then we can tabulate $R(t)$ at any point t from the formula

$$R(t) = \frac{1}{d}\,[\Delta F(t) - \tfrac{1}{2}\Delta^2 F(t) + \tfrac{1}{3}\Delta^3 F(t) - \tfrac{1}{4}\Delta^4 F(t) + \cdots] \,. \tag{27}$$

For most statistical data the first two terms of this series are sufficient to determine the values of $R(t)$. Since, however, the value of k in the logistic is sensitive to small variations in the determination of $R(t)$, it is important to employ considerable care in computing this variable. The second differences of $R(t)$ are often quite erratic so that the application of formula (27) is not always desirable without some preliminary smoothing of the first differences.

The value of b can be estimated in several ways. Thus, from formula (11) of Section 3, we know that b is related to the abscissa, t_0, of the critical point by the equation

$$\log_e b = at_0 \,.$$

We also know that the ordinate of the critical point, y_0, is given by

$$y_0 = \tfrac{1}{2}k . \tag{28}$$

Hence, by smoothing the data in the neighborhood of the value $y_0 = \frac{1}{2}k$, it is usually possible to estimate quite accurately the corresponding value of t_0 and from it the value of b by means of (28).

An alternative method is derived from the equation

$$\frac{k}{y_t} = 1 + b\, e^{-at} .$$

If we sum both sides of this equation from $t = m$ to $t = n$, that is, over the range of the data, we obtain

$$k\, M_0 = (n - m + 1) + b/L ,$$

where we employ the abbreviations

$$M_0 = \sum_{t=m}^{n} \frac{1}{y_t} , \quad L = \frac{e^{-a} - 1}{e^{-a(n+1)} - e^{-am}} .$$

Hence b is computed from the formula

$$b = L[k\, M_0 - (n - m + 1)] . \tag{29}$$

Example. We shall apply this method to the population data of the United States from the first census in 1790 to the census of 1910, following in part the computations of Hotelling. In the table given below we record the original population data, their reciprocals, and the rates of increase as estimated by Hotelling, who used a method differing somewhat from the one suggested above.

Year	t	Population (y) in millions	$1/y$	Rate of increase $R(t)$
1790	10	3.929	.2545 176	....
1800	20	5.308	.1883 948	.03005
1810	30	7.240	.1381 215	.02990
1820	40	9.638	.1037 559	.02898
1830	50	12.866	.0777 242	.02890
1840	60	17.069	.0585 857	.02931
1850	70	23.192	.0431 183	.03055
1860	80	31.443	.0318 035	.02517
1870	90	38.558	.0259 349	.02288
1880	100	50.156	.0199 378	.02456
1890	110	62.948	.0158 861	.02079
1900	120	75.995	.0131 588	.01907
1910	130	91.972	.0108 729	.01670
			.9818 120	.30686

To these data we now fit equation (25) by the method of least squares and thus obtain:

$$R(t) = 0.031239 - 0.00015949y .$$

Hence we compute

$$a = 0.031239 \,, \quad k = \frac{0.031239}{0.00015949} = 195.868 \,.$$

Since ½ k = 97.934 is greater than any value of y in the data, it is clear that the critical point is beyond the last value of t recorded in the table. For this reason the determination of b by the critical point method is not practical. We thus employ formula (29) in which we let $m = 1$, $n = 13$, $M_0 = 0.9818120$, and $L = 0.376648$. We thus obtain $b = 67.5352$.

The values obtained from this logistic are given in the table in Section 7.

PROBLEMS

1. Compute the logistic for the production of wheat by the method of the rate of increase. For your data use the production at five year intervals from the table given in Section 8.

2. Compute the logistic for the index of industrial production by the method of the rate of increase. Use as data the index at five year intervals from the table given in Section 8.

3. In Section 5 of Chapter 19 there is given an index of Spanish trade from 1505 to 1650. Using the items at intervals of 10 years, fit a logistic to the data by the method of the rate of increase. Note that the data must first be adjusted by subtracting some constant, approximately 60, which represents the value of the lower asymptote.

6. The Biological Basis for the Logistic

Since the use of the logistic curve as the true representation of growth rests essentially upon the empirical assumption that the rate of growth is proportional to a quadratic function of the population itself, it is both interesting and important to fortify this proposition by independent biological observations. Raymond Pearl has made extensive studies which bear upon this point. Because of the importance of the logistic thesis in its application to human population and to the growth of industrial production, this excursion into the biological foundations of the theory will contribute essentially to a better understanding of the economic problem.

It is a universal observation that nature imposes an upper limit to the size of biological organisms. The individuals of any given species, when subjected to biometric measurements, conform to a normal distribution. This, it must be observed, is in sharp contrast to the distribution curve of special ability, as we have seen from the examples of Chapter 2. It is natural, then, to inquire whether a population of separate individuals will increase in the same manner as a population of cells, controlled by the mechanism of a single living body. In the second case, the activity of glands furnishes an obvious bio-chemical control of the growth function, but in the first case there is no such apparent agency.

The celebrated English economist, Thomas R. Malthus (1766–1834) thought to find this controlling agency of population growth in the assumption "that population has a tendency to increase faster than food," but the data for modern populations do not tend to confirm this proposition. The population of France has reached a stable state without any apparent relationship to the supply of food, and there are strong indications that the rate of growth of the United States is decelerating, while the available food supply far exceeds the population's needs.

In order to explain the phenomenon of a declining rate of population growth in the face of an over-supply of food, we might assume that man's ability to reason about his environment has a tendency to check an exponential increase. That is to say, psychic elements, rath-

Observed and Calculated Values for the Growth in Weight of the Male White Rat*

Age in days	Obs. Wt. in grams	Cal. Wt. in grams	Age in days	Obs. Wt. in grams	Cal. Wt. in grams	Age in days	Obs. Wt. in grams	Cal. Wt. in grams
10	13.5	14.1	46	50.5	52.8	107	177.6	178.1
11	13.3	14.5	49	56.7	58.3	112	183.8	185.5
12	14.8	15.0	52	62.5	64.2	117	191.4	192.2
13	15.3	15.5	55	68.5	70.4	124	197.3	200.6
14	15.2	16.1	58	73.9	76.8	131	202.5	208.1
15	16.5	16.7	61	81.7	83.4	138	209.7	214.5
17	17.8	17.9	64	89.1	90.1	143	218.3	218.6
19	19.5	19.3	67	99.3	97.0	150	225.4	223.7
21	21.2	20.8	70	106.3	103.8	157	227.0	228.2
23	22.9	22.4	73	113.8	110.7	164	231.4	232.1
25	25,3	24.2	76	121.3	117.6	171	235.8	235.7
27	27.4	26.1	79	128.2	124.3	178	239.4	238.9
29	29.5	28.2	82	135.0	130.9	185	239.8	241.9
31	31.8	30.5	85	143.8	137.4	216	252.9	252.7
34	34.9	33.2	88	148.4	143.7	256	265.4	264.4
37	37.8	38.3	92	152.3	151.7	365	279.0	279.6
40	42.2	42.7	97	160.0	161.2			
43	46.3	48.6	102	168.8	170.0		$\sigma = 4.96$	

* Data from H. H. Donaldson, **The Rat Philadelphia,** Wistar Institute. 1915.

er than external physical mechanisms, might tend to stimulate population control. But this argument would lack validity if it is found that populations of lower life forms also grow according to logistic law.

We first consider the growth of an individual organism in order to ascertain the mathematical and statistical characteristics of the development of a collection of cells functioning under the control of a central mechanism. In the following table there is recorded the actual weight in grams of the male white rat over the period of a year, together with the calculated weight as graduated by the curve

$$y = 7 + \frac{273}{1 + e^{4.3204 - 7.2196t + 30.0878t^2 - 0.5291t^3}}. \tag{30}$$

The data and the graduated curve are graphically represented in Figure 50.

It is clear from the data and from the graduation curve (30) that the growth of individual organisms does not conform strictly to the logistic. The coefficient of the exponent is a cubic function of the time, which indicates that the initial growth is more rapid than in those data for which the logistic law holds. This conclusion is also confirmed by data on the growth of the pumpkin (*Cucurbita Pepo*) which is graduated by a function similar to that given in equation (30).[10]

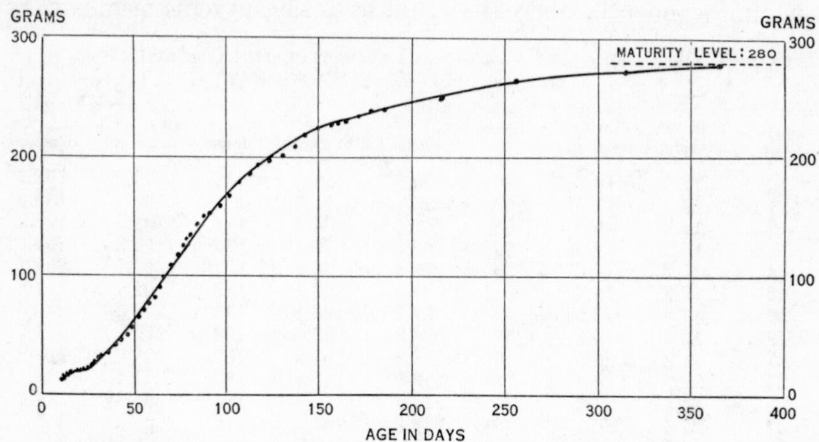

FIGURE 50.—GROWTH OF MALE WHITE RATS. (DONALDSON).

Having now observed that there is an essential difference between the growth of individual organisms, and populations which increase by the logistic law, we next inquire whether populations of individual organisms, as distinct from collections of cells governed by a single mechanism, follow the logistic law.

This question was extensively studied by Pearl, who used, as his experimental material, colonies of the fruit fly (*Drosophila melanogaster*). In the experiment, the data for which are recorded below, a colony of fruit flies, a mutant from *Quintuple*, was started with 2 males, each 15 days old, one male and 3 females each 2 days old, 12

---

[10] See T. B. Robertson: *The Chemical Basis of Growth and Senescence.* Philadelphia, 1923.

pupae and a smaller number of eggs and larvae. Population counts were made 10 times until the problem of managing the food supply became difficult. The data, together with their estimated values computed from the logistic

$$y = \frac{346.14}{1 + e^{5.34 - 0.22t}}, \tag{31}$$

are given in the accompanying table. The excellent agreement between the observed and calculated population is exhibited in Figure 51.

GROWTH OF POPULATION OF QUINTUPLE STOCK OF DROSOPHILA IN A PINT BOTTLE*

Date of Census	Obs. Pop.	Cal. Pop.	Date of Census	Obs. Pop.	Cal. Pop.
Oct. 6	6	6.0	Oct. 24	163	162.6
Oct. 9	10	11.3	Oct. 27	226	218.0
Oct. 13	21	25.9	Oct. 30	265	265.0
Oct. 15	52	38.5	Nov. 3	282	306.8
Oct. 18	67	67.0	Nov. 7	319	324.5
Oct. 21	104	109.2			

* Data from Pearl: **The Biology of Population Growth**, p. 224.

A similar phenomenon is observed in the growth of yeast cells, a population which may be regarded as somewhere between a population of independent organisms such as fruit flies, and a population of cells controlled by a central mechanism. In an experiment performed by T. Carlson, a few cells of yeast were dropped into a proper medium for their development and the entire colony kept at a moderately warm temperature. The census was taken daily until the asymptotic value of the growth had been attained. When the data

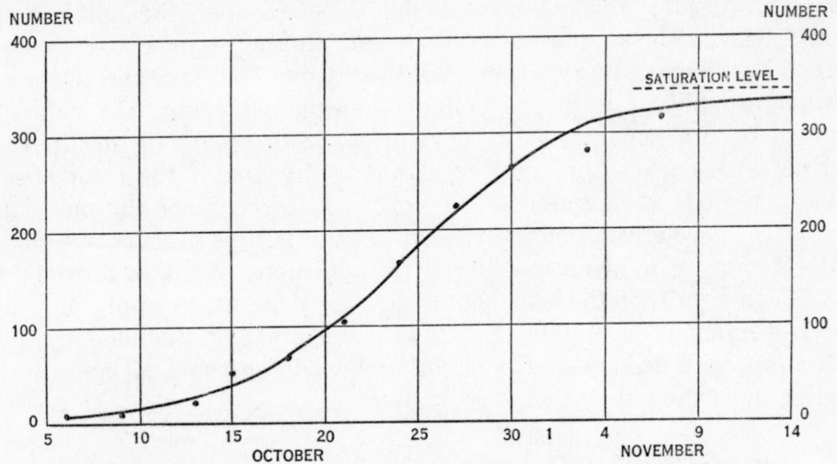

FIGURE 51.—GROWTH OF A POPULATION OF FRUIT FLIES. (PEARL).

thus secured were graduated, it was found that they were excellently represented by the logistic.[11]

The tentative conclusion which we may derive from these studies may be formulated in the statement *that populations which grow under the direction of a central mechanism tend to increase according to the generalized logistic law described by formula* (2) *in which* ϕ(t) *is a cubic function of the time, while populations subject to no such central mechanisms tend to increase according to the special logistic law in which* ϕ(t) *is a linear function of the time.* In the next section we shall indicate an economic application of this biological principle.

7. *The Logistic of Population*

Among all the series with which economics deals probably the most uniform is that of population. Here we see the operation of a steady law of growth which is so uniform from one period to another that forecasts of unusual accuracy are possible not only by years but by decades. This makes the data of population growth exceptionally attractive to statisticians.

It is obvious that the exponential law of growth, $y = a\, e^{bt}$, should apply with some exactness to a young population, since this law is merely another way of stating the reasonable proposition that the rate of growth is proportional to the population; that is, $dy/dt = by$.

But it is equally apparent that some mechanism must eventually operate to decelerate growth, if for no other reason than that territorial limitations must eventually put a bound upon the number of people who can be supported within them. But as we have already observed in the preceding section, this Malthusian doctrine does not necessarily supply us with the complete mechanism since the rate of growth of the population of the United States began to decline as early as 1914 when the country was entering one of the most spectacular periods of abundance in recorded history. Since the mechanism of the deceleration of the rate of growth is thus obscure, we shall not attempt an explanation of the phenomenon. What is important here is to note that the exponential law of growth can apply only at the beginning of a population growth and must be modified by another law such as that of the logistic which imposes an ultimate limitation upon the population.

---

[11] "Über Geswchwindikeit und Grösse der Hefevermehrung in Würze," *Biochem. Zeitsehrift,* Vol. 57, 1913, pp. 313–334.

We have already discussed the fitting of the logistic to the population of the United States in the example of Section 5. The method of Pearl-Reed, the method of least squares (Schultz), and the method of the rate of increase (Hotelling) agree to within small statistical errors as to the values of the parameters. We list the three estimates in the following table, where the parameters are defined by the logistic in the form given in equation (1) of Section 1; that is,

$$y = \frac{k}{1 + b\,e^{-at}}. \tag{32}$$

CONSTANTS OF THE LOGISTIC OF POPULATION FOR THE UNITED STATES

Constants	Pearl-Reed	H. Schultz	H. Hotelling
a	0.031396	0.031352	0.031482
b	67.6315	67.1750	64.5352
k	196.5968	196.2624	195.868

These values refer to an origin in 1780 with the time taken in

POPULATION ESTIMATES FOR THE UNITED STATES
(Unit = 1 million)

Year	t	Observed	Pearl-Reed	Schultz	Hotelling
1780	0		2.879	2.879	2.858
1790	10	3.929	3.900	3.918	3.885
1800	20	5.308	5.300	5.321	5.271
1810	30	7.240	7.183	7.209	7.134
1820	40	9.638	9.702	9.732	9.621
1830	50	12.866	13.043	13.076	12.917
1840	60	17.069	17.427	17.463	17.236
1850	70	23.192	23.100	23.135	22.820
1860	80	31.443	30.307	30.337	29.949
1870	90	38.558	39.252	39.273	38.710
1880	100	50.156	50.045	50.047	49.330
1890	110	62.948	62.624	62.598	61.719
1900	120	75.995	76.709	76.647	75.614
1910	130	91.972	91.792	91.685	90.526
1920	140	105.711	107.188	107.036	105.792
1930	150	122.775	122.157	121.958	120.682
1940	160	131.410	136.037	135.794	134.539
1950	170		148.350	148.072	146.878
1960	180		158.854	158.549	157.443
1970	190		167.520	167.196	166.191
1980	200		174.473	174.173	173.233
1990	210		179.929	179.585	178.776
2000	220		184.136	183.788	183.062
2020	240		189.744	189.396	188.797
2040	260		192.879	192.534	192.018
2060	280		194.595	194.253	193.788
2080	300		195.523	195.184	194.749
2100	320		196.022	195.685	195.267

years. The accompanying table gives the estimates of population by these various methods.

Only inconsequential variations exist between the ordinates of the logistic as obtained by these methods. The graphical representation of these values is shown in Figure 52.

It is instructive next to inquire when the acceleration of growth of the population became negative. It seems to the writer a hazardous procedure to forecast from the logistic curve until the actual

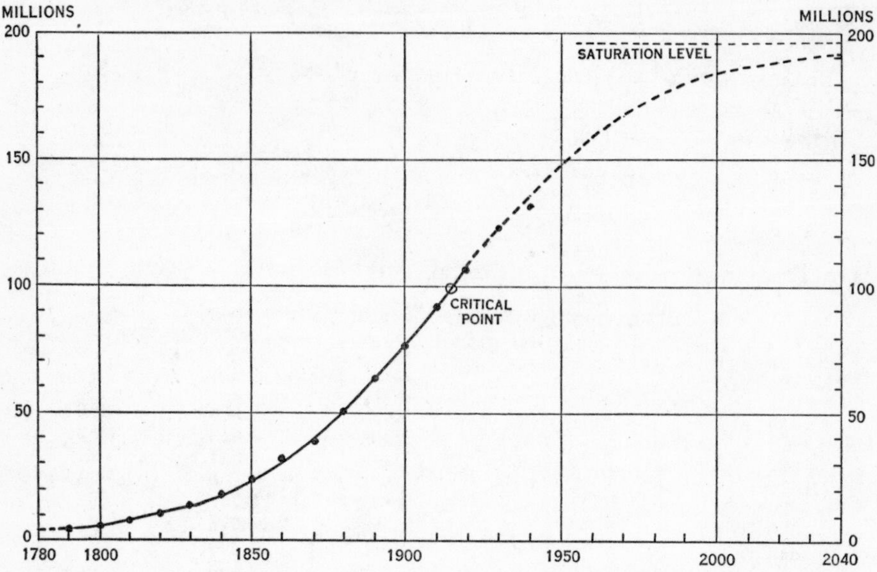

FIGURE 52.—THE LOGISTIC CURVE FOR THE POPULATION OF THE UNITED STATES.

growth has passed this critical value. From the Pearl-Reed estimates we at once compute

$$t = (\log_e 67.6315)/0.031396 = 134.2232;$$

since the origin was 1780, this gives approximately March, 1914.

We have devoted considerable space to the discussion of this curve because of its very fundamental nature in our general economy. Other time series which describe the historical behavior of such economic variables as price and production are highly erratic when compared with that of population growth. It is fortunate, indeed, that this curve is so uniform since its stability contributes something to the stability of other series. If per capita estimates of economic variation can be approximately predicted, then it is clear that the total variation can be estimated without essential loss of accuracy.

In order to account for the logistic character of population growth Pearl has made a rather elaborate study of the influence of the density of population on the birth rate and has found a small negative correlation, $r = -0.175$ with a probable error of ± 0.057, after other influences have been accounted for. This confirmed a study made by J. L. Brownell in 1894.[12] Pearl reaches the conclusion:[13]

> The bearing of the results set forth in this chapter on the general problem of the causes lying back of the logistic curve is evident. As any population confined within definite special limits goes up on the logistic curve its density automatically becomes greater and greater. But if, as the evidence indicates, increasing density has associated with it the biological effect of a reduction in the rate of reproduction of the population exhibiting it, then obviously there is in this relationship a factor which may appear as a *vera causa* in damping the time rate of growth in the upper half of the logistic curve.

Factors extraneous to normal growth by the logistic law are observable also in other population statistics. A notable example of this is the growth of educational institutions, which has been considerably greater than the normal growth of the population. This has been due in part to urban concentration, to increasing standards of living, and, perhaps, also to an increase in general belief in the virtues of education itself.

We should consider also in connection with the material of this section the important problem of the growth of cities. Does this growth also conform to the logistic law? The significance of this question is readily ascertained when one considers the problem of estimating the future adequacy of such public works as water supplies, electrical and other utilities, transportation facilities, school systems, and the like.

The answer to this question appears to be that upon the normal logistic growth of cities there is superimposed an adjustment due to the rapid shift of the population from rural to urban living. This shift is observed from the following data on urban concentration, which have been furnished the author by the courtesy of L. E. Truesdell of the U. S. Bureau of the Census:

Urban Concentration in Per Cent

Year	1820	1830	1840	1850	1860	1870	1880	1890	1900	1910	1920	1930
Per Cent Urban	7.0	8.4	11.6	16.8	20.8	26.2	29.6	35.4	40.0	45.8	51.4	56.2

[12] "The Significance of a Decreasing Birth-rate," *Annals of the Academy of Political and Social Science*, Vol. 5, 1894–95, pp. 48–89.

[13] *The Biology of Population Growth*, p. 157.

These data show that the percentage increase is strictly linear over the period of time considered, the average increase being 5.2% per decade. Hence cities have tended to grow faster than the population, until recent years, and estimates of their future size must take into account this general movement of the population. It seems quite reasonable to suppose that as industrial production ceases to advance, the rate of increase in urban concentration will also decline with it. The census of 1940 appears to confirm this observation, since there has been a marked decline in the rate of growth of many American cities during the ten years between 1930 and 1940.

The question naturally arises as to whether the growth of cities, themselves subjected to central planning, the direction of Chambers of Commerce, etc., may not be more closely related to the growth of individual organisms than to the growth of colonies of individuals. The following data, which are graphically represented in Figure 53, indicate that the growth of New York City and Chicago has been greater than the growth of the population of the country itself and that the graduation of the data by the simple logistic would not be entirely satisfactory. An exercise bearing on this point will be found in problem 2 below.

THE GROWTH OF POPULATION IN NEW YORK CITY AND CHICAGO

New York City						Chicago			
Year	Pop.	Year	Pop.	Year	Pop.	Year	Pop.	Year	Pop.
1790	33,131	1840	348,943	1890	2,507,414	1840	4,853	1890	1,099,850
1800	63,787	1850	612,385	1900	3,437,202	1850	29,963	1900	1,698,575
1810	100,775	1860	1,174,779	1910	4,766,883	1860	109,260	1910	2,185,283
1820	130,881	1870	1,478,103	1920	5,620,048	1870	298,977	1920	2,701,705
1830	217,985	1880	1,911,698	1930	6,930,446	1880	503,185	1930	3,376,438
				1940	7,380,259			1940	3,384,556

PROBLEMS

1. The following table gives the population data for France expressed in units of a million:

Year	1801	1821	1841	1861	1866	1872	1876
Population	26.931	29.871	33.401	35.845	36.495	36.103	36.906
Year	1881	1886	1891	1896	1901	1906	1911
Population	37.672	38.219	38.343	38.518	38.962	39.252	39.602

Assuming an initial lower limit of population for this cycle of growth as 6.604 (Pearl's estimate), fit a logistic to these data. Compare your estimates since 1911 with the actual population figures. What influence is noted from the

World War? Comment on Pearl's remark (*Studies in Human Biology*): "France is near the end of her present cycle of population growth." Compute the data of the point of inflection. Compare your logistic with that obtained by Pearl,

$$y = 6.604 + \frac{35.975}{1 + 0.808\, e^{-0.0197t}},$$

origin in 1870, t in units of five years.

2. Correct for urban concentration the figures given in this Section showing the growth of Chicago. To do this divide all the urban concentration figures since 1860 by the figure for 1860. Then divide the population figures by these ratios. Now compare your corrected population data with the growth of the country as a whole. What conclusions do you draw?

3. The German population as given below shows evidence of having had two growth cycles, divided approximately at the year 1870. Show that the following curve (from Pearl) furnishes a good approximation to the data and discuss from it the characteristics of the growth.

$$y = \frac{119.552}{1 + e^{1.9416 - 0.0331t + 0.00038t^2 - 0.00000021t^3}}.$$

Year	1816	1822	1831	1840	1855	1861
Population	24.833	27.040	29.770	32.790	36.114	38.140
Year	1871	1880	1890	1900	1910	
Population	41.059	45.230	49.430	56.367	64.930	

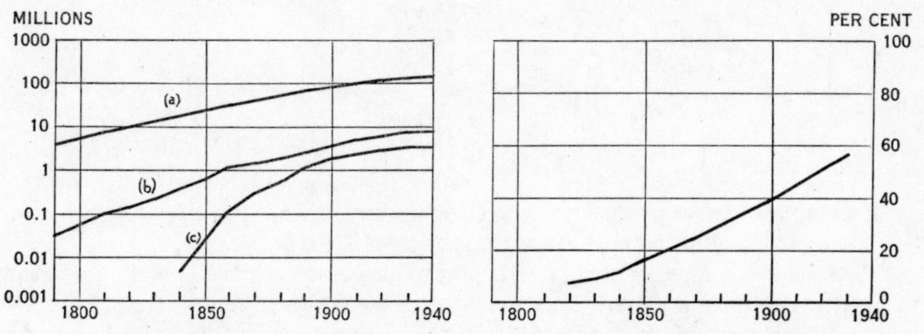

FIGURE 53.—POPULATION GROWTH OF CITIES COMPARED WITH POPULATION GROWTH OF THE COUNTRY AS A WHOLE. CURVE (a) THE UNITED STATES; (b) NEW YORK; (c) CHICAGO. ALSO THE PER CENT OF URBAN CONCENTRATION.

8. *The Growth of Production*

The great wealth of the United States and the remarkably high standard of living attained by its population are due in the final analysis to the growth of production and trade over the past century and a half. Carl Snyder, who devoted many years to the statistics of production, makes the following comment:[14]

> The picture that these measures (the per capita growth of production and trade in the United States from about 1800 to 1929 . . . varying but little from an average of about 2.8 per cent per annum) gives is that of an amazingly even rate of growth not merely from generation to generation but actually of *each* separate decennium throughout the last century. As if there was at work a kind of momentum or inertia that sweeps on in spite of all obstacles.

But these remarks, it would appear, must be somewhat altered in the light of the behavior of the series of production data during the past decennium. The annual growth has not been maintained. The saturation level of automobile production has clearly been reached and the constantly recurring difficulties of the steel industry may be traced to the apparent fact that its development has surpassed society's capacity to absorb its production in peaceful pursuits. Like other organisms, the mechanism of industrial production is subject

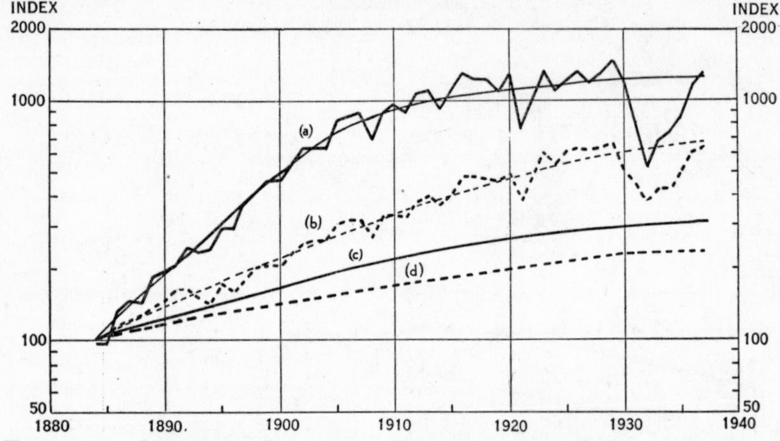

FIGURE 54.—INDEXES OF INDUSTRIAL PRODUCTION AND POPULATION FOR THE PITTSBURGH DISTRICT AND THE UNITED STATES.

This chart compares the growth of production in a district with the growth in production for the country as a whole. The series describe: (a) Production in the Pittsburgh District (Data from the Bureau of Business Research, University of Pittsburgh); (b) Production in the United States; (c) Population in Pittsburgh District; (d) Population of the United States. Logarithmic Scale. Trend point for January, 1884 = 100.

to the laws of organic growth; the annual average of increase which we have cited above must finally yield to the leveling process of the logistic law.

[14] "The Concepts of Momentum and Inertia in Economics," Chapter 4 in *Stabilization of Employment*, edited by C. F. Roos. Bloomington, Ind., 1933, pp. 76–77. See also *Capitalism the Creator*, New York, 1940, pp. 54–60.

Strong evidence for the truth of this thesis is furnished by the investigations of the Bureau of Business Research of the University of Pittsburgh under the direction of R. J. Watkins. This study shows the trend of industrial production for the Pittsburgh district and is based upon 12 statistical series covering manufacturing and coal mining.

In Figure 54 the trend for the Pittsburgh district has been compared with the trend of industrial production for the United States for the period 1884–1937. The index used has been constructed from the Warren M. Persons' indexes of manufacturing and mining for the period 1884–1930 and from the Federal Reserve Board indexes for the subsequent period. Weights were assigned in the ratio of seven for manufacturing and one for mining.

There is one striking difference to be observed between production in the Pittsburgh district and production for the United States as a whole. The former appears to grow more rapidly and to attain maturity earlier than the latter. There is observed here, perhaps, the same difference noted between the growth of male white rats and the growth of a colony of fruit flies. In the first instance, a central mechanism governed the growth, while in the second, the growth and the maturity of the population appeared to be a mechanism of the population itself. It seems fairly logical to assume that the production growth of a district, with its centralized government and its civic organization, might resemble more closely the growth of a self-contained organism than the growth of a population of separate units controlled only by the mechanism of the population itself. At least the hypothesis is worth stating and could be verified or disproved by a study of a sufficient number of other unified areas of production.

If the law of biological growth does hold, indeed, within statistical limits for the growth of industry, this is certainly a very important matter from the standpoint of predictive economics.

In a very suggestive work published in 1930 and using data for the most part prior to the year 1925, S. S. Kuznets gave a number of logistics pertaining to industrial, agricultural, and other indexes.[15] Hence, in his work we have essentially a series of forecasts into the very interesting period which followed 1925. Although it is probable that Kuznets' logistics were not corrected by the method of least squares and are to be regarded as approximations to the trend rather than curves fitted with sufficient care to form a basis for forecasting,

[15] *Secular Movements in Production and Prices,* Boston, 1930, xxiv + 536 pp.

some of the logistics come remarkably close to the truth as one may see from the curve for the production of copper, Chart (d) in Figure 55.

It is interesting and instructive to examine the four logistics of Figure 55, which were computed from the following parameters, the variable t being taken in units of five years:

Constants	Wheat	Corn	Industrial Production	Copper
a	0.35075	0.30230	0.78178	0.60928
b	3.6702	2.9168	22.5978	9.7499
k	845.4	3,128.2	77.0656	699.5
Origin	1865	1865	1883	1885

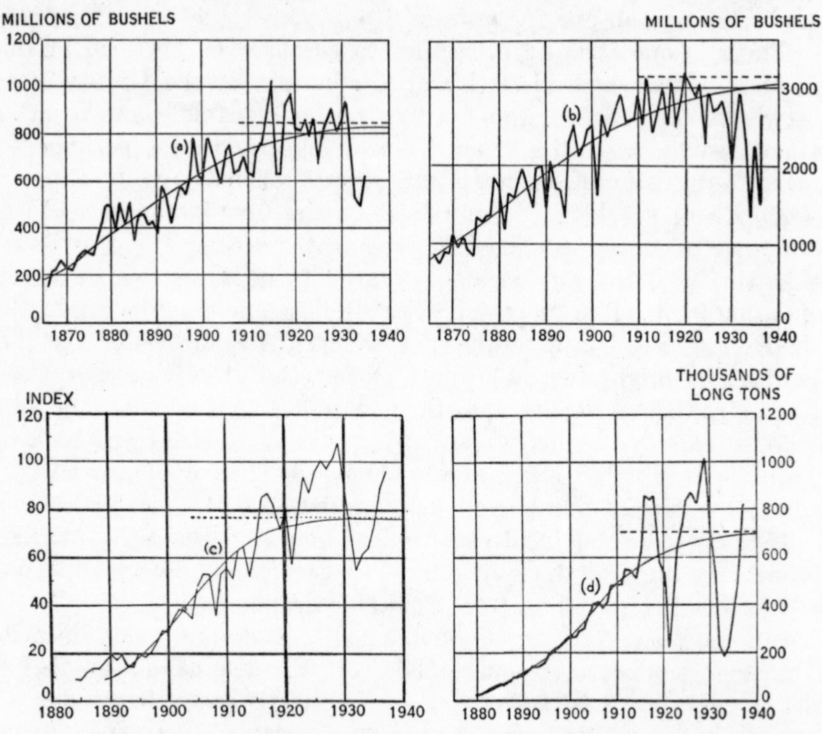

FIGURE 55.—LOGISTICS OF PRODUCTION IN THE UNITED STATES.

The series describe: (a) The Production of Wheat; (b) The Production of Corn; (c) Index of Industrial Production; (d) Production of Copper.

With the exception of the logistic for industrial production, the curves were fitted to the data prior to and including the year 1925. These logistics, therefore, are essentially forecasters of the trends of production and of the asymptotic limit beyond which overproduction may be assumed to occur. Both the production of wheat and the production of corn have been affected adversely by the period of drough in the middle of the decade from 1930 to 1940, and by governmental restrictions upon acreage planted. That both series will tend to oscillate about the established equilibrium lines in the future may be expected.

The logistic of the index of industrial production may well be conservative since it is not corrected for the growth of population. However, an inspection of the logistic for the production of pig iron given in Figure 49 shows an optimum which the events of the last few years have denied. Saturation production is seen to be around 43,000,000 long tons annually. It is interesting to speculate when, if ever, the production of pig iron will attain this asymptotic value. An inspection of the graph reveals three maxima in the production curve, one due to the use of pig iron in the World War, a second around 1924 due probably to the rapid expansion of the automobile industry during this period, and the third in 1929 when the building cycle reached its maximum.

We next inspect the table of per capita production of pig iron in Section 4 and we observe that there has been a steady increase since 1855 in the use of iron. This per capita use reached the incredible value of 0.39 tons in 1916, due of course to the war, another maximum of 0.36 in 1923, due to the expansion of the automobile industry, and a third maximum of 0.34 in 1929, due to building. The amazing magnitude of the depression is clearly shown from the fact that in 1932 the per capita use of pig iron dropped to 0.068 tons, a value lower than any since 1879.

Since it is improbable that another industry comparable to that of automobiles will be developed in the next few years, we cannot expect a large per capita production from such a source. But war is not improbable, and building booms seem to follow a somewhat irregular cycle of from 17 to 20 years in length. Hence we may expect to see again a per capita production around 0.35 tons from one or the other of these two sources. But a per capita production of 0.35 tons for a population of 123,000,000 people will yield a total in excess of 43,000,000 long tons. Hence we may expect to see the asymptotic figure exceeded during the next war or during the next building cycle.

From the table of parameters given above, including also those for pig iron computed in Section 4, it is interesting to obtain the dates of the respective critical points by means of formula (11) of Section 2. These are found to be the following: wheat, 1885; corn, 1882; pig iron, 1907; industrial production, 1903; copper, 1904. It is interesting to observe that the critical points for the grains agree and that the critical points for the metals and for industrial production are also essentially the same.

Production of Wheat
(Unit = 1,000,000 bushels)

Year	Prod.	Year	Prod.	Year	Prod.	Year	Prod.	Year	Prod.	Year	Prod.
1865	....	1877	364.2	1889	434.4	1901	788.6	1913	763.4	1925	676.4
1866	152.0	1878	420.1	1890	378.1	1902	724.8	1914	891.0	1926	831.0
1867	212.4	1879	496.4	1891	584.5	1903	663.9	1915	1025.8	1927	878.4
1868	224.0	1880	498.6	1892	528.0	1904	596.9	1916	636.3	1928	914.9
1869	260.1	1881	383.3	1893	427.6	1905	726.8	1917	636.7	1929	812.6
1870	235.9	1882	504.2	1894	516.5	1906	756.8	1918	921.4	1930	857.4
1871	230.7	1883	421.1	1895	569.5	1907	638.0	1919	968.0	1931	932.2
1872	250.0	1884	512.8	1896	544.2	1908	644.7	1920	833.0	1932	745.8
1873	281.3	1885	357.1	1897	610.3	1909	700.4	1921	814.9	1933	529.0
1874	308.1	1886	457.2	1898	772.2	1910	635.1	1922	867.6	1934	496.6
1875	292.1	1887	456.3	1899	636.1	1911	621.3	1923	797.4	1935	626.3
1876	289.4	1888	415.9	1900	602.7	1912	730.3	1924	864.4	1936	636.5
										1937	874.0

Production of Corn
(Unit = 1,000,000 bushels)

Year	Prod.	Year	Prod.	Year	Prod.	Year	Prod.	Year	Prod.	Year	Prod.
1865	....	1877	1342.6	1889	1998.7	1901	1613.5	1913	2447.0	1925	2917.0
1866	867.9	1878	1388.2	1890	1460.4	1902	2619.5	1914	2672.8	1926	2692.2
1867	768.3	1879	1823.2	1891	2055.8	1903	2346.9	1915	2994.8	1927	2763.1
1868	906.5	1880	1717.4	1892	1713.7	1904	2528.7	1916	2566.9	1928	2818.9
1869	874.3	1881	1194.9	1893	1707.6	1905	2748.9	1917	3065.2	1929	2535.4
1870	1094.3	1882	1617.0	1894	1339.7	1906	2897.7	1918	2502.7	1930	2059.6
1871	991.9	1883	1551.1	1895	2311.0	1907	2512.1	1919	2811.3	1931	2588.5
1872	1092.7	1884	1795.5	1896	2503.5	1908	2545.0	1920	3208.6	1932	2906.9
1873	932.3	1885	1936.2	1897	2144.6	1909	2572.3	1921	3068.6	1933	2350.7
1874	850.1	1886	1665.4	1898	2261.1	1910	2886.3	1922	2906.0	1934	1377.1
1875	1321.1	1887	1456.2	1899	2454.6	1911	2531.5	1923	3053.6	1935	2296.7
1876	1283.8	1888	1987.8	1900	2505.1	1912	3124.7	1924	2309.4	1936	1524.3
										1937	2645.0

Index of Industrial Production
(1926 = 100)

Year	Index	Year	Index	Year	Index	Year	Index	Year	Index	Year	Index
1884	8.7	1894	13.9	1904	34.1	1914	52.1	1924	87.1	1934	64.2
1885	8.6	1895	19.9	1905	47.8	1915	66.2	1925	95.7	1935	73.9
1886	12.2	1896	17.8	1906	52.7	1916	85.0	1926	100.0	1936	88.6
1887	13.6	1897	20.1	1907	52.6	1917	86.8	1927	97.2	1937	96.0
1888	13.5	1898	24.5	1908	35.4	1918	82.2	1928	101.0	1938	
1889	15.9	1899	29.4	1909	53.6	1919	71.7	1929	108.1	1939	
1890	19.2	1900	28.5	1910	55.8	1920	80.1	1930	86.2	1940	
1891	17.1	1901	34.4	1911	50.7	1921	57.3	1931	70.2	1941	
1892	19.0	1902	37.8	1912	62.8	1922	77.9	1932	54.8	1942	
1893	14.8	1903	36.8	1913	64.8	1923	92.9	1933	61.3	1943	

PRODUCTION OF COPPER

(Unit = 1000 long tons)

Year	Prod.	Year	Prod.	Year	Prod.	Year	Prod.	Year	Prod.	Year	Prod.
1880	27.0	1890	116.0	1900	482.2	1910	482.2	1920	539.8	1929	1006.2
1881	32.0	1891	126.8	1901	268.8	1911	489.8	1921	225.7	1930	690.5
1882	40.5	1892	154.0	1902	294.4	1912	555.0	1922	424.2	1931	528.9
1883	51.6	1893	147.0	1903	311.6	1913	546.7	1923	640.6	1932	238.1
1884	64.7	1894	158.1	1904	362.7	1914	513.4	1924	729.6	1933	190.7
1885	74.1	1895	169.9	1905	402.6	1915	619.6	1925	842.1	1934	239.3
1886	70.4	1896	205.4	1906	409.8	1916	860.6	1926	872.4	1935	369.5
1887	81.0	1897	220.6	1907	387.9	1917	842.0	1927	830.0	1936	592.2
1888	101.1	1898	235.1	1908	420.8	1918	852.0	1928	909.1	1937	812.0
1889	101.2	1899	253.9	1909	487.9	1919	574.3				

The actual data from which the logistics in Figure 55 have been computed are contained in the following tables:

A fundamental lesson may be learned from these logistics. The era of the great scientific revolution which began approximately with the discoveries of Galileo (1564–1642), Tycho Brahe (1546–1601), Johann Kepler (1571–1630), and Sir Isaac Newton (1642–1727) is reaching its maturity. The amazing energies of science, directed by the patterns set by these great leaders, have given us in rapid succession the steam engine, the dynamo, the telegraph and telephone, the automobile, the radio, the airplane, and all the other wonders of the modern world. This transition from the past to the present regime may be estimated by the per capita increase in the use of iron. If we are attaining the upper asymptote of the production of this basic commodity, then also the maturity of technological science must be close at hand. But there can be no real regrets if this should happen to be true, since in the process of scientific growth the lot of the human race has been immeasurably elevated. The standards of living in America and in those other nations, which desire to profit by the new knowledge, have been greatly raised.

PROBLEMS

1. Compare graphically the increase in prices in the United States (Use the annual averages in the table of general prices given in Section 7. Chapter 12) with the increase in industrial production since 1884. Would you say that the logistic law applies to prices as well as to production?

2. Obtain some production data other than that given in this chapter and examine them for their logistic character.

3. The following data measure the approximate influence of Rome over the period of its rise and fall:

Year	Index	Year	Index	Year	Index	Year	Index
800 B.C.	0	500 B.C.	4.91	200 B.C.	32.16	100 A.D.	61.14
750	.71	450	6.01	150	53.01	150	57.25
700	1.41	400	8.12	100	61.49	200	47.36
650	2.47	350	7.77	50	62.55	250	33.57
600	2.83	300	10.60	1	61.14	300	26.38
550	3.88	250	20.50	50 A.D.	59.37	350	17.67
						400	16.26

Consider these data from the point of view of this section. Are they logistic in character? What conclusions do you derive from them?

4. Can a curve of the type given in Section 2 be used to graduate the data of problem 3? Suggest such a curve.

5. Noting that equation (3) of Section 2 is of the form

$$\frac{dy}{dt} = g(t)\, yF(y/k)\,, \tag{33}$$

where $F(z)$ is a function such that $F(1) = 0$, observe that the following equation is of the same type:

$$\frac{dy}{dt} = cy \log(y/k)\,. \tag{34}$$

Show that this equation has the solution

$$y = ka^{f(t)}\,, \text{ where } f(t) = e^{ct}\,. \tag{35}$$

This curve was first discussed by Benjamin Gompertz in a paper presented to the Royal Philosophical Society of London in 1825 in connection with the graduation of the curve of mortality and is known generally as the *Gompertz curve.* It is occasionally used instead of the logistic to describe growth phenomena, but the analytical difficulties which it presents make it generally inferior as a statistical tool. R. B. Prescott has employed the Gompertz curve in a study of the production of automobiles and cotton in the United States. Methods for fitting it to data are given in the *Text Book of the Institute of Actuaries.* Part 2, 2nd ed., 1902. For an example, see p. 80.

6. Show that the second derivative of y as defined by equation (34) in problem 5 is given by

$$\frac{d^2y}{dt^2} = c^2 y \log(y/k)\,[\log(y/k) + 1].$$

Hence, show that a point of inflection exists when

$$\log(y/k) = -1\,. \tag{36}$$

7. Solve (36) for t and show that

$$t = -\frac{1}{c} \log(-\log a)\,.$$

8. Show that if c is negative and less than 1, then the function (35) of problem 5 resembles the logistic. Show that as $t \to +\infty$, $y \to k$, and as $t \to -\infty$, $y \to 0$.

SELECTED BIBLIOGRAPHY ON THE GROWTH OF POPULATION AND INDUSTRY

BOLZA, H. "Bemerkungen zur Bevölkerungsentwicklung und ihre Gesetzmäszigkeiten," *Berichte der Phys.-Med. Gesellschaft zu Wurzburg*, Vol. 63, 1940, pp. 97–120.

DAVIS, H. T. *The Theory of Economic Time Series.* Bloomington, Ind., 1940. Chapter 6.

HOTELLING, H. "Differential Equations Subject to Error, and Population Estimates," *Journal of the American Statistical Association*, Vol. 22, 1927, pp. 283–314.

KUZNETS, S. S. *Secular Movements in Production and Prices.* Boston, 1930, xxiv + 536 pp.

LOTKA, A. J. *Elements of Human Biology.* Baltimore, 1925. Chapter 7.

LUYTEN, W. J. (See E. B. WILSON).

OSTWALD, W. *Die Zeitlichen Eigenschaften der Entwickelungsvorgange.* Leipzig, 1908.

PEARL, RAYMOND. (1) (with L. J. Reed). "On the Rate of Growth of the Population of the United States since 1790 and its Mathematical Representation," *Proceedings of the National Academy of Sciences*, Vol. 6, 1920, pp. 275–288.

(2) (with L. J. Reed). "On the Mathematical Theory of Population Growth," *Metron*, Vol. 3, 1923, pp. 6–19.

(3) (with L. J. Reed). "The Probable Error of Certain Constants of the Population Growth Curve," *American Journal of Hygiene*, Vol. 4, 1924, pp. 237–240.

(4) *Studies in Human Biology*, Baltimore, 1924. Chapter 24.

(5) *The Biology of Population Growth.* New York, 1925.

PRESCOTT, R. B. "Law of Growth in Forecasting Demand," *Journal of the American Statistical Association*, Vol. 18, 1922-23, pp. 471–479.

PUFFER, RUTH R. (See E. B. WILSON).

REED, L. J. [See Raymond Pearl].

ROBERTSON, T. B. (1) *The Chemical Basis of Growth and Senescence.* 1923.

(2) *Archiv. für die Entwickelungsmechanik der Organismen*, Vol. 25, 1907, p. 4; Vol. 26, 1908, p. 108.

SCHULTZ, H. "The Standard Error of Forecast from a Curve," *Journal of the American Statistical Association*, Vol. 25, 1930, pp. 139–185.

THORTON, H. G. *Annals of Applied Biology*, 1922, p. 265.

TRUESDELL, L. E. "Growth of Urban Population in the United States of America." *U. S. Department of Commerce*, 1937.

VERHULST, P. F. "Recherches mathématiques sur la loi d'accroissement de la population," *Nouv. Mem. de l'Acad. Roy. de Bruxelles*, Vol. 18, 1845, pp. 1–38; Vol. 20, 1847, pp. 1–32.

WILSON, E. B. (1) (with RUTH R. PUFFER). "Least Squares and Laws of Population Growth," *Proceedings of the American Academy of Arts and Sciences*, Vol. 68, 1933, pp. 285–382.

2. "The Logistic or Autocatalytic Grid," *Proceedings of the National Academy of Sciences*, Vol. 11, 1925, pp. 451–456.

(3) (with W. J. LUYTEN). "The Population of New York City and its Environs," *Proceedings of the National Academy of Sciences*, Vol. 11, 1925, pp. 137–143.

CHAPTER 12

The Equation of Exchange

1. *Historical Note*

As we have already observed in previous chapters, one of the most intriguing problems in economics is that presented by the relationship of money to prices. Many fallacious views have been held on this subject and disastrous experiments have been tried from time to time based upon monetary theories that have proved to be false.

In earlier sections of this book we have been concerned mainly with the static aspects of money and prices, but it is clear to anyone who has visited the wheat pit or the stock exchange that prices are in constant flux and that the value of money itself is never stable. One must then conclude that the problem of money and prices is essentially dynamic in its character and must be studied with respect to variations in time.

Perhaps the best approach to the subject of monetary relationships is through what is called the *quantity theory of money*. Basic to this theory is a mathematical relationship called the *equation of exchange,* which assumes that money, M, and credit, M', are related to price, P, and trade, T, by the equation

$$MV + M'V' = PT. \tag{1}$$

The parameters V and V' are called respectively, the *velocities* of money and credit.

Since the first term in this equation, namely, MV, is of the order of 10% of the second, namely, $M'V'$, it is often convenient in monetary discussions to write equation (1) in the simpler form

$$MV = PT, \tag{2}$$

where M refers mainly to bank credit and V to its velocity.

The equation of exchange was first written down and discussed by Simon Newcomb (1835–1909), that prolific genius who not only established a high reputation in economics, but was also the leading astronomer of his time. The equation and its implications appeared in Newcomb's *Principles of Political Economy,* published in 1886.

Although this fundamental relationship between money, trade, velocity, and prices attracted the immediate attention of economists, it was not until 1895 that any attempt was made to examine the variables separately and to subject them to statistical scrutiny. In that year Pierre des Essars published a study based upon the observed velocity of deposits in certain individual banks in different European countries.[1]

The next attempt to measure the variables was made by E. W. Kemmerer, who published in 1909 his notable work: *Money and Credit Instruments in their Relations to General Prices.* About this study Irving Fisher says: "Professor Kemmerer's calculation is, I believe, the first serious attempt ever made to test statistically the so-called 'quantity theory' of money. The results show a correspondence which is very surprising when we consider the exceedingly rough and fragmentary character of the data employed." Kemmerer considered the value of the variable over the period from 1879 to 1908, but the lack of adequate data, particularly with respect to trade, seriously impaired the conclusions.

A new scrutiny of the problem was called for. This appeared in 1911 in the now classical study on *The Purchasing Power of Money,* published by Irving Fisher with the assistance of H. G. Brown.[2] This elaborate work is essentially an examination into the constituents of the equation of exchange in the form in which it has been given above in equation (1).

These important works attracted the renewed attention of the economists to the *quantity theory of money,* and a vigorous debate has progressed since that time over the fundamental interpretation of the variables. Strange to say, most of the debate has been on a priori principles; until recently, few serious attempts were made to appraise the statistical relationships between the variables.

A notable exception to this is found in the work of Carl Snyder. This statistician, over a period of years, assembled data from many sources in order to measure the variables in the equation of exchange. His theory and the contributing data are given in his work, *Business Cycles and Business Measurements.*[3] A summary of his theory will be found in a paper, "Industrial Growth and Monetary Theory," published in the *Economic Forum.*[4] The postulates of Snyder's theory

[1] "La vitesse de la circulation de la monnaie," *Journal de la Société de Statistique de Paris,* 1895, p. 143.

[2] New York, 1911, xxii + 505 pp.; second edition, 1931.

[3] New York, 1927, xv + 326 pp.

[4] 1933, pp. 275–290.

have recently been formulated in mathematical terms by E. V. Huntington.[5]

Current data are now available through The Standard Statistics Company which give the velocity of bank deposits by months, the series extending to 1919. A fairly adequate series on bank debits also exists to 1919. J. W. Angell in his book on *The Behavior of Money,* published in 1936, gives comprehensive data on circulating currency and circulating deposits from 1890 to 1934 inclusive.

2. The Variables in the Equation of Exchange

Before considering in detail the constituents of equation (1), let us inquire into the nature of the relationship which we have set up. In a sense the equation of exchange is a tautology, since on one side the expression $MV + M'V'$ is equal to the amount of money spent in a given unit of time, while on the other side the quantity PT is the value of the things purchased by the money. An instant's consideration will show us, however, that PT is not equivalent to the national income since $M'V'$ alone reached the amazing figure of 1,678 billions of dollars in 1929, whereas the total annual income for that year was estimated to be 79.1 billions of dollars.

The principal confusion over the nature of the equation of exchange is found in a misunderstanding of the character of the relationship. Although the equation is tautological, nevertheless it defines one of the variables in terms of the other five. But the other five variables must themselves be defined in measurable units before any meaning can be assigned to the one dependent upon them. Moreover, after the variables have been defined independently, it may happen that a functional relationship will be observed between one or more of them. This relationship will be an *economic law,* and when it is combined with the original equation of exchange the latter loses its tautological character.

With the equation of exchange, as with many other equations in physics, chemistry, and other sciences, a major gain is found in the attention which is focused upon the measurement of the different variables. If these variables have been well chosen, then great insight into the problems involving these variables in other connections may be acquired. An instructive example is found in the theory of electrical conduction. The equation

$$E = I R , \tag{3}$$

[5] "On the Mathematical Hypotheses Underlying Carl Snyder's Trade-Credit Ratio Theorem," *Econometrica,* Vol. 6, 1938, pp. 177–179.

expresses the relationship between E, the electromotive force, I the current, and R the resistance, when electricity is flowing through a simple circuit.

This equation may be regarded as a *law of physics,* provided the three symbols are measured in proper units. Moreover, any two of the variables is sufficient to define the third. One of the first problems in the history of electricity was that of devising methods for the independent measurement of E, I, and R. The first quantity is associated with the battery, or other source of electromotive force, the second is the quantity driven through the wire, the third is associated with the material of the wire itself.

But is one approaches the problem without reference to preconceived images of the three quantities, it is obvious that the force which drives something through the wire must be equal to what is driven, multiplied by some parameter representing the retarding influence of the wire. The equation in this sense is a mere tautology and it emerges into a law of physics only after careful independent definitions have been given to the three variables involved.

A similar remark applies to equation (1), since what we spend, as represented by the symbols on the left hand side, must be precisely equal to what we buy, as defined by the product PT. But this futile tautology disappears, just as it does in equation (3) above, as soon as we have given precise and independent meaning to the six parameters.

A great deal of the mystery associated with this equation disappears when the variables have been independently described and statistical methods devised for their measurement. We shall proceed, therefore, to a careful consideration of the six quantities and the meanings that are to be associated with them.

3. *Circulating Money* (M)

The quantity M in the equation of exchange denotes circulating money. Since a penumbra of uncertainty surrounds this definition, just as it does most definitions in economics which are unsupported by statistical data, we shall give it a more precise meaning through the elements of a statistical series.

Circulating money has meant different things at different times and in different countries. Before the institution of banking, circulating money was for the most part gold and silver coins. At times it has been principally paper notes, supported by the credit of the issuing government, as is the case with most countries with modern banking

Year	M (in millions of dollars)	Population as of July 1	Per Capita M (in dollars)	M_b = Vault Cash (in millions of dollars)	$K = M_b/M$
1890	941	63,056,438	14.92	488	0.519
1891	1,000	64,361,124	15.54	498	0.498
1892	1,016	65,665,810	15.47	586	0.576
1893	1,081	66,970,496	16.14	516	0.477
1894	972	68,275,182	14.24	689	0.709
1895	971	69,579,868	13.96	631	0.650
1896	974	70,884,554	13.74	532	0.546
1897	1,013	72,189,240	14.03	628	0.620
1898	1,150	73,493,926	15.65	688	0.598
1899	1,181	74,798,612	15.79	723	0.612
1900	1,305	76,129,408	17.14	750	0.575
1901	1,368	77,747,402	17.60	808	0.590
1902	1,401	79,365,396	17.65	848	0.605
1903	1,510	80,983,390	18.65	857	0.568
1904	1,529	82,601,384	18.51	991	0.648
1905	1,594	84,219,378	18.93	994	0.624
1906	1,720	85,837,372	20.04	1,016	0.591
1907	1,659	87,445,366	18.97	1,114	0.672
1908	1,670	89,073,360	18.75	1,368	0.820
1909	1,644	90,691,354	18.13	1,452	0.884
1910	1,678	92,267,080	18.24	1,424	0.849
1911	1,660	93,682,189	17.72	1,554	0.936
1912	1,712	95,097,298	18.00	1,573	0.919
1913	1,703	96,512,407	17.65	1,561	0.917
1914	1,820	97,927,516	18.59	1,639	0.901
1915	1,862	99,342,625	18.74	1,458	0.783
1916	2,163	100,757,735	21.47	1,486	0.687
1917	2,564	102,172,845	25.09	1,502	0.588
1918	3,585	103,587,955	34.61	897	0.250
1919	3,879	105,003,065	36.94	997	0.250
1920	4,391	106,543,031	41.21	1,076	0.257
1921	3,964	108,207,853	36.63	947	0.245
1922	3,633	109,872,675	33.07	830	0.239
1923	4,026	111,537,497	36.10	797	0.228
1924	3,964	113,202,319	34.79	912	0.198
1925	3,864	114,867,141	33.64	951	0.232
1926	3,890	116,531,963	33.38	998	0.246
1927	3,843	118,196,785	32.51	1,008	0.256
1928	3,909	119,861,607	32.61	888	0.227
1929	3,926	121,526,429	32.31	820	0.209
1930	3,656	123,091,000	29.70	866	0.237
1931	3,938	124,113,000	31.73	884	0.224
1932	4,904	124,974,000	39.24	792	0.162
1933	5,048	125,770,000	40.14	676	0.134
1934	4,660	126,626,000	36.80	714	0.153
1935	4,784	127,521,000	37.51	785	0.164
1936	5,222	128,429,000	40.66	1,019	0.195
1937	5,489	129,337,000	42.44	958	0.175
1938	5,417	130,245,000	41.59	1,044	0.193

systems. It is interesting to note that the internal circulating currency of Germany, after the great inflation of 1922–23, with a metal base of perhaps 0.3 of one per cent of the world's monetary gold, possessed approximately the same stability as the circulating currency in the United States, backed by more than 60 per cent of the world's monetary gold supply.

Following J. W. Angell, who gives excellent statistical summaries in his book on *The Behavior of Money,* we shall define M to be the total currency issued and not yet redeemed, diminished by the currency held in the Federal treasury, the currency in Federal Reserve banks, the currency with Federal Reserve agents, and the currency in the vaults of all banks.

In the table on page 246 we give the series for M (outside currency), the population as of July 1, the per capita value of M, the vault cash, M_b and the ratio $K = M_b/M$, these data referring to continental United States. From 1890 to 1934 the monetary data are taken from Angell's book; for the subsequent years they are Angell's esti-

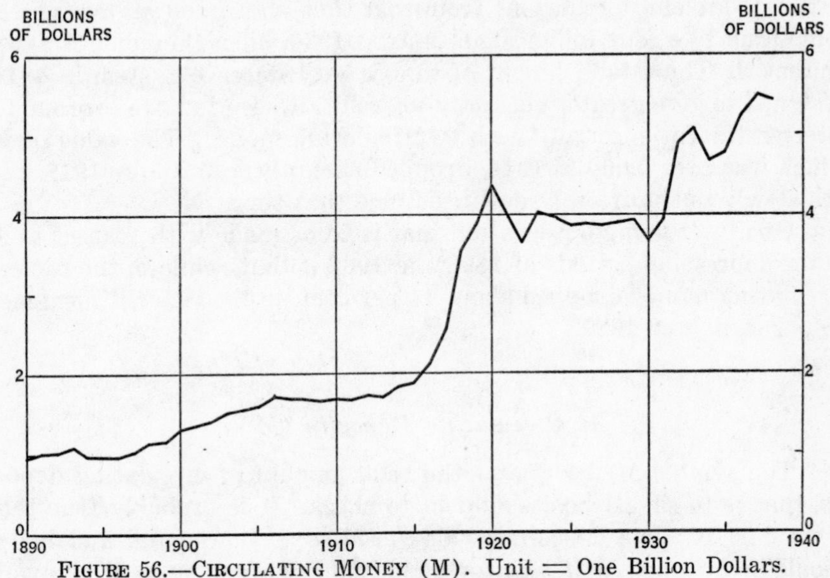

FIGURE 56.—CIRCULATING MONEY (M). Unit = One Billion Dollars.

mates based upon Treasury data. The value of M prior to 1909 differ slightly from those computed by Irving Fisher and published in his book on *The Purchasing Power of Money,* to which reference has previously been made. Fisher's values from 1896 to 1909 inclusive, in billion-dollar units, were the following: 0.87, 0.88, 0.96, 1.03, 1.17, 1.22, 1.26, 1.38, 1.37, 1.45, 1.59, 1.63, 1.63, 1.63.

The series for M is graphically represented in Figure 56, with respect to which some rather interesting observations may be made. From 1890 to 1915 there was a steady and essentially uniform increase in M, which could be attributed mainly to the growth of population. During this time the per capita value of M changed from approximately \$15.00 to approximately \$18.00, an annual increase of one per cent. The major fluctuation in this period is observed in the depression years from 1893 to 1897, when both M and per capita M declined. The unusual stability of the money series from 1897 to 1915 was reflected in all the other series of this period, which makes it one of the best for the exploration of the interrelationships between production and price indexes. For this reason this period may be taken as an almost perfect example of a stable economic system operating under a mild positive trend.

But the World War put an end to this stable economy and we find an abrupt change in all the series of the next period, including that for M. We note a sharp increase in circulating money from 1915 to 1920 and violent fluctuations from that time on around an average of something like four billion dollars until 1930 when the amount again increased. The establishment of the Federal Reserve System in 1914, designed to give greater elasticity to credit, is seen to have profoundly affected the ratio of vault cash to circulating money. The value of K, which was over 0.900 in 1914, dropped abruptly to 0.250 by 1918, and has slowly but uniformly declined since that time.

One interesting observation that is to be made with respect to M in the depression periods of 1893 and 1932 is that, while in the former circulating money dropped about 11 per cent, in the latter it increased 25 per cent over 1929.

4. Circulating Deposits (M')

The symbol M' designates the total amount of circulating deposits, that is to say, deposits subject to check. It is probably true that some part of time deposits is also used to pay accounts and hence should be included in M'. Unfortunately there are at present no available data for estimating this part of time deposits, which should be added to M', but since the amount is presumably small it is probable that no essential error will be introduced into our calculations by neglecting it.

The following table gives the values of circulating deposits (M'), total deposits (M'_t), total money ($M + M'_t$), circulating money ($M + M'_t$), and the ratios $h = M/M'_t$ and $H = M/M'$. The figures for

Year	Circulating Deposits, M' (in millions of dollars)		Total Deposits, M'_t (in millions of dollars)		Total Money ($M + M'_t$) (in millions of dollars)	Total Circulating Money ($M + M'$) (in millions of dollars)	$h = M/M'_t$	$H = M/M'$
	Total	Per cap. (in dollars)	Total	Per cap. (in dollars)				
1890	2,295	36.40	3,993	63.32	4,934	3,236	0.236	0.410
1891	2,351	36.53	4,126	64.11	5,126	3,351	0.242	0.425
1892	2,629	40.04	4,572	69.63	5,588	3,645	0.222	0.386
1893	2,524	37.69	4,516	67.43	5,597	3,605	0.239	0.428
1894	2,592	37.96	4,587	67.18	5,559	3,564	0.212	0.375
1895	2,744	39.44	4,838	69.53	5,809	3,715	0.201	0.354
1896	2,703	38.13	4,841	68.29	5,815	3,677	0.201	0.360
1897	2,763	38.27	4,979	68.97	5,992	3,776	0.203	0.367
1898	3,251	44.23	5,615	76.40	6,765	4,401	0.205	0.354
1899	3,941	52.69	6,545	87.50	7,726	5,122	0.180	0.299
1900	4,304	56.54	7,104	93.31	8,409	5,609	0.184	0.303
1901	5,054	65.01	8,097	104.14	9,465	6,422	0.169	0.271
1902	5,491	69.19	8,910	112.27	10,311	6,892	0.157	0.255
1903	5,687	70.22	9,416	116.27	10,926	7,197	0.160	0.266
1904	5,963	72.19	9,880	119.61	11,409	7,492	0.155	0.256
1905	6,634	78.77	11,126	132.11	12,720	8,228	0.143	0.240
1906	6,953	81.00	11,862	138.19	13,582	8,673	0.145	0.247
1907	7,290	83.37	12,870	147.18	14,529	8,949	0.129	0.228
1908	6,652	74.68	12,565	141.06	14,235	8,322	0.133	0.251
1909	6,886	75.93	13,669	150.72	15,313	8,530	0.120	0.239
1910	7,707	83.53	14,710	159.43	16,388	9,385	0.114	0.218
1911	8,192	87.44	15,547	165.95	17,207	9,852	0.107	0.203
1912	8,204	86.27	16,683	175.43	18,330	9,916	0.103	0.209
1913	8,089	83.81	17,133	177.52	18,836	9,792	0.099	0.211
1914	9,356	95.54	18,108	184.91	19,928	11,176	0.101	0.195
1915	9,265	93.26	18,875	190.00	20,738	11,127	0.099	0.201
1916	11,784	116.95	22,230	220.63	24,393	13,947	0.097	0.184
1917	13,021	127.44	26,106	255.51	28,670	15,585	0.098	0.197
1918	15,050	145.29	28,606	276.15	32,190	18,635	0.125	0.238
1919	17,697	168.53	32,790	312.27	36,669	21,576	0.118	0.219
1920	18,656	175.10	36,657	344.05	41,047	23,047	0.112	0.235
1921	17,270	159.60	34,628	320.01	38,592	21,234	0.114	0.229
1922	16,507	150.24	36,388	331.18	40,021	20,140	0.100	0.220
1923	17,311	155.20	39,551	354.60	43,577	21,337	0.102	0.232
1924	18,174	160.54	41,864	369.82	45,802	22,112	0.094	0.217
1925	19,934	173.54	45,486	395.99	49,350	23,798	0.083	0.194
1926	20,178	173.15	47,719	409.49	51,608	24,068	0.082	0.193
1927	22,861	193.41	50,305	425.60	54,148	26,704	0.076	0.168
1928	23,356	194.86	52,639	439.16	56,548	27,265	0.074	0.167
1929	23,408	192.62	52,549	432.41	56,475	27,334	0.075	0.168
1930	22,661	184.10	52,325	425.09	55,981	26,317	0.070	0.161
1931	20,506	165.22	49,996	402.83	53,934	24,444	0.079	0.192
1932	16,124	129.02	41,249	330.06	46,153	21,028	0.119	0.304
1933	15,484	123.11	37,138	295.29	42,186	20,532	0.136	0.326
1934	18,903	149.28	42,011	331.77	46,671	23,563	0.111	0.247
1935	22,092	173.24	45,994	360.68	50,778	26,876	0.104	0.217
1936	25,876	201.48	50,656	394.43	55,878	31,098	0.103	0.202
1937	26,257	203.01	52,162	403.30	57,651	31,748	0.105	0.209
1938	26,086	200.28	52,277	401.37	57,694	31,503	0.104	0.208

M' from 1890 to 1908 inclusive are from W. C. Mitchell's *Business Cycles: The Problem and its Setting*; the values from 1908 to 1934, excepting the per capita figures, are taken from Angell's book, and the subsequent values are estimates kindly furnished the author by Angell. Mitchell's estimates from 1896 to 1909 show a slight variation from those computed by Irving Fisher.[6]

The series for M' is graphically represented in Figure 57. From this figure and from the numerical values of the ratios h, H, and K some rather instructive observations may be made with regard to them.

We note that the ratio H showed a steady and uniform decrease

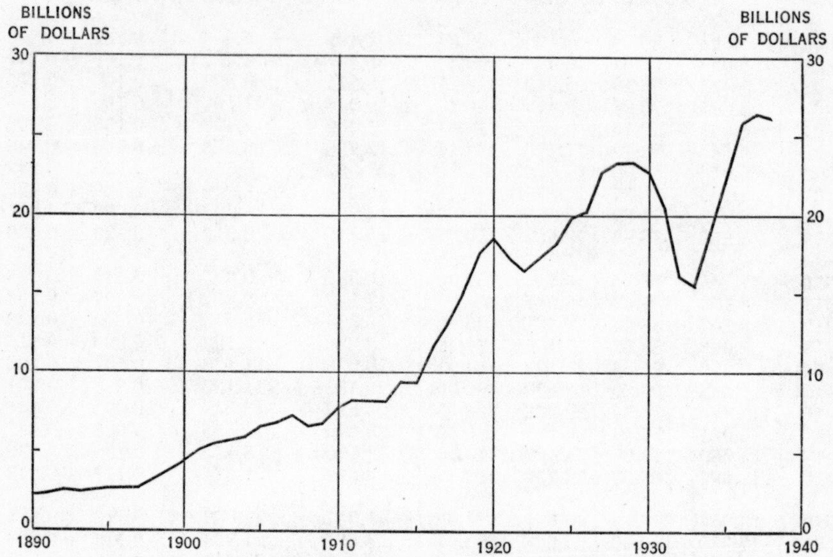

FIGURE 57.—CIRCULATING DEPOSITS (M′). Unit = One Billion Dollars.

over the forty year period from 1890 to 1930. This meant that there was a steady increase in the use of checks in the trading habits of the people. But in 1931, as the depression deepened, the ratio showed a violent reversal. As M' decreased from its peak of 23,408 in 1929 to its minimum of 15,484 in 1933, circulating money increased to 5,048. Thus in a period of four years H regained most of what it had lost in the preceding four decades.

A large credit expansion is also to be noticed in the period from 1920 to 1930. Prior to that time the curves for M and M' showed a

[6] Fisher's values (expressed in billions of dollars) were: 2.68, 2.80, 3.19, 3.90, 4.20, 5.13, 5.43, 5.70, 5.80, 6.54, 6.84, 7.13, 6.57, 6.75.

remarkable similarity to one another and after 1910 the ratio H remained reasonably stable around an average of approximately 0.2. But in the inflationary period which began shortly after the price collapse of 1920, the ratio suffered a sudden drop. While M remained essentially unchanged, M' rose rapidly from a low of 16,507 in 1922 to its peak of 23,408 in 1929.

The spectacular rise of both M and M' from 1914 to 1920 is attributable to the war. During this period there was a great increase in trade and an expanding currency was needed to meet the demand. We have already commented upon the spectacular drop in the ratio K as the result of the establishment of the Federal Reserve System in 1914, which released large holdings of vault cash and allowed a concomitant increase in M. It is rather a pity from the standpoint of the theory of economics that this remarkable phenomenon should have taken place at the beginning of the World War, when trade inflation masked the natural results of so drastic a change in the banking system of the nation.

5. *The Velocity of Circulating Deposits* (V')

The symbol V' in the equation of exchange means the velocity of circulating deposits. Since this parameter plays a more important role in the theory of trade and prices than does V, the velocity of circulating currency, and since its statistical determination is much easier, we shall give to it our primary attention.

The term velocity, which may be either V or V', and which we shall designate for the moment by v, is used in the following sense: Suppose that e is the total amount of money spent by an individual in some unit of time and that m is the average amount of money which he possesses during that time. Then v, which is obviously a function of the interval of time, is the ratio of e to m; that is,

$$v = e/m\,.$$

For example, if an individual earns \$300 per month and spends it during that period of time, he will have \$300 on the first day of the month and nothing on the last day. His average bank account will be less than \$300. If he spends his money uniformly, that is to say, the same amount each day, then his average bank account will be \$150, and his monthly velocity will be

$$v = \$300/\$150 = 2\,.$$

On the assumption just made the yearly velocity would be $12 \times 2 = 24$, a velocity which is not far from the velocity of currency, but which is lower, on the average, than the observed velocity of circulating deposits. We shall find later that the average value of V' over a long period of time was 41.8, a value which includes the data from New York City where the velocity is normally higher than in other parts of the country.

If we refer to the example just given, we see that certain modifications must be made in the calculations because of the fact that debts are generally paid at the beginning of the month. Hence the individual with an income of \$300 per month may, for example, pay \$160 on the first day of the month; he may then spend perhaps \$110 uniformly over the remainder of the month, and transfer the remaining \$30 to his savings account, where it is removed from circulating deposits. Under this schedule the individual would then spend \$270. His average bank account would be $\$30 + \frac{1}{2} \times \$110 = \$85$, and the monthly velocity is computed as the ratio

$$v = \$270/\$85 = 3.2 .$$

Hence we reach a more realistic value for the yearly velocity, namely, $12 \times 3.2 = 38.4$

It is obvious that a study of family cash accounts would permit one to compute with some accuracy the value of V'. Since such budgetary data have not been available, the computation has been made by a study of bank deposits and the data for bank debits.[7]

If we consider, then, the data available from banks, it is clear that the velocity of deposits can be computed by dividing the total amount of checks drawn each month in a given center by the average of the demand deposits for the same period. The actual procedure in the calculation has been described by W. R. Burgess in his careful study on the velocity of bank deposits. (See *Bibliography*). Although the calculation is a straightforward process, certain care must be exercised to take account of the turnover of time deposits and to exclude the effects of government withdrawals. When these corrections have been applied we then compute the velocity, usually given in annual figures, from the formula

[7] It is of some interest to know the relationship between bank debits, namely the total exchange of money by checks, and bank clearings, that is, the total exchange of money by checks which pass through the clearing house. A statistical study by the author's student, E. L. Godfrey, based upon annual debits and clearings from 1900 to 1937 inclusive, indicates that the ratio

$$u = \frac{\text{Bank debits}}{\text{Bank clearings}}$$

has the value $u = 2.00$ with a standard error of $+0.24$.

$$V = \frac{\text{Bank Debits per unit of time}}{\text{Average Circulating Deposits}} \times n,$$

where n is the number of times the selected unit of time is contained in a year.

The great variation of the annual velocity from one financial center to another is shown in the following table, which shows the average velocity for 141 cities including New York City, and the velocity for nine of these cities separately. We observe from the table that the range of the velocity was from 9.5 for Syracuse to 77.1 for New York City. The average for the nine cities listed was 33.5 with a probable error of 11.2, which gives a coefficient of variation, σ/A, equal to 0.50.

AVERAGE ANNUAL VELOCITY OF BANK DEPOSITS

Year	1919	1920	1921	1922	1923	1924	1925	Avr.
141 cities	42.3	41.9	38.5	40.5	41.4	40.9	44.2	41.4
Chicago	46.3	48.0	44.1	44.7	45.2	42.7	44.0	45.0
New York City	75.2	74.1	68.3	75.8	79.1	79.6	87.7	77.1
Boston	36.6	37.2	30.7	31.7	34.8	35.2	38.3	34.9
San Francisco	40.3	40.5	40.1	38.9	40.2	38.0	39.0	39.6
Albany	35.3	31.5	27.7	25.8	26.2	26.4	28.5	28.8
Rochester	18.4	20.7	20.7	20.7	22.5	23.8	30.3	22.4
Syracuse	10.3	11.6	8.9	8.6	9.6	8.9	8.9	9.5
Binghampton, N. Y.	21.0	24.9	22.7	22.1	23.0	20.8	20.6	22.2
Buffalo	18.1	20.7	18.7	20.6	26.2	24.9	26.2	22.2

The following estimates of the velocity of bank deposits are obtained from several sources. From 1896 to 1912 the values are taken from Irving Fisher's *The Purchasing Power of Money*; from 1912 to 1918 they are computed from the formula

$$V' = 12.3\, I/M' , \tag{4}$$

where I is the total national income; for 1919 and 1920 they are taken from Carl Snyder; from 1921 to 1934 they are Angell's estimates

Year	V'	Year	V'	Year	V'	Year	V'
1896	36.6	1907	45.3	1918	48.8	1929	71.7
1897	39.4	1908	44.8	1919	42.3	1930	48.6
1898	40.6	1909	52.7	1920	41.9	1931	36.3
1899	42.0	1910	52.7	1921	36.1	1932	28.7
1900	38.3	1911	53.4	1922	38.7	1933	26.7
1901	40.6	1912	53.4	1923	43.4	1934	24.5
1902	40.5	1913	50.8	1924	41.4	1935	24.2
1903	39.7	1914	41.8	1925	43.7	1936	24.1
1904	39.6	1915	45.4	1926	45.5	1937	23.4
1905	42.7	1916	45.8	1927	49.6	1938	20.0
1906	46.3	1917	49.9	1928	58.6		

Av. of $V' = 41.79$, $\sigma_{V'} = 10.00$.

based upon the data on bank debits for 141 cities including New York City; since 1934 they are estimates by the author.

Formula (4), by means of which values of V' were interpolated between the estimates of Fisher and Snyder was empirically derived. It would seem, however, that there should be some reasonably fixed ratio between the total exchange of money (bank debits) in a year and the total annual income. This assumption would imply, merely, that each exchange of money would add its percentage to national income and that income is thus derived as a necessary concomitant of the total exchange of money.

The test of this thesis is found in the following table of values of the quantity

$$k = M'V'/I \, .$$

The values of the income, I, are taken from the table given in Section 2 of Chapter 2; the values of the product $M'V'$ are taken for the year 1909 to 1912 from Fisher, and for the years from 1919 to 1934 they are computed from the data in Sections 4 and 5 of this chapter. The unit is in billions.

Year	$M'V'$	I	k	Year	$M'V'$	I	k
1909	353	27.2	12.98	1926	918	78.5	11.69
1910	381	30.1	12.66	1927	1134	77.2	14.69
1911	388	29.4	13.20	1928	1369	80.5	17.01
1912	436	31.8	13.40	1929	1678	79.1	21.21
....	......	......	....	1930	1101	72.2	15.25
1919	749	67.4	11.11	1931	744	60.1	12.38
1920	782	74.3	10.52	1932	463	46.5	9.96
1921	623	52.6	11.84	1933	413	44.4	9.30
1922	639	61.7	10.36	1934	463	50.4	9.19
1923	751	69.8	10.76	1935	535	54.9	9.74
1924	752	69.6	10.80	1936	624	62.4	10.00
1925	871	77.1	11.30				

Av. of $k = 12.27$, $\sigma_k = 2.55$.

It is clear from this table that k is not entirely independent of the velocity, since the large velocities which prevailed in the inflationary period around 1929 gave an abnormal increase to k and the subsequent depression abnormally reduced the value of k. In spite of these difficulties, however, formula (4) would appear to give a value of V' in stable periods, which would probably not be in error in excess of the error that exists in the values as directly computed.

In order to exhibit this highly important relationship between bank debits and national income, index numbers of both series were computed with 1926 = 100 as base. These indexes are graphically represented in Figure 58, together with similar indexes for industrial production and national income. We see from this figure that bank debits, while highly correlated with the national income, tend to rise higher in speculative periods and drop lower in depressions than national income. This difference is probably a good measure of the psychic factor which essentially enters into all price phenomena, since the variation between bank debits and national income is considerably greater than the variation between actual industrial production and

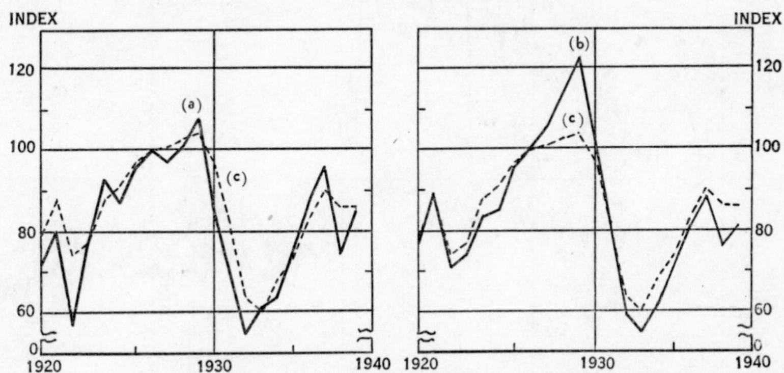

FIGURE 58.—THE FIRST CHART SHOWS INDEX NUMBERS (1926 = 100) FOR INDUSTRIAL PRODUCTION (a) AND THE NATIONAL INCOME (c). THE SECOND CHART MAKES A SIMILAR COMPARISON BETWEEN THE INDEXES FOR BANK DEBITS (b) AND NATIONAL INCOME (c). THE SPECULATIVE FACTOR IS THUS SHOWN TO BE MEASURED BY THE BANK DEBITS SERIES.

national income. The optimism of the speculative period around 1929 and the pessimism of the deflationary period around 1932 were clearly not justified by the national incomes of the two periods.

One may observe that much of the speculative activity in debit figures is revealed more clearly in the banking data for New York City than in the similar data for other cities. Hence it is instructive to consider separately the velocity of deposits for this financial center compared with the same velocity for cities outside of New York City. Figure 59 compares the two velocities. We note the incredible increase of the New York velocity at the time of the bull-market inflation from an average of 68.77 (1919 through 1925) to an average of 131.7 in 1929, and a comparable violent drop during the depression period, when the average fell to 34.90 (1932 through 1938). The outside velocity showed a much smaller fluctuation, rising from an average of 37.76 before the inflation to 47.1 for 1929, and then falling to an average of 26.54.

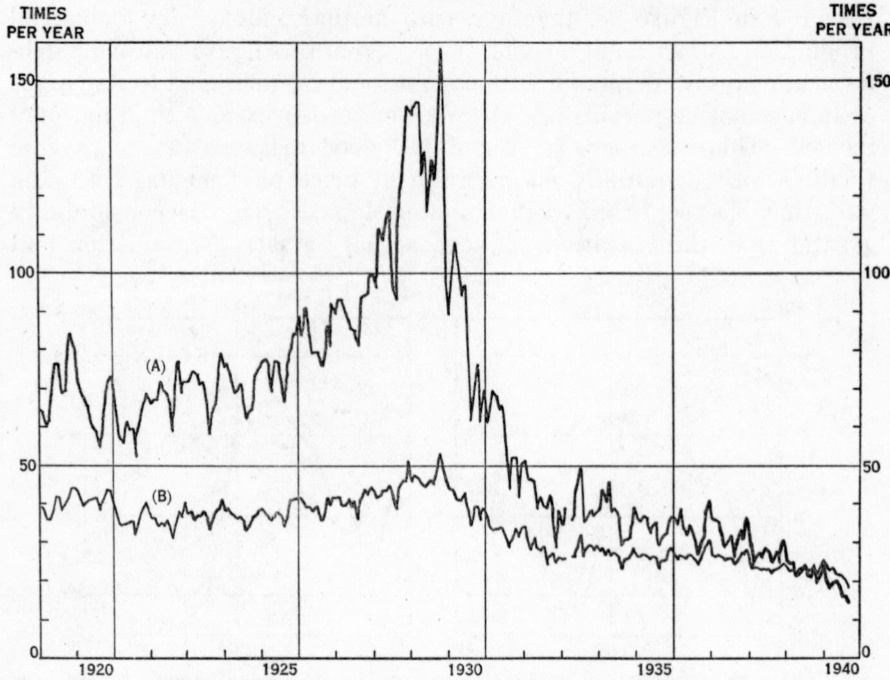

FIGURE 59.—THE VELOCITY OF BANK DEPOSITS. VELOCITY IN NEW YORK CITY (A); VELOCITY IN 100 CITIES OUTSIDE OF NEW YORK CITY (B).

6. *The Velocity of Circulating Money* (V)

The symbol V in the equation of exchange means the velocity of circulating money. This value is difficult to estimate and the first serious attempt made to approximate it was by Irving Fisher, who obtained values for the years from 1896 to 1912. W. S. Jevons recognized the difficulties of the computation in his *Money and the Mechanism of Exchange*[8] where he says:

> I have never met with any attempt to determine in any country the average rapidity of circulation, nor have I been able to think of any means whatever of approaching the investigation of the question, except in the inverse way. If we know the amount of exchanges effected, and the quantity of currency used, we might get by division the average number of times the currency is turned over; but the data, as already stated, are quite wanting.

Fisher's theory is based upon the assumption that most money does not circulate many times before it returns to the bank, but for the most part only once. He thus assumes that

[8] Published in New York in 1876, xviii + 349 pp. This work is an unusually clear treatment of the problem of money and exchange. See, in particular, p. 336.

. . . [much] money circulates in general only once outside of banks; but that when it passes through the hands of nondepositors (which practically means wage-earners) it circulates once more, thus adding the volume of wage payments to the volume of ordinary money circulation, which, as we have seen, is equal to the flow of money through banks.

We falsely picture the circulation of money in modern socity when we allow ourselves to think of it as consisting of a perpetual succession of transfers from person to person. Were it such a succession it would be, as Jevons said, beyond the reach of statistics. But we may form a truer picture by thinking of banks as the home of money, and the circulation of money as a temporary excursion from that home. If this description be true, the circulation of money is not very different from the circulation of checks. Each performs one transaction or, at most, a few transactions outside of the bank, and then returns home to report its circuit.[9]

Fisher divides those who circulate money into three classes: (1) commercial depositors, who handle money once; (2) other depositors, such as salaried and professional classes; and (3) nondepositors, who are wage earners for the most part.

Obviously the largest term in the computation of the velocity of money would be given by the total money deposited in banks during some unit of time. If we designate by C_b, O_b, and N_b the money deposited respectively by the three classes, then the total deposit would be the sum of these three terms, namely $C_b + O_b + N_b$. Figures were available for making an estimate of this total deposit for July 1, 1896 and for March 16, 1909. Thus in 1896 the daily deposit was 37.4 millions, which, when multiplied by the 305 settling days for the year, gives a total annual deposit of 11.4 billions. A similar estimate for 1909 yields the value 19.1. It was deemed necessary by Fisher, however, to correct these figures for the time of the month since "on July 1, 1896 many June bills must have been paid by cash as well as by check and on March 16, 1909, the middle of the month, there must have been a slackness of settlements by cash as well as by check." Hence, the first estimate was multiplied by 0.68 and the second by 1.17, giving new estimates of 7.8 and 22.3 billions respectively. The average of 11.4 and 7.8, namely, 9.6 billions, was assumed to be the total annual money deposits for the year 1896, and a similar average of 19.1 and 22.3, namely, 20.7 billions, was the estimated annual money deposits for the year 1909.

The second term in the computation of V would be that money which would circulate once outside of banks, that is to say, the total expenditure of nondepositors. This would be the sum of the payments of the nondepositors to commercial depositors, N_c, and to

[9] *The Purchasing Power of Money*, Second edition, New York, 1931, pp. 287–288.

other depositors, N_o. This sum, $N_c + N_o$, Fisher estimated to be between 5 and 6.5 billions of dollars in 1896 and 13.1 billions in 1909. Thus the estimates for the second figure are distributed as follows:

Trade and transportation	4.3 millions at $640	$ 2,752 millions
Manufacturing and mechanical pursuits	6.9 millions at $550	3,790 millions
Agricultural pursuits	12.4 millions at $300	3,720 millions
Domestic and personal service	7.4 millions at $250	1,850 millions
Clerks, etc. having no bank account		1,000 millions
Total		$13,112 millions

To the sum, $C_b + O_b + N_b + N_c + N_o$, must now be added an estimate of other money circulations such as interclass circulations and money exchanges not accounted for by the two large classes just described. This correction term is probably small and is estimated by Fisher to be 0.9 billions in 1896 and 1.3 billions in 1909. Hence one obtains for the total estimate of money circulated the following:

Circulation Classes	1896	1909
Money deposited $(C_b + O_b + N_b)$	9.6	20.7
Expenditure of Non-depositors $(N_c + N_o)$	5.7	13.1
Other circulation	0.9	1.3
Total (in billions)	16.3	35.1

Since total circulating money in 1896 was 0.87 billions and in 1909 was 1.63 billions (Fisher's estimates), the velocity of money would then be for the two years respectively $16.2/.87 = 18.6$ and $35.1/1.63 = 21.5$.

Having once estalished these two velocities, Fisher then interpolated velocities for the intervening years. He first made a table giving the linearly interpolated values of V between the velocities 18.6 and 21.5. A second table was then constructed so that the ratio of MV to $M'V'$ between the two dates was linearly interpolated. From the fluctuations in M new determinations of V were made, which were averaged with the ones given in the first table.

The following table of V and MV is taken from the second edition of Fisher's *The Purchasing Power of Money,* in which certain minor corrections were made in his first table and estimates for the years 1910, 1911, and 1912 were added:

The average value of V is found to be 20.9, with a standard deviation of 0.94. We thus infer that the velocity of money is much more stable than the velocity of deposits and that on the average it is about half the value of V'.

Year	V	MV	Year	V	MV	Year	V	MV
1896	18.8	16	1902	21.6	27	1908	19.7	32
1897	19.9	18	1903	20.9	29	1909	21.1	34
1898	20.2	20–	1904	20.4	28	1910	21	34
1899	21.5	22	1905	21.6	31+	1911	21	34
1900	20.4	24	1906	21.5	34	1912	22	38
1901	21.8	27	1907	21.3	35			

7. *Price* (*P*)

We turn next to a consideration of the concept of price, P, which appears in the right-hand member of the equation of exchange. In its simplest form price may be regarded as the ratio of exchange between two commodities such as, for example, wheat and corn. If one bushel of wheat may be exchanged for two of corn, then the ratio of exchange is two; we may then say that the price of a bushel of wheat is two bushels of corn. If, however, two bushels of wheat may be exchanged for three of rye, then the price of wheat may be said to equal 1.5 bushels of rye. But in order to simplify exchange, a common unit is chosen to which all commodities may be referred, and this unit is designated as money. In ordinary parlance, then, the price of a commodity means the exchange ratio between a unit of the commodity and a unit of money. Thus we say that the price of a bushel of wheat is $1.50, that of corn is $0.75, and that of rye is $1.00.

In earlier periods, before the advent of banking, the precious metals, principally gold and silver, were coined into convenient units and used as the common standard for determining price. Thus it is possible in the modern world to speak of the price of wheat in the middle ages by giving the number of grains of gold for which a bushel was then exchanged. To say that the price of wheat in the year 1420 was 19 cents merely means that one bushel of wheat was exchanged for 4.41 grains of gold. This is on the assumption that 480 grains = 1 Troy ounce = $20.67+ the old standard definition of the equivalence of dollars and gold.

It is a curious fact that the gold equivalence of money can be changed abruptly without any essential repercussions on price. On February 1, 1934 the United States Government changed the gold content of the dollar from 23.22 grains to 13.7143 grains. That is to say, the price of an ounce of gold changed abruptly from $20.67+ to $35.00. All monetary gold was redeemed at the former figure and newly-mined gold was purchased at the latter figure. There were immediate effects of this abrupt change in the price of gold in international exchange. Prior to the first indications in 1933 that the United

States contemplated a change in the gold standard, the pound had fallen from its par value of $4.8665 to $3.280 in December, 1932. But pronouncements by the president in March, 1933 that a new standard was imminent, caused an immediate rise in the value of the pound. By February, 1934, The Gold Reserve Act having been approved by Congress on January 30, 1934, the pound had risen as high as $5.033. But the effect on internal prices was unimportant. From March, 1933 to February, 1934 the sensitive index of wholesale commodity prices moved from 60.2 to 73.6, the difference being only 61 per cent of the standard deviation of this series. Prices had fallen to a low level as a result of the business decline, which began in 1929, and they were certain to rebound somewhat from their lows as the result of the natural elastic stresses in the price structure. The subsequent history of prices, particularly the decline which began in the fall of 1937, furnishes complete evidence that prices are not functionally related to the price of gold, except as this price affects international exchange and except as trade in gold, a somewhat unimportant commodity, affects the general level. The production of gold, however, received an unprecedented stimulus, as one might expect from a consideration of the curve of supply.

In order to compare the prices of one period with those of another, it is obvious that it would be more convenient to have a measure which is independent of the monetary unit employed and the various arbitrary units characteristically used in the trade in commodities, namely, bushels, tons, pounds, etc. Such a measure is found in index numbers. We have already introduced a definition of these numbers sufficient for our present purpose in Section 5 of Chapter 1. A more adequate consideration of problems relating to the definition of a level of prices will be given in Chapter 15.

It is obvious that a price level cannot be constructed from the data of one commodity. But if this commodity were an essential one, the general movement of other prices would probably conform somewhat closely to an average value of the price of the single commodity. It is upon this assumption that we shall attempt to examine in what we might call a macroscopic manner the variation in English prices over the long period of time between 1260 and 1930. In particular this study will reveal the great price revolution of the sixteenth century which is so instructive for us as students of general price movements of the twentieth century.

We shall use as the basis of our examination the series for the price of wheat, a series which is derived from the remarkably comprehensive studies of J. E. T. Rogers (1823–1890), published in his seven-volume work, *A History of Agricultural Prices in England.*[10] We shall consider a ten-year average of wheat prices, which will sufficiently smooth out the annual variation and will provide us with a series that indicates the major price fluctuations of the last seven centuries. These ten-year averages are given in the accompanying table and are graphically represented in Figure 60.[11]

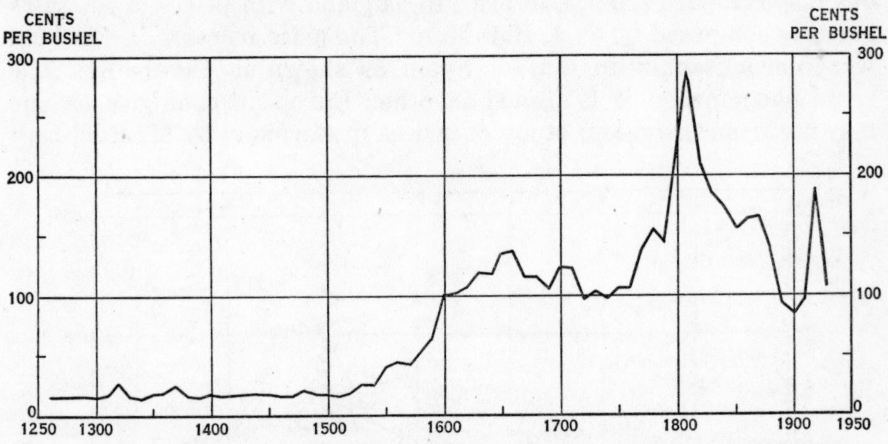

FIGURE 60.—TEN-YEAR AVERAGES OF WHEAT PRICES IN ENGLAND, 1260–1940.

TEN-YEAR AVERAGES OF ENGLISH WHEAT PRICES IN CENTS PER BUSHEL

Year	Price	Year	Price	Year	Price	Year	Price	Year	Price	Year	Price
1260	14.5	1380	16.0	1500	17.1	1620	108.2	1740	99.2	1860	163.2
1270	16.2	1390	13.9	1510	15.7	1630	119.9	1750	107.3	1870	165.1
1280	16.4	1400	17.6	1520	19.6	1640	118.8	1760	107.3	1880	136.8
1290	16.5	1410	15.8	1530	24.8	1650	134.5	1770	137.6	1890	93.1
1300	15.7	1420	17.1	1540	24.5	1660	137.1	1780	153.7	1900	83.8
1310	17.9	1430	17.5	1550	40.3	1670	114.1	1790	143.8	1910	97.8
1320	27.4	1440	19.0	1560	45.2	1680	115.0	1800	228.3	1920	188.5
1330	16.4	1450	17.0	1570	41.1	1690	104.9	1810	284.5	1930	108.4
1340	13.2	1460	15.9	1580	52.0	1700	123.2	1820	209.1		
1350	18.8	1470	16.4	1590	63.6	1710	121.8	1830	184.6		
1360	19.8	1480	20.2	1600	100.6	1720	97.0	1840	172.9		
1370	23.8	1490	16.6	1610	101.3	1730	103.3	1850	156.7		

The most interesting observation that we can make from a study of the graph of this long series is that the great price revolution began in the early part of the sixteenth century and reached its culmi-

[10] Oxford, Vol. 1, 2 (1866); Vols. 3, 4, 5, 6 (1887); Vol. 7 (1902).

[11] These data, reduced to equivalent cents per bushel based on equivalent values of gold and silver, are from N. C. Murray, *Wheat Prices in England,* Clement, Curtis, and Company, Chicago, 1931.

nation about the middle of the seventeenth century. The cause of this revolution has been attributed to the discovery of the abundant mines in America, which added large quantities of gold and silver first to the meager supply in Spain, and thence to all of Europe. It is a point worthy of special comment that the rise of prices in Spain was almost immediately transferred to other countries. Thus, if we form from wheat prices in England an index number with 1600 as the base year,[12] one may compare the rise in price in England with prices in Spain as recently computed by E. J. Hamilton.[13] The price increase in England was concomitant with that of Spain as shown in Figure 61. The same phenomenon is exhibited in other European countries as one may see from the recent study on prices in Germany by M. J. Elsas.[14]

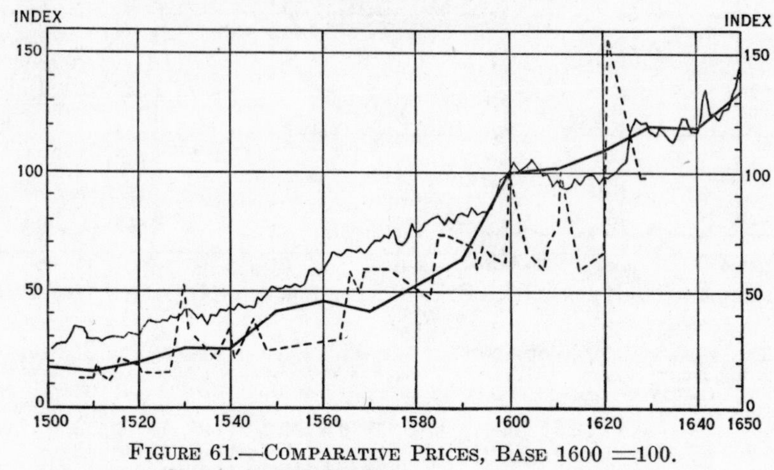

FIGURE 61.—COMPARATIVE PRICES, BASE 1600 = 100.
———: wheat prices in England,
- - - - -: wheat prices in Munich,
———: general price index in Spain (adapted from Hamilton).

And index based upon the price of wheat in Munich is also shown in Figure 61 and this tends to confirm the opinion that prices rose more rapidly on the continent than they did in England. The flow of treasure into continental countries was not impeded by ocean barriers as it was in England, and not until the time of Sir Francis Drake, who returned with his first spoils in 1573, and the buccaneers of the Span-

[12] By a base we mean a year whose price level is selected as a norm to which the price levels of other years are referred. The price level of the base year is generally set equal to 100.

[13] *American Treasure and the Price Revolution in Spain, 1501–1650,* Cambridge, Mass., 1934, xxxv + 428. pp.

[14] *Umriss einer Geschichte der Preise und Löhne in Deutschland,* Vol. 1, Leiden, 1936, x+ 808 pp.

ish Main, was sufficient treasure diverted into England to cause a spectacular rise in prices.

A second observation may be made with respect to the series of wheat prices. The price revolution reached its end by the middle of the seventeenth century and from that time until the beginning of the nineteenth century prices remained unusually stable at the high level which had been attained. Only a moderate fluctuation is apparent in the series and the economic history of that long period reveals no evidence of anything but a stable economic development, with the possible exception of the speculative fury of the South Sea Bubble around 1720.

On the contrary, the price history of the nineteenth and twentieth centuries is one of great disturbance. The nineteenth century was ushered in with the wars of the Napoleonic era and the consequent disruption of world economy. Tremendous surges were set up in the price structure, although the average level was not materially changed from that which had been attained in the price revolution. Although the price of wheat for the decennium centering around 1900 had reached the lowest value in three centuries, the World War introduced another violent perturbation in prices.

The story told by wheat prices is amply confirmed when we broaden our range to include a more general index of prices. Since the study contemplated in the present chapter concerns American indexes rather than those of England, we shall change, at the beginning of the nineteenth century, to the general commodity price index for the United States. This index has been constructed by G. F. Warren and F. A. Pearson for the years 1797–1889, and thereafter by the U. S. Bureau of Labor Statistics. It is graphically represented in Figure 1, Chapter 1.

From the graph of this index we note one important fact. War is the great price inflator. Thus, peaks appear as the result of the War of 1812, the Civil War, and the World War. These peaks are approximately fifty years apart and there is a striking similarity of price action in each of the three subsequent periods. After the cessation of hostilities there is an abrupt drop in prices, presumably occasioned by the collapse in farm values which have been inflated by war demand. For a brief period prices move along a small shelf, which was longer after the World War than after either of the other two wars, a phenomenon which may perhaps have been due to the large influx of gold during that time. The respite from deflation is short-lived, however, and prices again take their long drop to the first deflation minimum. The fall of prices is then halted and a mild inflation occurs, which is probably monetary in its origin. When the force of this inflation has been exhausted, the prices then continue to fall and reach their minimum value approximately twenty-five years after the beginning of the deflation. It is a melancholy reflection that prices then continue to rise, stimulated doubtless by a long period of increasing trade, until the era of economic prosperity culminates in another war and the creation of a new price cycle.

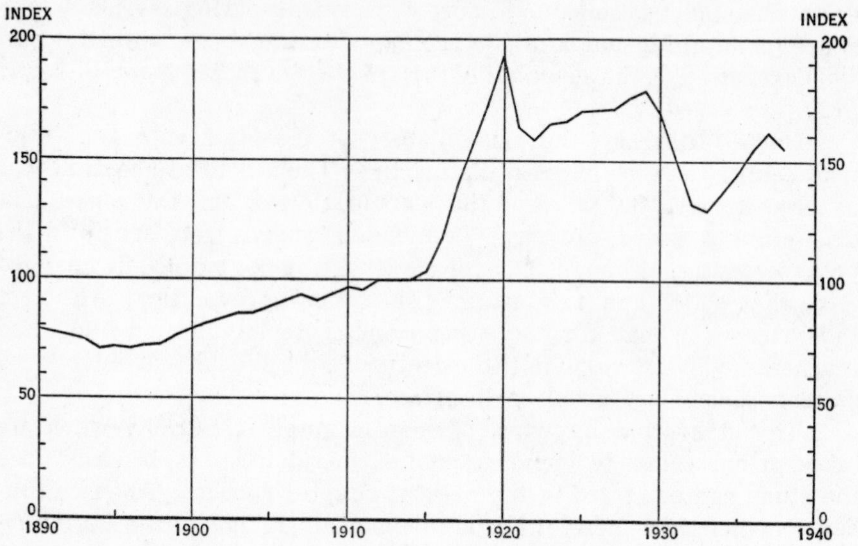

FIGURE 62.—GENERAL INDEX OF PRICES IN THE UNITED STATES. BASE: 1913 = 100.

But the question naturally arises: Can commodity prices be substituted for P in the equation of exchange? It is obvious that this equation is far more inclusive in its character, since all goods and services, of which commodities are only a part, are purchased by the total $MV + M'V'$ of the left-hand member.

In order to obtain a price index which would reflect changes in the *general level* of prices, Carl Snyder constructed for the Federal Reserve Bank of New York City a comprehensive series, which is entirely adequate to represent the parameter P in the right-hand member of the equation of exchange. These data are given in the accompanying table and they are graphically represented in Figure 62.

8. *Trade* (T)

We come finally to a consideration of the remaining variable in the equation of exchange, namely trade, which we have indicated by T. Since price has been represented by an index number, which is a

INDEX OF GENERAL PRICES

Year	Jan.	Feb.	Mar.	Apr.	May	June	July	Aug.	Sept.	Oct.	Nov.	Dec.	Av.
1890	77	77	77	77	78	78	77	78	79	78	77	77	78
1891	77	77	78	78	77	77	77	76	76	76	76	76	77
1892	75	76	75	75	76	76	75	76	76	76	76	77	76
1893	78	78	78	77	76	75	73	74	73	74	74	73	75
1894	72	71	71	71	70	71	71	71	72	71	71	71	71
1895	71	71	71	72	73	73	73	73	73	73	72	72	72
1896	72	72	71	71	71	71	71	70	70	71	72	72	71
1897	71	71	71	71	71	71	71	72	73	73	73	73	72
1898	73	74	73	73	74	73	73	73	73	74	74	74	73
1899	75	75	75	76	77	77	77	77	79	79	79	79	77
1900	80	80	80	80	79	79	79	79	79	80	80	80	79
1901	80	80	80	81	81	81	81	81	81	82	82	83	81
1902	82	82	82	83	84	84	84	84	85	87	85	86	84
1903	86	86	86	86	86	86	85	85	85	85	85	84	86
1904	85	86	86	85	85	85	86	86	86	87	87	87	86
1905	88	88	88	89	87	87	88	88	88	89	89	89	88
1906	90	90	90	90	90	90	90	90	91	92	92	93	91
1907	93	93	93	94	93	93	93	93	93	93	91	91	93
1908	91	90	90	90	91	91	91	91	91	91	92	92	91
1909	93	93	93	93	94	95	95	95	95	96	97	97	94
1910	97	97	98	97	98	97	98	97	97	96	96	96	97
1911	96	96	96	96	96	96	96	96	96	97	96	97	96
1912	97	98	99	100	100	100	100	100	100	101	100	100	100
1913	100	100	100	100	100	99	100	100	100	100	100	100	100
1914	100	100	100	100	100	100	100	101	101	100	99	100	100
1915	100	100	100	101	101	101	102	103	104	107	107	108	103
1916	110	111	113	114	114	115	115	117	120	122	126	127	117
1917	128	130	132	136	139	142	141	142	142	142	141	143	139
1918	144	146	147	149	151	153	145	158	160	162	162	164	157
1919	163	161	162	164	167	170	174	176	176	178	181	184	173
1920	188	189	192	196	198	199	198	195	195	192	187	180	193
1921	177	172	170	167	164	162	160	160	159	159	159	158	163
1922	156	155	155	156	158	158	159	160	160	161	162	163	158
1923	163	164	165	165	166	166	165	165	165	166	166	166	165
1924	167	167	166	165	165	164	165	166	165	165	166	168	166
1925	169	169	169	168	168	170	170	171	171	172	173	173	170
1926	173	172	171	171	171	171	171	171	172	171	172	171	171
1927	170	170	170	169	170	171	170	171	173	173	173	173	171
1928	173	173	174	175	177	176	176	176	178	177	177	178	176
1929	179	179	180	179	179	179	181	182	183	181	174	174	179
1930	174	173	173	174	172	169	167	166	167	163	161	158	168
1931	157	157	157	155	153	150	149	149	147	144	144	140	150
1932	138	136	137	134	132	129	129	132	132	131	130	128	132
1933	127	124	124	124	127	128	132	132	133	133	133	132	129
1934	133	136	136	137	136	137	138	138	139	139	140	140	137
1935	141	142	141	142	143	144	145	146	147	148	149	150	145
1936	150	150	151	150	150	152	154	156	156	156	158	159	154
1937	161	162	163	162	162	162	163	164	161	158	156	155	161
1938	155	154	152	152	152	152	155	154	154	155	154	155	154
1939	155	154	153	152	152	152	153	152	155	155	154	154	153

ratio having the dimensions of pure number, it is clear that trade must be dimensionally the same as total MV, that is to say, it must be expressed in terms of dollars per year.

Total trade is clearly not equal to the total annual value of production and services. This is equivalent to total income and we have already shown that this quantity is approximately one-twelfth of bank debits, that is to say, of $M'V'$. If goods were transferred directly from the producer to the consumer in one transaction, then obviously PT would be exactly equal to total income. But the stream of goods passing from production to consumption flows through many hands and in each exchange there is involved the ancillary exchange of money, which equals in annual total the total quantity MV. Hence, if we wish to represent PT more explicitly, we must write

$$PT = p_1q_1 + p_2q_2 + \cdots + p_nq_n ,$$

where $q_1, q_2, \cdots, q_n$ are the individual quantities of goods and services which are purchased during a year, and where $p_1, p_2, \cdots, p_n$ are their corresponding prices. But it is clear that many of these q_i are the same. Thus, if q_1 is wheat sold to the miller, then q_2 may be the same wheat sold as flour to the wholesaler, q_3 the same wheat sold to the baker, and q_4 the same wheat sold once more to the ultimate consumer as bread. In these transactions the prices will not be the same and in each transaction there will be added a quantity of service with its corresponding price.

The quantity T is, therefore, a kind of mathematical index of the *volume of transactions* per year, expressed in the units of dollars per year. Statistics are not available for its direct evaluation. It must be computed by dividing MV by P.

However, its trend must be that of the trend of production and its fluctuations should coincide with those of production. This follows from the fact that there must be a reasonably high stability in the number of transactions which take place for each commodity in its progress from production to consumption.

If, as in Figure 63, we compare the volume of trade with the index of industrial production, we note that the two curves are strikingly similar. The two trends show the same logistic characteristics, which we have noticed earlier in the production of pig iron. The industrial booms of 1906, 1917, and 1929, with the subsequent depressions of 1908, 1921, and 1932 are revealed in both graphs. The most striking difference is found in the abnormal rise of trade around 1929, which far exceeded in magnitude the industrial boom of the same period. This inflation we know was created by a great increase in stock speculation. Industrial production was unable to sustain the values which developed in the trade index and the subsequent depression followed.

Carl Snyder has constructed an index of the volume of trade by the combination of some fifty-six series by months back to the begin-

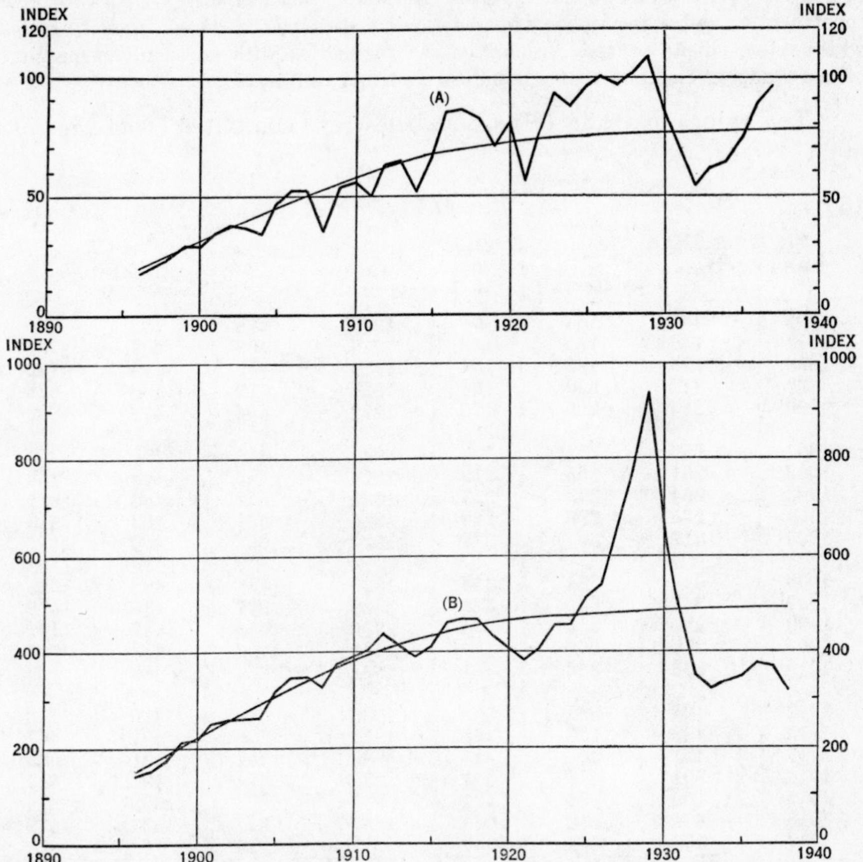

FIGURE 63.—COMPARISON OF THE INDEX OF VOLUME OF TRADE WITH THE INDEX OF INDUSTRIAL PRODUCTION. (A) INDEX OF INDUSTRIAL PRODUCTION; (B) INDEX OF TRADE.

ning of 1919. In this index 28 different factors were combined, divided into five separate categories as follows: (1) productive activity; (2) distribution to consumers; (3) primary distribution; (4) general business activity; (5) financial activity.

Snyder makes the following illuminating comment on the total volume of trade:

To sum up, the total trade of this nation now mounts up to unimaginable sums. According to our computation the aggregate value of all checks drawn exceeds 700 billions of dollars a year. This means a total volume of transactions in checks and money exceeding 800 billions. And by far the larger part of this vast trade relates to the production and distribution of food, clothing, and the astonishing variety of common needs and luxuries of everyday life, and to the command of human service which all this involves. Relatively but a minor part goes for new construction; and it seems, therefore, difficult to believe that those quantity series which relate chiefly to basic production can furnish us with an adequate measure of the trade or exchanges of a hundred and more millions of people.[15]

The values of trade (T) given below are computed from the formula

$$T = M'V'/P. \tag{5}$$

Year	Trade (T)	Trend Values $T(t)$	$M'V'$	Year	Trade (T)	Trend Values $T(t)$	$M'V'$
1896	139	154	99	1918	468	455	734
1897	156	169	112	1919	433	460	749
1898	179	185	131	1920	405	465	782
1899	212	202	163	1921	382	469	623
1900	215	219	170	1922	404	472	639
1901	256	237	208	1923	455	475	751
1902	261	255	219	1924	453	478	752
1903	264	273	227	1925	512	480	871
1904	265	290	228	1926	537	482	918
1905	317	307	279	1927	663	484	1134
1906	347	324	315	1928	778	485	1369
1907	347	340	323	1929	937	486	1678
1908	323	355	294	1930	655	487	1101
1909	375	369	353	1931	496	488	744
1910	393	382	381	1932	351	489	463
1911	404	395	388	1933	320	490	413
1912	438	406	438	1934	338	491	463
1913	411	416	411	1935	342	491	535
1914	391	426	391	1936	374	492	624
1915	409	434	421	1937	368	492	614
1916	462	442	540	1938	317	493	522
1917	468	449	650				

It is obvious that this value of T is smaller than the actual trade since the factor MV has been omitted. With the increased use of banks during the past half century, this error has become relatively negligible. The ratio of MV to $M'V'$ has steadily diminished from a value of 0.162 in 1896 to a value of 0.087 in 1912. It is safe to assume that the error in computing trade from formula (5) is not more than 10 per cent over the period under analysis.

A trend, $T(t)$ is fitted to the trade values obtained from formula

[15] *Business Cycles and Business Measurements*, New York, 1927, p. 180.

(5) on the assumption that the trend is logistic in character. The actual details of this computation will not be given. The method employed was essentially that described and illustrated in Section 5.[16]

The values of T, and the estimates of $T(t)$, together with the associated values of $M'V'$ are given in the following table:

9. *Snyder's Theory of Price*

As a result of a long study of the variables in the equation of exchange, Carl Snyder has evolved a theory of price which merits careful attention, not only because of its apparent statistical validity, but because of the possibility which it offers of defining a mechanism for the stabilization of prices.

Although the general features of the theory have been set forth in many of Snyder's writings, a precise mathematical formulation was wanting. This formulation has been provided recently by E. V. Huntington, whose notable work in the field of mathematical logic gave him ideal qualifications for the task of postulation.[17]

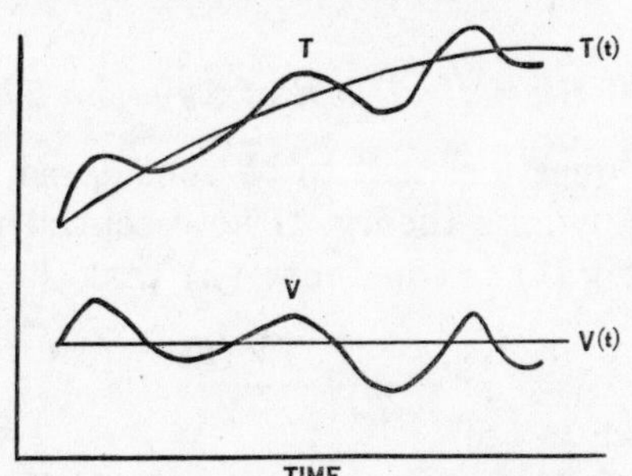

FIGURE 64.—CHART ILLUSTRATING SNYDER'S THEORY OF PRICES.

Snyder's theorem as stated by Huntington follows:

"In order to preserve the stability of the general price level (P), *we must keep the quantity of money* (M) *proportional to the long-time trend,* $T(t)$, *of the volume of trade; that is, we must make* $M = kT(t)$."

In this formulation the simpler form of the equation of exchange is used, namely,

$$MV = PT\,, \qquad (6)$$

where M is the total circulating money, mainly circulating deposits,

---

[16] Details of the computation are given in the author's treatise: *The Analysis of Economic Time Series,* Chap. 10, Section 8.

[17] See the *Bibliography* at the end of this chapter.

and V is its velocity. For the statistical verification of Snyder's theorem it will be convenient to think of M as essentially equivalent to M' as defined in Section 4, and V as equivalent to V'.

The first postulate of Snyder's theory is that the secular trend of V is nearly horizontal; that is,

$$V(t) = \text{constant}. \tag{7}$$

The second postulate of Snyder's theory states that the ratio of trade to the trend of trade is equal to the ratio of velocity to the trend of velocity. That is to say, in symbols, we have the equivalence

$$\frac{T}{T(t)} = \frac{V}{V(t)}. \tag{8}$$

Then, since by the first postulate $V(t)$ is a constant, it follows that P will be a constant provided M is proportional to $T(t)$. This is the statement of the theorem. The relationships between T, and V and their trends are illustrated in Figure 64.

10. The Statistical Test of Snyder's Theory

The important question next to be considered is that of the statistical validity of Snyder's theory. Two essential postulates must be examined: (1) that $V(t)$ is constant; (2) that the ratio

$$c = \frac{T}{T(t)} \cdot \frac{V(t)}{V} \tag{9}$$

is a constant, which is approximately equal to 1. The velocity we shall understand to be the velocity of deposits, the prime being dropped for convenience.

The first assumption, namely, that the trend of velocity, $V(t)$, is a constant, is difficult to establish directly. The range of the data is short and as one observes from the graph (Figure 65), velocity has been subjected to violent fluctuations during the past decade and a half. Thus one observes a decline from a maximum of more than 70 in 1929 to a minimum of around 20 in 1938. The average velocity, however, has remained relatively constant. Thus the average to 1917 inclusive was 44.50 with a standard error of 9.86, while for the subsequent period the average was 38.96 with a standard error of 12.72. We can say with reasonable certainty that there has been neither a secular increase nor a secular decrease over the period of 43 years under examination.

Unfortunately a computation of the value of c as defined by equation (9) shows that some modification of the theory is necessary. Thus the average value of c is found to be 1.0103 with a standard error of ± 0.1378. The largest value of c is for the year 1938, where this constant equals 1.3435. Hence the difference between c and its assumed value of 1.0000 exceeds twice the standard error in this case.

A check on this conclusion is obtained by making a direct computation of the general price index, using for this purpose the formula

$$P = \frac{V(t)}{c} \cdot \frac{M}{T(t)} = 41.36 \frac{M}{T(t)} . \tag{10}$$

The results of this computation are graphically shown in line (B) of Figure 66. One thus observes the great discrepancy between the computed and observed prices around 1920, 1929 and since 1932.

In scrutinizing the postulates of Snyder's system, it is upon the first one that suspicion falls because of its rigid and uncompromising character. In a world of change, it seems, strange, indeed, that the

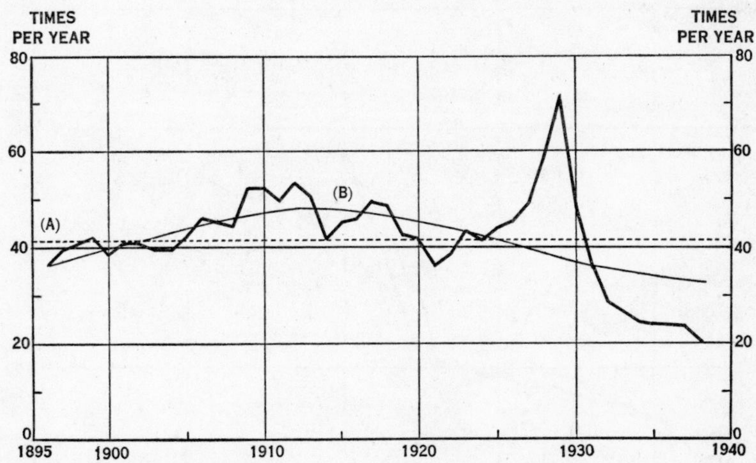

FIGURE 65.—ANNUAL AVERAGE OF THE VELOCITY OF DEPOSITS. LINE (A) IS THE CONSTANT SECULAR TREND OF VELOCITY; LINE (B) IS A HARMONIC APPROXIMATION TO $V(t)$ WITH A PERIOD OF FIFTY YEARS.

trend of velocity should be a constant. Particularly in a series where one witnesses such violent fluctuations as those which appear in the velocity factor and in which the psychic element seems to be so great, it strains belief to assume that one will find an unchanging pattern. Of course, the assumption is derived from an observation that the general spending mechanism is regimented by the institution of banking. Hence, it seems reasonable to suppose that in the long run about the same velocity of exchange will prevail in spite of the occasional extreme optimisms which can produce a velocity of 70, or the subsequent pessimisms which can reduce the velocity to 20.

An analysis of the discrepancies between Snyder's price and the observed price indicates that the trend of velocity is not constant, but that it is of a sinusoidal character about a constant value. This observation is easily made if one determines from equation (10) the values of $V(t)$ which will actually give the observed price. It is found from this that if a sine curve of period approximately equal to 50 years and of amplitude equal to 7.17 is added to the average velocity, then a much better agreement is obtained between the computed and the observed series.

In the following table we give the new values of $V(t)$, the resulting value of c, the values of Snyder's price, p_c, and the deviations, $P_c - P$, between it and the observed price. The graph of the velocity is given in Figure 65, the values of c are graphically represented in

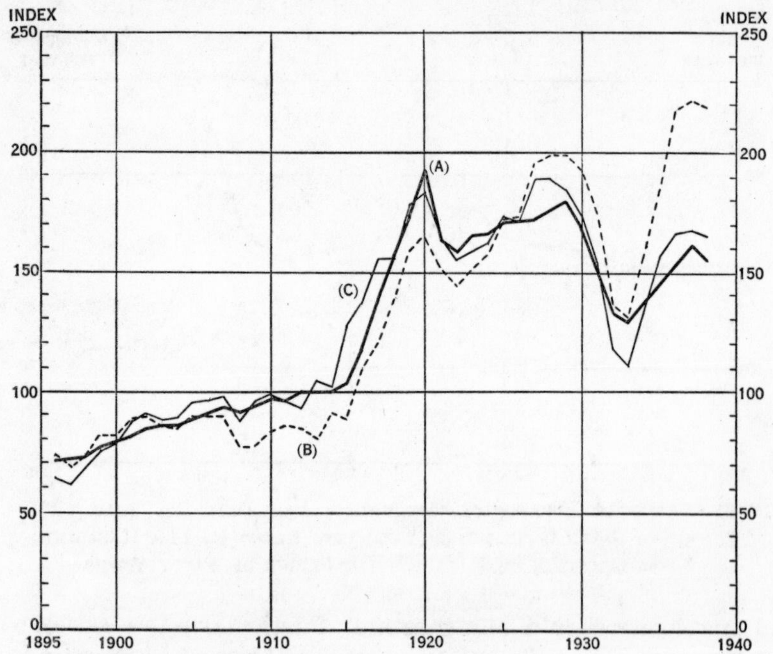

FIGURE 66.—COMPARISON OF THE COMPUTED PRICE INDEX WITH THE ACTUAL PRICE INDEX.

In this figure (A) is the General Price Index. Index (B) is computed on the assumption that $V(t)$ is a constant. Index (C) assumes that $V(t)$ is a harmonic of period equal to fifty years.

Figure 67, and the new computations of P_c are compared with the observed price in Figure 66.

Year	$V(t)$	c	P_c	$P_c - P$	Year	$V(t)$	c	P_c	$P_c - P$
1896	36.5	0.9002	64	— 7	1918	46.8	0.9864	155	— 2
1897	37.2	0.8716	61	—11	1919	46.2	1.0281	178	5
1898	38.0	0.9057	67	— 6	1920	45.6	0.9479	183	—10
1899	38.9	0.9720	76	— 1	1921	44.9	1.0131	165	2
1900	39.8	1.0228	78	— 1	1922	44.2	0.9775	155	— 3
1901	40.7	1.0829	87	6	1923	43.4	0.9579	158	— 7
1902	41.6	1.0513	90	6	1924	42.5	0.9729	162	— 4
1903	42.5	1.0352	88	2	1925	41.6	1.0154	173	3
1904	43.3	0.9991	89	3	1926	40.7	0.9966	171	0
1905	44.1	1.0665	95	7	1927	39.8	1.0991	188	17
1906	44.9	1.0387	96	5	1928	39.0	1.0675	188	12
1907	45.6	1.0273	98	5	1929	38.1	1.0245	184	5
1908	46.2	0.9384	87	— 4	1930	37.3	1.0323	173	5
1909	46.7	0.8989	87	— 7	1931	36.5	1.0220	153	3
1910	47.2	0.8956	95	— 2	1932	35.8	0.8954	118	—14
1911	47.6	0.9756	99	3	1933	35.2	0.8610	111	—18
1912	47.7	0.9637	96	— 4	1934	34.7	0.9750	133	— 4
1913	47.9	0.9316	93	— 7	1935	34.2	0.9843	156	11
1914	47.9	1.0517	95	5	1936	33.8	1.0662	166	12
1915	47.8	0.9923	102	— 1	1937	33.7	1.0773	167	6
1916	47.5	1.0840	127	10	1938	33.6	1.0802	165	11
1917	47.2	0.9859	136	— 3	Av.	41.7	0.9947		0.52

With the new determination of prices, there still remain one or two disagreements. The first of these is in the inflationary period of the bull market. It is possible that this discrepancy can be accounted for partially by the rigid system of weights used in the general index

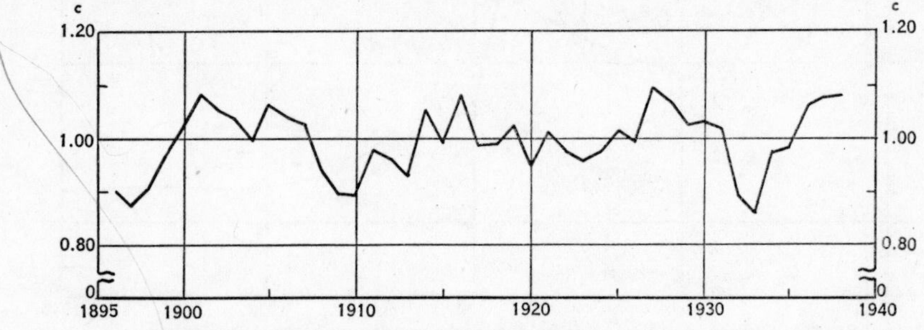

FIGURE 67.—VARIATIONS IN "SNYDER'S CONSTANT", (c).

of prices. Thus, the dominating characteristics of the period around 1929 was the spectacular rise in the price of stocks. The velocity of deposits also increased in a remarkable manner, as we have seen, and there was a corresponding rise in the volume of trade, which was only partially accounted for by the increase in industrial production. This great expansion of trade is undoubtedly to be explained by the increase in stockmarket transactions, which reached unprecedented heights. But in the computation of the general price index this spectacular increase in the price of stocks and its reaction upon the general level of prices were probably not sufficiently accounted for by the original weighting of five per cent, which was not changed over this period.

In connection with this revision of Snyder's first postulate, the question naturally arises as to the justification for introducing the new trend of velocity. The hypothesis has admittedly been advanced *ad hoc* in order to explain the major discrepancies of the Snyder theory, and until more evidence is adduced as to the reality of the observed cycle, the hypothesis must remain a tentative one. However, we have seen that prices themselves are intimately related to the war cycle, and the fact that the period in the velocity is also the average length of this phenomenon, may, perhaps, tentatively suggest a connection between the two phenomena.

One may observe in passing that there appears in recent years

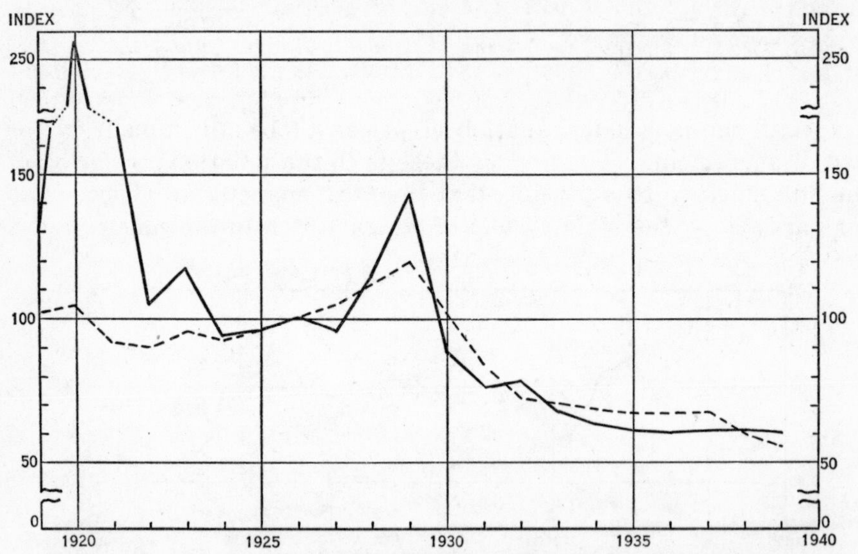

FIGURE 68.—COMPARISON OF THE INDEX OF "MONEY TENSION" WITH THE INDEX OF THE VELOCITY OF DEPOSITS. HEAVY LINE IS "MONEY TENSION" MEASURED BY INTEREST RATES; DOTTED LINE IS THE INDEX OF THE VELOCITY OF DEPOSITS.

to be a relationship between the velocity of money and the rate of interest, which has been created by the exigencies of large governmental deficit spending. If we consider the curve of money tension as measured by the reciprocal of the Standard Statistics Company's inverted interest rate over the period from 1919 to date, we note that a high correlation exists between the velocity factor (expressed as an index number with $1926 = 100$) and a similar index of money tension. The high tension observed in 1920 had no counterpart in the velocity index, but at this time there occurred one of the major readjustments of prices following the great war inflation. These data are graphically represented in Figure 68.

Our final conclusion from this study is that the agreement between computed and real prices appears to be quite satisfactory, when one considers the nature of the data, and the long range of time involved in the analysis. Certainly the major part of the variation in price can be accounted for by this theory.

11. *Gold and Silver and Their Relationship to the Level of Prices*

The next question concerns the relationship between world stocks of gold and silver and the variables in the equation of exchange. A complete discussion of this interesting but complicated question involves a consideration of world prices and the ratios of the currencies of the chief industrial countries. This problem we shall not consider here, since this would involve an analysis of the mechanism of foreign exchange, which will be discussed later in Chapter 20.

We may see, however, to what extent internal prices are presumably affected by gold and silver as the holdings of these metals affect the amount of currency in actual circulation. We have previously seen that money, M, which is for the most part fiduciary currency with a theoretical gold base, is about 25.9 per cent of circulating deposits, that is,

$$M = 0.259M'.$$

This percentage is obtained by averaging the ratio H of Section 4.

Moreover, since the average velocity of M is about 50 per cent of the velocity of M', that is,

$$V = 0.50V',$$

it is clear that MV would be on the average about $25.9 \times 0.50 = 12.9$ per cent of $M'V'$. Hence, any small increase in actual currency, caused by its issue against an increase in holdings of gold and silver, would have a negligible effect upon trade and prices. Any large increase would necessarily have profound repercussions upon the price system.

An instructive example of this is the great German inflation, which began with the World War and culminated in 1923. A comprehensive study of this unusual phenomenon has been given by C. Bresciani-Turroni, whose data we employ.[18] We note from the accompanying table the rapid increase in the issuance of paper marks as the financial condition of the government became more desperate. The total M' became submerged in the enormous issue of M and all business was of necessity transacted in the depreciated marks. The index number of wholesale prices, which was around 1.00 in 1914 and 2.45 at the end of the war, rose rapidly to 8.03 in December, 1919, to 14.4 a year later, to 34.9 in December, 1921, to 1.475 in December, 1922, and to the fantastic level of 1,262 billion at the end of the deflation in 1923.

CIRCULATION OF THE REICHSBANK
(Billions of paper marks)

Year	Jan.	Feb.	Mar.	Apr.	May	June	July	Aug.	Sept.	Oct.	Nov.	Dec.
1914	2.1	2.0	2.4	2.1	2.0	2.4	2.9	4.2	4.5	4.2	4.2	5.0
1915	4.7	4.9	5.6	5.3	5.3	5.8	5.5	5.6	6.2	5.9	6.0	6.9
1916	6.5	6.6	7.0	7.0	6.7	7.2	7.0	7.1	7.4	7.3	7.3	8.1
1917	7.9	8.1	8.6	8.3	8.3	8.7	8.9	9.3	10.2	10.4	10.6	11.5
1918	11.1	11.3	12.0	11.8	12.0	12.5	12.7	13.6	15.3	16.7	18.6	22.2
1919	23.6	24.1	25.5	26.6	28.2	30.0	29.3	28.5	29.8	30.9	31.9	35.7
1920	37.4	41.0	45.2	47.9	50.0	54.0	55.8	58.4	61.7	63.6	64.3	68.8
1921	66.6	67.4	69.4	70.8	71.8	75.3	77.4	80.1	86.4	91.5	100.9	113.6
1922	115	120	131	140	152	169	190	238	317	469	754	1280
1923	1984	3513	5518	6546	8564	17291	45594	663*	28229*	2.5†	400.3†	496.5†

* Trillions of marks; † Quadrillions of marks.

The lesson to be learned from this is not that there is virtue in a gold basis for currency, but merely that the ratio between M and M' should be held reasonably constant and that the issuance of M, or the expansion of M', should follow the trend of trade and not be governed by the exigencies of the national credit. More will be said on this subject in Chapter 20.

12. Summary

In the preceding pages of this chapter we have given a systematic study of the six variables which enter into the equation of exchange. We have discussed their independent measurement and have shown how each variable has its own special significance in the economy.

Far from being a mere tautology, the equation of exchange has been shown to have a position in the study of economics similar to that of the equation of conduction in the theory of electricity. The

[18] *The Economics of Inflation, London,* 1937, 464 pp. (First issued in Italian in 1931).

equation imposes one restraint upon six variables which have independent definition. From this mathematical foundation we can then explore safely the consequences of other postulates which relate one or more of the variables to the elements of other economic time series.

From the standpoint of the equation of exchange we can establish a theory of prices, which appears to have statistical validity, and which accounts for the major variation in this important variable. Our conclusion would be that the equation of exchange furnishes us with one of the most powerful instruments in interpreting economic movements and in exploring the consequences of major changes in economic policy.

PROBLEMS

1. Differencing the equation of exchange, $MV = PT$, show that an alternative form for it is given by the following expression:

$$\frac{\Delta M}{M} + \frac{\Delta V}{V} = \frac{\Delta T}{P} + \frac{\Delta T}{T}. \tag{11}$$

2. Making use of equation (11) in problem 1, determine the conditions under which money could increase but prices decline. Under what conditions would velocity increase, but trade decline?

3. From 1932 to 1938 we observe from the tables in this chapter that the percentage increase in circulating deposits was approximately 42 and the percentage increase in P was approximately 17. If $\Delta T = 0$, what was the value of $\Delta V/V$? Compare this with the observed change. What conclusion do you reach about trade during this period?

4. In a closed economic system, if a 10 per cent increase is observed in prices, if a 15 per cent increase is noted in trade, and if $\Delta V = 0$, how large was the initial supply of money if $\Delta M =$ \$100,000,000?

5. How much of a decline in an initial velocity of money equal to 30 would be required to balance an increase of 5 per cent in the supply of circulating money so that neither price nor trade would change?

6. During the period of the German inflation we find the following values for the index numbers of wholesale prices according to Bresciani-Turroni (*loc cit.*):

Index Numbers of Wholesale Prices in Germany
(1913 = 100)

Year	Jan.	Feb.	Mar.	Apr.	May	June	July	Aug.	Sept.	Oct.	Nov.	Dec.
1918	204	198	198	204	203	209	208	235	230	234	234	245
1919	262	270	274	286	297	308	339	422	493	562	678	803
1920	1260	1680	1710	1570	1510	1380	1370	1450	1500	1470	1510	1440
1921	1440	1380	1340	1330	1310	1370	1430	1920	2070	2460	3420	3490
1922	3670	4100	5430	6350	6460	7030	10060	19200	28700	56600	115400	147500

During the period in question the trade remained reasonably constant. On this assumption, and making use of the circulation table in Section 11, compute the increase in the velocity of money from January of one year to January of the next. How much did the velocity increase between January 1922 and December 1922?

7. If the total income of a city of 40,000 people is $22,400,000, what approximately is the value of the bank debits for the year, on the assumption that the velocity of deposits is 20? Would this answer be modified if some particular year were specified? How would you modify the problem if the year were 1926?

8. In the city of problem 7, approximately how large were the circulating deposits?

9. How many families had incomes in excess of $25,000 in the city of problem 7?

10. Making use of formula (11) of problem 1 estimate the answer to the following question: If a community of 40,000 people gains an industry which keeps an average balance in the bank of $50,000, and if both the velocity of money and price remain fixed, how much approximately is added to the income of the city?

11. Under the conditions of problem 10 compute the approximate increase in the trade of the city created by the new industry.

12. An individual finds from his bank statement that he had the following amounts on deposit during the month of June: June 1, $425.26, June 5, $793.53, June 10, $686.82, June 15, $519.96, June 20, $368.65, June 25, $162.29, June 30, $150.25. On the basis of these figures, what was his monthly velocity?

13. Compare the velocities of money of the following two families, each of which has a monthly income of $300. Both families pay $70 for food, $30 for clothing, $60 house rent, $25 for household operation, $25 for transportation, $10 for gifts and taxes, $40 for miscellaneous items, and save $40. The first family charges food, clothing, transportation, and household operation, paying for these items at the beginning of each month. The second family distributes its payments for these items by paying cash uniformly over the month. Both pay house rent at the beginning of the month. Both distribute gifts and miscellaneous items over the month and both transfer their savings to a time account at the end of each month.

14. How large a balance should each family describe in problem 13 add to his checking account in order to maintain an annual velocity of 20?

15. If in problem 13 the savings of the second family were expended over the month, by what per cent would the velocity be increased?

16. Under the condition of problem 15, how much should the second family add to its checking account in order to maintain a velocity of 20?

17. If in problem 13 the savings of the first family were expended over the month, by what per cent would the velocity be increased?

18. Under the condition of problem 17, compute the amount that the first family should add to its checking account in order to maintain a velocity of 20.

19. In a certain city its three banks report the following demand deposits: (a) $9,905,708.70; (b) $4,403,707.18; (c) $1,902,585.41, the report being made as of January 1, 1941. Estimate the size of the city and its probable annual income.

20. If in a country it is observed that the index of production has a secular trend of one per cent per annum, how fast should the money supply increase if prices are to be kept constant?

21. If in the United States the money supply is not increased beyond its value in 1938, and if trade advances 10 per cent by 1945, what would be the expected price level if velocity maintains a value of 20?

22. Answer the question given in problem 21, if the trend of velocity follows a sinusoidal pattern as indicated in Figure 65.

SELECTED BIBLIOGRAPHY ON THE EQUATION OF EXCHANGE

ANDERSON, O. "Ist die Quantitätstheorie statistisch nachweisbar?" *Zeitschrift für Nationalökonomie*, Vol. 2, 1931, pp. 523 ff.

ANGELL, J. W. (1) *The Theory of International Prices.* Cambridge, Mass., 1926, xiv + 571 pp.

(2) *The Behavior of Money.* New York, 1936, xiv + 207 pp.

BRESCIANI-TURRONI, C. *The Economics of Inflation.* (English Translation). London, 1937, 464 pp. Italian edition, published by the University of Bocconi in 1931. See in particular, Chapter 4.

BURGESS, W. R. "Velocity of Bank Deposits," *Journal of the American Statistical Association*, 1923, pp. 727–740.

ESSARS, PIERRE DES. "La vitesse de la circulation de la monnaie," *Journal de la Société de Statistique de Paris*, 1896, p. 143.

EVANS, G. C. *Mathematical Introduction to Economics.* New York and London, 1930, xi + 177 pp. In particular, Chapter 9.

FISHER, IRVING. *The Purchasing Power of Money.* New York, 1911, xxii + 505 pp.; second edition, 1931.

(2) "Our Unstable Dollar and the So-Called Business Cycle," *Journal of the American Statistical Association*, 1925, pp. 179–202.

(3) *Booms and Depressions.* New York, 1932, xxi + 258 pp.

HAMILTON, E. J. *American Treasure and the Price Revolution in Spain, 1501–1650.* Cambridge, Mass., 1934, xxxv + 428 pp.

HAWTREY, R. G. *Currency and Credit.* London, 1934, ix + 477 pp.

HUNTINGTON, E. V. "On the Mathematical Hypotheses Underlying Carl Snyder's Trade-Credit-Ratio Theorem," *Econometrica*, Vol. 6, 1938, pp. 177–179.

KEMMERER, E. W. *Money and Credit Instruments in their Relations to General Prices.* New York, 1909.

KEYNES, J. M. *A Treatise on Money.* Vol. 1, New York, 1930, xvii + 363 pp.; Vol. 2, viii + 424 pp. In particular, Chapters 10 and 24.

MARGET, A. W. (1) "The Relation between the Velocity of Circulation of Money and the Velocity of Circulation of Goods," *Journal of Political Economy*, Vol. 40, 1932, p. 502.

(2) *The Theory of Prices.* Vol. 1, New York, 1938, xxv + 624 pp.

MARSCHAK, J. *Elastizität der Nachfrage.* Tübingen, 1931, xix + 143 pp.

MISES, L. VON. *The Theory of Money and Credit.* English translation by H. E. Batson, London, 1934, 445 pp. First German edition, 1912; second edition, 1924.

NEWCOMB, SIMON. *Principles of Political Economy.* New York, 1886.

ROOS, C. F. *Dynamic Economics.* Bloomington, Ind., 1934, xvi + 275 pp. In particular, Chapter 13.

SNYDER, CARL. (1) *Business Cycles and Business Measurements.* New York 1927, xv + 326 pp.

(2) "Industrial Growth and Monetary Theory," *Economic Forum,* 1933, pp. 275–290.

(3) "New Measures in the Equation of Exchange," *American Economic Review,* 1924,

(4) "New Measures of the Relations of Credit and Trade," *Proceedings of the Academy of Political Science,* 1930,

(5) "Further Measures of the General Price Level and the Trade-Credit Relations for Great Britain," *Le revue de l'institut de statistique,* 2nd year, book 3, 1934.

(6) "Deposits Activity as a Measure of Business Activity," *Review of Economic Statistics,* 1924.

(7) "A New Index of the General Price Level from 1875," *Journal of the American Statistical Association,* 1924,

(8) "The Problem of Money and Economic Stability," *Quarterly Journal of Economics,* 1925.

SPRAGUE, O. M. W. "Fisher's Purchasing Power of Money," *Quarterly Journal of Economics,* Vol. 26, 1911.

STAMP, SIR JOSIAH. (1) *Papers on Gold and the Price Level.* London, 1932.

(2) *The Present Position of Monetary Science.*

VINER, JACOB. *Studies in the Theory of International Trade,* New York, 1937, xv + 650 pp.

CHAPTER 13

INTEREST AND INVESTMENT

1. Definitions

By the word interest is generally meant the amount of money which is earned in a given length of time by principal that has been profitably invested. Thus if a principal, denoted by P, at the end of a period of time has increased to $P + I$, then I is called the interest made by the investment. The *rate of interest*, denoted by i, is the ratio of I to P; that is, $i = I/P$.

Simple interest is interest that is proportional to the time during which the capital has been invested. In actual business practice simple interest is usually computed at intervals not to exceed one year, and generally for shorter periods such as three or four months.

Interest after it has been earned is frequently reinvested, that is to say, it is in effect added to capital. This interest then in its turn earns interest, which may again be added to principal. When interest is thus reinvested at stated intervals throughout a period of time, the difference between the final principal and the original principal is called *compound interest*.

The sum of the original principal and the accrued interest is called the total amount; it is generally designated by the letter S. If P is invested for n intervals of time at simple interest at rate i, then S is given by the formula

$$S = P + Pin . \tag{1}$$

If P is invested at compound interest for n intervals of time at rates $i_1, i_2, i_3, \cdots, i_n$, then the compound amount is given by the formula

$$S = P(1 + i_1)(1 + i_2)(1 + i_3) \cdots (1 + i_n) . \tag{2}$$

If the rates of interest are all equal, then this quantity reduces to the simple form

$$S = P(1 + i)^n . \tag{3}$$

As we have explained above, interest is often compounded more than once a year. If we let i, called the *effective rate*, refer to periods of one year, then it is useful to have a relationship between this rate and the rate j, called the *nominal rate,* which is compounded m times a year. If interest is compounded m times per year, then the rate for one interval will be j/m. Hence the total amount to which one dollar will accumulate in the year will be $(1 + j/m)^m$. This quantity is equal to the unit principal plus the effective rate, that is,

$$1 + i = (1 + j/m)^m . \tag{4}$$

Consequently the compound amount in terms of the nominal rate becomes

$$S = P(1 + j/m)^{mn} . \tag{5}$$

If we solve equation (4) for the nominal rate of interest, we obtain j in terms of the effective rate. We thus obtain the formula

$$j = m[(1 + i)^{1/m} - 1] . \tag{6}$$

In business practice m is usually 2 or 4, that is to say, money is usually compounded semi-annually or quarterly. Bonds usually pay their interest twice or four times a year, and banks lend money on notes due in 90 days or in six months. However, in instances such as that of monthly installment buying, or the payment of rents, or where insurance premiums are paid monthly, the value of m may be 12.

It is instructive to observe what happens to formula (5) if m becomes infinite, that is to say, if money is compounded at every instant of time. At first sight such an assumption might seem to be unrealistic, but in large banking systems where loans are made and received a great many times every day there is certainly observed an approximation to instantaneous compound interest. Populations, also, have a tendency to grow by the instantaneous compound interest law over short periods of time and there are many biological and physical examples of its application.

When money is compounded instantaneously we refer to the nominal rate as the force of interest and designate it by the Greek letter δ (delta). If, then, in (4) we replace j by δ and recall the limit [1]

$$\lim_{r=0} (1 + r)^{1/r} = e = 2.71828 \cdots ,$$

we shall have

$$1 + i = \lim_{m=\infty} [(1 + \delta/m)^{(m/\delta)}]^{\delta} = e^{\delta} .$$

Hence formula (5) assumes the simple form

[1] See, for example, H. T. Davis and W. F. C. Nelson: *Elements of Statistics,* 2nd ed., 1937, pp. 359–360.

(7) $$S = P e^{n\delta} ,$$

which is generally referred to as the *compound interest* law. It is also, although somewhat erroneously, called the *law of biological growth.* Biological organisms under assumptions of unlimited food and unlimited opportunity to expand, do increase according to this law for short periods of time. However, as we have seen in our discussion of the logistic curve and its applications, their rate of growth diminishes after a while and ultimately the population reaches a place of constant equilibrium.

At first sight one might believe that the assumption of unlimited compounding would materially increase the value of the effective rate. That this is not the case is easily seen by computing the effective rate for nominal rates corresponding to 2, 4, and 12 conversions a year and also for the force of interest. Letting $j = \delta = .06$, we obtain for the corresponding effective rates the following:

Conversion Period (m)	2	4	12	∞
Effective Rate (i)	.060900	.061364	.061678	.061837

If in formula (6) m is allowed to increase indefinitely, it will be found that $j = \delta$ is related to the effective rate by the formula

(8) $$\delta = \log_e(1 + i) .$$

In practical business affairs it is customary to employ interest tables which are based upon formula (5).[2] But since the difference between (5) and (7) is small compared with the variation occasioned by changes in the interest rate itself, and since (7) is mathematically simpler to deal with than (5), it is useful in some arguments to employ the concept of the force of interest.

It will be convenient in later sections to have available a short table of the values of j in terms of i for certain particular values of m. This table is given below.

Values of $j = m[(1 + i)^{1/m} - 1]$

m	1%	1½%	2%	3%	4%	5%	6%	7%	m
2	0.009975	0.01494	0.01990	0.02978	0.03961	0.04939	0.05913	0.06882	2
4	0.009963	0.01492	0.01985	0.02967	0.03941	0.04909	0.05870	0.06823	4
6	0.009959	0.01491	0.01984	0.02963	0.03935	0.04899	0.05855	0.06804	6
12	0.009954	0.01490	0.01982	0.02960	0.03928	0.04889	0.05841	0.06785	12
∞	0.009950	0.01489	0.01980	0.02956	0.03922	0.04879	0.05827	0.06766	∞

[2] See, for example, J. W. Glover: *Tables of Applied Mathematics in Finance, Insurance, Statistics.* Ann Arbor, Michigan, 1923.

The compound interest function, $s_n = (1 + i)^n$, has been extensively tabulated for small differences in i and over a long range in n. A brief table to four decimal places is found in Table I at the end of this volume.

Example 1. Compare the compound amount for 12 years of $100 at 6% effective with the compound amount at 6% nominal, converted four times a year, and also with the compound amount accumulated at a force of interest equal to .06.

Solution. Using Table I, we have

$$x_1 = \$100\,(1.06)^{12} = \$201.22\,,$$
$$x_2 = \$100\,(1.015)^{48} = \$204.35\,.$$

Using logarithms in the calculation, we have finally

$$x_3 = \$100\; e^{0.06 \times 12} = \$100\; e^{0.72} = \$205.44\,.$$

Example 2. A man has three investments, the first of $1,000 at 4% nominal, converted four times a year, the second of $1,500 at 6% effective, and the third of $2,000 at 3% nominal, converted twice a year. How much will he have accumulated at the end of 5 years? What average rate of interest does his money earn?

Solution. From Table I we compute the accumulation

$$S = \$1{,}000\;(1.01)^{20} + \$1{,}500\;(1.06)^{5} + \$2{,}000\;(1.015)^{10}$$
$$= \$1{,}220.20 + \$2{,}007.30 + \$2{,}321.00 = \$5{,}548.50\,.$$

Since the man has a total of $4,500 invested for 5 years, we obtain the average effective rate of interest, i, from the equation

$$\$4{,}500\;(1 + i)^5 = \$5{,}548.50\,.$$

Taking logarithms of both sides we obtain

$$\log\,(1 + i) = \frac{1}{5}\,(\log 5548.50 - \log 4500) = 0.01819\,.$$

Hence we get $1 + i = 1.0428$, which shows that the average rate of interest earned was 4.28 per cent. This answer could also have been obtained by direct interpolation in Table I. Thus we see that $(1 + i)^5 = 5548.50/4500 = 1.2330$. Entering Table I for $n = 5$ with this value, we see that the rate of interest is between 4% and 5%. Hence, by interpolation, we get

$$i = .04 + .01\,\frac{163}{596} = .0427\,.$$

PROBLEMS

1. Find the compound amount of $1,000 invested for 10 years at 5% effective.

2. Compute the compound amount of $1,000 invested at 5% nominal, compounded twice a year, for 10 years.

3. Find the compound amount of $1,000 invested for one year at 5%, for a second year at 4%, and for a third year at 3%. Compare this with $1,000 invested for 3 years at 4%.

4. What average annual rate of interest is realized by the investment of

problem 3? *Hint*: Set the compound amount equal to $\$1{,}000(1+i)^3$ and solve for i.

5. Compute the nominal rate of interest compounded 4 times a year which is equivalent to an effective rate of 6%.

6. Compute the effective rate of interest corresponding to a nominal rate of 6% compounded 4 times a year.

7. Prove that the time in which money doubles itself at the effective rate i is approximately n years where n is defined by

$$n = \frac{0.69}{i} + \frac{1}{3}.$$

Hint: Let $(1+i)^n = 2$. Take logarithms to the base e of both sides and use the expansion $\log_e(1+i) = i - i^2/2 + i^3/3 - \cdots$.

8. Compare the compound amounts of $1,000 invested for 10 years at 5% effective, at 5% nominal, compounded twice a year, and at the force of interest 5%.

2. The Variability of the Interest Rate

In many business transactions it is customary to assume that a fixed rate of interest will prevail over a given interval of time. Thus, when a house is purchased on time payments a certain rate of interest is written into the mortgage; when a bond is issued a fixed rate is specified for the payment of dividends and when the bond is purchased it is purchased to yield a certain rate of interest on the investment. But in spite of these apparently rigid contracts, the rate of interest will actually vary during the life of the mortgage and of the bond. To verify this one has merely to observe the constant fluctuations in the book values of certain bonds as they are quoted on the

Year	Interest Rate	Year	Interest Rate	Year	Interest Rate	Year	Interest Rate	Year	Interest Rate
1871	6.84	1886	4.77	1901	4.28	1916	3.43	1931	2.64
1872	8.85	1887	5.75	1902	4.92	1917	4.74	1932	2.84
1873	10.13	1888	4.88	1903	5.47	1918	5.87	1933	1.87
1874	6.01	1889	4.86	1904	4.21	1919	5.42	1934	1.14
1875	5.51	1890	5.75	1905	4.40	1920	7.37	1935	0.91
1876	5.10	1891	5.39	1906	5.68	1921	6.53	1936	0.75
1877	5.21	1892	4.11	1907	6.36	1922	4.43	1937	0.94
1878	4.80	1893	6.66	1908	4.38	1923	4.98	1938	0.93
1879	5.05	1894	3.04	1909	3.98	1924	3.91	1939	0.75
1880	5.23	1895	.366	1910	5.00	1925	4.03	1940	0.64
1881	5.19	1896	5.82	1911	4.03	1926	4.24		
1882	5.67	1897	3.53	1912	4.74	1927	4.01		
1883	5.57	1898	3.83	1913	5.60	1928	4.84		
1884	5.21	1899	4.12	1914	4.78	1929	5.78		
1885	4.14	1900	4.39	1915	3.45	1930	3.56		

market. It will be found that this variation is roughly correlated with the current rate of interest.

In order to obtain a realistic view of this ebb and flow of interest rates, let us consider the table on page 285 of monthly interest rates on 4 to 6 months commercial paper.

These data from 1908 are graphically represented in Figure 69-a, which shows the remarkable variability in the monthly interest rate. Referring to the table itself, the reader may observe the unusual average of more than 10% which prevailed during the year 1873, an average which was partially occasioned by a rate of 17% during the month of October. This abnormally high average is to be contrasted with the equally remarkable low average of 0.75% which prevailed throughout the year 1936.

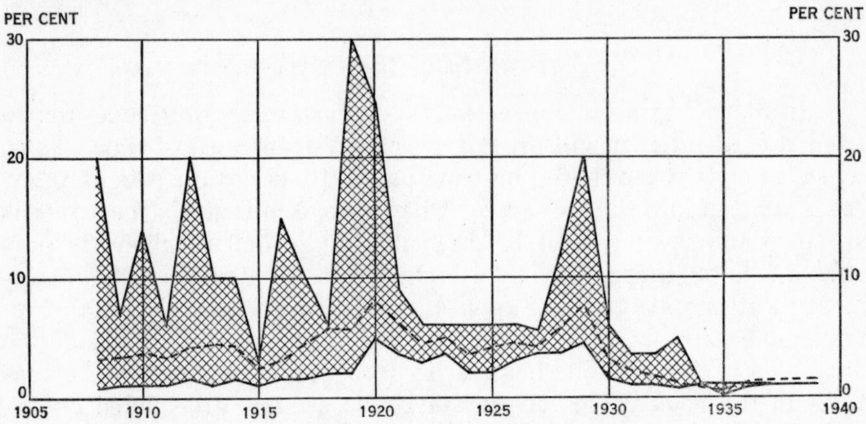

FIGURE 69-a.—VARIABILITY OF THE INTEREST RATE. THE DARK AREA SHOWS THE ANNUAL RANGE OF CALL MONEY RATES; THE DOTTED LINE SHOWS THE ANNUAL AVERAGE OF THE INTEREST RATE OF 4 TO 6 MONTHS COMMERCIAL PAPER.

An instructive computation can be made to illustrate the effect upon income of a variable rate of interest. There is one school of economic thought, led by J. M. Keynes, which believes that a higher general economy is possible under low rather than under high interest rates. It will be instructive to consider the following example for its bearing upon the variations created in capital by a changing rate of interest.

A capitalist has a fund of $100,000 in 1913, which he proposes to use in the following manner. He will lend his money at the current rate of interest. From the income thus obtained he proposes to maintain a standard of living equivalent to that which could be purchased for $3,000 in 1913, and he will then add all that remains of his income to his capital fund. The question is to determine the variation in his capital fund over the subsequent period, which, it will be observed, includes one of the most prosperous eras in American history.

We must first compute the annual variation in the amount which the capitalist will need in order to maintain his assumed standard of living. This is obtained by multiplying \$3,000 by some index of prices, let us say the index of general prices constructed for the Federal Reserve Bank of New York City by Carl Snyder. This index, together with the living income, is given in the following table:

Year	Price Index (I)	Living Income \$3,000 × I	Year	Price Index (I)	Living Income \$3,000 × I
1913	1.00	\$3,000	1926	1.71	\$5,130
1914	1.00	3,000	1927	1.71	5,130
1915	1.03	3,090	1928	1.76	5,280
1916	1.17	3,510	1929	1.79	5,370
1917	1.39	4,170	1930	1.68	5,040
1918	1.57	4,710	1931	1.50	4,500
1919	1.73	5,190	1932	1.32	3,960
1920	1.93	5,790	1933	1.29	3,870
1921	1.63	4,890	1934	1.37	4,110
1922	1.58	4,740	1935	1.45	4,350
1923	1.65	4,950	1936	1.54	4,620
1924	1.66	4,980	1937	1.61	4,830
1925	1.70	5,100	1938	1.53	4,590

From these figures we can now compute the annual capital increment by subtracting the annual living income from the amount earned by the principal. Thus, if P is the principal available at the beginning of any year, and if i is the current rate of interest, then the principal of the next year, P', will be given by

$$P' = P + Pi - 3000\,I\,.$$

The following table shows the fluctuating fortunes of the capital fund as computed by this formula:

Year	Principal	Interest	Increment	Year	Principal	Interest	Increment
1913	\$100,000	\$5,600	\$2,600	1926	\$117,454	\$4,980	\$– 150
1914	102,600	4,904	1,904	1927	117,304	4,704	– 426
1915	107,504	3,709	619	1928	116,878	5,657	377
1916	108,123	3,709	199	1929	117,255	6,777	1,407
1917	108,322	5,134	964	1930	118,662	4,224	– 816
1918	109,286	6,415	1,705	1931	117,846	3,111	–1,389
1919	110,991	6,016	826	1932	116,457	3,307	– 653
1920	111,817	8,241	2,451	1933	115,804	2,166	–1,704
1921	114,268	7,462	2,572	1934	114,100	1,301	–2,809
1922	116,840	5,176	436	1935	111,291	1,013	–3,337
1923	117,276	5,840	890	1936	107,954	819	–3,810
1924	118,166	4,620	–360	1937	104,144	979	–3,851
1925	117,806	4,748	–352	1938	100,293	1,003	–3,587
				1939	96,706	....	....

Several lessons can be learned from this table. The first, perhaps, is contained in the observation that the rate of interest in any calculation cannot be considered independently of the level of prices. Irving Fisher has repeatedly called attention to this relationship. Thus he says:[3]

> If, last year, I borrowed 100 dollars and am to pay 105 this year, my *nominal* or money rate of interest is 5 per cent. But if, meanwhile, the dollar has swollen so that, when the date arrives, 105 dollars have become worth 106 of last year's dollars, my *real* interest is not five per cent but six per cent. In a depression, therefore, when interest is meant to be low, the real interest amounts, sometimes, to over 50 per cent per annum!

So large an increase in interest could not be explained on the basis of the tables given above, but Fisher also observes the fact that in periods of depression lenders take into account the value of the security offered and then they raise their rates instead of lowering them.

The second lesson to be learned from the table is contained in a comparison of the first and the final capital. The net result has been that the conservative policy of the capitalist has left him after 26 years with a loss of more than $3,000 in his initial principal. This illustrates the essential fallacy in attempts to create large fortunes by means of capital increases from interest alone. There are comparatively few examples of the successful operation of this principle over any substantially long period of time. It is an instructive exercise for students to show that one cent put out at compound interest at 6% from the beginning of the Christian era is equivalent at current prices to a ball of gold with radius more than 75 times the distance from the earth to the sun. In the example just considered we see that the fluctuations of the rate of interest and of the index of prices work together to keep down abnormal accumulations in such capital funds.

The third lesson is found in the economic effects of a low interest rate, that is to say, low with respect to the index of prices. One school of thought believes that many of our economic ills can be traced to high interest rates. Lower these, runs the argument, or even reduce them to zero, and the flow of capital occasioned by "easy money" will restore production and quicken the pulse of business. The flaw in this argument is seen when one considers what will happen to the distribution of income. The capital structure of those high on the curve will be impaired, as in the example given above. The concentration ratio will be lowered and with it will come all the attendant

---

[3] From *Booms and Depressions.* New York, 1932, p. 38.

ills of this disturbance to the Pareto pattern. As the concentration ratio drops, there will be an attempt to lower prices to compensate for the reduction in income occasioned by the falling rate of interest. Since the volume of money changes slowly, the velocity of money must fall exactly as it has been observed to do in the period of low rates of interest.

It must be observed, however, that capital is not invested, for the most part, in commercial paper and hence the schedule given in the example is not entirely realistic. By far the greatest part of capital is found in bonds, in mortgages on real estate, and in stocks of corporations. But in all of these investments the rate of interest, which is called the yield in the case of bonds and the dividend ratio in the case of stocks, plays a role that is essentially like that illustrated by the example. Hence, the record of an investment trust over the period covered by the table would not be greatly different from the record of our theoretical capitalist.

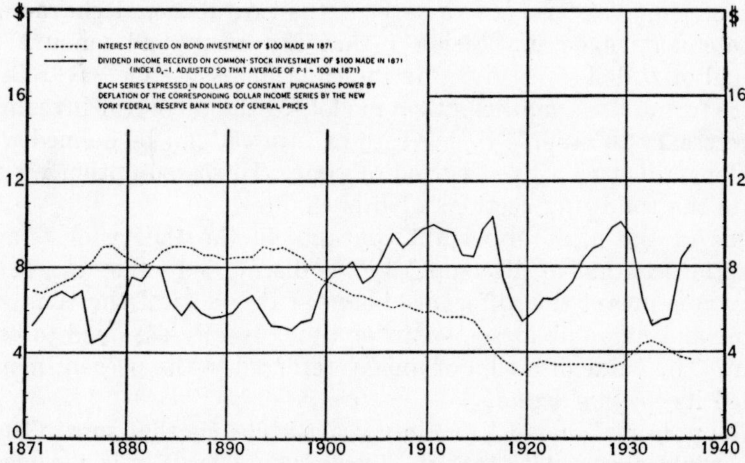

FIGURE 69-b.—VARIABILITY OF THE INTEREST RATE AS SHOWN BY THE YIELDS ON BONDS AND THE DIVIDEND RATIO OBTAINED FROM AN INVESTMENT IN COMMON STOCKS.

The Cowles Commission for Research in Economics, under the direction of Alfred Cowles, has made an extensive study of the problem of the variability of the interest rate as it applies to dividend income received over a long period of time from investments in common stocks. In Figure 69-b the comparison is made graphically between the interest received on a bond investment of $100 and the dividend investment of a similar amount in common stocks. These series, with origin in 1871, are expressed in dollars of constant purchasing power through deflation by the index of general prices.[4]

PROBLEMS

1. Show that if $i_1, i_2, \cdots, i_n$ are the rates of interest for n successive years, the average rate of interest is computed from the geometrical average

$$1+i=[(1+i_1)(1+i_2)\cdots(1+i_n)]^{1/n}.$$

2. What average rate of interest was earned by commercial paper between 1916 and 1920 inclusive?

3. Answer the question of problem 1 for the years 1931 to 1935 inclusive?

4. Compare bond yields with interest rates on commerical paper.

5. Discuss the proposition: Business activity is stimulated by low rates of interest.

3. Discount

Having in the preceding section discussed the difficulties inherent in attempting to define a fixed rate of interest over any considerable length of time, we are now aware of the postulational character of the statement made in Section 1 that the compound amount of a principal of P dollars is given by the equation $S=P(1+i)^n$. But in order to formulate a mathematical model for the theory of investment, it is necessary to assume that a rate of interest can be defined which holds constant over a fixed period of time. This assumption we shall make in the following sections of this chapter.

One of the most important concepts in the theory of financial transactions is that of discount. By the discounted value of a sum of money, x, is meant the difference between its value at the time when it is due and its value at some earlier time, usually assumed to be the present. The value of a sum of money referred to the present moment is called its *present value.*

The present value of 1 due in n years is clearly that sum of money which would accumulate to 1 in n years; that is, if x is the present value, then we have

$$x(1+i)^n=1\ ;$$

or, solving for x,

$$x=\frac{1}{(1+i)^n}=(1+i)^{-n}\ .$$

It is customary in the theory of investment to employ the abbrev-

[4] See Alfred Cowles, *Common-Stock Indexes, 1871–1937,* Principia Press, 1938, xii + 499 pp. Second edition, 1939.

iation $v = (1 + i)^{-1}$. Hence we may write as the discounted value of 1,

$$x = v^n . \tag{9}$$

In terms of the nominal rate of interest this becomes

$$x = v^{mn} \text{ (at rate } j/m). \tag{10}$$

Similarly, when the force of interest is employed, we have

$$x = e^{-n\delta} , \tag{11}$$

as the discounted value of 1.

The function v^n has been extensively tabulated. A brief table to four decimal places is found in Table II at the end of this volume. Values to eight places together with their logarithms to seven places are given by J. W. Glover in his *Tables of Applied Mathematics*, Ann Arbor, Michigan, 1923.

Example 1. Compare the present values of $1,000 due in 10 years as computed by formulas (9), (10), and (11), where $i = .06$, $j = .06$, $m = 4$, $\delta = .06$.

Solution. Using Table II, we find

$$x_1 = \$1{,}000\, v^{10} \text{ (at rate .06)} = \$558.40 ;$$

$$x_2 = \$1{,}000\, v^{40} \text{ (at rate .01}\tfrac{1}{2}) = \$551.30 ;$$

and, employing logarithms, for the computation,

$$x_3 = \$1{,}000\, e^{-0.6} = \$548.81 .$$

Example 2. A man purchases a lot by paying $100 down and $200 each half year for four years. If money is worth 6% nominal, $m = 2$, what is the cash value of the lot?

Solution. The cash value of the lot is the present value of the partial payments. Hence, the cash value of the lot is given by the sum

$$x = \$100 + \$200\, v + \$200\, v^2 + \$200\, v^3 + \cdots + \$200\, v^8 ,$$

where the interest used in computing the present values is $.06/2 = .03$.

Using Table II, we obtain

$$x = \$100 + \$194.18 + \$188.52 + \cdots + \$157.88$$
$$= \$1503.94 .$$

PROBLEMS

1. Find the discounted value of $1,000 due in 10 years at 5%.

2. Compute the discounted value of $1,000 due in 10 years at 5% nominal, compounded twice a year.

3. Find the discounted value of $1,000 discounted one year at 5%, a second

year at 4%, and a third year at 3%. Compare this with the discounted value for 3 years at 4%.

4. A man buys a property worth $10,000 and he pays for it $2,000 cash, $3,000 at the end of one year, $2,000 at the end of two years, $1,000 at the end of three years, and the balance at the end of four years. If money is worth 4% effective, how much did he pay the last year?

5. Answer problem 4 on the basis that money is worth 4% nominal, converted 4 times per year.

6. A man owes the following debts: $1,000 due in one year, $2,000 due in two years, and $3,000 due in three years. He decides to amortize his indebtedness by paying $1,000 cash, $1,500 for each of two successive years, and the balance at the end of the third year. How large is the last payment if money is worth 5%?

7. Answer problem 6 if money is worth 4% converted twice a year.

8. What would be the answer to problem 6 if the amounts are discounted at a force of interest equal to 5%?

4. Annuities

By an annuity we shall mean a series of payments, usually equal in amount, which are made at equal intervals of time. If the annuity begins and ends at specific dates, then the series of payments is called an *annuity certain*. Such annuities are common in most business transactions, as, for example, in the payment of rent on a lease, the purchase of real estate or other property by fixed payments, the payment of interest on bonds, etc. If the annuity payments either begin or terminate on the occasion of some event which cannot be foretold, then the annuity is said to be a *contingent annuity*. The most conspicuous example of this is found in life insurance, where the premiums are paid throughout the life of an individual or over a specified fixed number of years, unless the death of the policyholder occurs within the period.

When the payments are equal in amount, the total payment made in one year is called the *annual rent*. The time between the first payment and the last payment is called the *term* of the annuity.

Let us assume that a is the annual rent of an annuity, that n is the time in years, and that the annual rents as they come due are allowed to accumulate at rate of interest i until the end of the term. This sum, called the *amount of the annuity*, we shall represent by the symbol $a\, s_{\overline{n|}}$, where $s_{\overline{n|}}$ is the amount of an annuity of 1 per annum.

In order to compute $s_{\overline{n|}}$ we write

$$s_{\overline{n|}} = (1+i)^{n-1} + (1+i)^{n-2} + \cdots + (1+i) + 1\,,$$

$$s_{\overline{n|}} = 1 + (1+i) + (1+i)^2 + \cdots + (1+i)^{n-1}.$$

Employing the formula

$$s = \frac{a - rl}{1 - r},$$

which gives the sum of the geometrical progression

$$s = a + ar + ar^2 + \cdots + ar^{n-1}, \quad l = ar^{n-1},$$

we obtain

$$s_{\overline{n|}} = \frac{(1+i)^n - 1}{i}. \tag{12}$$

This function has been extensively tabulated by J. W. Glover in his *Tables of Applied Mathematics,* which we have previously mentioned. A brief table will be found in Table III at the end of this book.

If in this formula i is replaced by a nominal rate j, converted m times per year, then the sum may be written

$$s_{\overline{n|}} = \frac{\left(1 + \frac{j}{m}\right)^{mn} - 1}{\left(1 + \frac{j}{m}\right)^{m} - 1} = \left(\frac{1}{s_{\overline{m|}}}\right) s_{\overline{mn|}} \text{ (at rate } j/m). \tag{13}$$

If the force of interest is used, that is, if $m = \delta$, this formula becomes

$$s_{\overline{n|}} = \frac{e^{n\delta} - 1}{e^{\delta} - 1} = e^{\frac{1}{2}(n-1)} \frac{\sinh \frac{1}{2}n\delta}{\sinh \frac{1}{2}\delta}, \tag{14}$$

where $\sinh x$ is the hyperbolic sine of x.

If the annuity is paid in p installments during the year, then the sum of the annuity becomes

$$\begin{aligned} s^{(p)}_{\overline{n|}} &= \frac{1}{p}(1+i)^{n-1/p} + \frac{1}{p}(1+i)^{n-2/p} + \cdots + \frac{1}{p}(1+i)^{1/p} + \frac{1}{p}, \\ &= \frac{(1+i)^n - 1}{p[(1+i)^{1/p} - 1]} = \frac{i}{j(p)} s_{\overline{n|}}, \end{aligned} \tag{15}$$

where we use the abbreviation

$$j(p) = p[(1+i)^{1/p} - 1].$$

If the rate of interest is nominal, converted m times per year, then the sum given in (15) becomes

(16)
$$s_{\overline{n|}}^{(p)} = \frac{(1+\frac{j}{m})^{mn}-1}{p[(1+\frac{j}{m})^{m/p}-1]}$$

If m is allowed to approach infinity, and if j is replaced by the force of interest δ, this formula has the limiting form

(17)
$$s_{\overline{n|}}^{(p)} = \frac{e^{n\delta}-1}{p(e^{\delta/p}-1)} .$$

In business practice, when payment are made p times per year, it is usual to assume also that the interest is nominal, converted $m = p$ times per year. In this case formulas (16) and (17) assume the simpler forms

(18)
$$s_{\overline{n|}}^{(p)} = \frac{1}{p} s_{\overline{np|}} \quad (\text{at rate } j/p) ,$$

and where $p = m \to \infty$, $j = \delta$,

(19)
$$s_{\overline{n|}}^{(\infty)} = \frac{e^{n\delta}-1}{\delta} :$$

Example 1. A man accumulates $100 per year for 10 years, the first sum being paid into the account one year from date. How much will he have in his fund at the time of the last payment (a) if the rate of interest is 6% effective; (b) if the rate of interest is 6% nominal, $m = 4$, and the payments are $25 every quarter?

Solution. Using formula (12) and Table III, we get for (a)

$$x_1 = \$100\, s_{\overline{10|}} = \$1318.08 .$$

The answer to (b) is obtained from formula (18), where $p = 4$, $j = .06$.

$$x_2 = \$25\, s_{\overline{40|}} \ (\text{at rate } 1\tfrac{1}{2}\%) = \$1356.70 .$$

Example 2. Compare the second answer in the first example with the accumulated value determined from formula (19).

Solution. We let $n = 10$, $\delta = .06$, and thus obtain

$$x_3 = \$100 \times 13.7020 = \$1370.20 .$$

PROBLEMS

1. A man saves $1,000 per year for 10 years. How much will he have at the end of that time if money can be accumulated at 5%?

2. Solve problem 1 using the force of interest, $\delta = .05$.

3. Find the answer to problem 1 if money is paid in two installments per year and the interest is 5% converted twice a year.

4. Solve problem 1 if the money is paid in two installments per year, but the interest is 5% effective.

5. What is the answer to problem 1 if the interest is 5% nominal, converted twice a year?

6. A man saves $500 annually for 5 years and $750 annually for 7 years. If money is worth 5% effective, what is his accumulation?

5. *The Present Value of an Annuity*

In the practical problems of business the present value of an annuity is frequently desired. As we shall see later, the *book value*, or the purchase price of bonds, is determined from the present value of an annuity. By such a *present value* we mean the present value of the sum or amount, which we described in Section 4.

Thus in the first case, where payments are made annually for n years, the first payment a year from date, and where the interest rate is i, we obtain for the present value of the annuity the following:

$$(20) \qquad a_{\overline{n|}} = v + v^2 + v^3 + \cdots + v^n$$

$$= v^n s_{\overline{n|}} = \frac{1 - v^n}{i}.$$

This function, together with its reciprocal, and the logarithms of both have been extensively tabulated by J. W. Glover in his work on *Tables*, which we have previously mentioned. Values of $a_{\overline{n|}}$ will be found in Table IV at the end of this book.

Introducing the nominal rate of interest into (20), we obtain the formula:

$$(21) \qquad a_{\overline{n|}} = \left(\frac{1}{s_{\overline{n|}}}\right) a_{\overline{mn|}} \quad (\text{at rate } j/m),$$

which, in terms of the force of interest, becomes

$$(22) \qquad a_{\overline{n|}} = \frac{1 - e^{-n\delta}}{e^{\delta} - 1}.$$

If the annuity is paid in p installments during the year, then the present value becomes

$$(23) \qquad a_{\overline{n|}}^{(p)} = \frac{i}{j(p)} a_{\overline{n|}},$$

where we use the abbreviation

$$j(p) = p[(1+i)^{1/p} - 1] .$$

If the rate of interest is nominal, converted m times per year, then the sum given in (23) becomes

$$(24) \qquad a^{(p)}_{\overline{n|}} = \frac{1 - (1 + \frac{j}{m})^{-mn}}{p\left[\left(1 + \frac{j}{m}\right)^{m/p} - 1\right]} .$$

If m is allowed to approach infinity, and if j is replaced by the force of interest δ, this formula has the limiting form

$$(25) \qquad a^{(p)}_{\overline{n|}} = \frac{1 - e^{-n\delta}}{p(e^{\delta/p} - 1)} .$$

In usual business price formula (24) is seldom if ever used except when $m = p$. In this case formulas (24) and (25) assume the simpler forms

$$(26) \qquad a^{(p)}_{\overline{n|}} = \frac{1}{p} a_{\overline{np|}} \text{ (at rate } j/p) ,$$

and where $p = m \to \infty$, $j = \delta$,

$$(27) \qquad a^{(\infty)}_{\overline{n|}} = \frac{1 - e^{-n\delta}}{\delta} .$$

Example 1. A man buys a house paying \$1,000 cash and \$600 each half year for six years. If money is worth 4% converted twice a year, what is the cash value of the house?

Solution. In this case we use formula (26) to find the present value of the annuity. Hence, making use of Table IV, we compute

$$x = \$1{,}000 + \$600\, a_{\overline{12|}} \text{ (at 2\%)}$$

$$= \$1{,}000 + \$6{,}345.18 = \$7{,}345.18 .$$

Example 2. What would be the value of the house in example 1, if the annuity were \$1,200 computed at a rate of interest equivalent to a force of interest of .04?

Solution. In this case we use formula (22) and thus obtain

$$x = \$1{,}000 + \$1{,}200 \frac{1 - e^{-.24}}{e^{.04} - 1}$$

$$= \$1{,}000 + \$6{,}273.96 = \$7{,}273.96$$

PROBLEMS

1. Find the present value of an annuity of \$100 for 10 years at 5% effective; at 5% converted twice a year.

2. Compute the present value of an annuity of \$100 for 10 years, the first payment made 3 years from date, if money is worth 6% converted twice a year.

3. A man buys a house for \$1,000 cash and 8 annual payments of \$1,200. If money is worth 5% effective, what is the cash value of the house?

4. A man buys a house for \$1,000 cash and 16 annual payments of \$600. What is the cash value at 5% effective; at 5% nominal, converted twice a year?

5. How long would be required to purchase a house valued at \$10,000 by paying an annuity of \$1,200 per year, if money is worth 4%? How large would the last payment be?

6. Compute the present value of an annuity of \$500 per year for 12 years, assuming that the discounts are made at a force of interest equal to .05.

7. Obtain the answer to problem 6 discounting at the effective rate of interest equal to .05.

8. If a property worth \$1,000 is purchased for \$100 cash and 11 annual payments of \$100, what was the rate of interest charged?

9. A man buys a house worth \$8,000 for which he pays \$1,000 cash and the balance in 10 equal annual installments at 5% effective. How much is the annual installment?

10. A man, beginning when his son is 10 years old, sets aside enough money each year so that his son, entering college at the age of 18, will have \$800 a year for 4 years. How much must the man set aside annually if money yields 4% effective?

6. *Perpetuities*

By a *perpetuity* we mean a series of payments which are assumed to be made for a sufficiently large number of times so that they may be regarded mathematically as if they continued forever.

It is clear that the amount of a perpetuity exceeds all bounds, but this is not true of the present value. Thus we readily see that the sum of \$2,000 will provide a perpetuity of \$100 per year, if it is invested at 5%; hence \$2,000 is the present value of such a perpetuity.

The formula for the present value of a perpetuity is readily obtained by letting $n \to \infty$ in formula (20) of Section 5. Since the limit of v^n is zero as $n \to \infty$, we thus obtain

$$a_\infty = \frac{1}{i}. \tag{28}$$

In many applications of perpetuities it is useful to assume that the payments are made k intervals apart. In this case we have

$$a_\infty(k) = v^k + v^{2k} + v^{3k} + \cdots$$
$$= \frac{v^k}{1 - v^k} = \frac{1}{v^{-k} - 1} = \frac{1}{i\left[\frac{(1+i)^k - 1}{i}\right]}.$$

Since the expression in brackets is merely $s_{\overline{k|}}$ we obtain the useful formula

$$(29) \qquad a_\infty(k) = \frac{1}{i\, s_{\overline{k|}}}.$$

Example 1. Compare the present value of a perpetuity of \$200 paid every two years with one of \$100 paid every year, if money is worth 5%.

Solution. Using formula (28) we obtain

$$x_1 = \frac{\$100}{.05} = \$2,000.$$

Using formula (29) we get

$$x_2 = \frac{\$200}{.05 \times s_{\overline{2|}}} = \frac{\$200}{.05 \times 2.05} = \$1,951.22.$$

The difference is seen to equal \$48.78.

Example 2. A building brings an annual net rental of \$2,500 after taxes and operating expenses have been paid. If \$1,500 must be spent every three years to keep the building in repair, what is its value just after repairs have been made? What is its value one year before repairs must be made? Assume that money is worth 5%.

Solution. For the first value we obtain

$$x_1 = \frac{\$2,500}{.05} - \frac{\$1500}{.05 \times s_{\overline{3|}}} = \$50,000 - \$9,516 = \$40,484.$$

In the second instance, the perpetuity representing repairs must be accumulated for two years. We thus obtain

$$x_2 = \$50,000 - (1.05)^2 \times \$9,516 = \$50,000 - \$10,491 = \$39,509.$$

7. *Capitalized Cost*

By the *capitalized cost* of an article we shall mean its first cost plus the cost of keeping it in repair, or of replacing it when it wears out.

The formula for the capitalized cost of an article is derived immediately from the perpetuity formulas of Section 6. Thus, if C' is the first cost of an article, and if C must be paid every k years to keep the article in repair, or to replace it, the present value, or capitalized cost, is given by

$$(30) \qquad C_\infty = C' + \frac{C}{i\, s_{\overline{k|}}}\,.$$

In some instances C' and C will be the same. For example, the cost of renewing a street pavement should equal approximately the cost of the original pavement, since there is no salvage value in such a project. In this case, when $C' = C$, formula (30) becomes

$$(31) \qquad C_\infty = \frac{C}{i\, a_{\overline{k|}}}\,.$$

The derivation of this formula follows from (30), since we have

$$C_\infty = C + \frac{C}{i\, s_k} = C[1 + \frac{1}{(1+i)^n - 1}]\,,$$

$$= C\,\frac{(1+i)^n}{(1+i)^n - 1} = C\,\frac{1}{i[\frac{1-v^n}{i}]} = \frac{C}{i\, a_{\overline{k|}}}\,.$$

Example. Determine which is the better proposition. To pay \$200,000 for a pavement which will last 10 years, or to pay \$300,000 for a pavement which will last for 18 years, if money is worth 4%?

Solution. The capitalized costs of the two pavements are respectively

$$x_1 = \frac{\$200{,}000}{.04 \times a_{\overline{10|}}} = \$616{,}500\,, \qquad x_2 = \frac{\$300{,}000}{.04 \times a_{\overline{18|}}} = \$592{,}450\,.$$

Even disregarding the practical fact that traffic will not be disturbed more than once in 18 years if the second pavement is laid, the second proposition is a better financial transaction since is capitalized cost is lower than that of the first bid.

PROBLEMS

1. Find the amount which could be expended in the purchase of a machine which runs automatically, if the cost of operation otherwise is \$1,500 per year. Assume that money is worth 5% effective.

2. What amount will provide for the construction and maintenance of a house which costs \$10,000 to build, and which required annual repairs of \$200, taxes amounting to \$250, and extensive repairs of \$2,000 every 10 years, if money is worth 4%?

3. Find the value of a property, which provides a net profit of \$500 every other year, if it is sold one year before the profit is due. Interest is 4% effective.

4. Telephone poles costing \$25 each must be replaced every 8 years. If they

could be treated chemically so as to last 15 years, what amount could be paid for the treatment? Assume an interest of 5% effective.

5. A man buys an automobile for $1,000 and plans to replace it every 3 years. If he estimates his trade-in value at $300, what is the capitalized cost of the automobile at 5%?

6. Which is the better bargain for a city, to build a pavement for $100,000, which must be replaced every 10 years, or to build a pavement for $200,000 that will last for 17 years? Capitalize at 4% effective.

8. *Bonds*

One of the most important forms of investment is a bond, by which we mean a certificate of ownership in a definite portion of a debt due from a government, a municipality, a business corporation, or an individual. For convenience of reference bonds may be put into the following categories: (a) government bonds; (b) municipal bonds; (c) industrial bonds; (d) railroad bonds; (e) utility bonds; (f) real estate bonds; (g) bonds of foreign governments; (h) miscellaneous bonds.

The simplest type of bond is a promise to pay a stipulated sum of money on or after a given date and to pay interest, or *dividends,* in the intervening time at a specified rate of interest. The stipulated sum is called the *redemption value* of the bond, the sum on which the interest is computed is called the *par value,* and the interest named is called the *dividend rate.*[4a] The redemption value and the par value are usually the same, although sometimes, in order to attract buyers, bonds may bear a higher redemption than par value.

We shall designate by C the par value of a bond, by C_1 the price to be paid on redemption, by n the number of years before redemption, by r the dividend rate, and by i the yield. The yield is usually different from the dividend rate since the yield is roughly equal to the market rate of interest, whereas the dividend rate is a constant value specified at the time the bond is issued.

In computing the value of a bond several things must be taken into account. The first of these is the security offered by the debtor and this should be the most important consideration of the investor. If, for example, bonds are issued on an apartment house, which is being constructed in a period of high prices, and if the bond issue is say 80 per cent of the cost of construction, then the risk involved in the purchase of such a bond is high. The record of such bond issues is very bad and defaults are frequent on such issues. The same thing

[4a] The term *coupon rate* is sometimes used instead of *dividend rate,* although the latter is customary in most texts on the theory of investment.

is true of foreign bonds, which, however, usually have a speculative attraction on account of their high yields. The lure of high interest will often offset the obvious risk of losing all or a part of the principal.

The second factor in determining the value of a bond is the redemption price. The third factor is the dividend rate, and the fourth the time to the maturity of the bond. This time to maturity is not always fixed. Thus bonds are sometimes issued by corporations which specify that they are *callable*, that is to say, subject to redemption at the option of the corporation. Consequently if interest rates fall after the bonds are issued, the issue can be redeemed in part or in full and reissued at the lower prevailing rate. If part of an issue is to be retired, the order of the retirement of the bonds is often determined by lot.

9. *Evaluating a Bond*

The evaluation of a bond is a purely mathematical problem provided the five elements mentioned in Section 8, namely, C, C_1, n, r, and i are all known. We do not need specifically to include the degree of risk assumed by the purchaser since this enters into the determination of the yield.

Let A_n, called the book value, designate the value of the bond n years before its maturity. When one purchases a bond he receives two things, the first, a promise to pay the redemption value C_1 in n years, and the second, an annuity of Cr dollars per year. If these annual dividends are paid in p installments, then the periodic payments are rC/p.

Considering the simplest case first, namely, where the annual dividends are paid in one installment, we see that the book value, A_n, is given by the formula

(32) $$A_n = C_1 v^n + rC\, a_{\overline{n}|} \quad \text{(computed at rate } i\text{)}.$$

If the dividends are paid p times a year, where p is customarily 2 or 4, then the book value is given by

(33) $$A_n = C_1 v^n + rC\, a^{(p)}_{\overline{n}|}.$$

Example 1. Let us find the book value of a \$100 bond bought to yield 5%, which is redeemed in 10 years for \$120 and which pays dividends of 1% each quarter.

Solution. From the problem we have the following known values: $C_1 = \$120$, $C = \$100$, $n = 10$, $r = .04$, $p = 4$, $i = .05$. Substituting these values in formula (33) we obtain

$$A_{10} = \$120 \times 0.6139 + \$4 \times a^{(4)}_{\overline{10}|}$$

$$A_{10} = \$73.67 + \$4 \times 7.8649$$
$$= \$73.67 + \$31.46 = \$105.13.$$

If a bond is purchased between dividend dates, then the book value must be accumulated to the date of purchase.

By definition, the *premium* on a bond, designated by P, is the difference between the book value and the par value,

$$P = A_n - C$$
$$= C_1 v^n + rC\, a_{\overline{n|}}^{(p)} - C\,.$$

If we write $C_1 = (1+k)C$, then this formula may be reduced to the simpler form

(34) $$P = C[(r - j_{(p)})a_{\overline{n|}}^{(p)} + k\, v^n]\,,$$

or if $C_1 = C$, that is, if $k = 0$,

(35) $$P = C(r - j_{(p)})\, a_{\overline{n|}}^{(p)}\,.$$

This reduction is easily proved as follows:

We have by definition $a_{\overline{n|}}^{(p)} = (1 - v^n)/j_{(p)}$; hence, we get

$$P = rC\, a_{\overline{n|}}^{(p)} - C(1 - v^n) + kC\, v^n$$
$$= rC\, a_{\overline{n|}}^{(p)} - C\, j_{(p)}\left[\frac{1 - v^n}{j_{(p)}}\right] + kC\, v^n$$
$$= C[r - j_{(p)}]\, a_{\overline{n|}}^{(p)} + kC\, v^n\,.$$

If the conversion periods of a nominal rate of interest j corresponds to the payment periods of the bond, that is, if $m = p$, then this formula assumes an even simpler form, namely,

(36) $$P = C\frac{(r - j)}{p}\, a_{\overline{np|}} \text{ (at rate } j/p) + kC\, v^n \text{ (at rate } j/p)\,.$$

Example 2. We shall compute the premium of the bond given in the first example.

Solution. As before we have

$$C = \$100, k = 0.2, n = 10, r = .04, p = 4, i = .05.$$

Substituting these values in formula (34) we get

$$P_{10} = \$100(0.04 - 0.04909) \times 7.8649 + \$20 \times 0.6139$$
$$= -\$7.15 + \$12.29 = \$5.13.$$

The book value is thus $100 + $5.13 = $105.13, which agrees with the answer obtained in the first method of solution.

PROBLEMS

1. Compute the selling price of a $1,000 bond with dividend rate at 4% effective, redeemable at par in 10 years, bought to yield 3%.

2. Find the selling price of the bond in problem 1 if it is bought to yield 5%.

3. A $100 bond pays interest semiannually at 4%. If it is redeemable at par in 15 years, what is its selling value if it yields 5% nominal, converted twice a year?

4. Find the premium on a $500 bond, due in 5 years, dividend rate 3%, if it is purchased to yield 2% effective.

5. Find the premium on the bond of problem 4 if the yield is 4% effective.

6. Evaluate the following bonds as of January 1, 1941:

A and B Co., 4% annually, due in 1949, to yield 3%, par $1,000.
P and Q RR., 2% semiannually, due in 1955, to yield 5% nominal, par $500.
City of M., 3% semiannually, due in 1950, to yield 4% nominal, par $100.

7. The following table gives the value of a bond 10 years before redemption in terms of the nominal investment rate, converted twice a year:

Nominal Yield	Dividend rate, paid semiannually					
	3½%	4%	4½%	5%	5½%	6%
4.50	92.02	96.01	100.00	103.99	107.98	111.97
4.60	91.26	95.23	99.21	103.18	107.15	111.12
4.70	90.51	94.47	98.42	102.37	106.33	110.28
4.80	89.77	93.71	97.64	101.57	105.51	109.44
4.90	89.04	92.95	96.87	100.78	104.70	108.61
5.00	88.31	92.21	96.10	100.00	103.90	107.79

From this table determine the yield for a 4% bond, dividends paid semiannually, bought for $94.75.

8. From the table of problem 7, determine the yield for a 6% bond, dividends paid semiannually, bought for $110.50.

10. *Depreciation*

The theory of depreciation is one of the most important in practical economics, since most physical objects begin to lose value immediately after they have been created and finally must be discarded. The theory applies especially to factors of production, machinery, buildings, and the like, and the capitalization of industrial plants must take special account of the depreciation of equipment.

We shall designate by C the *initial cost* of some factor of production, by S the *scrap value*, and by W the *wearing value* defined by the equation

$$W = C - S. \tag{37}$$

In making an accounting of the value of the factor of production this wearing value must be distributed over the period of the life of the factor, which we shall assume is estimated to be n years. The simplest formula for computing the annual depreciation, denoted by D, is called the *straight line formula*, and is merely

$$D = \frac{C - S}{n} = \frac{W}{n} . \tag{38}$$

The book value for the year t, designated by $V(t)$, is then given by

$$V(t) = C - Dt . \tag{39}$$

The *sinking fund method*, on the other hand, assumes that the total depreciation at time t is just equal to the amount in a sinking fund which has been created from annual payments R to replace the factor when it has worn out.

The annual amount, called the *replacement charge*, is clearly given by

$$R = \frac{W}{s_{\overline{n|}}} , \tag{40}$$

where $s_{\overline{n|}}$ is computed at the investment rate i.

The book value, $V(t)$, is then equal to

$$V(t) = C - R\, s_{\overline{t|}} . \tag{41}$$

Example 1. If the initial cost of a fleet of trucks is \$10,000, and if the units must be replaced in 5 years when the scrap value is \$3,000, what is the annual depreciation by the straight line method? Compare this with the annual replacement charge as computed by the sinking fund method, where interest is 5%.

Solution. By the straight line formula we obtain

$$D = \frac{\$10{,}000 - \$3{,}000}{5} = \$1{,}400 .$$

On the other hand the replacement charge by the sinking fund method is

$$R = \frac{\$7{,}000}{s_{\overline{5|}}} = \$1266.80 .$$

Example 2. At the end of three years, what is the book value of the fleet of trucks of example 1?

Solution. Using formula (39) we get

$$V(3) = \$10{,}000 - 3 \times \$1{,}400 = \$5{,}800 .$$

By the sinking fund formula (41) we get

$$V(3) = \$10{,}000 - \$3{,}993.66 = \$6{,}006.34 .$$

PROBLEMS

1. Determine the annual depreciation of a machine costing \$1,500, which lasts for 8 years and has a scrap value of \$300. Use the straight line method.

2. Compute the book value of the machine described in problem 1, namely, the difference between the original cost and the amount in the depreciation fund. Make a graph showing the depreciation fund and the book value for each year.

3. Solve problem 1 using the sinking fund method, interest at 6%.

4. Solve problem 2 using the sinking fund method, interest at 6%.

5. Compute the annual depreciation for a factory with the following assets:

(a) Plant: Cost, \$50,000; Life, 10 years; Scrap value, \$5,000.
(b) Machinery: Cost, \$20,000; Life, 8 years; Scrap value, \$4,000.
(c) Other equipment: Cost, \$10,000; Life 6 years; Scrap value, \$1,000.

Use the straight line method.

6. Solve problem 5 using the sinking fund method, interest at 5%.

11. The Evaluation of a Machine

The problem of depreciation may readily be extended to include the evaluation of a machine whose annual output is known as a function of the time. Thus, let us assume that a machine in the year s from some arbitrary origin produces $u(s)$ units of a certain commodity which sells for p dollars per unit, and let us represent the cost in the year s by $Q(s)$. If n is the life of the machine, and if the annual rate of interest is represented by the variable force of interest $\delta(r)$, then the value of the machine at the end of t years is given by the function

$$(42)\quad v(t) = \int_t^n [p\,u(s) - Q(s)]\, e^{-\int_t^s \delta(r)\,dr}\, ds + S\, e^{-\int_t^n \delta(r)\,dr} .$$

Since $v(n) = S$, it is clear that S is the scrap value.[5]

An interesting problem is obtained if we assume that the cost is a linear function of the value, $v(s)$, that is to say, if

$$Q(s) = a(s) + b(s)\, v(s) .$$

If this cost is substituted in (42), we obtain the integral equation

(43)

$$v(t) = \int_t^n [p\,u(s) - a(s) - b(s)\, v(s)]\, e^{-\int_t^s \delta(r)\,dr}\, ds + S\, e^{-\int_t^n \delta(r)\,dr} .$$

This particular equation is readily solved if we take derivatives of both sides of (43). We thus get[6]

[5] This problem is taken from H. Hotelling (see *Bibliography*).
[6] See problem 1 below for this differentiation.

$$v'(t) = [\delta(t) + b(t)]\, v(t) - p\, u(t) + a(t)\,. \tag{44}$$

The solution of this equation which satisfies the condition $v(n) = S$ is then found to be[7]

$$v(t) = \int_t^n [p\, u(s) - a(s)]\, e^{-\int_t^s \gamma(r)\, dr}\, ds + S\, e^{-\int_t^n \gamma(r)\, dr}, \tag{45}$$

where we employ the abbreviation $\gamma(r) = \delta(r) + b(r)$.

Example. If $u(s) = ae^{-\lambda s}$, $a(s) = be^{\mu s}$, $S = 0$, $\delta(r) + b(r) = \gamma$ (a constant), determine the value of the machine.

Solution. The value of the machine after t years is found by substituting the given functions in equation (45). We thus obtain

$$v(t) = \int_t^n [pa\, e^{-\lambda s} - b\, e^{\mu s}] e^{\gamma t}\, e^{-\gamma s}\, ds\,,$$

which reduces, upon integration, to the value

$$v(t) = pa\, e^{\gamma t}\, E(\lambda + \gamma) + b\, e^{\gamma t}\, E(\gamma - \mu)\,,$$

where we employ the abbreviation

$$E(x) = \frac{e^{-xt} - e^{-xn}}{x}\,.$$

12. *The Composite Life of Factors of Production*

If the wearing values and the replacement charges of a number of factors of production, which together make up a manufacturing unit, are known, then it is possible to determine what is called the *composite life* of the unit.

Thus, if $W_1, W_2, \cdots, W_r$ are the wearing values of the factors, and if $R_1, R_2, \cdots, R_r$ are the corresponding replacement charges, then the composite life, n, of the unit is defined by the equation

$$R = \frac{W}{s_{\overline{n|}}}\,,$$

where we employ the abbreviations

$$R = R_1 + R_2 + \cdots R_r\,, \text{ and } W = W_1 + W_2 + \cdots + W_r\,.$$

The value of n may be obtained from the tables of values of $s_{\overline{n|}}$ by interpolation, or explicitly from the formula

$$n = \frac{\log(1 + \frac{W}{R} i)}{\log(1 + i)}\,.$$

[7] For the solution of this differential equation see problem 2 below.

In the case of the machine discussed in the preceding section the problem is more complex. Thus we see, that if C is the original cost of the machine, and if the other factors which enter into equation (42) are known, then the life, n, can be computed from the equation

$$V(0) = C .$$

The complexity of the problem can be seen from the illustrative example of Section 11, where the life of the machine must be obtained by solving the following exponential equation for n:

$$C = pa\, E(\lambda + \gamma)_{t=0} + b\, E(\gamma - \mu)_{t=0} .$$

PROBLEMS

1. Observing that the derivative of the function

$$y(t) = \int_{B(t)}^{A(t)} K(t, s)\, ds ,$$

is given by

$$\frac{dy}{dt} = \int_{B(t)}^{A(t)} \frac{\partial}{\partial t} K(t, s)\, ds + \frac{dA}{dt} K(t, A) - \frac{dB}{dt} K(t, B) ,$$

establish equation (44).

2. Observing that the solution of the linear differential equation

$$\frac{dy}{dt} + P(t) y = Q(t)$$

is given by

$$y = e^{-\int^{t} P(s) ds} [\int^{t} Q(s) e^{\int^{s} P(r) dr} ds + C],$$

show that the function defined by equation (45) is the solution of (44) which satisfies the condition $v(n) = S$.

3. Given the following specifications for a machine which has a life of 10 years:

$$p = 5, \qquad u(s) = 1000 e^{-.05s} , \qquad a(s) = 1000\, e^{.04s} ,\ S = 0, \quad \mu = 0.10,$$

determine its value after it has been in operation 5 years.

4. Compute the composite life of the plant described in problem 5, Section 10, using interest at 5% effective.

5. Find the composite life at 5%, converted semiannually, of the following items:

(a) Cost: \$10,000, $n = 7$, Scrap value: \$2,000.
(b) Cost: 5,000, $n = 5$, Scrap value: 1,000.
(c) Cost: 1,000, $n = 12$, Scrap value: 2,500.

SELECTED BIBLIOGRAPHY ON INTEREST AND INVESTMENT

COWLES, ALFRED (and associates) *Common-Stock Indexes, 1871–1937,* Principia Press, 1938; 2nd ed., 1939; xii + 499 pp.

EVANS, G. C. *Mathematical Introduction to Economics.* Chapter 8.

FISHER, I. *The Theory of Interest.* New York, 1930, xxvii + 566 pp.

HOTELLING, H. "A General Mathematical Theory of Depreciation," *Journal of the American Statistical Association,* 1925.

KNIGHT, F. H. (1) "Interest", *Encyclopaedia of the Social Sciences,* Vol. 8, 1932, pp. 131–143.

(2) "Capital, Time, and the Interest Rate," *Economica,* Vol. 14, 1934, pp. 257–286.

LANGE, O. (1) "The Place of Interest in the Theory of Production," *Review of Economic Studies,* Vol. 3, 1936, pp. 160–192.

(2) "The Rate of Interest and the Optimum Propensity to Consume," *Economica,* 1938, pp. 12–32.

LOTKA, A. J. "Industrial Replacement," *Skandinavisk Aktuarietidskrift,* 1933, pp. 51–63.

PREINREICH, G. A. D. (1) "Annual Survey of Economic Theory: The Theory of Depreciation," *Econometrica,* Vol. 6, 1938, pp. 219–241.

(2) "The Economic Life of Industrial Equipment," *Ibid.,* Vol. 8, 1940, pp. 12–44.

ROOS, C. F. "A Mathematical Theory of Depreciation and Replacement," *American Journal of Mathematics,* Vol. 50, 1928.

SKINNER, E. B. *The Mathematical Theory of Investment,* New York, 1913; 2nd ed., 1924, xi + 269 pp.

(Numerous other texts in this subject have appeared in recent years. Skinner, however, appears to have been the first American writer to have produced a text in this field and his book exerted great influence in introducing the theory of finance into mathematical curricula).

TAYLOR, J. S. "A Statistical Theory of Depreciation," *Journal of the American Statistical Association,* 1923, pp. 1010–1023.

WICKSELL, K. *Lectures on Political Economy.* Volume 1, New York, 1934, xxiii + 299 pp. In particular, pp. 258–299.

CHAPTER 14

INSURANCE—EXPECTATION

1. The Origins of Insurance

Since economics is a study of the behavior of individuals with respect to the production and use of goods, it is inevitable that we must devote some attention to the hazards of ownership. A sudden drop in prices can destroy the value of goods, but so also in a more direct physical way can floods, fires, and other visitations of nature. Since, moreover, economics is concerned with human welfare, the study of the principles of life insurance is also a proper subject for our study.

That branch of economics which deals with the protection of ownership and well-being against contingent events is called the *theory of insurance.* Since insurance, therefore, must deal with the chances of the occurrence of such events, it is necessary for us to understand something about the laws of probability before we can deal adequately with insurance problems.

The origin of insurance is very old. Thus Demosthenes describes the marine loans of the ancient Greeks, where money was advanced on cargoes to be repaid with substantial interest if the ships arrived safely in port, but which was not to be repaid at all if the ships were lost. The first known case of direct marine insurance, independent of loans, where guarantee against loss was made for a premium payment, is found in Belgium about the beginning of the fourteenth century.

Both life and fire insurance were of much later date than marine insurance, their origins being found in the seventeenth century. Although the citizens of London petitioned Charles I in 1635 and 1638 for a patent of monopoly to insure houses against loss by fire, it was not until the great fire of 1666 that practical measures to insure against such losses were finally undertaken.

The first known life insurance policy was made in London in 1583 when sixteen underwriters, for a premium of 8%, insured the life of William Gibbons for one year for £383 6s. 8d. Gibbons died just before the end of the year, and although the underwriters at first refused to pay the insurance on a technicality involving the length of a legal year, the court ruled in favor of Gibbons' estate. Since the age of Gibbons is not known it is impossible to compare the rate cited with modern rates.

Only a few cases of life insurance appear in the court records of the seventeenth century, and not until an adequate mathematical theory of probability was developed could life insurance assume a status essentially different from that of gambling.

VOL. XVII.] PHILOSOPHICAL TRANSACTIONS. 465

of mankind, than any thing of the kind yet extant. It exhibits the number of people in the city of Breslaw of all ages, from the birth to extreme old age, and thereby shows the chances of mortality of all ages; and likewise, how to make a certain estimate of the value of annuities for lives, which hitherto has been only done by an imaginary valuation; also the chances there are, that a person of any age proposed, may live to any other age given; with many more, as I shall hereafter show. This table shows the number of persons that are living in the ages current as annexed to them.

Age. Curt.	Persons.	Age. Curt.	Persons.	Age. Curt.	Persons.	Age. Curt.	Persons	Age. Curt.	Persons.	Age. Curt.	Persons.	Age.	Persons.
												7	5547
1	1000	15	628	29	539	43	417	57	272	71	131	14	4584
2	855	16	622	30	531	44	407	58	262	72	120	21	4270
3	798	17	616	31	523	45	397	59	252	73	109	28	3964
4	760	18	610	32	515	46	387	60	242	74	98	35	3604
5	732	19	604	33	507	47	377	61	232	75	88	42	3178
6	710	20	598	34	499	48	367	62	222	76	78	49	2709
7	692	21	592	35	490	49	357	63	212	77	68	56	2194
8	680	22	586	36	481	50	346	64	202	78	58	63	1694
9	670	23	579	37	472	51	335	65	192	79	49	70	1204
10	661	24	573	38	463	52	324	66	182	80	41	77	692
11	653	25	567	39	454	53	313	67	172	81	34	84	253
12	646	26	560	40	445	54	302	68	162	82	28	100	107
13	640	27	553	41	436	55	292	69	152	83	23		
14	634	28	546	42	427	56	282	70	142	84	20	Total	34000

Thus it appears, that the whole people of Breslaw consist of 34000 souls, being the sum total of the persons of all ages in the table. The first use hereof is to show the proportion of men able to bear arms, which are those between 18 and 56, rather than 16 and 60; the one being generally too weak to bear the fatigues of war, and the weight of arms, and the other too infirm from age, notwithstanding particular instances to the contrary. By the table there are found in this city 11997 persons under 18, and 3950 above 56, which together make 15947; so that the remainder to 34000, being 18053, are persons between those ages; at least one half of these are males, or 9027: so that the whole force this city can raise of fencible men, as the Scotch call them, is about 9000, or [illegible], or somewhat more than a quarter of the number of souls: which may perhaps pass for a rule for all other places.

The second use of this table is to show the different degrees of mortality, or rather vitality, in all ages; for if the number of persons of any age, remaining after one year, be divided by the difference between that and the number of the age proposed, it shows the odds there is, that a person of that age does not die in a year. As for instance, a person of 25 years of age has the odds of:

FIGURE 70.—FACSIMILE OF THE PAGE IN THE TRANSACTIONS OF THE ROYAL PHILOSOPHICAL SOCIETY OF LONDON (ANNO 1692–93) IN WHICH EDMUND HALLEY, ASTRONOMER OF NOTE AND FRIEND OF SIR ISAAC NEWTON, GAVE THE FIRST TABLE OF MORTALITY. MODERN LIFE INSURANCE MAY BE SAID TO DATE FROM THE PUBLICATION OF THIS TABLE.

Life insurance awaited both an adequate foundation in the theory of probability, and the development of carefully constructed tables of mortality. The first of these two foundations was laid by Jacob Bernoulli (1654–1705) in his great work, *Ars Conjectandi,* which was published posthumously in 1713. Here appeared a systematic statement of the laws of chance in a form suitable for the construction of a theory of actuarial science.

The second of the two foundations of life insurance was initiated by Edmund Halley (1656–1742), astronomer of note and friend of Sir Isaac Newton. Halley it was who made the first table of mortality (see Figure 70).[1] Finding that the vital statistics of the English parishes failed to give the age of death, Halley made a world-wide search for records which would give these essential data. He finally found that the city of Breslau in Silesia had kept such records and he succeeded in obtaining the registers for the five years from 1687 to 1691. Included in these data were the records of some 6193 births and 5869 deaths. Since no census of the city was available, Halley was forced to make an estimate for it. The principal value of Halley's table is found in the fact that it pointed the way toward the modern theory of insurance.

2. The Mortality Table

Since life insurance is probably the most completely developed insurance from the mathematical point of view, we shall confine ourselves to a discussion of its principles.

The basis of life insurance, as also in all other forms of insurance, is the *experience table*. In the case of life insurance, this table gives the mortality expectation for an initial group of individuals all assumed to be of the same age. This table consists of five columns. The first of these gives the age, x; the second gives the number living at this age, a number designated by l_x; the third column shows the number dying during the year, denoted by d_x; the fourth contains the probability of dying during the year, the ratio q_x; and the fifth gives the probability, p_x of surviving the year.

The relationships between these variables are indicated as follows:

$$(1) \qquad q_x = \frac{d_x}{l_x} = \frac{l_x - l_{x+1}}{l_x} \; ; \quad p_x = 1 - q_x = \frac{l_{x+1}}{l_x} = \frac{l_x - d_x}{l_x} \, .$$

Extensive statistical attention has been devoted to the problem of constructing mortality tables. Such tables naturally differ from country to country, from race to race, and from occupation to occupation. Changes also take place at different times in the same country and race because of scientific improvements in medicine, sanitation, modes of living, etc. Thus, for example, there has been a

[1] Published under the title: "An Estimate of the Degrees of Mortality of Mankind, drawn from curious Tables of the Births and Funerals at the City of Breslaw; with an Attempt to ascertain the Price of Annuities on Lives," *Transactions of the Royal Philosophical Society of London*, Vol. 17, 1692–93, pp. 483–491.

remarkable improvement in the conditions of health in the United States during the present century. Although the length of life has not been materially changed, the average length of life has been greatly extended. As a result, older mortality tables such as the celebrated *American Experience Table,* based upon the records of the Mutual Life Insurance Company of New York and published in 1868, no longer represent actual experience.

Since, however, the American Experience Table is generally used in computing life insurance premiums, we shall use it here as a basis of our illustrative calculations.

The American Experience Table, given in Table V at the end of the book, records the values of l_x, d_x, q_x, and p_x for ages from $x = 10$ to $x = 95$ on the assumption that the initial population was 100,000 persons at age 10.

A few examples will illustrate the use of this table. We use the customary notation, ${}_np_x$, to designate the probability that a person age x survives for n years.

Example 1. What is the probability of surviving from age 25 to age 40?

Solution. We compute directly

$$ {}_{15}p_{25} = \frac{l_{40}}{l_{25}} = \frac{78106}{89032} = 0.87728\ . $$

Example 2. A man 50 years old has a daughter age 25. What is the probability that both will survive 15 years?

Solution. This is a problem in joint probability. We first compute the probabilities that both separately will survive 15 years. We thus find

$$ {}_{15}p_{50} = \frac{l_{65}}{l_{50}} = \frac{49341}{69804} = 0.70685\ , \quad {}_{15}p_{25} = \frac{l_{40}}{l_{25}} = 0.87728\ . $$

The probability that both will survive 15 years is then the product of these two probabilities, namely,

$$ p = 0.70685 \times 0.87728 = 0.62011\ . $$

Example 3. What is the probability that at least one of the two persons in example 2 will be alive in 15 years?

Solution. This is a problem in the probability of mutually exclusive events. These mutually exclusive events are the following: (a) both may survive; (b) the father may survive and the daughter not; (c) the daughter may survive, but the father not. The sum of the probabilities of these events is the desired answer. We thus compute

Both survive:	0.62011
Father survives, but daughter not: $0.70685 \times (1 - 0.87728) =$	0.08674
Daughter survives, but father not: $0.87728 \times (1 - 0.70685) =$	0.25717
Probability that at least one survives:	0.96402

We may now check this answer by computing the remaining joint probability, namely that neither survives, and subtracting this value from 1. We thus obtain

$$1-(0.29315\times 0.12272)=0.96402\,.$$

PROBLEMS

1. Compute the probability that a man age 20 will live to be 50.

2. If a man at age 45 starts a project which will require 10 years, what is the probability that he will live to complete it?

3. A father is age 45 and a son age 15. What is the probability that both will survive one year? ten years?

4. A man is 50 years of age and his wife 45. What is the probability that both survive jointly 5 years?

5. The probabilities that A, B, and C live five years are respectively 0.9, 0.8, and 0.7. What is the probability that at least one survives five years?

6. In problem 5 compute the probability that at least two survive.

7. Approximately 4,000,000 men were engaged in the American Army during the World War. Assuming that half of these were age 25, one-third were 30, and one-sixth were 35 at the end of the war on November 11, 1918, how many survived to November 11, 1940?

8. Make a graph of l_x from age 10 to the end of the table.

9. Make a graph of q_x from age 10 to the end of the table.

10. A man age 45 and a wife age 42 have a child age 12. What is the probability that all will be alive when the man is 50?

11. If a man age 30 joins a pension plan to provide him with a retiring allowance at age 65, what is his chance of benefiting by the plan?

12. A university has a faculty of 500 members of average age 42. A group insurance plan is started to insure all members. How many deaths, on the average, should be expected in 10 years?

3. *Life Annuities*

In Chapter 13 we considered the evaluation of annuities certain. Specified amounts were to be paid at specified times and at a given rate of interest. The accumulation and the present value of such a series of payments were therefore mathematically determined values.

In *life annuities,* on the other hand, we deal with contingent annuities, where specified amounts are to be paid over a period of time which is determined by the duration of one or more lives.

By an *endowment* we shall mean a promise to pay a specified sum of money to an individual providing he shall survive to that date. The present value of an endowment of 1 payable in n years to an individual age x we shall designate by ${}_nE_x$. Its value is evidently given by the formula

$$(2) \qquad {}_nE_x = v^n \, {}_np_x = v^n \frac{l_{x+n}}{l_x} ,$$

where ${}_np_x$ is the probability, defined in the preceding section, that the individual survives for n years.

By the present value of a life annuity associated with the life of an individual of age x, or simply a life annuity, we mean the sum of all the endowments. Designating this present value by a_x, we have

$$(3) \qquad a_x = {}_1E_x + {}_2E_x + {}_3E_x + \cdots \text{ to end of table}$$

$$= \frac{vl_{x+1} + v^2 l_{x+2} + \cdots \text{ to end of tables}}{l_x} .$$

The quantities $D_{x+r} = v^{x+r} \, l_{x+r}$ have been tabulated and will be found in the first column of Table VI at the end of this book. These values are computed for an assumed rate of 3½%. They, together with the values of two other quantities soon to be described, form what are called *Commutation Columns*.

It is also clear that a table of the values of the function

$$(4) \qquad N_x = D_x + D_{x+1} + D_{x+2} + \cdots \text{ to end of table}$$

would be convenient in computing a_x. Such a set of values, the second entry in the Commutation Columns, is provided in Table VI.

We now see that the present value of a life annuity can be written

$$(5) \qquad a_x = \frac{D_{x+1} + D_{x+2} + \cdots}{D_x} = \frac{N_{x+1}}{D_x} .$$

Example 1. For what sum can a life annuity of $1,000 per annum be purchased by a person age 25?

Solution. By formula (5) and Table VI we have

$$a_{25} = \frac{N_{26}}{D_{25}} = \frac{732439.8}{37673.6} = 19.442 .$$

Hence the present value of the life annuity is given by

$$x = \$1{,}000 \, a_{25} = \$19{,}442 .$$

In the purchase of life annuities it is not unusual to start purchase some years in advance of the first payment. Thus a man at age 40 may decide to acquire a life annuity which will begin payment when he reaches the age of 65. The formula by means of which we may evaluate the present value of such a deferred annuity is readily derived.

Thus, let us designate by the symbol ${}_{n|}a_x$ the present value of a life annuity of 1 for a person age x, the first payment to be made $n+1$ years from the present. The value of the deferred annuity is then given by

$$
\begin{aligned}
{}_{n|}a_x &= {}_{n+1}E_x + {}_{n+2}E_x + {}_{n+3}E_x + \cdots \text{ to end of table} \\
&= \frac{v^{n+1}\, l_{x+n+1} + v^{n+2}\, l_{x+n+2} + \cdots}{l_x} \\
&= \frac{D_{x+n+1} + D_{x+n+2} + \cdots}{D_x}.
\end{aligned}
$$

Hence we obtain the formula

$$
{}_{n|}a_x = \frac{N_{x+n+1}}{D_x}. \tag{6}
$$

Example 2. Compare with the result of example 1 the cost of a life annuity of $1,000 per annum purchased by a person age 25, who specifies that the annuity is to begin when he reaches the age of 65.

Solution. Since the first payment is to be made in 40 years, we get by (6)

$$
{}_{40|}a_{25} = \frac{N_{66}}{D_{25}} = \frac{43{,}343.08}{37{,}673.6} = 1.1505\ .
$$

Multiplying this value by $1,000 we obtain

$$
x = \$1150.50\ .
$$

In business practice life annuities are frequently encountered which continue for n years, provided the annuitant survives so long, and then terminate. An annuity of this kind is called a *temporary annuity.* Its present value is customarily designated by the symbol ${}_{|n}a_x$, where one understands that the first payment is made at the end of the first year.

Since a life annuity is the sum of a temporary annuity for n years plus a life annuity deferred for n years, we can write

$$
a_x = {}_{|n}a_x + {}_{n|}a_x\ .
$$

From this we then obtain the formula for the present value of the temporary annuity since

$$
{}_{|n}a_x = a_x - {}_{n|}a_x = \frac{N_{x+1}}{D_x} - \frac{N_{x+n+1}}{D_x};
$$

that is to say,

$$
{}_{|n}a_x = \frac{N_{x+1} - N_{x+n+1}}{D_x}\ . \tag{7}
$$

Example 3. Compare the present value of a life annuity of $1,000 for 10 years for a person age 25, with the present value of an annuity certain of $1,000 for 10 years, interest at 3½%.

Solution. From formula (7) and the commutation Columns of Table VI we obtain

$$_{|10}a_{25}=\frac{N_{26}-N_{36}}{D_{25}}=\frac{732439.8-432326.5}{37673.6}=7.96614\ .$$

Hence the present value of the temporary annuity is $7,966. This is to be compared with $1,000 $a_{\overline{10|}}$ (at rate 3½%) = $8,317.

PROBLEMS

1. Compute the present value of an inheritance of $10,000, if this sum is to be paid to a young man age 18 when he reaches the age of 21. Compute this at 3½% and at 5%.

2. Find the present value of $1,000 $_{10}E_{15}$ at 4%. Compare this with the present value of $1,000 due in 10 years.

3. Compute the present value of a life annuity of $1,000 to a person age 40.

4. A man receives a life annuity of $1,000 when he reaches the age of 65. What is the cash equivalent of this annuity?

5. How large an annuity for life can be purchased by a person age 50 for $10,000?

6. Find the present value of a temporary life annuity of $500 for 20 years for a person age 45.

7. Which would be better for a person age 30 to own a temporary life annuity of $1,000 for 20 years (interest at 3½%), or an annuity certain of $1,000 for 18 years (interest at 3%)?

8. What annuity certain of $1,000 (interest at 3%) is equivalent to a temporary life annuity of $1,000 for 15 years (interest at 3½%) for a person age 25?

9. A man age 30 is to receive a life annuity of $500 when he reaches the age of 45. What is its present value?

10. A man wishes to give his son age 30 a life annuity on the son's 40th birthday. How large an annuity can he provide for $5,000?

4. Life Insurance

In its simplest form a life insurance policy is a promise to pay a stipulated sum of money upon the death of the policyholder. For this insurance the policyholder usually agrees to pay a life annuity in monthly or quarterly payments.

In order to compute such payments we must first find what is called the *net premium.* This is the amount that the insured would pay for his policy on the assumption (1) that nothing is charged by the issuing company for doing business; (2) that the mortality table is used as the basis of computation; and (3) that the payment is made at the end of the policy year in which the death occurs.

In order to find the net premium we must form the sum of the following mutually exclusive expectations, discounted to the present, for the policyholder of age x:

$$v\frac{d_x}{l_x}, \quad v^2\frac{d_{x+1}}{l_x}, \quad v^3\frac{d_{x+2}}{l_x}, \cdots .$$

The sum of these values is the net premium, which we shall designate by the symbol, A_x. If we employ the customary abbreviation

$$C_x = v^{x+1} d_x ,$$

then we can write the net premium in the form

$$A_x = \frac{C_x + C_{x+1} + C_{x+2} + \cdots \text{ to end of table}}{D_x}$$

Because of its usefulness the numerator of this fraction has been extensively tabulated and recorded in the Commutation Columns (Table VI) under the abbreviation M_x. We thus obtain the net premium under the simple form

$$(8) \qquad A_x = \frac{M_x}{D_x} .$$

Example 1. Compute the net premium for a policy of $1,000 taken out by a man age 25.

Solution. From Table VI we get

$$A_{25} = \frac{M_{25}}{D_{25}} = \frac{11631.14}{37673.6} = 0.30874 .$$

Hence the net premium is found to be

$$x = \$1{,}000\, A_{25} = \$308.74 .$$

One of the most common forms of insurance is that which is purchased by means of a life annuity. It is obvious that the present value of the life annuity is equated to the net premium of the policy. Such insurance is called *ordinary life,* and the annual amount paid by the policyholder is called the *net annual premium.*

If we designate this premium by P_x and note that it is always paid in advance, then we have the following equation for its determination:

$$P_x + P_x a_x = A_x .$$

From this we obtain

$$P_x = \frac{A_x}{1 + a_x} = \frac{M_x}{N_x}\,. \tag{9}$$

Example 2. Compute the annual net premium for the policy of example 1.

Solution. From Table VI we get

$$P_{25} = \frac{M_{25}}{N_{25}} = \frac{11631.14}{770113.4} = 0.015104\ ;$$

hence the annual net premium is equal to

$$x = \$1{,}000\,P_{25} = \$15.10\,.$$

PROBLEMS

1. Compute the net premium for an ordinary life policy of \$1,000 taken by a man age 50.

2. Find the net annual premium for the policy of problem 1.

3. If the net annual premium for a \$1,000 policy is \$23.50, how old is the policyholder?

4. If the net annual premium is \$63.66 for a man age 37, how large is the face of the policy?

5. The net annual premium for a policy of \$1,000 taken at age 35 is \$19.91. Noting that the first premium is paid in advance, how many years would be required for the premium payments to accumulate to \$1,000 at 3%?

5. *Types of Life Insurance*

In this section we shall consider several types of insurance which are commonly issued by life insurance companies. One of these is an insurance which is purchased by means of a cash payment and a temporary life annuity of $n - 1$ additional payments. Such a policy is called an n-payment policy, where n is usually 20 or 30 years.

In order to obtain the net annual premium we equate the single net premium to the sum of the cash payment of the net annual premium, which we designate by ${}_nP_x$, and the present value of the temporary life annuity. We thus obtain

$${}_nP_x + {}_nP_x \cdot {}_{|n-1}a_x = A_x\ ;$$

that is,

$${}_nP_x = \frac{A_x}{1 + {}_{|n-1}a_x}\,.$$

Replacing the terms in the right hand member by their commutation symbols, we obtain the formula

$$ {}_nP_x = \frac{M_x}{N_x - N_{x+n}} \, . $$

Example 1. Compute the net annual premium of a 20-year life policy of $1,000 purchased by a man age 25.

Solution. From the commutation columns, Table VI, we obtain

$$ {}_{20}P_{25} = \frac{M_{25}}{N_{25} - N_{45}} = \frac{11631.14}{770113.4 - 253745.5} $$
$$ = 0.022525 \; ; $$

hence the net annual premium equals $1,000 ${}_{20}P_{25} = \$22.53$.

Another common form of insurance is known as *term insurance*, where a person of age x is insured for a period of n years. Designating the net premium by the symbol $|_nA_x$, we see that this is given by

$$ |_nA_x = \frac{C_x + C_{x+1} + \cdots + C_{x+n-1}}{D_x} \, . $$

Since we can write the numerator as the difference $M_x - M_{x+n}$, we obtain

$$ {}_nA_x = \frac{M_x - M_{x+n}}{D_x} \, . $$

If we designate by ${}_nP_x$ the net annual premium for a term insurance of 1 for n years, then we may write

$$ |_nP_x + |_nP_x \cdot |_{n-1}a_x = {}_nA_x \, . $$

Solving for the net annual premium and replacing the symbols by their equivalent values in terms of the commutation symbols, we obtain the formula

$$ (10) \qquad |_nP_x = \frac{|_nA_x}{1 + |_{n-1}a_x} = \frac{M_x - M_{x+n}}{N_x - N_{x+n}} \, . $$

Example 2. Compare the net annual premium for a term insurance of $1,000 to a person of age 25, $n = 20$ years, with the net annual premium found in example 1.

Solution. From formula (10) and the Commutation Columns (Table VI), we get

$$ |_{20}P_{25} = \frac{M_{25} - M_{45}}{N_{25} - N_{45}} = \frac{11631.14 - 7192.809}{770113.4 - 253745.5} $$
$$ = 0.0085953 \, . $$

Hence the net annual premium is equal to $1,000 $|_{20}P_{25} = \$8.60$. This is to be compared with $22.53 found in example 1.

Another common form of insurance is *endowment insurance,* in which the company agrees to pay a given sum in the event either of the death of the policyholder, or of his surviving n years.

It is clear that such an insurance may be regarded as a term insurance plus a pure endowment payable at the end of n years. Denoting the single net premium for such an insurance by ${}_e\Pi_{xn}$, we write

$$\begin{aligned} {}_e\Pi_{xn} &= |_n A_x + {}_n E_x \\ &= \frac{M_x - M_{x+n}}{D_x} + \frac{D_{x+n}}{D_x} \\ &= \frac{M_x - M_{x+n} + D_{x+n}}{D_x} . \end{aligned}$$

In order to find the net annual premium, we observe that the net premium is to be purchased by a cash payment and a temporary annuity for $n-1$ years. If we designate the net annual premium by ${}_eP_{xn}$, we then have

$$(11) \qquad {}_eP_{xn} + {}_eP_{xn} \cdot |_{n-1}a_x = {}_e\Pi_{xn} .$$

From this equation we then obtain the formula

$$(12) \qquad {}_eP_{xn} = \frac{{}_e\Pi_{xn}}{1 + |_{n-1}a_x} = \frac{M_x - M_{x+n} + D_{x+n}}{N_x - N_{x+n}} .$$

Example 3. Compute the net annual premium for a 20-year endowment policy of $1,000 for a person age 25.

Solution. From Table VI we evaluate formula (12) and thus obtain

$$\begin{aligned} {}_eP_{25 \cdot 20} &= \frac{M_{25} - M_{45} + D_{45}}{N_{25} - N_{45}} = \frac{20211.931}{516367.9} \\ &= 0.0391425 . \end{aligned}$$

Hence, multiplying by $1,000, we obtain as the desired net annual premium the quantity $39.14.

PROBLEMS

1. Compute the net annual premium of a 20-year life policy of $1,000 purchased by a man age 45.

2. What is the net annual premium for a 10-year term insurance of $1,000 purchased by a man age 45?

3. Find the net annual premium for a 20-year endowment policy of $1,000 purchased by a man age 45.

4. If the net annual premium of a 20-year life policy of $1,000 is $44.21, how old is the policyholder?

5. Compare the accumulation of 20 annually spaced payments of $39.14 (first payment cash) at 3% with the face value of a 20-year endowment policy purchased by a man age 25 for the same amount.

6. *The Loading Factor*

In preceding examples we have obtained the net annual premium for several types of policies at $1,000 for a man of age 25. The computations were based on the American Experience Table with interest at $3\frac{1}{2}\%$. In the following table we summarize these values and also include the net annual premium as computed from the American Experience Table with interest at 3%.

Type of Policy	Net Annual Premium (American Experience at 3½%)	Net Annual Premium (American Experience at 3%)
Ordinary Life	$15.10	$16.11
20-year Life	22.53	24.98
20-year Term	8.60	8.66
20-Year Endowment	39.14	41.01

But in the actual sale of insurance policies these net annual premiums are never the ones actually quoted. We give below the figures quoted in 1940 by one of the leading American companies, the computations being based upon the American Experience Table with interest figured at 3%.

Type of Policy	Quoted Net Annual Premium Based on American Experience at 3%
Ordinary Life	$21.49
20-year Life	31.83
20-year Term[2]	11.55
20-year Endowment	49.33

The difference between the net annual premium and the *gross*, or *office premium*, is called *loading*. This difference is distributed over the overhead of the issuing company and includes the cost of administering the business, the expense incurred in obtaining new business, etc. When this difference exceeds the legitimate costs of the business and the expense of possible contingencies, then a surplus will accumulate which is distributed to the policyholders in the form of dividends. It is clear that this surplus depends in part upon the current rate of interest, that is to say, the rate of interest which the company is able to realize on the investment of its assets. When the interest rate is high, the premiums are high, and when the interest rate is low, the premiums fall with it. It is an interesting proposition to consider

[2] Convertible within 7 years.

what would be the economic consequencies if the current rate of interest should remain for any considerable length of time below the 3% assumed in the computation of net annual premiums on the basis of the American Experience Table.

7. *Terminal Reserves*

It will be observed that there is a considerable difference between the net annual premium of an ordinary life policy bought at age 25 and the value paid for the insurance for a single year at the same age. These values are respectively \$15.10 and \$7.79. But if the holder of the life policy survives until the age of 65 he will still pay \$15.10 for his insurance, whereas insurance for a single year would cost \$38.77. We thus see that in the early ages more is paid annually for insurance than for an equivalent term insurance, while at advanced ages the premiums are smaller.

The excess paid in early years for insurance is accumulated as a reserve to meet the deficiencies of later years. The accumulation of this excess payment is called the *terminal reserve,* and constitutes what is termed the value of the policy at the end of the year in question.

Let us designate by ${}_nV_x$ the reserve at the end of n years for an ordinary life policy issued to a person at age x.

The single net premium for the new policy at age $x + n$ is A_{x+n}, while the present value of the unpaid premiums is $P_x(1 + a_{x+n})$. The difference between these amounts is the terminal reserve; that is

$$(13) \qquad {}_nV_x = A_{x+n} - P_x(1 + a_{x+n}) .$$

The values of A_{x+n}, P_x, and a_{x+n} have all been given earlier in terms of the commutation symbols. Substituting these in (13) we readily obtain

$$(14) \qquad {}_nV_x = \frac{N_x M_{x+n} - M_x N_{x+n}}{N_x D_{x+n}} .$$

This quantity is what is usually called the *loan* or *cash surrender* value of the policy.

Example. Compute the terminal reserve on an ordinary life policy of \$1,000 issued at age 25 after it has run for 20 years.

Solution. Substituting in (14) we obtain

$$\begin{aligned} {}_{20}V_{25} &= \frac{N_{25} M_{45} - M_{25} N_{45}}{N_{25} D_{45}} \\ &= 0.213.04 \end{aligned}$$

Multiplying this value by $1,000 we obtain as the terminal reserve the sum $213.04.

PROBLEMS

1. Compute ${}_{30}V_{30}$.

2. Find the values of ${}_{40}V_{25}$.

3. Show numerically that ${}_{70}V_{25}$ differs very little from 1. What conclusion can we reach about the value of ${}_{95-x}V_x$?

4. Find the terminal reserves at the end of 10 years for an ordinary life policy of $1,000 taken by a man at the age of 37.

5. Assuming that 1,000 people at the age of 30 take out ordinary life policies of $1,000 compute the total amount paid each year for the first two years, the average losses on the policies each year, the accumulation at 3½% of the reserves, and hence the terminal reserves for each year.

SELECTED BIBLIOGRAPHY ON INSURANCE AND EXPECTATION

DOWLING, L. W. *Mathematics of Life Insurance.* New York, 1925.

FORSYTHE, C. H. *Mathematical Theory of Life Insurance.* New York, 1924.

FREEMAN, H. *An Elementary Treatise on Actuarial Mathematics.* Cambridge, 1931.

GLOVER, J. W. *Tables of Applied Mathematics in Finance, Insurance, Statistics.* Ann Arbor, Michigan, 1923.

HENDERSON, R. *Graduation of Mortality and Other Tables.* New York, 1919.

KENT, F. C. *Mathematics of Life Insurance.* New York, 1925.

KNIGHT, F. H. *Risk, Uncertainty, and Profit.* Boston, 1921.

MAGEE, J. H. *General Insurance.* Chicago, 1936.

RIEGAL, R. *Insurance Principles and Practice.* New York, 1929.

CHAPTER 15

INDEX NUMBERS FROM THE ECONOMIC POINT OF VIEW

1. The Problem of Index Numbers

In the study of economic time series one of the most important questions to be answered is that of the relative changes which take place in the variables from one period to another. The phenomenon of changing prices is apparent on every hand and we find amazing variations occurring over very short periods of time. Thus 70 cents spent in 1913 on wholesale commodities would have purchased as much as $1.54 in 1920, or $1.00 in 1926, or 65 cents in 1932. At the time of the Civil War 61 cents in 1861 would have obtained as much as $1.32 in 1864. Even more astonishing variations take place in the values of securities. Thus during the period of the great bull market, which culminated in 1929, we find that industrial stocks quoted at $90, as an average, in April, 1926, had appreciated to $219 by August, 1929. In November of that same year these stocks had fallen in quoted price to $135 and by June, 1932 to $31.

These great variations which we have cited naturally cause abnormal strains and stresses in the industrial system, and one of the primary aims of economic science is to ascertain the causes and to suggest remedies for these sudden and devastating changes. It is natural that one should first seek for a proper means of measuring the weekly, monthly, and annual variations in the various quantities that concern us in economics. This means of measurement is furnished by what are called index numbers, which we have already discussed briefly in Section 5 of Chapter 1. By an *index number,* as we have said earlier, we shall understand a ratio, generally expressed as a percentage, which is designed to indicate the level at any given date of the items of a time series.

We shall not attempt here to discuss the theory of the construction of index numbers, a subject which belongs more naturally to statistics, but we shall be concerned principally with the economic use and importance of such numbers. We shall state, however, a few of the considerations which enter into the problem of comparing the purchasing power of a dollar in one year with its purchasing power in another.

For this purpose we shall designate price by p and quantity by q, using the subscript 0 to denote the base, or comparison, year, and the subscript 1 to denote the year for which the index is desired. It has been customary in the application of index numbers to select as base some year not too remote from the present, a year, perhaps, which might be conceived as a reasonably normal one. In earlier work the year 1913 was employed as a base, and in more recent times 1926 has been similarly designated.

The comparison year having been selected, we may assume that the following prices and quantities, n in number, are known for it:

Prices for the base year: $p_0\, p'_0\, p''_0 \cdots p_0^{(n-1)}$

Quantities for base year: $q_0\, q'_0\, q''_0 \cdots q_0^{(n-1)}$

Similarly, for the year which is to be compared with the base year, we shall have the following prices and quantities:

Prices for the second year: $p_1\, p'_1\, p''_1 \cdots p_1^{(n-1)}$

Quantities for second year: $q_1\, q'_1\, q''_1 \cdots q_1^{(n-1)}$

It will be convenient to employ the abbreviation

$$\sum pq = pq + p'q' + p''q'' + \cdots + p^{(n-1)}q^{(n-1)},$$

and also to specify the four possible product sums by the following letters

$$I = \sum p_0 q_0\,, \quad I' = \sum p_1 q_0; \quad J = \sum p_0 q_1\,, \quad J' = \sum p_1 q_1\,.$$

The problem of index numbers is to construct a function of the $2n$ prices and the $2n$ quantities which describes exactly and uniquely the level of prices in one year when this level is compared with that of the other year.

Although this problem is inherently difficult, and although purely economic considerations have not yet been brought into complete accord with those raised by the requirements of statistics, practical measures of the comparative level of prices have been devised. We shall examine some of these measures here and their relationship to the problem as it is to be regarded from the point of view of economics.

2. *Types of Index Numbers and their Properties*

Although Irving Fisher in his treatise on *The Making of Index Numbers* lists 134 different formulas which have been suggested for the construction of index numbers, it will be sufficient for our purpose to mention only three. The first of these was used by E. Laspeyres in 1864 in Germany and is the ratio

$$i = I'/I. \tag{1}$$

The second was formulated by H. Paasche in 1874 and is the ratio

$$j = J'/J. \tag{2}$$

The third was called the "ideal" formula by Irving Fisher and is the geometrical mean of the indexes of Laspeyres and Paasche, that is

$$k = \sqrt{i \cdot j}. \tag{3}$$

Example 1. In order to illustrate these three indexes numerically, let us compute the agricultural price index for the year 1930 with 1926 as base.

Solution. Using production and price data for ten agricultural commodities, we first construct the following table of values for pq:

VALUES OF pq FOR YEARS 1926 AND 1930

Crops	p_0	p_1	q_0	q_1	$p_0 q_0$	$p_1 q_1$	$p_0 q_1$	$p_1 q_0$
Corn	.75	.84	2692	2060	2019.0000	1730.4000	1545.0000	2261.2800
Wheat	1.45	.87	831.0	858.2	1204.9500	746.6340	1244.3900	722.9700
Oats	.41	.39	1247	1278	511.2700	498.4200	523.9800	486.3300
Cotton	.175	.136	8989	6966	1573.0750	947.3760	1219.0500	1222.5040
Potatoes	1.420	.904	354.3	333.2	503.1060	301.2128	473.1440	320.2872
Hay	23.41	19.89	96.07	74.21	2248.9987	1476.0369	1737.2561	1910.8323
Sugar	.043	.034	12952	13169	556.9360	447.7460	566.2670	440.3680
Tobacco	.182	.144	1298	1635	236.2360	235.4400	297.5700	186.9120
Barley	.64	.52	184.9	304.6	118.3360	158.3920	194.9440	96.1480
Rye	.92	.61	40.80	45.38	37.5360	27.6818	41.7496	24.8880
Totals					9009.4437	6569.3395	7843.3507	7672.5195

In this table all prices are expressed in dollars. The quantities are in 1,000,000 units, where the units are bushels for corn, wheat, oats, potatoes, barley, and rye, pounds for cotton, sugar, and tobacco, and tons for hay. The products are thus in millions of dollars.

From the totals given in this table we immediately have the following values:

$$I = 9009.4437, \quad I' = 7672.5195; \quad J = 7843.3507, \quad J' = 6569.3395.$$

Introducing these values into formulas (1), (2), and (3), we immediately obtain

$$i = \frac{7672.5195}{9009.4437} = 0.8516, \quad j = \frac{6569.3395}{7843.3507} = 0.8376, \quad k = \sqrt{0.8516 \times 0.8376} = 0.8446.$$

In his study on index numbers mentioned above, Irving Fisher undertook the task of segregating the most perfect index number from the 134 formulas, which he had found. His line of attack was the formulation of two tests and the elimination of formulas which failed to meet one or both of them.

The first criterion was called the *time reversal test,* and it may be defined as follows:

If P_{ab} is the index number for year b with year a as base, and if P_{ba} is the index number for year a with year b as base, then P_{ab} and P_{ba} should satisfy the equation

$$P_{ab} \times P_{ba} = 1 . \tag{4}$$

If the product $P_{ab} \times P_{ba}$ is greater than 1, then an *upward bias* is said to exist; if the product is less than 1, the *bias* is *downward.*

It is clear from this definition that the time reversal test reduces to a study of the product of an index number by the same number in which the subscripts "0" and "1" of p and q have been interchanged.

Example 2. As an example, let us apply the time reversal test to the index number

$$P_{01} = \frac{I' + J'}{I + J},$$

where we make use of the abbreviations given in Section 1.

Solution. Interchanging subscripts of p and q, we obtain

$$P_{10} = \frac{J + I}{J' + I'},$$

which is seen to be the reciprocal of P_{01}. Thus the index meets the time reversal test.

Of the 134 formulas tested by this criterion, 41 were found to meet the test. These were then subjected to a second criterion called the *factor reversal test.* This may be described as follows: Suppose that an index of prices, P, and an index of quantity change, Q, have been constructed. The factor reversal test then requires that the product of P and Q shall equal the ratio of the expenditure in the comparison year to the expenditure in the base year. That is to say, in symbols we require that

$$P \cdot Q = \frac{\Sigma p_1 q_1}{\Sigma p_0 q_0}. \tag{5}$$

Since the quantity index is obtained from the price index merely by interchanging p and q, leaving the subscripts unchanged, the factor reversal test consists in showing that the product of the price index by the same formula, in which the p's and q's have been interchanged, is equal to the ratio of the expenditures. Some economists, especially Haberler, feel that this test has no economic significance.

Example 3. Show that the "ideal" formula defined by equation (3) above meets the factor reversal test.

Solution. From the explicit formula, and making use of the abbreviations of Section 1, we obtain the following expressions for P and Q:

$$P = \sqrt{\frac{I' \cdot J'}{I \cdot J}}, \qquad Q = \sqrt{\frac{J \cdot J'}{I \cdot I'}}.$$

The product of P by Q is readily seen to reduce to the ratio J'/I, as is required by the test.

Of the 41 formulas which had met the time reversal test, 13 were found also to satisfy the criterion of factor reversal. From this group Fisher selected his "ideal formula" as being the simplest.

But Fisher also observed that the *Edgeworth-Marshall aggregative* index number, given by the formula

$$P_A = \frac{I' + J'}{I + J}, \tag{6}$$

was a close approximation to the ideal for normal ranges of the price and quantity variables. Thus if we designate the ideal by P_I, and if we employ the abbreviations $\coth^2\alpha = IJ'/JI'$, $\coth^2\beta = JJ'/II'$, where $\coth\theta$ is the hyperbolic cotangent of θ, then the following relationship holds:

$$P_A = \coth(\alpha + \beta) P_I. \tag{7}$$

Testing this formula numerically, Fisher found that when $\coth^2\alpha$ ranges from 0.90 to 1.10 and $\coth^2\beta$ ranges from 0.50 to 2.00, the maximum range of the coefficient $\coth(\alpha + \beta)$ is from 0.983 to 1.016. Hence under all usual conditions the index number formula P_A will give an answer that is within two per cent of the value calculated by the ideal.

Unfortunately the ideal formula does not meet a third criterion which has been called the *circular test.* If we designate by P_{ab} the index number for the year b with a as base, then the circular test requires the following equality for any value of n:

$$P_{1n} = P_{12}P_{23}P_{34} \cdots P_{n-1,n}. \tag{8}$$

The amount by which the circular test fails has been called by Irving Fisher the *circular gap*. The geometrical average

$$(9) \qquad P_G = \frac{\Pi p_1^{\alpha}}{\Pi p_0^{\alpha}} ,$$

where α is any number and Π implies that the products are to be formed, is readily seen to satisfy the circular test. This index number also satisfies the time reversal criterion, but it fails to satisfy the factor reversal test.

Example 4. As an example, we shall compute the circular gaps obtained by the Laspeyres and Paasche formulas given by (1) and (2) above. We shall use for this computation agricultural prices and quantities for the years 1926, 1927, 1928, and 1929, representing these respectively by p_1, p_2, p_3, p_4 and q_1, q_2, q_3, and q_4.

Solution. Let us represent by I_{ij} the sum $\Sigma p_i q_j$. The values of I_{ij} necessary for our calculation are recorded in the following table:[1]

VALUES OF $I_{ij} = \Sigma p_i q_j$

j	$i = 1$	2	3	4
1	9009.4	8891.2	9278.8	9169.3
2	9292.4	9060.8	9422.9	9848.7
3	....	9304.0	9636.6	9584.4
4	8432.1	....	8675.0	8556.6

Using the formula of Laspeyres we compute the two indexes of prices for the year 1929 with 1926 as base, first by the circular method, and second by the direct method. We thus obtain

$$P_{14}^{(1)} = \frac{I_{21}}{I_{11}} \frac{I_{32}}{I_{22}} \frac{I_{43}}{I_{33}} = 1.0208 \qquad P_{14}^{(2)} = \frac{I_{41}}{I_{11}} = 1.0177 .$$

The circular gap is thus seen to equal numerically the difference between these values, that is to say 0.0031.

The same computation, using the formula of Paasche, gives the following values:

$$P_{14}^{(3)} = \frac{I_{22}}{I_{12}} \frac{I_{33}}{I_{23}} \frac{I_{44}}{I_{34}} = 0.9939, \quad P_{14}^{(4)} = \frac{I_{44}}{I_{14}} = 1.0147 .$$

In this case the circular gap is numerically equal to 0.0208, and the sign is reversed from that in the first computation.

No formula was found by Fisher's study which satisfied all three

[1] For the computation of these values see Davis and Nelson: *Elements of Statistics*, 2nd ed., 1937, p. 113.

tests. R. Frisch, in discussing the situation, makes the following comment:[2]

> The difficulties here discussed are unavoidable so long as we maintain the atomistic viewpoint and consider the p's and q's as independent variables. On this assumption (and assuming certain continuity properties of the index-number formula), I have indeed proved that three such fundamental tests as the commensurability, determinateness, and circular tests cannot be satisfied at the same time.[3] And, even if some of the tests are abandoned (Fisher is, for instance, willing to give up the circular test), the remaining ones do not lead to a unique formula.

3. Differential Derivation of Index Numbers

An ingenious interpretation of index numbers has been made by F. Divisia (see *Bibliography*), which enables one to see readily the assumptions which have been made when one assumes one form in preference to another for the computation of an index. The original work of Divisia has been extended and interpreted by R. Roy. (see *Bibliography*).

Let us assume that the sum $\sum pq$ can be represented by the product PQ, where P is a general price level and Q a measure of the physical volume of goods, that is to say, let

$$P \cdot Q = \Sigma pq \,. \tag{10}$$

Then, precisely as we did in Section 5 of Chapter 8, we form the differential

$$PdQ + QdP = \Sigma(pdq + qdp) \,. \tag{11}$$

Dividing this expression by PQ we obtain

$$\frac{dQ}{Q} + \frac{dP}{P} = \frac{\Sigma pdq}{\Sigma pq} + \frac{\Sigma qdp}{\Sigma pq} \,. \tag{12}$$

We now separate this differential into two parts, forming the following equations:

$$\frac{dQ}{Q} = \frac{\Sigma pdq}{\Sigma pq} \,, \qquad \frac{dP}{P} = \frac{\Sigma qdp}{\Sigma pq} \,. \tag{13}$$

The integral of the first of these expressions may now be called

---

[2] See *Bibliography*: Frisch (2), p. 7.

[3] *Journal of the American Statistical Association*, Dec. 1930. By the *commensurability test*, Frisch means that the index number "shall not change by changing the unit of measurement for any of the individual goods"; by the *determinateness test* he means that the index "shall not become zero, infinite, or indeterminate, if an individual price or quantity becomes zero."

an index of quantity, and the integral of the second an index of price. It is with the second equation that we shall be concerned.

If we assume, first, that all the values of q are proportional to those observed in the base year, that is, if $q = \lambda q_0$, then we can write

$$\frac{dP}{P} = \frac{\Sigma q dp}{\Sigma pq} = \frac{\Sigma \lambda q_0 dp}{\Sigma \lambda q_0 p} = \frac{d(\Sigma q_0 p)}{\Sigma q_0 p}. \tag{14}$$

Integrating this equation and dividing by P_0 we readily obtain

$$\frac{P}{P_0} = \frac{\Sigma(q_0 p)}{\Sigma q_0 p_0}, \tag{15}$$

which is recognized at once as the index of Laspeyres. In similar fashion the index of Paasche follows from the assumption that $q = \lambda q_1$.

If we next break up the summations into partial sums designated by subscripts to the Σ's, then it is clear that we can express the price differential in the following form:

$$\frac{dP}{P} = \frac{\Sigma_1(qdp) + \Sigma_2(qdp) + \cdots + \Sigma_n(qdp)}{\Sigma(pq)}, \tag{16}$$

$$= \frac{\Sigma_1(qdp)}{\Sigma_1(pq)}\left(\frac{\Sigma_1(pq)}{\Sigma(pq)}\right) + \frac{\Sigma_2(qdp)}{\Sigma_2(pq)}\left(\frac{\Sigma_2(pq)}{\Sigma(pq)}\right) + \cdots$$

$$+ \frac{\Sigma_n(qdp)}{\Sigma_n(pq)}\left(\frac{\Sigma_n(pq)}{\Sigma(pq)}\right).$$

If we designate the partial differentials by dP_i/P_i, and their coefficients by α_i, then we can write (16) as follows:

$$\frac{dP}{P} = \alpha_1 \frac{dP_1}{P_1} + \alpha_2 \frac{dP_2}{P_2} + \cdots + \alpha_n \frac{dP_n}{P_n}. \tag{17}$$

We observe in this that the sum of the coefficients equals 1, that is,

$$\alpha_1 + \alpha_2 + \alpha_3 + \cdots + \alpha_n = 1. \tag{18}$$

It will be seen now that the "ideal" formula can be obtained from (17) by assuming that $\alpha_1 = \alpha_2 = \frac{1}{2}$, and that $dP_1/P_1 = dI'/I'$, $dP_2/P_2 = dJ'/J'$. We thus obtain

$$\frac{dP}{P} = \frac{1}{2}\left(\frac{dI'}{I'} + \frac{dJ'}{J'}\right). \tag{19}$$

When this equation is integrated and the resulting function divided by P_0, the "ideal" formula is immediately obtained.

More generally, if in (17) all the values of α_i are assumed to be constants, then we obtain the following index, which, if each partial summation applies to a single year, satisfies the circular criterion:

$$\frac{P}{P_0}=\left(\frac{P_1}{P_0}\right)^{\alpha_1}\left(\frac{P_2}{P_0}\right)^{\alpha_2}\cdots\left(\frac{P_n}{P_0}\right)^{\alpha_n}. \tag{20}$$

PROBLEMS

1. Show that the "ideal" formula satisfies the time reversal test.
2. Prove that the index number

$$I_G=\left\{\frac{p_1}{p_0}\frac{p'_1}{p'_0}\frac{p''_1}{p''_0}\cdots\frac{p_1{}^{(n-1)}}{p_0{}^{(n-1)}}\right\}^{1/n}$$

satisfies the time reversal test and hence has no bias.

3. Making use of the conclusion reached in problem 2 show that the index number

$$I_A=\frac{\Sigma\,(p_1/p_0)}{n}$$

always has an upward bias. (*Hint*: Make use of the theorem that an arithmetic average of positive quantities always equals or exceeds the geometric average of the same quantities).

4. Making use of the conclusion in problem 2 show that the index number

$$I_H=\frac{n}{\Sigma\,(p_0/p_1)}$$

always has a downward bias. (*Hint*: Make use of the theorem that a harmonic average of positive quantities always equals or is less than the geometric average of the same quantities).

5. Show that the index number

$$I_C=\sqrt{\left(\frac{I'+J'}{I+J}\right)\left(\frac{J'}{I}\right)\left(\frac{I+I'}{J+J'}\right)}$$

satisfies the factor reversal test. Does it also satisfy the time reversal test?

6. Show that if in equation (17) we set $P_1=I'$ and $P_2=J'$, and if we define

$$\alpha_1=\frac{IJ'}{IJ'+I'J}\,,\qquad \alpha_2=\frac{I'J}{IJ'+I'J}\,,$$

then P is the harmonic aggregative index

$$P=\frac{2}{\dfrac{I}{I'}+\dfrac{J}{J'}}\,.$$

7. Using the table of Example 4, compute the circular gap of the "ideal" formula between the years 1926 and 1929.

8. Making use of the table in Example 1, compute the quantity index for the year 1930, with 1926 as base, by means of the formulas of Laspeyres and Paasche.

4. Index Numbers and the Utility Surface

The failure of the criteria, which we have set forth in Section 2, to define a unique index number has led to attempts on the part of a number of writers to refer the problem to a comparison of utilities. Perhaps the first of these investigations was made by A. A. Konüs in 1924, whose work was known only through an account of it published by L. V. Bortkiewicz. The original article was made available in English in 1939 (see *Bibliography*). A history of the problem and its present status will be found in an admirable survey of the theory of index numbers by R. Frisch to whom reference has already been made in Section 2. [See *Bibliography,* Frisch (2)]. Since it will be impossible for us to examine the numerous ramifications of this elegant but difficult subject, we shall content ourselves here by indicating merely the general nature of the argument.

We shift our point of view now to the cost of living and we ask what is the index which measures the *true* difference in cost of living between one price situation and another? The word true is now used in the sense of a comparison of satisfactions as determined from the relative positions of the base and comparison points on the indifference map discussed in Section 6 of Chapter 3.

Let us assume that for some base year there will exist a certain variety of prices $\{p_0\}$, and at the time of some comparison year a second variety $\{p_1\}$. Let us then consider the planes of expenditure which correspond to these two price varieties, namely,

$$(21) \qquad E_0 = \sum p_0 q\,, \quad \text{and} \quad E_1 = \sum p_1 q\,,$$

where q designates the quantities purchased at the given prices for the fixed money expenditures E_0 and E_1. For simplicity in notation subscripts have not been fixed to the q's, although the reader will understand from the summation signs that such subscripts are tacitly understood.

We now propose to prove the theorem that *if the indifference surfaces are concave, then the true index of the change in the cost of living,* i′, *between the base year and the comparison year, where by true we mean that index which compares the respective utilities, will be less than the index number of Laspeyres,* i, *but greater than the index number of Paasche,* j. *That is to say, we shall establish the inequality*

$$i > i' > j \,. \tag{22}$$

The reasoning may be followed more readily if we consider only two commodities; the extension to the general case is immediate. Let us then consider the two situations which are graphically illustrated in Figure 71 for two quantities q_1 and q_2.

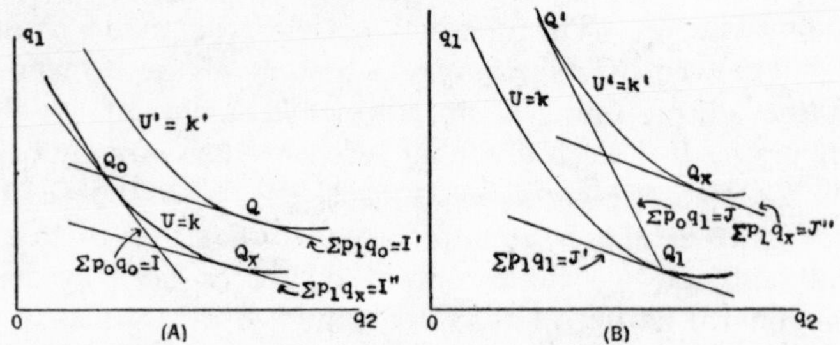

Figure 71.—Budget Lines on an Indifference Map Showing Various Utility Relationships.

The first chart, (A) of Figure 71, shows an indifference map in which are drawn the budget lines

$$\Sigma p_0 q_0 = I \,, \quad \Sigma p_1 q_0 = I' \,. \tag{23}$$

But because of the concavity of the indifference lines, the budget equation which represents the same utility at the new prices, namely, the equation $\Sigma p_1 q_x = I''$, will lie below the second equation given in (23). Hence, designating by i' the ratio I''/I, and noting that $i = I'/I$, we reach the inequality $i > i'$.

The second chart, (B) of Figure 71, shows an indifference map in which are drawn the budget lines

$$\Sigma p_0 q_1 = J \,, \quad \Sigma p_1 q_1 = J'. \tag{24}$$

But because of the concavity of the indifference lines, the budget equation which represents the same utility at the prices of the comparison year, namely, the equation $\Sigma p_1 q_x = J''$, will lie above the second equation given in (24). Hence, designating by i' the ratio J''/J, and noting that $j = J'/J$, we obtain the second inequality $i' > j$. The theorem follows immediately from the two inequalities which we have just established.

5. *Conclusion*

Although it will not be profitable for us to go further into this interesting subject, a few remarks may be pertinent about the general situation. If the true index of the cost of living is bounded above by i and below by j, then it follows that $i > j$ and consequently, that

$$I' \times J > I \times J'.$$

But this inequality is not a mathematically necessary one as can be proved readily by examples. Consequently, we should expect to find, and sometimes do find, sets of prices and quantities for which the inequality does not hold. It is interesting to observe, however, that for most statistical data the inequality is found to prevail, which lends considerable strength to the validity of the argument given in the last section. Thus, in Example 1 of Section 2 we found that $i = 0.8516$, which exceeded slightly the value $j = 0.8376$. We observe, furthermore, that since the "ideal" formula is the geometrical average of i and j, its value lies between the values of i and j and thus is closer to the true index than either of them.

But in some instances the difference between i and j is significantly large and the question naturally arises as to the best method of estimating i' in such cases. For example, employing the utility function $U(q_1, q_2) = q_1 + q_2 + \log_e(q_1 q_2)$, and an artificial schedule of prices, R. Frisch has shown [see *Bibliography*, Frisch (3)] that $i = 3.00$, $j = 1.43$, and $i' = 1.84$. Fisher's ideal formula gives a value of 2.07, which, while closer than the other indexes is still in error by 0.23. Bowley, and Frisch have given methods for the approximation of i', but the intricate nature of the analysis makes it undesirable to attempt an exposition here. The reader will find it profitable to consult the original articles.

PROBLEMS

1. Assuming that an individual has a budget equal to 34.00 in a year in which the following price schedule prevails for two commodities:

$$p_0: \quad 3.00, \quad 5.00,$$

show that his utility function

$$U = 24x + 32y - x^2 - y^2$$

has its maximum value of $U = 202.14$ for the following quantities:

$$q_0: \quad 4.76, \quad 3.94.$$

In a subsequent year new prices are found to prevail as follows:

$$p_1: \quad 2.00, \quad 6.00.$$

Show that the lowest expenditure that will give the same utility as before is 31.04, and that this corresponds to the following quantities:

$$q_1: \quad 7.54, \quad 2.66.$$

2. Using the prices and quantities for the two years discussed in problem 1, compute the values of i, i', and j and show that these agree with the theorem of Section 4.

3. From the results of problem 2 compute the value of the "ideal" index k and compare this with the value of i'.

4. The following prices and quantities are observed to prevail in a base year:

$$p_0: \quad 2.00, \quad 6.00;$$
$$q_0: \quad 7.4, \quad 2.2 \; .$$

Assuming the same utility function as in problem 1, show that $U = 188.4$ and that this value is a maximum for the assumed budget.

In a subsequent year the following new prices are observed:

$$p_1: \quad 3.00, \quad 5.00.$$

Show that the smallest budget that will give the same utility at the new prices is 31.00 and that the corresponding quantities are the following:

$$q_1: \quad 4.5, \quad 3.5.$$

5. Using the prices and quantities for the two years discussed in problem 4, compute the values of i, i', and j, and show that they have the proper order of magnitude.

6. R. Frisch has proposed a scheme for comparing utilities at different price and quantity levels which he has called the *double-expenditure method.* The basis of this method is the assumption that utilities are approximately equal whenever $D_1 = D_2$, where we define $D_1 = I\,I'$ and $D_2 = J\,J'$. Test this hypothesis numerically for the data given in problems 1 and 4.

SELECTED BIBLIOGRAPHY ON THE THEORY OF INDEX NUMBERS

ALLEN, R. G. D. "On the Marginal Utility of Money and its Application," *Economica*, Vol. 13, 1933, pp. 186–209.

BORTKIEWICZ, L. V. *Nordic Statistical Journal*, 1923, 1924, 1932.

BOWLEY, A. L. "Notes on Index Numbers," *Economic Journal*, Vol. 38, 1928, pp. 216–237.

DIVISIA, F. (1) "L'indice monétaire et la théorie de la monnaie," *Revue d'Economie politique*, Vol. 39, 1925, pp. 842–861, 980–1008, 1121–1151; Vol. 40, 1926, pp. 49–87.

(2) *Economique rationnelle.* Paris, 1927, xxxii + 443 pp.

FISHER, IRVING. *The Making of Index Numbers*, Boston, 1922; 3rd edition, 1927.

FRISCH, R. (1) *New Methods of Measuring Marginal Utility*, Tübingen, 1932, 142 pp.

(2) "Annual Survey of General Economic Theory: The Problem of Index Numbers," *Econometrica*, Vol. 4, 1936, pp. 1–38.

(3) "The Double-Expenditure Method," *Econometrica*, Vol. 6, 1938, pp. 85–90.

GINI. C. (1) "Quelques considérations au sujet de la construction des nombres indices et des questions analogues," *Metron*, Vol. 4, July 15, 1924, pp. 3-162.

(2) "On the Circular Test of Index Numbers," *Ibid.*, Vol. 9, Aug. 15, 1931, pp. 3–24.

HABERLER, G. VON. *Der Sinn der Indexzahlen*, Tübingen, 1927.

KONÜS. A. A. "The Problem of the True Index of the Cost of Living," *Econometrica*, Vol. 7, 1939, pp. 10–29. Translation of the original Russian article published in the *Economic Bulletin, Conjuncture-Institute of Moscow*, 1924.

LEONTIEF, W. "Composite Commodities and the Problem of Index Numbers," *Econometrica*, Vol. 4, 1936, pp. 39–59.

MITCHELL, W. C. *The Making and Use of Index Numbers*, U. S. Bureau of Labor Statistics, Bulletin No. 284, 1921.

RAWLES, T. H. "The Definition and Consistency of Index Numbers," *Report of the Research Conference of the Cowles Commission*, 1936, pp. 95–97.

ROY, RENÉ. "Les indes économiques," pp. 5–79 in *Études économétriques*, Paris, 1935.

SCHULTZ, H. "A Misunderstanding in Index-Number Theory: The True Konus Condition on Cost-of-Living Index Numbers and its Limitations," *Econometrica*, Vol. 7, 1939, pp. 1–9.

STAEHLE, H. (1) "The Reaction of Consumers to Changes in Prices and Income: A Quantitative Study in Immigrants' Behavior," *Econometrica*, Vol. 2, 1934, pp. 59–72.

(2) "A Development of the Economic Theory of Price Index Numbers," *Review of Economic Studies*, Vol. 2, 1934–35, pp. 163–188.

WALD, A. "A New Formula for the Index of Cost of Living," *Econometrica*, Vol. 7, 1939, pp. 319–331.

CHAPTER 16

Time Series and Their Correlation

1. *Time Series*

In the first chapter of this book we defined a *time series* to be a series of data observed successively in time. For purposes of discussion such a series may be represented by the sequence

$$(1) \qquad y = y_t\,, \quad t = 1, 2, 3, \cdots, N\,,$$

where t is the number of some specified unit of time measured from some arbitrarily chosen origin. Most time series in economics are given to us in terms of monthly, or yearly observations, although some series, such as the Dow-Jones stock price averages, are given daily, hourly, and even at intervals as short as 20 minutes.

If the items of the series are sufficiently closely spaced, or if a discussion about the series is not impaired by the assumption of a continuous variation, we may employ the functional notation

$$(2) \qquad y = y(t)\,, \quad t_0 \leqq t \leqq t_1\,,$$

where t is a continuous variable over the specified range.

Until the present century studies of the action of economic time series were greatly hampered by lack of adequate data, but today many series have been constructed and some of these extend many years into the past. Thus we have an accurate series showing the price of wheat in England since the twelfth century, as we have already seen in Chapter 12. Another series shows the monthly fluctuations of commodity prices in the United States since 1800, and recent research has extended this information into the period before the American Revolution. A third series gives the index of railroad stock prices since 1830, and more recently the Cowles Commission for Research in Economics has constructed a complete index of stock prices since 1870. We have already had occasion in Chapter 12 to use the data on Spanish prices in the spectacular trade expansion of the sixteenth and early seventeenth centuries, a remarkable time series constructed by E. J. Hamilton.

Economic time series include many types of indexes, but conspicuous among them are two great classes. The first relates to prices and money, the second to physical production. An example of the first is obviously the price of commodities, a graphical representation of which is found in Figure 1 of Chapter 1; an example of the second is the production of pig iron, which is shown in Figure 49 of Chapter 11. It is clear, of course, that all indexes interesting to economists cannot be included in one or the other category, as we see from the existence of indexes of commercial paper rates, of unemployment, of the volume of sales on the New York Stock Exchange, of the ratio of stock dividends to stock prices, etc. But for the most part we shall be interested in those indexes which relate in one way or another to prices and production.

We list below a few of the many series which are the objects of special study in economics:

(1) The index of commodity prices.
(2) The production of pig iron, copper, and other metals.
(3) The price of stocks on the New York Stock Exchange.
(4) The index of high grade bond yields.
(5) Time money rates.
(6) Commercial paper rates.
(7) Price indexes of agricultural commodities.
(8) Indexes of agricultural production.
(9) Volume of stock sales on the New York Stock Exchange.
(10) Volume of new orders for (a) consumers' goods; (b) capital goods.
(11) Bank clearings.
(12) Loans and discounts.
(13) The growth of population.
(14) Indexes relating to gold production and gold movements.
(15) Prices of metals and metal products.
(16) Industrial production.
(17) The velocity of money and bank credits.
(18) Price index of building materials.
(19) Car loadings.
(20) Index of new building.

In this chapter it will be of interest to us to examine those aspects of the dynamics of time series which relate, first, to secular trends, and, second, to the cyclical or near cyclical characteristics of the series. About these phenomena J. A. Schumpeter has made the following comment (see *Bibliography*):

> There would be little overstatement in saying that trend-analysis will be the central problem of our science in the immediate future and the center of our difficulties as well . . . The trends we want are very different from those we get by fitting a curve through unanalyzed material. But this opens up a host of questions, for example, . . . Whether it is the trend which is the "generating" phenomenon of cycles or the cycles which generate the trend; whether or not the trend is a distinct economic phenomenon at all, attributable to one factor, or a well-defined set of factors; whether all the points on our raw graphs have on principle equal right to exert an influence on its slope, and, if not, what credentials we are to ask of every one point before admitting it.

2. Trends

By a *trend,* or as it is more commonly called, a *secular trend,* we mean that characteristic of a time series which tends to extend consistently throughout the entire period.

In most economic time series it is sufficient to assume that the trend is linear, that is to say, is of the form

$$y = a + bt \,. \tag{3}$$

The parameter b is the slope of the line, and, in general, this quantity is of greatest interest to the economist since it determines the direction in which the economic phenomenon under discussion is tending. In a discussion of price series, when b is positive, we say that the market is *bullish;* when b is negative the market is *bearish.* Men concerned with long-time commitments, such as bankers who purchase bond issues, manufacturers of goods used in heavy industry, etc., are more interested in the trend than in the daily, weekly, or monthly variations of the series.

In Chapter 11 we have commented at considerable length upon the trends of population and industrial production in the United States. There we saw that both of these essential time series were logistic in character. The economy appears to contain within itself those factors which impose an upper limit to the capacity for growth. But over long portions of the series linear trends will furnish excellent descriptions of the data. They must not be extrapolated too far into the future, however, and must be used with caution in making forecasts.

Another type of trend is a straight line fitted to data which are graphically represented on a logarithmic scale. Much caution must be employed in extrapolating this trend, or in using it as a criterion for the description of a normal period. The reason for this is readily apprehended when we write the linear expression.

$$\log y = a + bt\,, \tag{4}$$

in the form

$$y = Ae^{bt}, \quad \log A = a\,. \tag{5}$$

As we have seen in Chapter 13 the function forming the right hand member of this equation is the function of compound interest. For positive values of b this function increases rapidly and even moderate extrapolations beyond the range of data, which it may accurately describe, will usually lead to unrealistic values. The compound interest law appears to be valid only over relatively short periods of time.

One of the most widely used trends is the weighted moving average, because it is easy to apply, and also because it makes no essential postulate as to the functional character of the trend which it defines. In this average the trend values are computed from the data by means of the formula

$$y_t = \frac{\sum_{s=-\lambda}^{\lambda} W_s x_{t+s}}{\sum_{s=-\lambda}^{\lambda} W_s}\,. \tag{6}$$

where W_s is a weight function. Usually W_s is a constant or the binomial coefficient $W_s = {}_{2\lambda}C_{\lambda+s}$. The *parameter* λ of the moving average is generally chosen sufficiently large to remove the major harmonic swings in the data. The quantity 2λ is called *the length of the moving average* and should be chosen equal to, or some multiple of, the periodic movement which is to be removed from the data. Thus seasonal variation can be eliminated by a moving average of 12 months.

It is clear that for continuous data, $x(t)$, the equivalent of formula (6) may be written

$$y_t = \frac{\int_{-\lambda}^{\lambda} W(s)\, x(t+s)\, ds}{\int_{-\lambda}^{\lambda} W(s)\, ds} = \frac{\int_{t-\lambda}^{t+\lambda} W(r-t)\, x(r)\, dr}{\int_{-\lambda}^{\lambda} W(s)\, ds}\,, \tag{7}$$

where $W(s)$ is the weight function.

3. Fitting Linear Trends to Time Series

A simple technique is available for fitting the trend line

$$y = a + bt \tag{8}$$

to the data of economic time series. We shall assume that the data to which it is to be fitted are given as equally spaced items, $N = 2p + 1$, in number. No essential restriction is implied by this assumption, since, in general, if the data are not given in this form, one usually finds it possible by interpolation to approximate them by a series of equally spaced items. In particular, in the case of economic time series the items of the series are usually recorded by weeks, months, or years, and hence are given to us as equally spaced data. Moreover, in practical analysis, the inclusion or the omission of a single item to obtain a series in which N is odd, is usually of negligible significance.

We shall assume, therefore, that the data are arranged in the following form:

(9)

t	$-p$, $-p+1$, $\cdots$, -2, -1, 0, 1, 2, $\cdots$, p
y_t	y_{-p}, y_{-p+1}, $\cdots$, y_{-2}, y_{-1}, y_0, y_1, y_2, $\cdots$, y_p

By the zero*th* and first moments we shall mean the following sums:

$$M_0 = \sum_{t=-p}^{p} y_t\,, \qquad M_1 = \sum_{t=-p}^{p} t\, y_t\,. \tag{10}$$

Numerous devices and tables have been developed for the determination of the coefficients of equation (8) so that the straight line will fit the data. We shall adopt as most suitable for our purpose the method of least squares, which assumes that the best fit of (8) to the data (9) is given by those values of a and b which minimize the sum

$$I = \sum_{t=-p}^{p} [y_t - y(t)]^2,$$

where we abbreviate the right hand member of (8) by $y(t)$.

We set the derivatives of I with respect to a and b respectively equal to zero and thus obtain:

$$\frac{\partial I}{\partial a} = -2 \sum_{t=-p}^{p} [y_t - y(t)] \frac{\partial y}{\partial a} = 0\,, \quad \frac{\partial I}{\partial b} = -2 \sum_{t=-p}^{p} [y_t - y(t)] \frac{\partial y}{\partial b} = 0\,.$$

Expressed in terms of the moments defined by (10), these equations become

$$\sum_{t=-p}^{p} y(t) = M_0 , \qquad \sum_{t=-p}^{p} ty(t) = M_1 .$$

Taking note of the sums

$$\sum_{t=-p}^{p} t = 0 , \qquad \sum_{t=-p}^{p} t^2 = \frac{1}{3} p(p+1)(2p+1) = \frac{1}{12} N(N-1)(N+1) ,$$

we immediately derive the result *that the coefficients of* (8) *are computed from the data by means of the formulas*

$$a = AM_0 , \qquad b = A'M_1 , \tag{11}$$

where we use the abbreviations

$$\begin{aligned} A &= \frac{1}{2p+1} = \frac{1}{N} , \\ A' &= \frac{3}{p(p+1)(2p+1)} = \frac{12}{N(N-1)(N+1)} . \end{aligned} \tag{12}$$

These coefficients have been extensively calculated and will be found to 10 significant figures for values of p from 1 to 150 in the author's *Tables of the Higher Mathematical Functions.*[1] An abridgment is found in Table VII of this volume.

We next observe that *the average of the deviations of the data from the linear trend will be zero.*

In order to prove this we compute the sum

$$S = \sum_{t=-p}^{p} [y_t - y(t)] = M_0 - a(2p+1) .$$

But from the explicit formula for a as given in (11) this sum is seen to equal zero, which establishes the proposition.

If the variance of the original series is designated by σ^2, that is, if

$$\sigma^2 = \frac{1}{N}\left[\sum_{t=-p}^{p} y^2 - \frac{M_0^2}{N} \right], \quad N = 2p+1 ,$$

then the variance of the residuals, that is to say, of the deviations from the linear trend, is given by

$$\sigma_1^2 = \sigma^2 - \frac{A'M_1^2}{N} . \tag{13}$$

Since the mean deviation is zero, we have for σ_1^2 the following:

$$\sigma_1^2 = \frac{1}{N} \sum_{t=-p}^{p} [y_t - y(t)]^2, \quad N = 2p + 1 ,$$

$$= \frac{1}{N} \sum_{t=-p}^{p} [y_t^2 - 2y_t\, y(t) + y^2(t)] ,$$

$$= \frac{1}{N} \sum_{t=-p}^{p} [y_t^2 - 2y_t(a + bt) + (a^2 + 2abt + b^2t^2)] ,$$

$$= \frac{1}{N} [\sum_{t=-p}^{p} y_t^2 - 2aM_0 - 2bM_1 + (2p + 1)a^2 + \tfrac{1}{3}p(p + 1)(2p + 1)b^2] ,$$

$$= \frac{1}{N} [\sum_{t=-p}^{p} y_t^2 - \frac{M_0^2}{N}] + \frac{M_0^2}{N} - 2a\frac{M_0}{N} - 2b\frac{M_1}{N} + a^2 + \tfrac{1}{3}p(p + 1)b^2 .$$

Introducing the explicit values of a and b from (11) into this expression and observing that the first term is σ^2, we find by a simple algebraic manipulation that the terms combine to yield (13).

Example. As an example, let us fit a straight line to the following data and compute the variance of the deviations from this trend.

THE COWLES COMMISSION—STANDARD STATISTICS INDEX OF INDUSTRIAL STOCK PRICES

Year	Jan.	Feb.	Mar.	Apr.	May	June	July	Aug.	Sept.	Oct.	Nov.	Dec.	Aver.
1897	22.1	21.7	21.6	21.0	21.0	22.0	23.3	25.1	25.9	24.7	23.5	24.3	23.0
1898	24.6	25.0	23.9	23.8	26.1	27.4	28.0	29.1	28.8	28.0	29.6	32.2	27.2
1899	34.4	34.9	37.0	38.2	36.0	34.7	35.7	37.6	37.7	38.0	38.5	34.2	36.4
1900	34.9	35.6	34.9	34.7	32.0	30.4	31.1	31.8	31.1	32.3	35.8	37.2	33.5
1901	37.2	37.8	39.2	42.4	38.9	44.1	41.3	41.1	40.2	38.6	38.4	37.2	39.7
1902	38.6	39.2	39.3	40.3	39.8	38.7	39.9	39.9	40.0	38.8	36.9	35.4	38.9
1903	37.8	38.9	37.8	36.1	35.0	32.6	29.9	28.5	27.2	25.3	24.7	26.2	31.7
1904	27.0	26.3	26.1	26.5	25.8	25.8	27.1	28.1	29.8	32.4	36.1	36.7	29.0
1905	37.4	39.3	40.6	40.9	38.3	38.2	39.8	41.4	41.0	42.3	43.1	46.7	40.8
1906	49.4	49.1	46.9	46.9	45.1	45.2	43.6	47.7	49.6	49.8	48.8	49.4	47.6
1907	48.4	47.2	42.5	41.9	40.2	39.0	40.8	36.5	34.6	29.1	27.3	28.5	38.0
1908	30.4	29.4	32.0	33.9	35.8	35.7	38.1	41.1	39.4	40.2	43.7	43.7	37.0
1909	43.6	41.4	41.4	44.4	47.4	49.3	50.3	52.6	53.5	54.0	55.2	55.8	49.1
1910	54.5	50.7	52.6	51.5	49.6	46.7	43.9	45.5	45.7	48.5	49.3	46.9	48.8
1911	47.6	49.1	48.2	47.7	49.1	49.9	49.5	46.5	42.7	41.7	44.0	45.3	46.8
1912	45.6	44.7	47.0	50.1	50.2	51.2	51.4	52.8	53.8	54.1	52.8	49.8	50.3
1913	49.3	46.6	45.6	45.7	44.4	41.2	42.0	44.4	45.2	43.2	41.7	42.1	44.3

Solution. We first evaluate the zeroth and first moments about the mid item, June, 1905, as the origin. Since there are 204 items in the series we omit the last, and thus have $N = 203$, $p = 101$. These moments, together with the arithmetic mean (A), the standard deviation, σ, and the variance, σ^2, computed from them, are given below as follows:

[1] Vol. 2, 1935, pp. 325–329.

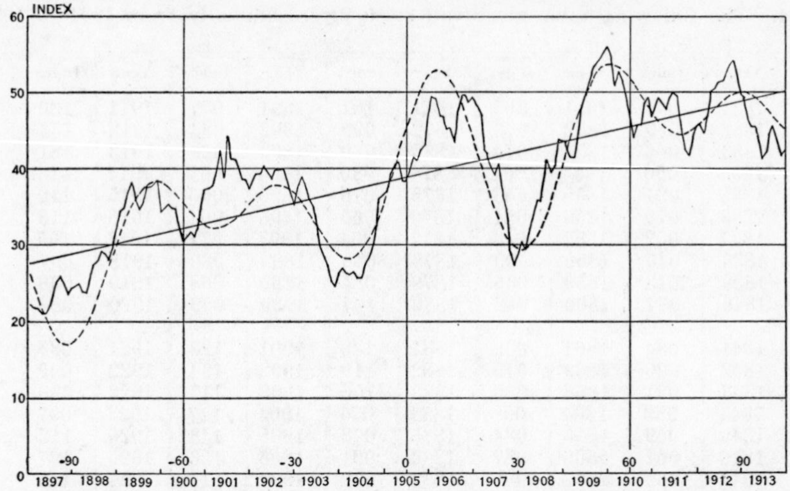

FIGURE 72.—THE COWLES COMMISSION—STANDARD STATISTICS INDEX OF INDUSTRIAL PRICES SHOWING LINEAR TREND AND HARMONIC APPROXIMATION.

$$M_0 = 7900.6\,, \quad M_1 = 76629.2, \quad A = 38.9192\,, \quad \sigma = 8.6873\,, \quad \sigma^2 = 75.4695\,.$$

From formulas (11) and (12), we compute $a = 38.9192$ and $b = 0.1099$. The trend is thus found to be

$$y = 38.9192 + 0.1099t\,.$$

The fit of this line to the data is graphically shown in Figure 72.

In order to find the variance of the residuals from the trend we substitute the values given above in formula (13) and thus obtain

$$\sigma_1{}^2 = \sigma^2 - \frac{A' M_1{}^2}{N} = \sigma^2 - b\frac{M_1}{N}\,,$$

$$= 75.4695 - 41.4855 = 33.9840\,.$$

PROBLEMS

1. The following table gives the fire losses in the United States in millions of dollars over a period of eleven years. Fit a straight line to the data.

Years	1915	1916	1917	1918	1919	1920	1921	1922	1923	1924	1925
Losses	172	258	290	259	321	448	495	507	535	549	570

2. Compare the variance of the time series of problem 1 with the variance of the data after the trend has been removed.

3. To the data showing urban concentration as given in Section 7, Chapter 11 fit a straight line. What has been the average annual change in urban concentration?

4. The following table gives rail stock prices annually from 1831 to 1930:

Year	Index	Year	Index	Year	Index	Year	Index	Year	Index
1831	049	1851	065	1871	101	1891	077	1911	130
1832	050	1852	073	1872	099	1892	083	1912	133
1833	066	1853	074	1873	089	1893	068	1913	121
1834	060	1854	061	1874	080	1894	063	1914	118
1835	081	1855	053	1875	076	1895	066	1915	110
1836	070	1856	051	1876	069	1896	064	1916	118
1837	052	1857	043	1877	054	1897	071	1917	105
1838	046	1858	039	1878	065	1898	080	1918	097
1839	043	1859	035	1879	084	1899	098	1919	098
1840	037	1860	042	1880	107	1900	099	1920	088
1841	034	1861	039	1881	136	1901	123	1921	085
1842	025	1862	049	1882	119	1902	134	1922	099
1843	031	1863	085	1883	106	1903	117	1923	096
1844	050	1864	098	1884	076	1904	117	1924	097
1845	049	1865	084	1885	073	1905	148	1925	112
1846	051	1866	087	1886	091	1906	153	1926	127
1847	056	1867	081	1887	092	1907	115	1927	145
1848	050	1868	097	1888	080	1908	113	1928	152
1849	053	1869	102	1889	082	1909	138	1929	169
1850	058	1870	100	1890	081	1910	128	1930	145

Graph these data and fit a straight line to them. By what per cent have railroad securities appreciated annually on the average?

5. Given $\sigma = 32.2615$ for the data of problem 1, by what per cent is the variance reduced when the trend is removed?

6. If y_t represents the items in the data of problem 1 and $y(t)$ the trend, evaluate the difference $D(t) = y_t - y(t)$ and represent $D(t)$ graphically.

7. Solve problem 6 using the data of problem 4. Are there conspicuous cyclical movements in rail stock prices?

4. The Harmonic Analysis of Time Series

When the trend has been removed from a time series there will often be observed a cyclical, or almost cyclical, structure in the resulting residuals. These harmonic characteristics of time series are the features which have been generically classified as *business cycles.* In this chapter we shall not be concerned with the economic aspects of the cycles, but rather with their mathematical description and their statistical determination.

It is but natural that we should turn for our analytical tool to the theory of *harmonic analysis.*

By a *harmonic* we mean a term of the form

$$y = A \cos \frac{2\pi t}{T} + B \sin \frac{2\pi t}{T} , \tag{14}$$

an expression which may be written also in the form

(15) $$y = R \cos \left(\frac{2\pi t}{T} - \alpha\right) ,$$

where we use the abbreviations

(16) $$R = \sqrt{A^2 + B^2} , \quad \alpha = \arctan \frac{B}{A} .$$

The quantity T is called the *period* of the harmonic, the quantity R the *amplitude,* and the quantity α the *phase angle.* We shall sometimes refer to A and B as the *components* of the harmonic. Figure 73 shows a typical harmonic term.

One of the important problems in the study of time series is that of determining the periods and the amplitudes of harmonic terms which may constitute the essential cyclical variation of the series. A number of methods have been devised to accomplish this reduction of a time series into its various elements.

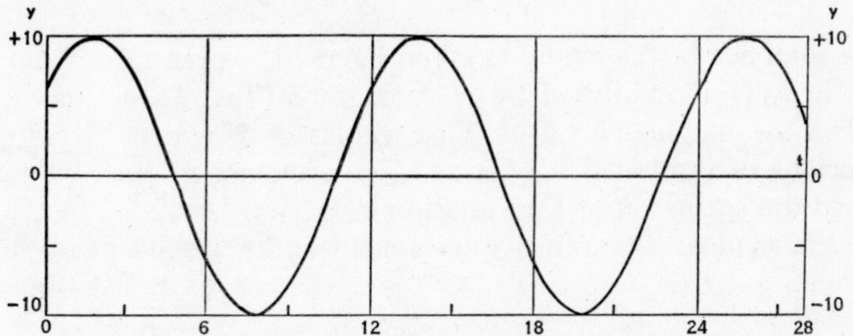

FIGURE 73.—GRAPHICAL REPRESENTATION OF THE HARMONIC TERM

$$y = 6 \cos \frac{2\pi t}{12} + 8 \sin \frac{2\pi t}{12} = 10 \cos \left(\frac{2\pi t}{12} - \alpha\right),$$

where $\alpha = 58° \; 8' = 0.3019\pi$ radians.

Most prominent among these methods is one invented by Sir Arthur Schuster (1851–1934), who applied it with conspicuous success to the study of sun spot cycles. This device, called the *periodogram method,* is somewhat laborious in numerical application, but it has certain theoretical features which have given it wide currency. It will be useful for us to understand the essential characteristics of this method.[2]

Let us, as in Section 1 of this chapter, designate the elements of a time series by the function $y = y(t)$ and let the range be from $t = -a$

[2] For a history of this and other methods of harmonic analysis see the author's treatise, *The Analysis of Economic Time Series,* Chap. 1, Section 8, and Chap. 2, Section 8.

to $t = +a$. We shall assume that this series is composed of one or more harmonic elements upon which, perhaps, there has been superimposed a set of random variations. We then compute the function

$$R^2(T) = A^2(T) + B^2(T), \tag{17}$$

where we use the abbreviations

$$\begin{aligned} A(T) &= \frac{1}{a}\int_{-a}^{a} y(s)\cos\frac{2\pi s}{T}\,ds\,, \\ B(T) &= \frac{1}{a}\int_{-a}^{a} y(s)\sin\frac{2\pi s}{T}\,ds\,. \end{aligned} \tag{18}$$

The *periodogram* of the function $y(t)$ is then defined to be the graph of the function

$$R = R(T), \qquad 0 < T < 2a\,. \tag{19}$$

As we shall see in the example given below, the presence of harmonic terms in $y(t)$ is exhibited by maxima in $R(T)$. These maxima are found in the neighborhood of those values of T which correspond to the periods of the harmonic terms. The sequence of such values of T is called the *spectrum* of the function $y(t)$.

As a typical example let us consider the periodogram for the function

$$y(t) = A\sin\left(\frac{2\pi t}{P} + \beta\right). \tag{20}$$

Substituting this function in equations (18) we obtain the values

$$\begin{aligned} A(T) &= A\sin\beta\left[\frac{\sin 2\pi(a/P + a/T)}{2\pi(a/P + a/T)} + \frac{\sin 2\pi(a/P - a/T)}{2\pi(a/P - a/T)}\right], \\ B(T) &= A\cos\beta\left[\frac{\sin 2\pi(a/P - a/T)}{2\pi(a/P - a/T)} - \frac{\sin 2\pi(a/P + a/T)}{2\pi(a/P + a/T)}\right], \end{aligned} \tag{21}$$

from which we compute

$$\begin{aligned} R^2(T) = A^2 \Bigg[& \frac{\sin^2 2\pi(a/P + a/T)}{4\pi^2(a/P + a/T)^2} + \frac{\sin^2 2\pi(a/P - a/T)}{4\pi^2(a/P - a/T)^2} \\ & - \cos 2\beta\,\frac{\sin 2\pi(a/P + a/T)\sin 2\pi(a/P - A/T)}{2\pi^2[(a/P)^2 - (a/T)^2]}\Bigg]. \end{aligned} \tag{22}$$

We see that the dominating term in this expression is the second, which assumes its maximum value of 1 when $T = P$. For this value (22) reduces to the following:

$$(23)\qquad R^2(P) = A^2 + A^2\left[\frac{\sin^2(4\pi a/P)}{16\pi^2 a^2/P^2} - \cos 2\beta\,\frac{\sin(4\pi a/P)}{2\pi a/P}\right].$$

Since a is always greater than P it is clear that the second term of this expression will be small in comparison with the first and $R^2(T)$ will have a maximum value in the neighborhood of $T = P$. This is the fundamental idea which underlies the use of periodogram analysis in the discovery of periodicities hidden in the data of an economic time series.

Since the second term of (22) is the dominating one, it is clear that $R^2(T)$ will have minima in the neighborhood of the values of T which make this term zero. Such zero values are obtained from the equation

$$2\left(\frac{a}{P} - \frac{a}{T}\right) = m\,,$$

where m is any positive or negative integer. Solving for T we get

$$(24)\qquad T = \frac{P}{1 - \dfrac{Pm}{2a}}\,.$$

In order to find the breadth of the peak around the maximum ordinate of the periodogram we obtain from formula (24) the values corresponding to $m = 1$ and $m = -1$, and compute their difference, Δ. We thus get

$$(25)\qquad T_1 = \frac{P}{1 - \dfrac{P}{2a}}\,,\qquad T_2 = \frac{P}{1 + \dfrac{P}{2a}}\,.$$

The difference, Δ, is thus found to be

$$(26)\qquad \Delta = T_1 - T_2 = \frac{P^2}{a[1 - \frac{1}{4}(P/a)^2]}\,,$$

which, in case P is small with respect to a, is approximately equal to P^2/a.

Example 1. As a numerical example let us compute the periodogram of the function

$$y = 100 \sin \left(\frac{2\pi t}{43} + \frac{\pi}{4}\right),$$

over an assumed range of length $2a = 204$.

Solution: If we employ the convenient variable $x = T/a$, we obtain for $R^2(x)$ the following:

$$(27) \qquad R^2(x) = 253.30 \left[\frac{\sin^2 2\pi(2.3721 + 1/x)}{(2.3721 + 1/x)^2} + \frac{\sin^2 2\pi(2.3721 - 1/x)}{(2.3721 - 1/x)^2}\right].$$

The periodogram $R = R(x)$ is shown in Figure 74. An inspection of the graph reveals the existence of a period at $x = 43/102 = 0.4216$. One notes also the existence of the minor maxima on either side of the major peak. This is a characteristic feature of all periodograms and clearly indicates why one must be careful in interpreting a periodogram not to construe these minor "shadows" of the real period as evidence of the existence of other periodicities.

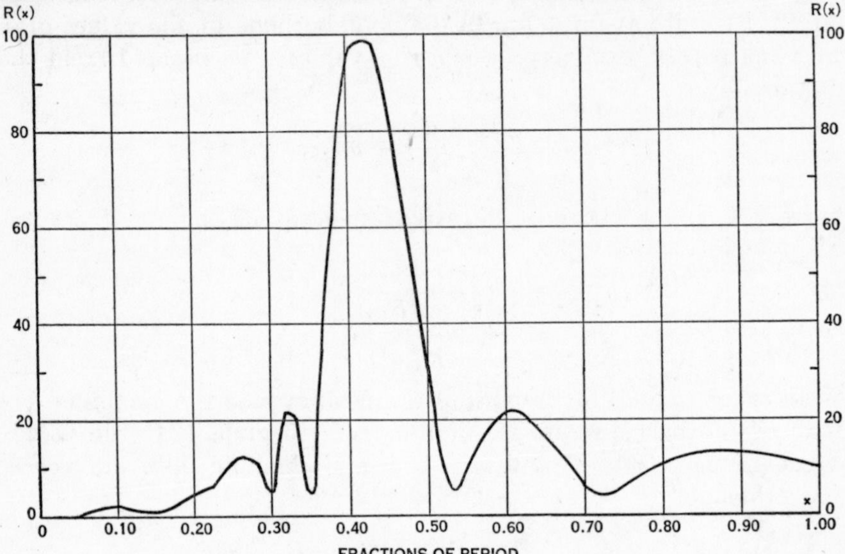

FIGURE 74.—PERIODOGRAM OF THE FUNCTION

$$y = 100 \sin\left(\frac{2\pi t}{43} + \frac{\pi}{4}\right)$$

Over an Assumed Range of Length $2a = 204$. Graphed as a Function of $x = T/a$, $T = 43$.

From formula (25) one obtains as the first minimum points about the period, the values

$$x_1 = \frac{1}{\mu - \frac{1}{2}} = 0.5342, \quad x_2 = \frac{1}{\mu + \frac{1}{2}} = 0.3484, \quad \mu = a/P.$$

The difference, $\Delta = x_1 - x_2 = 0.1858$ gives the breadth of the peak which corresponds to the period.

Example 2. As an example of the application of harmonic analysis to an economic time series, let us apply the theory of this section to discover the harmonic character of the data given in the illustrative example of Section 3.

Solution: The periodogram is given by the formula $R = R(T)$, where, instead of evaluating the integrals in (18), we form the corresponding sums

$$A(T) = \frac{2}{N'} \sum_{t=0}^{N'} y_t \cos \frac{2\pi t}{T}, \quad B(T) = \frac{2}{N'} \sum_{t=0}^{N'} y_t \sin \frac{2\pi t}{T}. \tag{28}$$

The upper limit of this summation, namely N', is chosen equal to the largest multiple of T in the total frequency N. That is to say, $N' = pT$, where p is an integer.

The values of the function $R = R(T)$, together with $A(T)$ and $B(T)$, T measured in months, are given in the following table. The periodogram is graphically represented in Figure 75.

VALUES OF THE PERIODOGRAM, $R = R(T)$, AND OF ASSOCIATED FUNCTIONS

T	$A(T)$	$B(T)$	$R(T)$	T	$A(T)$	$B(T)$	$R(T)$	T	$A(T)$	$B(T)$	$R(T)$
5	0.3303	–0.3630	0.49	27	–0.4641	–1.6146	1.68	49	....	....	......
6	–0.0512	–0.0451	0.07	28	–0.0904	–0.7596	0.77	50	0.6787	1.7503	1.88
7	0.2527	–0.5279	0.59	29	0.3142	–0.1324	0.34	51	1.5156	1.2726	1.98
8	0.4015	–0.5542	0.68	30	1.9689	–1.1335	2.27	52	3.2729	0.7629	3.36
9	0.3099	0.0268	0.31	31	1.5890	–2.1255	2.65	53	....	....	......
10	0.1285	–0.8032	0.81	32	0.8655	–2.7717	2.90	54	4.4952	–1.6909	4.80
11	0.5888	–0.8751	1.05	33	–0.3880	–2.5278	2.56	55	....	....	......
12	0.2899	–0.1979	0.35	34	–0.9417	–1.3009	1.61	56	4.0655	–3.9468	5.67
13	0.1624	–0.6629	0.67	35	0.4071	–0.8207	0.92	57	3.5829	–4.8465	6.03
14	0.2938	–0.7405	0.80	36	1.3489	–0.9518	1.65	58	2.9835	–5.5557	6.31
15	0.0389	–0.9052	0.91	37	2.2087	–1.7913	2.84	59	....	....	......
16	–0.0615	–1.8033	1.80	38	2.7310	–3.2399	4.24	60	1.3000	–6.3455	6.48
17	0.9988	0.4632	1.10	39	2.0657	–4.7943	5.22	61	....	....	......
18	–0.5108	–1.4312	1.52	40	0.3097	–5.6844	5.69	62	–0.0656	–6.3632	6.36
19	0.4925	–0.8658	1.00	41	–1.3556	–6.8962	7.03	63	....	....	......
20	–0.4825	–1.4112	1.49	42	–3.2202	–6.1361	6.93	64	–0.8771	–6.0510	6.11
21	–0.7487	–1.3599	1.55	43	–4.4805	–4.7522	6.53	65	–1.2753	–5.8382	5.98
22	–1.4919	–0.3644	1.54	44	–5.0474	–3.0482	5.90	66	–1.8471	–5.5631	5.86
23	–0.3539	0.6413	0.73	45	–5.1642	–1.2740	5.32	67	....	....	......
24	–0.1062	1.3355	1.34	46	–4.4907	–0.3416	4.50	68	–2.6333	–4.8163	5.49
25	0.7380	–1.1149	1.34	47	....	....	......	69	....	....	......
26	0.3719	–1.8259	1.86	48	–1.5920	2.0502	2.60	70	....	....	......

From the figure we see clearly defined periods at $T = 41$ months and at $T = 60$ months. The apparent period at $T = 32$ is probably a shadow of the principal peak. The spectrum of the series thus consists of the two values $T = 41$ and $T = 60$.

In Figure 72 there is graphically portrayed the approximation to the data which is attained by the function

$$y(t) = \text{Trend} + A(41) \cos \frac{2\pi t}{41} + B(41) \sin \frac{2\pi t}{41} + A(60) \cos \frac{2\pi t}{60} + B(60) \sin \frac{2\pi t}{60}.$$

This approximation is seen to be quite satisfactory.

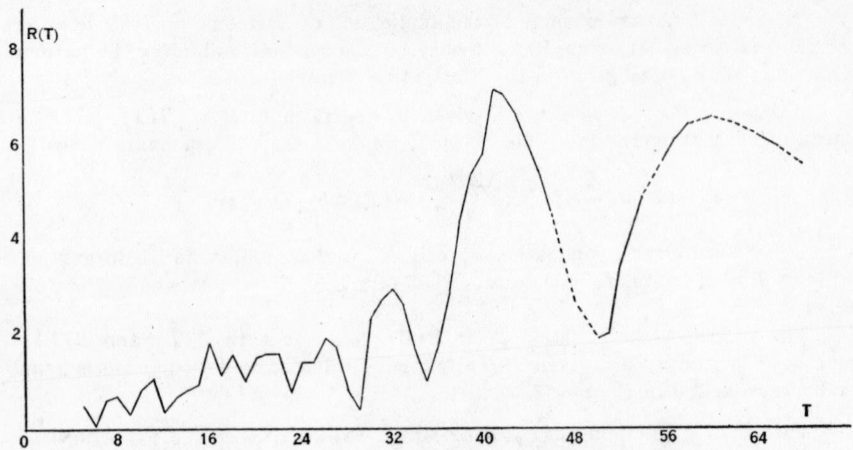

FIGURE 75.—PERIODOGRAM OF THE COWLES COMMISSION INDUSTRIAL STOCK PRICE INDEX, 1897–1913.

PROBLEMS

1. The following are the ordinates of a Schuster periodogram for a series of 300 items composed of pure harmonic terms. Graph the periodogram and determine (1) the periods of the original series and (2) the relative amplitudes of the separate harmonics.

T	*R*	*T*	*R*	*T*	*R*	*T*	*R*	*T*	*R*
5	0.07	15	0.22	25	4.52	39	4.02	56	7.67
6	0.10	16	0.47	26	1.88	40	7.84	57	8.38
7	0.11	17	1.77	28	1.13	42	14.56	58	8.63
8	0.25	18	1.10	29	0.91	44	19.59	60	6.82
9	0.23	19	1.19	30	0.94	45	19.01	62	8.54
10	0.43	20	0.32	31	2.37	46	17.31	65	4.66
11	1.28	21	0.67	32	1.29	48	12.35	66	3.57
12	9.38	22	1.72	34	1.61	50	5.23	67	1.19
13	0.43	23	0.19	36	3.45	51	3.53	68	2.01
14	0.83	24	3.64	38	1.14	52	0.63	72	1.29

2. The following are the ordinates of a Schuster periodogram for a series of 100 annual averages of commercial paper rates over the period 1831 to 1930. Graph the periodogram and determine the characteristic cycles.

T	*R*	*T*	*R*	*T*	*R*	*T*	*R*	*T*	*R*
5	0.35	14	0.77	23	0.46	32	0.61	41	0.86
6	0.42	15	0.74	24	0.30	33	0.64	42	0.82
7	0.22	16	1.16	25	0.33	34	1.04	43	0.77
8	0.41	17	1.55	26	0.49	35	1.04	44	0.76
9	0.57	18	1.50	27	0.50	36	1.03	45	0.74
10	0.49	19	1.13	28	0.53	37	1.02	46	0.70
11	0.64	20	0.89	29	0.59	38	0.99	48	0.63
12	0.88	21	0.82	30	0.62	39	0.95	50	0.62
13	0.37	22	0.58	31	0.61	40	0.91		

3. The ordinates of a Schuster periodogram of the monthly averages of freight-car loadings over the period from 1919 to 1932 are given in the following table:

T	5	6	7	8	9	10	11	12	13	14	15
R	5.70	46.67	4.41	7.07	14.27	12.12	8.83	75.28	7.87	8.84	20.38
T	16	17	18	19	20	21	22	23	24	25	26
R	14.82	12.72	19.06	8.08	6.46	9.81	11.36	17.69	18.92	2.71	6.87

Graph these data and show that freight-car loadings have two seasonal movements. The original series from which the periodogram was constructed are shown graphically in Figure 90 of Chapter 19.

4. The following data give the ordinates of the Schuster periodogram for the annual averages of the index rail stock prices given in problem 4 of Section 3 of this chapter:

T	R	T	R	T	R	T	R	T	R
5	1.81	14	4.44	23	3.03	32	8.25	41	19.62
6	5.06	15	6.93	24	4.16	33	4.22	42	20.73
7	2.35	16	7.22	25	11.70	34	1.13	43	21.43
8	0.12	17	10.00	26	13.18	35	2.30	44	21.58
9	9.57	18	11.28	27	14.78	36	5.69	45	21.27
10	1.41	19	12.19	28	14.92	37	8.50	46	20.77
11	6.51	20	16.01	29	13.98	38	13.11	48	19.27
12	3.18	21	11.42	30	12.72	39	14.93	50	18.55
13	3.81	22	6.71	31	10.85	40	17.42		

Graph the periodogram and determine the characteristic cyclical components of the series. Does the graph of the original data tend to confirm your conclusions?

5. Compute the periodogram for the function $y(s) = a^2 - s^2$.

6. If $y(s)$ is an integrable function defined over the interval $-a \leqq s \leqq a$, show that it is formally represented by the series:

$$y(s) = \tfrac{1}{2} A(\infty) + \sum_{n=1}^{\infty} A(a/n) \cos \frac{n\pi s}{a} + \sum_{n=1}^{\infty} B(a/n) \sin \frac{n\pi s}{a}.$$

Hint: Assume that $y(s)$ can be represented in the form

$$y(s) = a_0 + \sum_{n=1}^{\infty} a_n \cos \frac{n\pi s}{a} + \sum_{n=1}^{\infty} b_n \sin \frac{n\pi s}{a}.$$

Now multiply $y(s)$ by $\cos(n\pi s/a)$ and $\sin(n\pi s/a)$ and integrate between the limits of $-a$ and $+a$.

7. Graph three terms of the series

$$y(t) = \tfrac{1}{2} + \frac{4}{\pi^2}\left[\cos\frac{\pi t}{10} + \frac{1}{9}\cos\frac{3\pi t}{10} + \frac{1}{25}\cos\frac{5\pi t}{10} + \cdots\right]$$

and show that a close approximation is obtained to the function

$$y(t) = 1 - |t|/10, \qquad -10 \leqq t \leqq 10.$$

8. Integrating the square of $y(s)$ as defined in problem 6 between the limits $-a$ and $+a$, show that

$$R_1^2 + R_2^2 + R_3^2 + \cdots = 2\sigma^2,$$

where we define $R_n^2 = A^2(a/n) + B^2(a/n)$ and σ^2 is the variance of $y(s)$.

5. *Serial Correlation*

A method of analysis closely related to the theory of the periodogram is that of serial correlation. Although we find examples of the use of this method in earlier works it was not until about 1914 that serial correlations were applied extensively to economic data. In that year H. L. Moore computed the lag correlation between the yield per acre of crops and the production of pig iron. By this means he reached the conclusion . . . "that the cycles in the yield of crops per acre are intimately related to the cycles in the activity of industry, and that it takes between one and two years for good or bad crops to produce the maximum effect upon the activity of the pig-iron industry."[3] Two

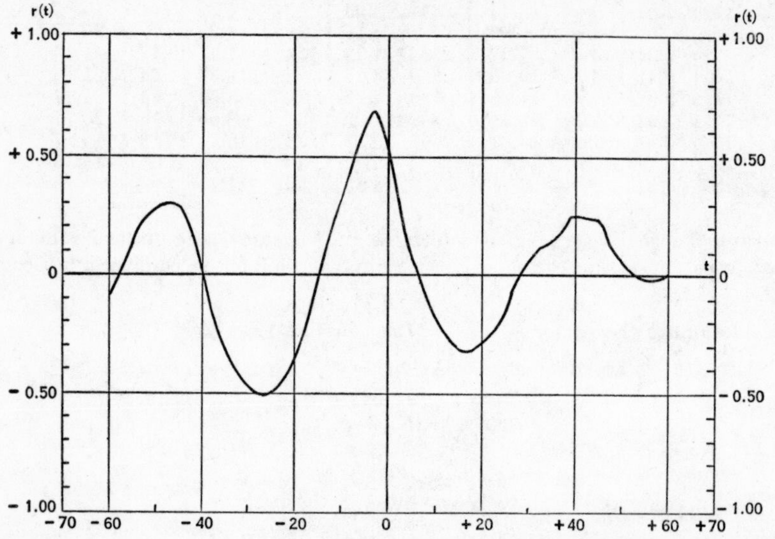

FIGURE 76.—SERIAL CORRELATION BETWEEN PIG IRON PRODUCTION AND INDUSTRIAL STOCK PRICES, t MEASURED IN MONTHS, IN WHICH THE PRODUCTION SERIES IS LAGGED BEHIND THE PRICE SERIES. BASE PERIOD 1897 TO 1913 INCLUSIVE.

years later Warren Persons made extensive use of serial correlation in studying the relationship between 21 American economic time se-

[3] *Economic Cycles: Their Law and Cause.* New York, 1914, p. 110.

ries.[4] In 1926 G. U. Yule asked his classical question: "Why do we sometimes get nonsense correlations between time series?" and in his answer established a scientific foundation for the investigation of serial correlation.[5] In this section it will be possible for us to give only a brief outline of the subject.[6]

If $x(t)$ and $y(t)$ represent the elements of two time series over some range of time which is sufficiently long so that the effects of omitting a few items in either series will have a negligible effect upon their variances (assumed to be unity) and upon their average values (assumed to be zero), then the *serial correlation* between them over range $-a \leqq t \leqq a$, is given by the integral

$$r(t) = \frac{1}{2a} \int_{-a}^{a} x(s)\, y(s+t)\, ds\,. \tag{29}$$

If t is a positive quantity, the series y will be said to lag behind the series x; if, on the contrary, t is a negative quantity, then the series x will be said to lag behind series y.

The serial correlation between pig iron production, $x(t)$, and industrial stock prices, $y(t)$, (represented by the Dow Jones averages), is shown in Figure 76, where t is measured in months. The maximum correlation is found for a negative lag of three months, which shows that the production of pig iron followed the movements of the stock market in the period under analysis, that is, during the years from 1897 to 1913 inclusive.

If $y(s)$ is identical with $x(s)$, then $r(t)$ is called an *autocorrelation function.* In other words, an autocorrelation function is merely the serial correlation of a function with itself. Thus, if we replace y by x in equation (29), we obtain the autocorrelation function

$$r(t) = \frac{1}{2a} \int_{-a}^{a} x(s)\, x(s+t)\, ds\,. \tag{30}$$

An example of such an autocorrelation function is shown in Figure 77, where $x(s)$ is the industrial stock price series (represented by the Dow Jones averages), with trend removed, over the period from 1897 to 1913 inclusive. The variable t is in months.

---

[4] "Construction of a Business Barometer Based upon Annual Data," *American Economic Review,* Vol. 6, 1916, pp. 739–769. See also Chapter 10 in the *Handbook of Mathematical Statistics,* edited by H. L. Rietz, Cambridge, Mass., 1924.

[5] *Journal of the Royal Statistical Society,* Vol. 89, 1926, pp. 1–64.

[6] For an historical account see G. Tintner, *The Variate Difference Method,* Cowles Commission Monograph No. 5, Bloomington, 1940, 175 pp.; also the author's work, *The Analysis of Economic Time Series,* Section 14, Chapter 1.

It will be observed from the graph that the function damps rapidly. It changes from positive to negative at approximately $t = \pm 10$, and again becomes positive at $t = \pm 40$. As we shall show later this may be interpreted as indicating a cycle in the series of approximately 40 months.

Another characteristic feature of the graph of $r(t)$ is found in the fact that it is a symmetric function. That is to say, the autocorrelation function has the property

$$r(t) = r(-t). \tag{31}$$

It will be useful in a later section for us to observe that the auto-

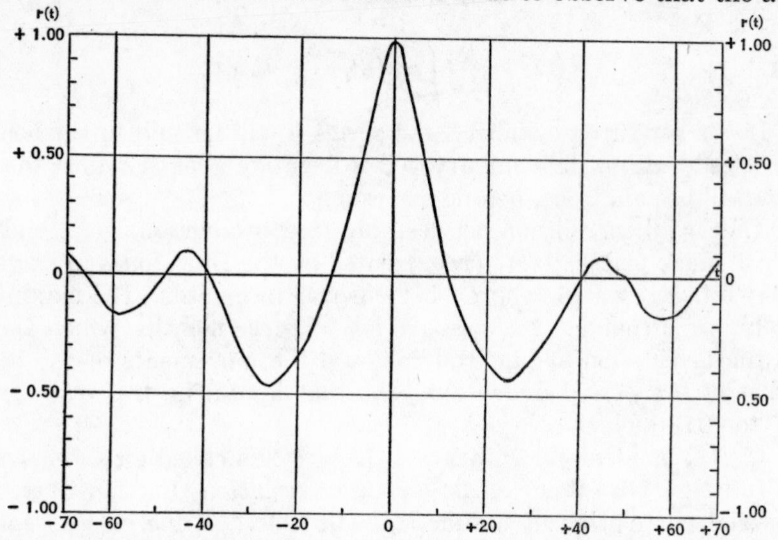

FIGURE 77.—AUTOCORRELATION FUNCTION FOR INDUSTRIAL STOCK PRICES, t MEASURED IN MONTHS. BASE PERIOD 1897 TO 1913 INCLUSIVE.

correlation function of industrial stocks may be closely approximated by the function

$$r(t) = \frac{\sin(2\pi t/40)}{(2\pi t/40)}. \tag{32}$$

We observe that this function vanishes at $t = \pm 20$, and at $t = \pm 40$. When $t = 0$ it has the limiting value 1. It also damps rapidly and at its first minimum at $t = 28.66$ it has the value 0.2172.

6. *Inverse Serial Correlation*

The problem of inverse serial correlation is the problem of inverting the integral

$$r(t) = \frac{1}{2a} \int_{-a}^{a} x(s)\, y(s+t)\, ds\,, \tag{33}$$

for either $x(s)$ or $y(s)$, assuming that one of these functions, together with $r(t)$, is known. The restrictions on the functions, which we noted in the preceding section, are assumed to hold.

It will be convenient for us to solve the problem over an infinite range. This imposes no real restrictions since the functions need merely be assumed zero outside of any finite region of definition.

For our present purpose, we shall consider the function

$$R(t) = \int_{-\infty}^{\infty} x(s)\, y(s+t)\, ds \tag{34}$$

instead of (33). The problem here is to determine either $x(s)$ or $y(s)$ from a knowledge of $R(t)$ and the other function.

Assuming proper integrability conditions for the formal operations which we shall need, we shall establish the following identities:

$$\begin{aligned} \alpha_1(\beta) &= a_x(\beta)\, a_y(\beta) + b_x(\beta)\, b_y(\beta), \\ \alpha_2(\beta) &= a_x(\beta)\, b_y(\beta) - a_y(\beta)\, b_x(\beta), \end{aligned} \tag{35}$$

where we designate

$$\alpha_1(\beta) = \int_{-\infty}^{\infty} R(t) \cos \beta t\, dt\,, \qquad \alpha_2(\beta) = \int_{-\infty}^{\infty} R(t) \sin \beta t\, dt\,;$$

$$a_x(\beta) = \int_{-\infty}^{\infty} x(t) \cos \beta t\, dt\,, \qquad b_x(\beta) = \int_{-\infty}^{\infty} x(t) \sin \beta t\, dt\,;$$

$$a_y(\beta) = \int_{-\infty}^{\infty} y(t) \cos \beta t\, dt\,, \qquad b_y(\beta) = \int_{-\infty}^{\infty} y(t) \sin \beta t\, dt\,.$$

In order to establish identities (35), we multiply both sides of (34), by $e^{\beta i t}$, where i is the imaginary unit $\sqrt{-1}$, and integrate over the infinite range. We thus get

$$\begin{aligned} \int_{-\infty}^{\infty} R(t) e^{\beta i t}\, dt &= \int_{-\infty}^{\infty} dt \int_{-\infty}^{\infty} x(s)\, y(s+t)\, e^{\beta i t}\, ds\,, \\ &= \int_{-\infty}^{\infty} dt \int_{-\infty}^{\infty} x(s)\, y(s+t)\, e^{-\beta i s}\, e^{i(t+s)}\, ds\,. \end{aligned}$$

Making the transformation $s + t = p$, we then obtain

$$\int_{-\infty}^{\infty} R(t)\, e^{\beta i t}\, dt = \int_{-\infty}^{\infty} y(p)\, e^{\beta i p}\, dp \int_{-\infty}^{\infty} x(s)\, e^{-\beta i s}\, ds\,. \tag{36}$$

Recalling the identity

$$e^{xi} = \cos x + i \sin x\,,$$

we now replace $e^{\beta i}$ and $e^{-\beta i}$ in (36) by their appropriate expansions and equate the real and imaginary parts of the equation. Identities (35) are thus attained.

The explicit determination either of $y(s)$ in terms of $x(s)$, or $x(s)$ in terms of $y(s)$, is now accomplished by a simple inversion of a Fourier integral.

It will be recalled that the Fourier integral

$$u(t) = \int_{-\infty}^{\infty} v(s)\, e^{sti}\, ds \tag{37}$$

is inverted by means of the formula

$$v(s) = \frac{1}{2\pi} \int_{-\infty}^{\infty} u(t)\, e^{-sti}\, ds\,, \tag{38}$$

provided $u(t)$ and $v(s)$ are functions properly defined over the infinite interval.[7]

Returning to equation (36), we see that if we define

$$\Psi(\beta) = \frac{\int_{-\infty}^{\infty} R(t)\, e^{\beta i t}\, dt}{\int_{-\infty}^{\infty} x(t)\, e^{-\beta i t}\, dt}\,, \tag{39}$$

then equation (36) takes the form

$$\Psi(\beta) = \int_{-\infty}^{\infty} y(p)\, e^{\beta i p}\, dp\,. \tag{40}$$

The inversion of this Fourier integral is now accomplished by means of (38), and thus we obtain

$$y(p) = \frac{1}{2\pi} \int_{-\infty}^{\infty} \Psi(\beta)\, e^{-p\beta i}\, d\beta\,.$$

In case $R(t)$ is an autocorrelation function, that is to say, if $x(s) = y(s)$, then the inversion is more complex. In this case identities (35) reduce to the single identity

[7] For a discussion of this transform and some of its applications see the author's work: *The Theory of Linear Operators*, Bloomington, Ind., 1936, pp. 262–270.

(41) $$\alpha(\beta) = a^2(\beta) + b^2(\beta).$$

Since the right hand member of this equation is the value of R^2 used in the Schuster periodogram analysis, we reach the important conclusion that *the Schuster periodogram is given by the square-root of the cosine transform of the autocorrelation function.* This is a very valuable theorem in application.

In the case of the autocorrelation function the inversion is not unique since we have

(42) $$x(s) = \frac{1}{2\pi}\int_{-\infty}^{\infty} \sqrt{\alpha}(\beta)\,[\cos p(\beta)\cos \beta s + \sin p(\beta)\sin \beta s]\,d\beta\,,$$

where $p(\beta)$ is an arbitrary odd function of β, that is,

$$p(-\beta) = -p(\beta).$$

To prove this identity we write

$$x_1(s) = \frac{1}{2\pi}\int_{-\infty}^{\infty} \sqrt{\alpha}(\beta)\cos p(\beta)\cos \beta s\, d\beta\,,$$

$$x_2(s) = \frac{1}{2\pi}\int_{-\infty}^{\infty} \sqrt{\alpha}(\beta)\sin p(\beta)\sin \beta s\, d\beta\,.$$

Inverting these integrals by the Fourier theorem, we obtain

(43)
$$\sqrt{\alpha(\beta)}\cos p(\beta) = \int_{-\infty}^{\infty} x_1(s)\cos \beta s\, ds = a(\beta),$$
$$\sqrt{\alpha(\beta)}\sin p(\beta) = \int_{-\infty}^{\infty} x_2(s)\sin \beta s\, ds = b(\beta),$$

since $x(s) = x_1(s) + x_2(s)$, and because of the fact that $p(-\beta) = -p(\beta)$, $x_2(-s) = -x_2(s)$. We observe also that $x_1(-s) = x_1(s)$.

Adding the squares of both sides of these equations, we obtain identity (41), which is at once seen to establish the inversion defined by (42).

While this lack of uniqueness, which we have just observed, might seem at first sight to be a blemish on the theory, it is, indeed, one of its most useful features. Thus we observe that the harmonic properties of any two functions $\phi(t)$ and $\theta(t)$ will be the same provided these functions have the same autocorrelation function. Such functions we shall call *harmonically equivalent.*

This observation often simplifies certain harmonic analyses, since a complex function, $\phi(t)$, frequently may be replaced by a simpler function, $\theta(t)$, harmonically equivalent to it, whose spectrum is known.

We shall illustrate the theory of this section by two examples.

Example 1. The autocorrelation function of some economic time series is approximated by the function

$$r(t) = \frac{\sin \lambda t}{\lambda t}.$$

Discuss the harmonic character of the time series.

Solution. We first compute

$$\alpha(\beta) = \int_{-\infty}^{\infty} r(t) \cos \beta t \, dt = \begin{cases} 0 & , \beta > \lambda. \\ \pi/\lambda & , \beta < \lambda, \end{cases}$$

The periodogram is thus seen to be zero from $\beta = 0$ to $\beta = \lambda$, and π/λ thereafter. The spectrum corresponding to such a periodogram is called *continuous.*

In order to find the function which has such a spectrum, we compute $x(s)$ by formula (42), setting $p = 0$ for convenience. By a simple integration we thus obtain

$$x(s) = \sqrt{\frac{\pi}{\lambda}} \frac{\sin \lambda s}{\lambda s},$$

which, except for the constant factor, is observed to equal $r(t)$. The reader will find it instructive to make a graph of this function.

This example shows why the periodograms of some economic time series are observed to increase rather sharply after some critical value of the trial period T, but give no evidence that the series possess harmonic components.

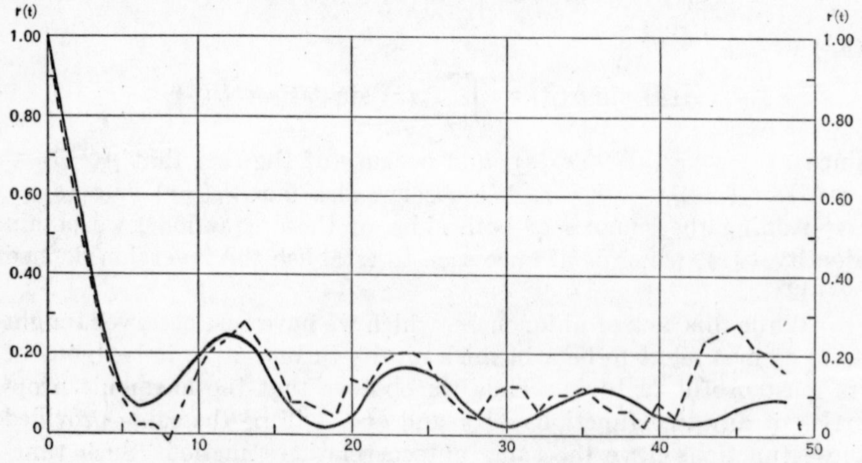

FIGURE 78.—AUTOCORRELATION OF SIR GILBERT WALKER'S ATMOSPHERIC-PRESSURE DATA AT PORT DARWIN.

Solid line is autocorrelation determined from function. Dotted line is autocorrelation from actual data.

Example 2. Sir Gilbert Walker (see *Bibliography*) found for certain data relating to atmospheric pressure at Port Darwin, Australia, the following function:

$$r(t) = 0.19\, e^{-0.0408t} \cos \frac{2\pi t}{12} + 0.15\, e^{-0.0202t} + 0.66\, e^{-0.3425t},$$

where t is measured in quarters of a year. In Figure 78 the graphs of this function and the actual autocorrelation determined from the data are compared. Discuss the harmonic properties of the data.

Solution. We first compute the function

$$\alpha(T) = \int_{-\infty}^{\infty} r(t) \cos \frac{2\pi t}{T}\, dt,$$

and thus obtain

$$\alpha(T) = \frac{4.66}{1 + 164.69(1 + 12/T)^2} + \frac{4.66}{1 + 164.69(1 - 12/T)^2} + \frac{7.43}{1 + 96751/T^2} + \frac{1.93}{1 + 336.56/T^2}.$$

The periodogram is then computed from the function

$$R(T) = \sqrt{\frac{2}{a}\alpha(T)},$$

where $2a = 177$, the number of items in the data analyzed. Figure 79 shows the actual periodogram together with the one harmonically equivalent to it. One will observe that $R(T)$ is a sort of smoothed average of the values of the periodogram computed directly from the data. There is evidence of the existence of a period at $T = 12$, but for no other value.

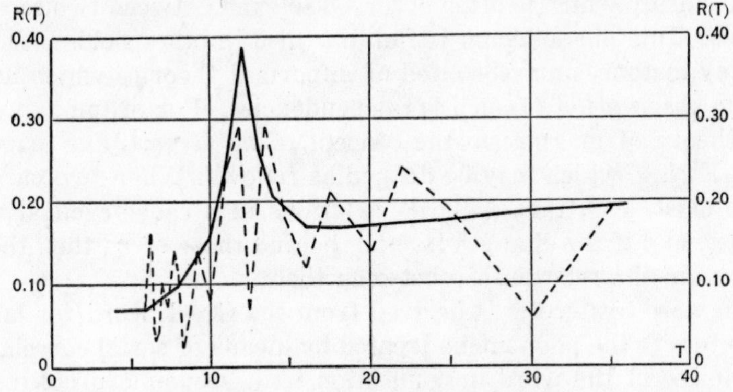

FIGURE 79.—PERIODOGRAM OF SIR GILBERT WALKER'S ATMOSPHERIC-PRESSURE DATA AT PORT DARWIN.

Solid line is periodogram determined from autocorrelation function. Dotted line is actual periodogram of the data.

PROBLEMS

1. Prove that for the function $y = A \sin(\beta t + \alpha)$, we have the limit

$$\sigma^2 = \lim_{a=\infty} \frac{1}{2a} \int_{-a}^{a} A^2 \sin^2(\beta t + \alpha)\, dt = \tfrac{1}{2}A^2.$$

2. For the function of problem 1, prove that

$$R(t) = \lim_{a=\infty} \frac{1}{2a} \int_{-a}^{a} A^2 \sin(\beta s + \alpha) \sin(\beta s + \alpha + \beta t)\, dt = \tfrac{1}{2}A^2 \cos \beta t\,.$$

3. Using the results of problems 1 and 2, which are called *limits in the mean,* show that the autocorrelation in the mean of the function $y = A \sin(\beta t + \alpha)$ is given by

$$r(t) = \cos \beta t\,.$$

4. In the same sense as that described in the preceding three problems show that the correlation between the functions

$$y(s) = A_1 \sin \beta_1 (s + a_1) + A_2 \sin \beta_2 (s + a_2) + \cdots + A_n \sin \beta_n (s + a_n)$$

$$x(s) = B_1 \sin \beta_1 (s + b_1) + B_2 \sin \beta_2 (s + b_2) + \cdots + B_n \sin \beta_n (s + b_n)$$

is given by

$$r = \frac{A_1 B_1 \cos \beta_1 (a_1 - b_1) + A_2 B_2 \cos \beta_2 (a_2 - b_2) + \cdots + A_n B_n \cos \beta_n (a_n - b_n)}{(A_1^2 + A_2^2 + \cdots + A_n^2)^{\frac{1}{2}} (B_1^2 + B_2^2 + \cdots + B_n^2)^{\frac{1}{2}}}\,.$$

5. In the formula derived in problem 4, set $A_i = B_i$ and $a_i = t + b_i$. Hence obtain the autocorrelation for y in the form

$$r(t) = \frac{A_1^2 \cos \beta_1 t + A_2^2 \cos \beta_2 t + \cdots + A_n^2 \cos \beta_n t}{A_1^2 + A_2^2 + \cdots + A_n^2}\,.$$

7. *The Concept of Hysteresis*

One of the most important applications of serial correlations in the theory of economic time series is found in its description of the lag-relationship which is often observed to exist between two economic variables. This phenomenon is familiar also in other fields of science and many instances may be cited of important theories which depend upon the observation of such lag-dependencies. For example, we find in the theory of magnetism the concept of *hysteresis,* due originally to J. A. Ewing, which may be defined as follows: When two variables x and y exist, such that cyclical variations in x cause cyclical variations in y, and if the changes in y lag behind those of x, then there is *hysteresis* in the relationship between them.

The word hysteresis is derived from the Greek word for lag and hence refers to the phenomena treated by means of serial correlations. The first use of the word in connection with economic problems was probably by C. F. Roos in 1925, who set up the relationship between demand, represented by $y(t)$, and price, $p(t)$, in the form of an integral equation

$$(44) \qquad y(t) = a\,p(t) + b + \int_{-\infty}^{t} \phi(t-s)\, p(s)\,ds\,,$$

where $\phi(z)$ approaches zero as z approaches negative infinity.[8] Equations of this type have previously been studied by Vito Volterra (1860–1940), who showed that they were admirably adapted to the investigation of what he called hereditary phenomena. Such phenomena include magnetic hysteresis and other types of lag relationships.[9]

The actual investigation of hysteresis phenomena in economic time series from the point of view of the present section was carried out by H. E. Jones in 1937, who exhibited hysteresis in the relationships between various economic variables.[10]

In order to formulate our problem more precisely, let us regard x and y as depending upon a parameter t,

$$(45) \qquad x = x(t)\,, \qquad y = y(t), \qquad t_0 \leqq t \leqq t_1\,,$$

such that $x(t_0) = x(t_1)$, $y(t_0) = y(t_1)$. Then if the point $P = (x,y)$ traces a non-intersecting curve from $P_0 = (x_0\,, y_0)$ to $P_1 = (x_1\,, y_1)$, we shall say that hysteresis exists between the variables x and y. The amount of hysteresis will be proportional to the area of the curve so traced.

In mechanics, and more roughly so in economic phenomena, there is frequently observed a relationship between x and y which may be defined by the differential equations:

$$(46) \qquad \frac{dx}{dt} = \alpha x - \beta y\,, \qquad \frac{dy}{dt} = \gamma x - \alpha y\,,$$

where $\Delta = \beta\gamma - \alpha^2 > 0$ and all the parameters are positive quantities.

These equations state that the growth of both variables is stimulated directly by the magnitude of one of them, but is adversely affected by the magnitude of the second. For example, business tends to increase as production rises and payrolls grow. But, unfortunately, prices may also advance and these increasing prices will exert an adverse influence upon business.

---

[8] "A Mathematical Theory of Competition," *American Journal of Mathematics*, Vol. 47, 1925, pp. 163–175. In particular, p. 173.

[9] *Leçons sur les équations intégrales.* Paris, 1913.

[10] "The Nature of Regression Functions in the Correlation Analysis of Time Series," *Econometrica*, Vol. 5, 1937, pp. 305–325. See also R. Frisch: "Note on the Phase Diagram of Two Variates," *Ibid.*, pp. 326–328.

In order to obtain the functional relationships between x and y we observe the following equation derived immediately from (46):

$$2\gamma x x' - 2\alpha(x y' + y x') + 2\beta y y' = 0\,, \tag{47}$$

where x' and y' indicate the derivatives of x and y respectively.

Integrating (47), we obtain the desired equation

$$\gamma x^2 - 2\alpha x y + \beta y^2 = \kappa\,, \tag{48}$$

where κ is a constant. From the conditions that $\beta\gamma - \alpha^2 > 0$, we see that (48) is the equation of an ellipse. A graphical example, due to H. E. Jones, is shown in Figure 80.

If we differentiate the first equation in system (46) and eliminate x' and y' by substituting their values as defined by the system, we shall obtain

$$\frac{d^2x}{dt^2} + (\beta\gamma - \alpha^2)x = 0\,. \tag{49}$$

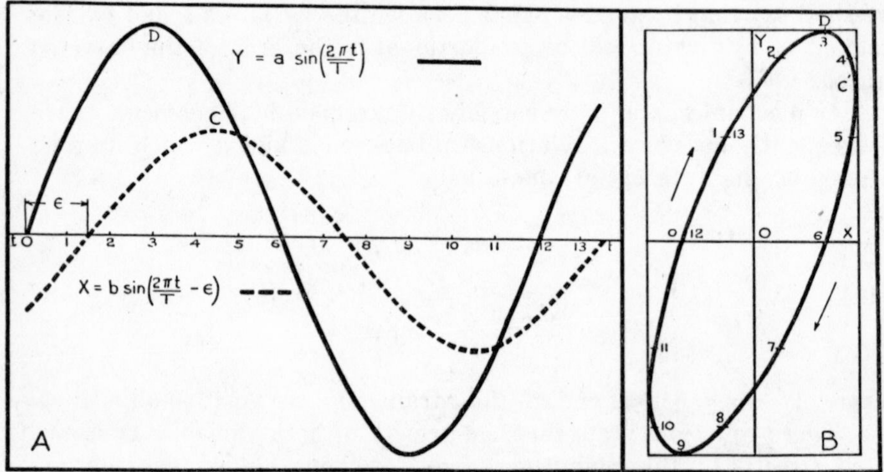

FIGURE 80.—DIAGRAM SHOWING ELLIPTICAL HYSTERESIS BETWEEN TWO HARMONIC CURVES. (From H. E. JONES).

This defines the harmonic

$$x = A\cos\left(\frac{2\pi}{T}t + a\right), \tag{50}$$

where $(2\pi/T)^2 = \beta\gamma - \alpha^2$, and where A and a are arbitrary constants. In similar fashion we also obtain

$$y = B \cos\left(\frac{2\pi}{T} t + b\right). \tag{51}$$

Eliminating t between (50) and (51) we obtain

$$B^2 x^2 - 2 \cos(a - b) AB\, xy + A^2 y^2 = A^2 B^2 \sin^2 (a - b). \tag{52}$$

This equation is observed to be essentially the same as (48) defining also an ellipse. If $a = b$, then the ellipse degenerates into two coincident lines, and there is no hysteresis between the variables. Maximum hysteresis is obtained when $a - b = \frac{1}{2}\pi$, that is to say, when the two components are completely out of phase.

If the two variables $x(t)$ and $y(t)$ are defined statistically, and if they are approximately sinusoidal, then (52) can be written in terms of statistical parameters in the form

$$\sigma_x^2 x^2 - 2\, \sigma_x \sigma_y r_{xy}\, xy + \sigma_y^2 y^2 = 2\, \sigma_x^2 \sigma_y^2 (1 - r^2_{xy}). \tag{53}$$

A system of variables such as the one which we have described above is very common in physics and other applied fields where harmonic, or almost harmonic, motions are observed. It is quite reasonable to suppose that such a system would also apply in economics. The postulates which underly (46) are simple and have a priori validity in many observed relationships between economic time series.

8. *Hysteresis with Damping*

In Section 5 we saw from the serial correlation between pig iron production and the stock market averages that, while there was definite indication of a hysteresis relationship between these two variables, the effect tended to damp out as one series was lagged at greater and greater intervals with respect to the second. This is a characteristic feature of related time series because of the existence of an erratic element, which is usually so prominent in all of them.

We shall indicate a method for obtaining the hysteresis curve when damping is present. The tool to be employed is serial correlation. Thus let us suppose that $x(t)$ is one series and $y(t)$ is the second. Then if $r_{xy}(t)$ is the serial correlation of the two variables, the lag between the two functions can be determined from the graph of $r = r_{xy}(t)$.

We next compute the harmonically equivalent variables

$$\xi(t) = \frac{1}{2\pi} \int_{-\infty}^{\infty} \sqrt{\alpha_1(\beta)} \cos \beta t \, d\beta, \tag{54}$$

$$\eta(t) = \frac{1}{2\pi} \int_{-\infty}^{\infty} \sqrt{\alpha_2(\beta)} \cos \beta(\alpha - t) \, d\beta,$$

where $\alpha_1(\beta)$ and $\alpha_2(\beta)$ are defined respectively by the following integrals in terms of the autocorrelations $r_x(t)$ of x and $r_y(t)$ of y:

$$(55) \qquad \alpha_1(\beta) = \int_{-\infty}^{\infty} r_x(t) \cos \beta\, t\, dt\,, \qquad \alpha_2(\beta) = \int_{-\infty}^{\infty} r_y(t) \cos \beta\, t\, dt\,.$$

The curve obtained from the parametric system

$$(56) \qquad \xi = \xi(t), \qquad \eta = \eta(t).$$

is then the hysteresis diagram of the original variables.

In the general case the curve defined by (56) will not be closed, but will tend to spiral inward around the origin as t carries $\xi(t)$ and η through successive cycles. Hence the average area of successive loops will contract as the hysteresis diminishes.

Example. An example of this type of hysteresis is furnished by the observed relationship between the Dow Jones industrial averages and pig iron production over the period from 1897 to 1913 inclusive (see Section 5 of this chapter). The autocorrelations of the two variables are satisfactorily described by the same function, namely,

$$r_x(t) = \frac{\sin \lambda t}{\lambda t}\,, \qquad \lambda = \frac{\pi}{20}\,,$$

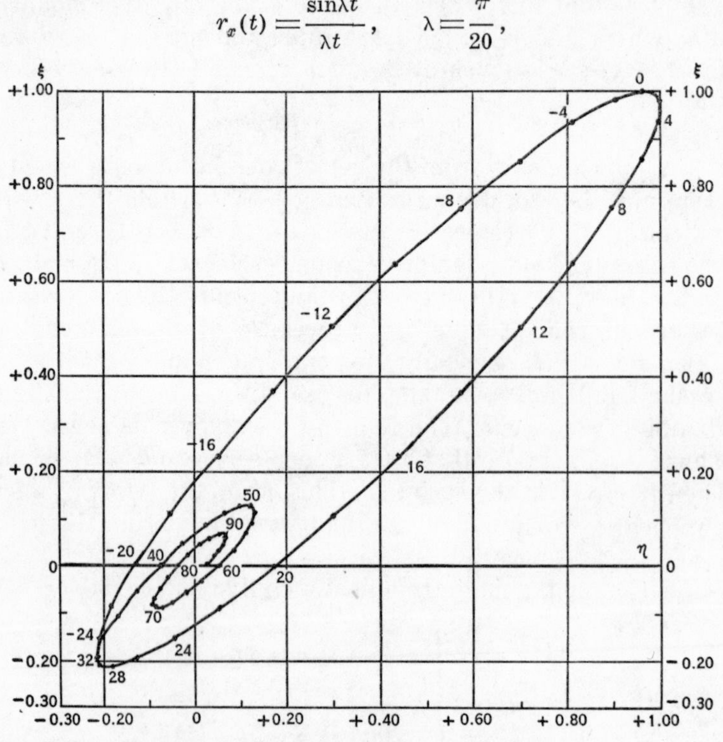

FIGURE 81.—HYSTERESIS DIAGRAM SHOWING THE EFFECTS OF DAMPING.

where t is measured in months. The problem is to determine the hysteresis relationship which exists between the two series.

Solution. We first observe from the statistical evidence that the serial correlation between the two variables shows a lag of three months between the two series, the stock market averages preceding the production of pig iron.

Our analysis would then proceed as follows:

We first compute the function

$$\alpha(\beta) = \int_{-\infty}^{\infty} \frac{\sin\lambda t}{\lambda t} \cos\beta t dt = \begin{cases} \pi/\lambda, & \beta < \lambda, \\ 0, & \beta > \lambda. \end{cases}$$

From this we then obtain by means of (54)

$$\xi(t) = \frac{1}{2\pi} \int_{-\infty}^{\infty} \sqrt{\alpha(\beta)} \cos \beta t d\beta ,$$

$$= \sqrt{\frac{\lambda}{\pi}} \frac{\sin\lambda t}{\lambda t} .$$

For the lagged variable (pig iron production) we obtain similarly

$$\eta(t) = \frac{1}{2\pi} \int_{-\infty}^{\infty} \sqrt{\alpha(\beta)} \cos \beta (\alpha - t) d\beta ,$$

$$= \sqrt{\frac{\lambda}{\pi}} \frac{\sin\lambda(\alpha - t)}{\lambda(\alpha - t)} .$$

Setting $\lambda = \pi/20$ and $\alpha = 3$, we then compute the hysteresis diagram from the functions

$$\xi(t) = S\left(\frac{\pi t}{20}\right), \qquad \eta(t) = S\left[\frac{\pi(3 - t)}{20}\right],$$

where we use the abbreviation

$$S(x) = \frac{\sin x}{x} .$$

We observe from the diagram, Figure 81, how successive loops rapidly diminish in area, showing the relative impermanence of the hysteresis relationship.[11]

---

[11] A. J. Lotka considered in 1923 a problem similar to the one which we have just described. Lotka discussed a system of two variables defined by the system:

$$x'(t) = -y + Bxy + cy^2 + Ex^2y + Fxy^2 + Gy^3 + \cdots$$

$$x'(t) = x + A'x^2 + B'xy + D'x^3 + E'x^2y + F'xy^2 + \cdots .$$

See his "Contributions to Quantitative Parasitology," *Journal of the Washington Academy of Science*, Vol. 13, 1923, pp. 152–158. Hysteresis loops of the character discussed in this section were discovered by him in this study .

PROBLEMS

1. Prove that if the hysteresis curve is the ellipse

$$\gamma x^2 - 2\alpha xy + \beta y^2 = \kappa \, ,$$

then the amount of hysteresis is proportional to $\pi\kappa/\sqrt{\Delta}$, where $\Delta = \beta\gamma - \alpha^2$.

2. Prove that if the hysteresis curve is the ellipse given in problem 1, then a rotation of axes which removes the term in xy leads to the equation

$$a'x'^2 + b'y'^2 = \kappa \, ,$$

where a' is the smaller and b' the larger of the roots of the equation

$$\lambda^2 - (\beta + \gamma)\lambda + \Delta = 0 \, .$$

3. Show that the amount of hysteresis defined by equation (52) is proportional to $AB\,\pi \sin (a-b)$.

4. Show that the amount of hysteresis defined by equation (53) is proportional to $2\pi\, \sigma_x\, \sigma_y\, (1 - r_{xy}{}^2)^{\frac{1}{2}}$.

5. If between the limits $-a \leqq t \leqq a$ the autocorrelations of two variables are satisfactorily described by the same function, $r(t) = \cos \lambda t$, and if one variable lags α units behind the other, discuss the hysteresis curve.

6. Graph the hysteresis curve of problem 5 when $\lambda = 2\pi/20$, $\alpha = 3$, and t is between the limits of -100 and $+100$.

7. Discuss the hysteresis curve defined by

$$\xi(t) = a(\sin t)/t \, , \qquad \eta(t) = a(\cos t)/t .$$

8. Graphically represent the hysteresis curve defined by

$$\xi(t) = e^{-t} \cos 2t \, , \qquad \eta(t) = e^{-t} \sin 2t \, , \qquad t \geqq 0 \, .$$

9. The Standard Error of Trends—Forecasting

In the foregoing analysis we have said nothing about the errors which obviously are to be found in trend lines determined from statistical data. The importance of this problem will be readily understood when we observe that our ability to forecast the future by an extrapolation of trends is strictly limited by the size of the errors.

The errors in trends are of two kinds, namely, those which enter the parameters of the fitted curve through sampling errors in the data, and those which enter through an improper choice of the functional representation itself. The problem is thus more complicated than that presented by sampling from frequency data, where the assumption of a normal, or almost normal, distribution is usually valid. This assumption thus eliminates errors of the second kind mentioned above.

The problem of the errors in the trend of a time series clearly presents unusual difficulties, since, if it were satisfactorily solved, we should be able to forecast, and to define the limits of our forecast, in terms of a probability judgment. But the present status of the problem of estimating the future trends of economic time series shows that the problem is far from attaining a satisfactory solution.[12]

In this section we shall indicate briefly a method of estimating the standard error of a trend line. In this analysis we shall make use of a suggestive method originating with the late Henry Schultz (see *Bibliography*), which we shall modify to the extent of defining a range of forecast. Because of the essential difficulties of the theory we shall state merely the results and refer the reader for details to the original article, or to the author's discussion in Chapter 11 of his *Analysis of Economic Time Series.*

Let us begin by assuming that the trend to be fitted to the data is represented by the function

$$y(t) = f(t; a, b, c, \cdots, m), \tag{57}$$

where $a, b, c, \cdots, m$ are the parameters to be adjusted.

Let us designate by $a_0, b_0, c_0, \cdots, m_0$ the values of the parameters for which (57) gives the best approximation within the range of the data, and let us designate the function (57) for these values by $y_0(t)$.

The standard error of the trend is then defined to be the square root of the function

$$\begin{aligned} \sigma_f^2(t) = \Bigg[& \left(\frac{\partial f}{\partial a}\right)_0^2 \sigma_a^2 + \left(\frac{\partial f}{\partial b}\right)_0^2 \sigma_b^2 + \cdots + \left(\frac{\partial f}{\partial m}\right)_0^2 \sigma_m^2 \\ & + 2\left(\frac{\partial f}{\partial a}\right)_0 \left(\frac{\partial f}{\partial b}\right)_0 \sigma_a \sigma_b r_{ab} + 2\left(\frac{\partial f}{\partial a}\right)_0 \left(\frac{\partial f}{\partial c}\right) \sigma_a \sigma_c r_{ac} + \cdots \Bigg], \end{aligned} \tag{58}$$

where σ_a^2, σ_b^2, etc. are the variances of the errors in the parameters, and where r_{ab}, r_{ac}, etc. are the correlations between these errors. The subscript to the partial derivatives means that these functions are to be evaluated at the initial values of the parameters.

Before one can compute numerically this standard error, it is necessary to have an estimate of the quantities $\sigma_a^2, \sigma_b^2, \cdots, r_{ab}, r_{ac}$, etc. Such an estimate may be attained as follows:

Let us employ the abbreviation

$$\varepsilon^2 = \frac{N}{N-m}\sigma_1^2, \qquad \sigma_1^2 = \frac{\Sigma \Delta^2(t)}{N}, \tag{59}$$

where $\Delta(t) = y_t - y_0(t)$, that is to say, the difference between the

[12] See, for example, Alfred Cowles, 3rd: "Can Stock Market Forecasters Forecast?" *Econometrica,* Vol. 1, 1933, pp. 309–324.

data and the estimate obtained for $y(t)$. Then the desired variances of the parameters and their correlation coefficients are given by the formulas:

$$\sigma_a^2 = \varepsilon^2[\alpha, \alpha]\ , \sigma_b^2 = \varepsilon^2[\beta, \beta]\ , \cdots, \quad \sigma_a\sigma_b r_{ab} = \varepsilon^2[\alpha, \beta]\ , \cdots, \tag{60}$$

where the bracket symbols are to be determined from the inversion of the following system of equations:

$$\begin{aligned} &[f_a f_a]\Delta a + [f_a f_b]\Delta b + \cdots + [f_a f_m]\Delta m = [f_a \Delta]\ , \\ &[f_b f_a]\Delta a + [f_b f_b]\Delta b + \cdots + [f_b f_m]\Delta m = [f_b \Delta]\ , \\ &\cdot \quad \cdot \quad \cdot \quad \cdot \quad \cdot \quad \cdot \quad \cdot \quad \cdot \\ &[f_m f_a]\Delta a + [f_m f_b]\Delta b + \cdots + [f_m f_m]\Delta m = [f_m \Delta]\ . \end{aligned} \tag{61}$$

In this system we have employed the following abbreviations:

$$[f_a f_b] = \sum_t \left(\frac{\partial f}{\partial a}\right)_0 \left(\frac{\partial f}{\partial b}\right)_0, \qquad [f_a \Delta] = \sum_t \left(\frac{\partial f}{\partial a}\right)_0 \Delta(t)\ ,$$

where we write $\Delta(t) = y_t - y_0(t)$.

The inversion of this system has the form

$$\begin{aligned} \Delta a &= [\alpha, \alpha][f_a\Delta] + [\alpha, \beta][f_b\Delta] + \cdots + [\alpha, \mu][f_m\Delta]\ , \\ \Delta b &= [\beta, \alpha][f_a\Delta] + [\beta, \beta][f_b\Delta] + \cdots + [\beta, \mu][f_m\Delta]\ , \\ &\cdot \quad \cdot \quad \cdot \quad \cdot \quad \cdot \quad \cdot \quad \cdot \quad \cdot \quad \cdot \quad \cdot \\ \Delta m &= [\mu, \alpha][f_a\Delta] + [\mu, \beta][f_b\Delta] + \cdots + [\mu, \mu][f_m\Delta]\ , \end{aligned}$$

which thus defines the brackets $[\alpha, \alpha]$, $[\beta, \beta]$, etc., and hence, the variances of the errors as given in equations (60).

Example 1. As an example we shall compute the standard error of forecast of the straight line

$$y = a + bt\ ,$$

which we shall assume is fitted to a set of data defined over the sequence of integers from $t = -p$ to $t = +p$.

Solution. From equation (58) we obtain

$$\begin{aligned} \sigma_f^2(t) &= \sigma_a^2 + 2\sigma_a\sigma_b r_{ab} t + \sigma_b^2 t^2\ , \\ &= \varepsilon^2\{[\alpha, \alpha] + 2[\alpha, \beta]t + [\beta, \beta]t^2\}\ , \end{aligned} \tag{62}$$

where ε^2 is given by $\varepsilon^2 = \{N/(N-1)\}\sigma_1^2$, the variance σ_1^2 being defined by equation (13) in Section 3.

In order to evaluate the bracket symbols we have the equations

$$(2p+1)\Delta a + \sum_{-p}^{p} t\,\Delta b = [\Delta]\ ,$$

$$\sum_{-p}^{p} t\,\Delta b + \sum_{-p}^{p} t^2 \Delta b = [t\Delta]\,.$$

Noting the sums

$$\sum_{-p}^{p} t^2 = \frac{p(p+1)(2p+1)}{3}, \quad \sum_{-p}^{p} t = 0\,,$$

we get

$$\Delta a = \frac{[\Delta]}{2p+1}, \quad \Delta b = \frac{3[t\Delta]}{p(p+1)(2p+1)}\,.$$

From these quantities, and noting that $N = 2p + 1$, we obtain the following:

$$[\alpha, \alpha] = \frac{1}{N}, \quad [\alpha, \beta] = 0\,, \quad [\beta, \beta] = \frac{12}{N(N^2-1)}.$$

Employing the abbreviations A and A' defined by equation (12) in Section 3, we immediately obtain from (62) the desired standard error of the trend, namely,

$$\sigma_f = \varepsilon(A + A't^2)^{\frac{1}{2}}. \tag{63}$$

An example of the application of the technique described above is shown graphically in Figure 82. A linear trend is fitted to 20 years of rail stock prices and this trend is then extrapolated four years into the future. About this trend there is then constructed a band whose upper bound is the graph of the function $y(t) + \sigma_f(t)$ and whose lower bound is the graph of $y(t) - \sigma_f(t)$. For reasons about to be discussed the value of N was chosen equal to 5.

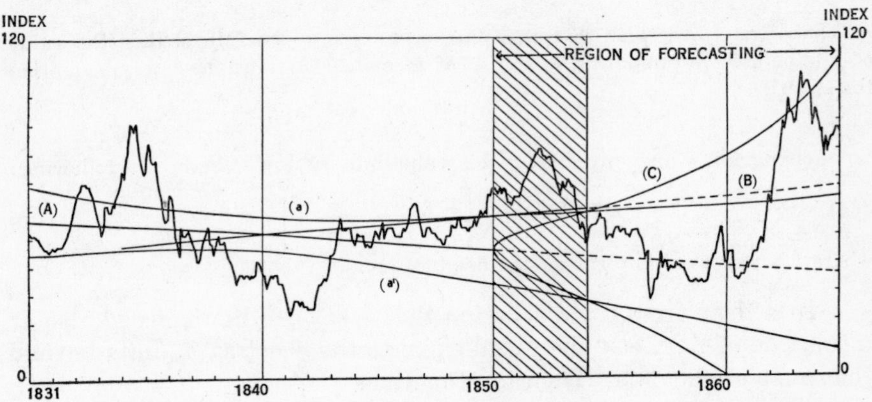

FIGURE 82.—THE STANDARD ERROR OF FORECAST FOR A LINEAR TREND FITTED TO RAIL STOCK PRICES.

(A) is original trend; (B) is new trend obtained by eliminating four years of data at one end and adding four years of data at the other; (C) is the graph of $y(t) \pm \sigma_f(t_m)$. Curves (a) and (a′) are limits of the standard error of forecast about the linear trend.

The derivation of formula (58) was originally made without regard to the fact that the items of an economic time series are serially correlated with one another. The importance of noting this is seen in the fact that, although ε^2 varies little whether the items are taken at monthly intervals, or as annual averages, the value of $\sigma_f^2(t)$ varies greatly with respect to the choice of the interval.

In order to avoid the difficulty of a technical discussion of what has been called the number of *degrees of freedom* of an economic time series, we shall introduce an empirical postulate to the effect that if $\sigma_f^2(t)$ has been computed for a set of N items, then the forecast of the trend is valid for one unit beyond the range of the data. Thus, for the example graphically shown in Figure 82, since the trend is extrapolated four years beyond the data, the range of which was 20 years, the value of N employed in computing the standard error of forecast must be $20/4 = 5$.

To state the postulate otherwise, let us assume that the mid point of the range is chosen as the origin, and that the data are given over $2p + 1 = N$ units. Suppose, then, that we wish to explore m units into the future. The number of degrees of freedom to be used in the computation of $\sigma_f(t)$ is given by N/m. The number m is called the *range of forecast.*

Example 2. As an example, let us consider the evaluation of $\sigma_f^2(t)$ for the straight line discussed in example 1.

Solution. If we wish to extrapolate m units into the future, then the value of p to be used in computing A and A' of formula (63) must be determined from the equation

$$2p + 1 = N/m.$$

Solving for p and introducing this value into (63) we obtain the following:

$$\sigma_f^2(t) = \varepsilon^2 \frac{m}{N}\left[1 + \frac{12}{N^2 - m^2} t^2\right], \tag{64}$$

where t is measured in terms of the original units.

It is clear from the discussion that $\sigma_f(t)$ can be regarded also as a function of m. Let t_m be taken equal to the abscissa m units beyond the range of the data. Then the functions

$$Y(m) = y(t) \pm \sigma_f(t_m) \tag{65}$$

will define a band about the trend which will indicate the region of error for trend forecasts of varying length. Such a region is shown in Figure 82.

The theory which we have developed in this section can be applied to harmonic approximations, such as that given in example 2 of Section 4, to the logistic discussed in Chapter 11, and to other types of trend. An example of its application to the logistic, which describes the trend of the production of pig iron, is shown in Figure 83. The original logistic was computed from the data prior to 1920 and the standard error band was estimated on the assumption of an extrapolation of 20 years. It is clear from the graph that only a slight modification in the trend would have been made by adding to the original data the production figures from 1920 to 1930. But it is also clear that

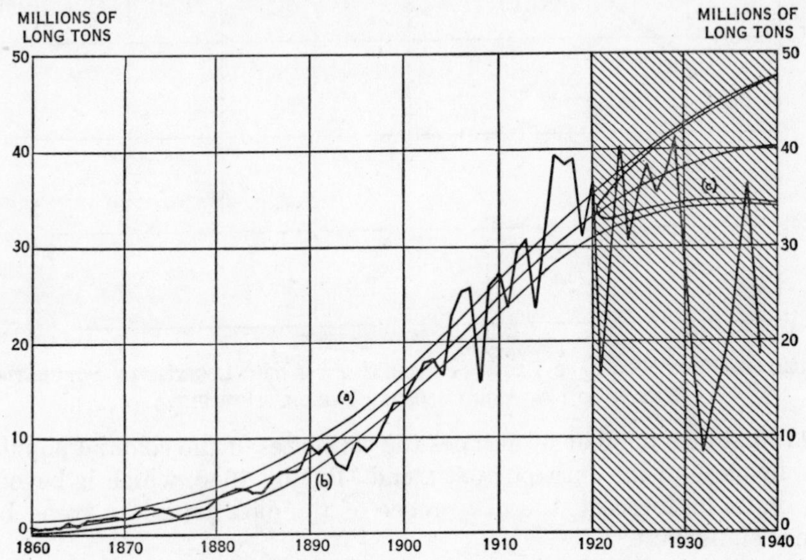

FIGURE 83.—THE REGION OF FORECAST AND STANDARD ERROR BANDS FOR THE LOGISTIC OF PIG IRON PRODUCTION.

Curves (a) and (b) are graphs of $y(t) + \sigma_f(t)$ and $y(t) - \sigma_f(t)$ respectively. Curve (c) is the graph of $y(t) \pm \sigma_f(t_m)$.

the violent decline occasioned by the depression of 1932 would have modified materially the original trend.

Let us note finally the significant fact that if $m = N$ in formula (64), then $\sigma_f^2(t)$ becomes infinite. This states the reasonable proposition that one cannot forecast over a range which equals, or exceeds, the range of the original data.

An interesting example of this is found in an application originally made by Schultz. Figure 84 shows the standard error band computed by the unmodified theory of this section for the logistic of population extrapolated into the past from the first United States census

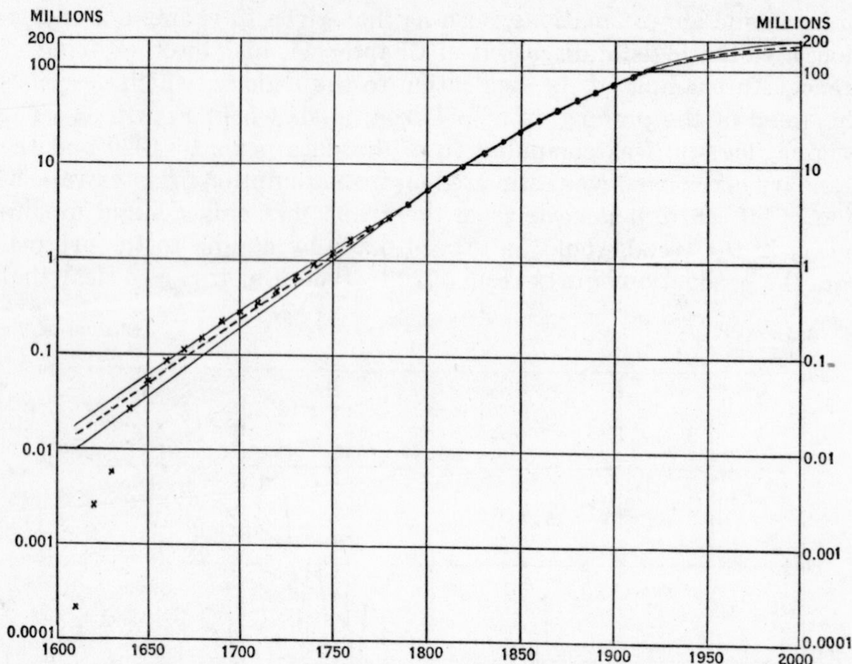

FIGURE 84.—THE STANDARD ERROR OF FORECAST FOR THE LOGISTIC OF POPULATION EXTENDED INTO THE COLONIAL PERIOD. (SCHULTZ).

of 1790. For a number of decades the estimates of the colonial population lie close to the extrapolated trend. But by 1640, which is beyond the limits of forecast, the divergence of the data from the trend becomes significant.

PROBLEMS

1. Compute and represent graphically the standard error of forecast for problem 1, Section 3. Fire losses in the United States during the five years preceding and the five years following the period of the data were as follows: 214, 217, 206, 204, 221, and 562, 473, 465, 459, 502. Discuss the standard error of forecase in the light of these figures.

2. Compute and represent graphically the standard error of forecast for the data of problem 4 for the period from 1901 to 1920 inclusive.

3. Extend your forecast for the data of problem 2 first to 1925 and then to 1930. What conclusions do you reach?

4. Show that the standard error of forecast for the harmonic sum

$$y = \tfrac{1}{2} a_0 + \sum_{m=1}^{n} \left(a_m \cos \frac{m\pi t}{a} + b_m \sin \frac{m\pi t}{a}\right)$$

is given by $\sigma_f = \varepsilon \sqrt{(n+1)/a}$, where we abbreviate

$$\varepsilon^2 = \frac{N}{N-n-1}\{\sigma^2 - \tfrac{1}{2}(R_1{}^2 + R_2{}^2 + \cdots + R_n{}^2)\},$$

in which $R_m{}^2 = a_m{}^2 + b_m{}^2$.

5. Making use of the result of problem 8, Section 4, show that as n tends toward infinity σ_f tends toward zero.

6. From the results of problem 4, and making use of the computations of the illustrative example of Section 3, compute the standard error of forecast for the function defined in Example 2 of Section 4.

7. Making use of your results from problem 6 estimate the values of the index of industrial stock prices for the last two months of 1915 and 1920. Compare with the observed values 64.8, 65.8, and 57.4, 51.7.

SELECTED BIBLIOGRAPHY ON TIME SERIES AND THEIR CORRELATION

ALTER, D. "A Group or Correlation Periodogram, with Application to the Rainfall of the British Isles," *Monthly Weather Review*, Vol. 55, 1927, pp. 263–266.

BARTELS, J. "Random Fluctuations, Persistence, and Quasi-Persistence in Geophysical and Cosmical Periodicities," *Terrestrial Magnetism*, Vol. 40, 1935, pp. 1-60.

BRUNT, D. *The Combination of Observations*, Second edition, Cambridge, 1931.

DAVIS, H. T. *The Analysis of Economic Time Series*, Principia Press, 1941.

EAGLE, A. *Fourier's Theorem and Harmonic Analysis*, London, 1925, Chapter 8.

FRISCH, R. "Note on the Phase Diagram of Two Variates," *Econometrica*, Vol. 5, 1937, pp. 326–328.

GREENSTEIN, B. "Periodogram Analysis with Special Application to Business Failures," *Econometrica*, Vol. 3, 1935, pp. 170–198.

HOTELLING, H. (See H. Working).

JONES, H. E. "The Nature of Regression Functions in the Correlation Analysis of Time Series," *Econometrica*, Vol. 5, 1937, pp. 305–325.

KOOPMANS, T. *Linear Regression Analysis of Economic Time Series*, Haarlem, 1936, 132 pp.

LOTKA, A. J. "Contributions to Quantitative Parasitology," *Journal of the Washington Academy of Science*, Vol. 13, 1923, pp. 152–158.

MOORE, H. L. *Economic Cycles: Their Law and Cause*, New York, 1914.

PERSONS, W. (1) "Construction of a Business Barometer Based upon Annual Data," *American Economic Review*, Vol. 6, 1916, pp. 739–769.

(2) "Correlation of Time Series," *Journal of the American Statistical Association*, Vol. 18, 1922–23, pp. 713–726. Republished as Chapter 10 in the *Handbook of Mathematical Statistics*, edited by H. L. Rietz, Cambridge, Mass., 1924.

ROBINSON, G. (See E. T. Whittaker)

ROOS, C. F. "A Mathematical Theory of Competition," *American Journal of Mathematics*, Vol. 47, 1925, pp. 163–175.

SCHULTZ, H. "The Standard Error of a Forecast from a Curve," *Journal of the American Statistical Association*, Vol. 25, 1930, pp. 139–185.

SCHUMPETER, J. A. "Mitchell's Business Cycles," *Quarterly Journal of Economics*, Vol. 45, 1930–31, pp. 150–172.

SCHUSTER, SIR ARTHUR. (1) "On Interference Phenomena," *Philosophical Magazine*, Vol. 37, (5), 1894, pp. 509–545.

(2) "On Hidden Periodicities," *Terrestrial Magnetism*, Vol. 3, 1897, p. 13.

(3) "The Periodogram and its Optical Analogy," *Proceedings of the Royal Society of London*, Vol. 77(A), 1906, pp. 136–140.

(4) "On the Periodicities of Sun Spots," *Philosophical Transactions of the Royal Society of London*, Vol. 206(A), 1906, pp. 69–100.

STUMPFF, K. *Grundlagen und Methoden der Periodenforschung*, Berlin, 1937, vii + 332 pp.

TINTNER, G. *The Variate Difference Method*. Cowles Commission Monograph No. 5, Principia Press, 1940, 175 pp.

VOLTERRA, V. (1) *Leçons sur les équations intégrales et les équations integro-differentielles*, Paris, 1913, 164 pp.

(2) *Leçons sur la théorie mathématique de la lutte pour la vie*. Paris, 1931.

WALKER, SIR GILBERT. "On Periodicity in Series of Related Terms, "*Proceedings of the Royal Society of London*, Vol. 131(A), 1931, pp. 518–532.

WHITTAKER, E. T. (With G. Robinson). *The Calculus of Observations*, London, 1929, Chapter 13.

WIENER, N. "Generalized Harmonic Analysis," *Acta Mathematica*, Vol. 55, 1930, pp. 117–258.

WILSON, E. B. "The Periodogram of Business Activity," *Quarterly Journal of Economics*, Vol. 48, 1934, pp. 375–417.

WOLD, H. *A Study in the Analysis of Stationary Time Series*, Uppsala, 1938, vi + 211 pp.

WORKING, H. (With H. Hotelling). "Application of the Theory of Error to the Interpretation of Trends," *Proceedings of the American Statistical Association*, Vol. 24, 1929, pp. 73–85.

YULE, G. U. (1) "Why Do We Sometimes Get Nonsense Correlations between Time Series?" *Journal of the Royal Statistical Society*, Vol. 89, 1926, pp. 1–64.

(2) "On a Method of Investigating Periodocities in Disturbed Series, with Special Reference to Wolfer's Sunspot Numbers," *Philosophical Transactions of the Royal Society*, Vol. 226(A), 1927, pp. 267–298.

CHAPTER 17

DYNAMIC CONCEPTS OF SUPPLY AND DEMAND

1. Demand as a Function of Time

In preceding chapters of the book we have employed curves of supply and demand, which were assumed to be independent of time. Economic statics depends fundamentally upon the assumption that such curves exist, and the question as to the possibility of their statistical determination is not generally essential to arguments based upon them. We have already indicated in Chapter 4 the statistical difficulties. A static demand curve could be constructed easily if we could determine the demand for some commodity in n identical communities in each of which the price was different. But actually prices are observed as the fluctuating values in a sequence of time, and the static demand curve must be constructed from these observations by the device discussed in Chapter 4.

Although arguments based upon the concept of static curves of supply and demand will always remain fundamental in many problems in economics, the fact that prices, as we observe them, are actually functions of time makes it inevitable that dynamical considerations must be introduced.

Several writers, notably G. C. Evans and C. F. Roos, have made attempts to describe the dynamic behavior of supply and demand curves. Thus, limiting our attention for the moment to demand, let us assume that the relationship between demand, y, and price, p, can be described by an equation of the form

$$y(t) = -ap(t) + b + c\frac{dp}{dt}, \tag{1}$$

where a, b, and c are positive constants.

If we set $c = 0$, then we obtain for the demand curve a straight line of the static type discussed in Chapter 4. But if $c > 0$, then the situation is modified by the assumption that the demand tends to increase as prices rise, and conversely, the demand tends to diminish as prices fall. If, on the contrary, we assume that $c < 0$, then demand is assumed to increase as prices fall, and diminish as prices rise. Which of these assumptions is realistic, or perhaps more properly, whether either of them is realistic, can be determined only by submitting the proposition to the final arbiter of all economic questions, namely, the data themselves.

It is also possible that $p'(t) = dp/dt$ is itself an independent economic variable and should be so regarded. In this case the demand function, instead of being a straight line, will be a plane as shown in the diagram. In this case we should speak of the plane of demand. Since, however, both p and p' depend upon a parameter t, the demand becomes a function of a single variable. It can then be represented as a space curve, which lies wholly on the plane of demand. This curve is then the space representation of a time series as is shown in Figure 85.

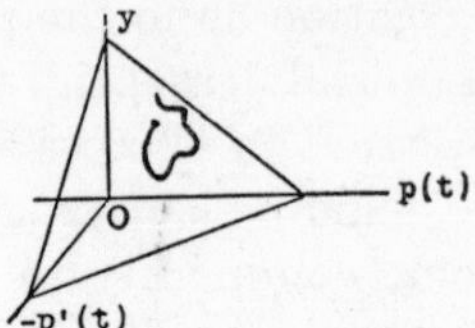

FIGURE 85.—DEMAND AS A FUNCTION OF PRICE AND THE DERIVATIVE OF PRICE.

2. Supply as a Function of Time

If demand is to be regarded as a function of time, it is clear that we must make a similar assumption with regard to supply. It will be convenient for the sake of illustration to write the dynamic supply curve in the form

$$u(t) = \alpha p(t) - \beta + \gamma \frac{dp}{dt}, \tag{2}$$

where α, β, and γ are assumed to be positive constants.

It is obvious that when the dynamic term, dp/dt, is absent, that is to say, when $\gamma = 0$, we have the case of linear supply in the static theory discussed in Chapter 4.

The first problem which presents itself is that of determining price when both demand and supply are dynamic variables. In order to solve this problem we assume that $y(t) = u(t)$, and hence obtain the equation

$$-ap + b + c\frac{dp}{dt} = \alpha p - \beta + \gamma \frac{dp}{dt}.$$

This differential equation can be written in the form

$$\frac{dp}{dt} + mp = k\,, \tag{3}$$

where we employ the abbreviations,

$$m = \frac{a+\alpha}{\gamma - c}\,, \qquad k = \frac{b+\beta}{\gamma - c}\,, \qquad \gamma \neq c\,.$$

The solution of (3) has the form

$$p(t) = p_0 + Ce^{-mt}, \tag{4}$$

where we write

$$p_0 = \frac{k}{m} = \frac{\beta + b}{\alpha + a}. \tag{5}$$

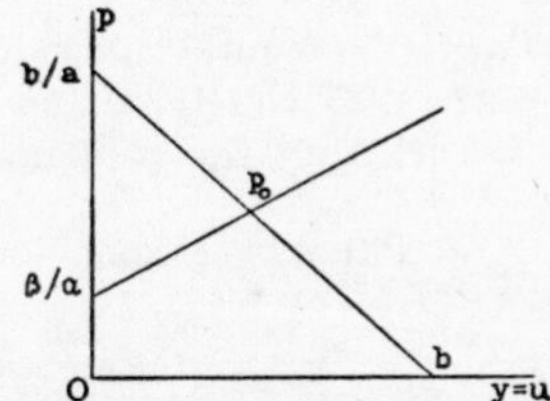

FIGURE 86.—LINEAR DEMAND AND SUPPLY CURVES.

We observe that p_0 is the classical price obtained by the intersection of the static demand and supply curves as shown in Figure 86.

If we assume that at $t = 0$, the price is P_0, that is, $p(0) = P_0$, then we can compute C in equation (4). Thus we find $P_0 = p_0 + C$, or $C = P_0 - p_0$. Hence we can write equation (4) in the form

$$p(t) = p_0 + (P_0 - p_0)\,e^{-mt}\,. \tag{6}$$

If $m > 0$, then as t increases $p(t)$ will tend toward p_0. But if $m < 0$, $p(t)$ will tend to increase and hence diverge more and more from the equilibrium position. But since prices are not observed to do this in general, we may assume that $m < 0$, or what is the same thing,

$$\gamma > c\,. \tag{7}$$

The case where $\gamma = c$ is trivial since the derivatives drop out and the problem reduces to that of static equilibrium.

PROBLEMS

1. The demand for a certain commodity is observed to be given by the function

$$y = A \cos mt + y_0 .$$

Prices are observed to be strictly oscillatory, that is to say, without essential damping or inflation, and they are also found to be connected with demand by the relationship shown in equation (1). Regarding (1) as a differential equation in $p(t)$ with y given, solve this equation and show that prices are harmonic but out of phase with demand.

2. The supply of a certain commodity is given by

$$u = B \cos nt + u_0 .$$

Prices are also observed to be oscillatory and are connected with supply by the relationship given in equation (2). Regarding (2) as a differential equation in $p(t)$ with u given, solve this equation and show that prices are harmonic, but out of phase with supply.

3. Show that the demand-price curve in problem 1 is an ellipse. Given $A = 10$, $m = 2$, $a = 1$, $b = 5$, $c = 1$, $y_0 = 10$, find its equation and represent it graphically.

4. The following tables give the monthly price of eggs in cents per dozen at New York City for the two years 1923 and 1924, and the monthly receipts of eggs (unit = 1,000 cases) at New York City for the same two years:

PRICE OF EGGS

Year	Jan.	Feb.	Mar.	Apr.	May	June	July	Aug.	Sept.	Oct.	Nov.	Dec.
1923	42	37	31	27	27	24	25	29	35	39	53	47
1924	42	39	25	24	25	27	29	33	39	44	52	57

SUPPLY OF EGGS

Year	Jan.	Feb.	Mar.	Apr.	May	June	July	Aug.	Sept.	Oct.	Nov.	Dec.
1923	386	447	981	924	1163	796	596	528	416	377	270	272
1924	301	410	717	1082	970	789	599	429	405	361	221	259

Graph these data and show that the situation is similar to that discussed in problem 2.

5. From the data given in problem 4 estimate the constants of the supply function given in problem 2, and then from the observed difference in phase between the two curves estimate as far as possible the constants in the relationship given in equation (2).

6. From the data given in problem 4 form a hysteresis diagram as described in Section 7 of Chapter 16.

3. *Profits under Dynamic Prices*

Since we are now considering a dynamic system with prices as variables of the time, it is necessary to make considerable modification in the study of the profit function.

In the case of variable demand, the profit function takes the form of an integral over time. Thus if we designate by π the profit acquired between the times $t = t_0$ and $t = t_1$, we have

$$\pi = \int_{t_0}^{t_1} [py - Q(u)]\, dt , \tag{8}$$

where y is the variable of demand and $Q(u)$ is the total cost of manufacturing and marketing u units. Since the possibility of overproduction is always present in every business enterprise, we shall not assume that u is equal to y.

In order to simplify the mathematical development we shall adopt the following simple forms for y, the demand; u, the supply; and $Q(u)$, the total cost:

$$y = -ap(t) + b + cp'(t) \,, u = \alpha p(t) - \beta + \gamma p'(t) \,, \tag{9}$$

$$Q(u) = Au^2 + Bu + C \,.$$

The problem of maximizing the profit π is clearly that of determining that function, $p = p(t)$, for t between the limits $t = t_0$ and $t = t_1$, which gives to the integral (8) its largest possible value. Such a function is called an *extremal.*

The mathematical discipline which was developed to solve problems of this type is called the *calculus of variations.* Since its essential features have been given in other places, and since it would go beyond the scope of the present work to consider many of its details, we shall limit our discussion to the barest outline of the subject. However, the calculus of variations appears destined to play an important role in the theory of economics, as it has in mechanics, not only in such a problem as the one before us of maximizing profit, but also perhaps in establishing the fundamentals of the dynamics of time series. It is essential, therefore, that we have at least a résumé of some of the immediately useful formulas of the subject.

4. Excursus on the Calculus of Variations

In Vergil's account of the wanderings of Aeneas, it is told that Queen Dido, wishing to secure a site for founding the new city of Carthage, was offered "as much land as could be surrounded by a bull's hide." Her crafty followers interpreted this to mean the amount of land that could be enclosed within a cord made from the bull's hide. The problem thus presented itself as to the form that the curve should assume in order to enclose a maximum area. The answer, a circle, was known to the Greeks, but it wasn't until centuries later that an adequate mathematical theory of this so-called *isoperimetric problem* of the calculus of variations was finally developed.

The systematic development of the calculus of variations began with John Bernoulli (1667–1748) and his brother James Bernoulli (1654–1705), who gave solutions of the problem of the *brachistochrone,* that is to say, the problem of determining the curve between two fixed points so that the time of descent along this curve from the higher to the lower point shall be shorter than the time along any other curve. The theories thus involved were broadened and deepened by Leonhard Euler (1707–1783), who published a comprehensive memoir on the subject in 1744. The next significant addition to the theory was made by Joseph Louis de Lagrange (1736–1813) in a series of papers published between 1762 and 1770, who formulated the analytical theory in a satisfactory way and gave numerous applications to mechanics and physics. Lagrange is generally regarded as the founder of the calculus of variations.

The second variation, through which the existence of a maximum or a minimum may be ascertained, was studied by A. M. Legendre (1752–1833), and the conditions which he discovered were extended by C. G. J. Jacobi (1804–1851) in a memoir published in 1837. As the problems embraced by the new calculus broadened, the older theories were found to be inadequate to answer many questions of existence which arose. A precise examination satisfactory to modern mathematics was made of these important problems by K. Weierstrass (1815–1897), who distinguished carefully between necessary and sufficient conditions for the existence of a maximum (or minimum), and developed an ingenious and powerful sufficiency proof. Modern research in the calculus of variations may be said to have originated with the papers of Weierstrass.

In a form sufficiently general for our purpose, the calculus of variations is concerned with the problem of determining the function $y = y(x)$ which will render the integral

$$I = \int_a^b F(x, y, y')\, dx \tag{10}$$

either a maximum or a minimum, provided such an *extremum* exists. When a maximum exists it will be understood that there exists a definite area within which the curve $y = y(x)$ lies and that the integral is greater when taken along this curve than for any other curve which lies within the region and which connects the same two points.

Such an area is shown in Figure 87. It will be necessary also to assume that $y(x)$ is continuous and has a derivative $y'(t)$ within the interval $(a \leqq x \leqq b)$, and that the interval can be subdivided into parts on each of which $y'(x)$ is continuous. When a function $y(x)$ exists, subject to the restrictions just stated, which renders the integral I a maximum or a minimum, this function is called an *extremal.*

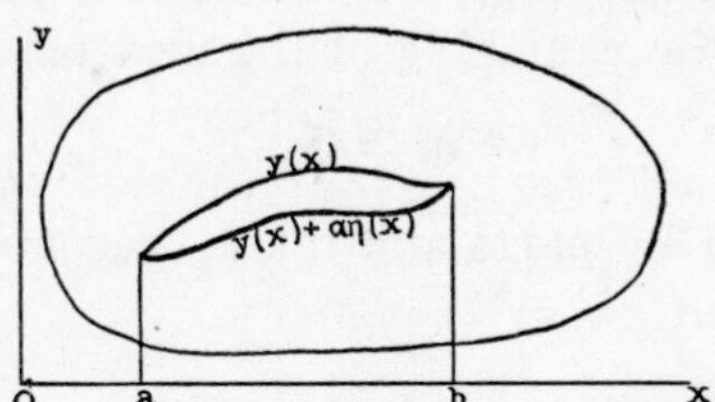

FIGURE 87.—REGION OF VARIATION.

In order to obtain a necessary condition which must be satisfied by $y(x)$, we replace $y(x)$ in (10) by $y(x) + \alpha\eta(x)$, where α is an arbitrary constant, and where $\eta(x)$ is an arbitrary function, continuous and of continuous derivative, which vanishes at $x = a$ and $x = b$; that is

$$\eta(a) = \eta(b) = 0 . \tag{11}$$

If we designate the new integral by $I(\alpha)$, that is,

$$I(\alpha) = \int_a^b F(x, y + \alpha\eta , y' + \alpha\eta')\, dx , \tag{12}$$

this integral may be regarded as a function of the parameter α and expanded as a power series in this variable.

Adopting the abbreviations

$$P = \frac{\partial^2 F}{\partial y^2} , \quad Q = \frac{\partial^2 F}{\partial y \partial y'} , \quad R = \frac{\partial^2 F}{\partial y'^2} , \quad F'_y = \frac{\partial F}{\partial y} , F'_{y'} = \frac{\partial F}{\partial y'} , \tag{13}$$

we see that equation (12) may be written

$$I(\alpha) = I(0) + \alpha \int_a^b (F'_y\, \eta + F'_{y'}\, \eta')\, dx \tag{14}$$

$$+ \frac{\alpha^2}{2!} \int_a^b [P\eta^2(x) + 2Q\eta(x)\eta'(x) + R\{\eta'(x)\}^2]\, dx + \cdots .$$

The coefficient of α is called the *first variation* and is designated by δI; the coefficient of $\alpha^2/2!$ is similarly called the *second variation* and is designated by $\delta^2 I$. It is the first variation, namely,

$$\delta I = \int_a^b (F'_y \eta + F'_{y'} \eta') dx , \tag{15}$$

that we shall first consider. It will be seen at once that if $y(x)$ is to be an extremal, then it is necessary that the coefficient of α in (14) reduce to zero. In other words, we obtain as a necessary condition to be satisfied by $y(x)$ the vanishing of the first variation,

$$\delta I = 0 .$$

Integrating (15) by parts and taking account of condition (11), we immediately obtain

$$\begin{aligned} \delta I &= F'_{y'} \eta(x) \Big|_a^b + \int_a^b (F'_y - \frac{d}{dx} F'_{y'}) \eta(x) dx \\ &= \int_a^b (F'_y - \frac{d}{dx} F'_{y'}) \eta(x) dx . \end{aligned} \tag{16}$$

The fundamental lemma of the calculus of variations is now invoked. This lemma states that if in the integral

$$\int_a^b p(x) \; q(x) dx$$

the function $p(x)$ is continuous between $x = a$ and $x = b$, and if the integral vanishes for all continuous functions $q(x)$, then $p(x)$ must be identically zero.

Employing this lemma, we obtain from (16) the condition which must be satisfied by all extremals in the form of the equation

$$\frac{\partial F}{\partial y} - \frac{d}{dx} \frac{\partial F}{\partial y'} = 0 . \tag{17}$$

This famous result is called the *equation of Euler,* and its fundamental throughout the entire theory of the calculus of variations.

We concern ourselves next with the second variation, namely,

$$\delta^2 I = \int_a^b [P\eta^2(x) + 2Q\eta(x)\eta'(x) + R\{\eta'(x)\}^2] dx . \tag{18}$$

It is at once clear from (14) that if $\delta I = 0$ and if $\delta^2 I$ is positive, then I is a minimum; and if $\delta I = 0$ and $\delta^2 I$ is positive, then I is a maximum. A sufficient condition that either of these extrema should be attained is that the quadratic form which forms the integrand of (18) should be either positively or negatively definite. This condition is merely that

$$(19) \qquad PR - Q^2 > 0 \, ,$$

with the auxiliary condition that P or $R > 0$ if the integral is a minimum, and that P or $R < 0$ if the integral is a maximum.

Legendre attained a more satisfactory form for the sufficiency condition by writing $\delta^2 I$ as follows:

$$(20) \qquad \delta^2 I = \int_a^b [P\eta^2 + 2Q\eta\eta' + R(\eta')^2 + \ (2\theta\eta\eta' + \theta'\eta^2)]dx \, ,$$

where θ is an arbitrary function.

Since the integral of the expression in parentheses is equal to $\theta\eta^2$ and since $\eta(a) = \eta(b) = 0$, the addition made to $\delta^2 I$ is zero.

Let us now define θ as the solution of the equation

$$R(P + \theta') = (Q + \theta)^2.$$

It follows that (20) can then be written in the form

$$\delta^2 I = \int_a^b R(\eta' + m\eta)^2 \, dx \, ,$$

where we use the abbreviation $m = (Q + \theta)/R$.

Hence the second variation will be positive provided R *does not change sign in the interval* (a, b). This is the sufficiency condition of Legendre for the existence of an extremum value for I.

Example. As a simple illustrative example, let us consider the integral

$$I = \int_b^a (1 + y'^2)^{\frac{1}{2}} \, dx \, ,$$

which expresses the length of an arc between $x = a$ and $x = b$. In other words, we are seeking to determine the shortest distance between two points

Solution. Since y is not contained explicitly in the integrand, $F = (1 + y'^2)^{\frac{1}{2}}$, the Euler equation (17) degenerates into

$$\frac{d}{dx}\frac{\partial F}{\partial y'} = 0 \, .$$

A first integral of this equation is $\partial F/\partial y' = c$; that is,

$$\frac{y'}{(1 + y'^2)^{\frac{1}{2}}} = c \, .$$

Squaring and collecting terms we obtain

$$y'^2 = \frac{c^2}{1 - c^2} \, ;$$

or, since c is an arbitrary constant, $y' = k$. The integral of this equation is merely the straight line $y = kx + K$, where K is also an arbitrary constant.

Computing P, Q, and R, we find $P = Q = 0$, $R = (1 + y'^2)^{-3/2}$. Hence, we have $R > 0$ throughout the interval (a, b); consequently the second variation $\delta^2 I$ is greater than zero, and the extremal, $y = kx + K$, furnishes a minimum. We have thus proved analytically the simple geometrical proposition that a straight line is the shortest distance between two points.

PROBLEMS

1. Show that an extremal for the integral

$$I = \int_a^b (1 + y'^2)^2 \, dx$$

is a straight line.

2. Is it true that an extremal for the integral

$$I = \int_a^b (1 + y'^2)^n \, dx$$

is a straight line for every value of n? Discuss fully.

3. Prove that a minimum value is given to the integral

$$I = \int_a^b y(1 + y'^2)^{\frac{1}{2}} \, dx$$

by the *catenary*

$$y = \tfrac{1}{2}c[e^{(t-a)/c} + e^{-(t-a)/c}].$$

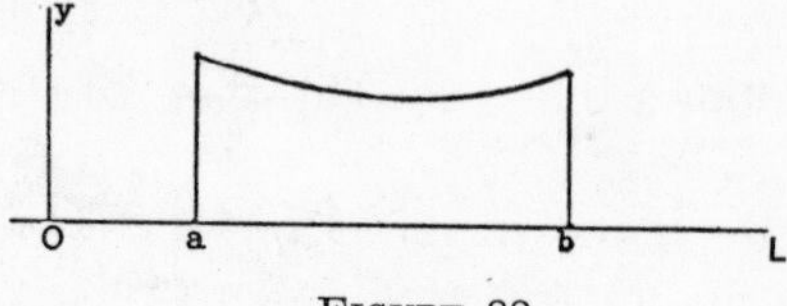

FIGURE 88

Show that this result proves the theorem that the catenary is the curve through two fixed points on one side of a line L, which generates the surface of smallest area, when it is revolved about L. See Figure 88.

4. Show that extremals for the integral

$$I = \int_a^b [n(n + 1)y^2 - (1 - x^2)y'^2] \, dx$$

are polynomials when n is a positive integer. Show that the integral is maximized for these functions provided $x^2 < 1$. These polynomials are called *Legendrian functions*. See, for example, W. E. Byerly: *An Elementary Treatise on Fourier Series*. Boston, 1893, Chapter 5.

5. For what integral is the function

$$y = A \sin nx + B \cos nx$$

an extremal? Evaluate the integral from $x = 0$ to $x = \pi/n$ for the two functions: $y = \sin nx$ and $y = x(\pi/n - x)$, and show that the former gives a higher (or lower) value to the integral than the latter.

6. Find the extremals for the integral

$$I = \int_a^b x^2 \, y'^2 \, dx \, .$$

7. What functions are extremals for the integral

$$I = \int_a^b x^{-2} \, y'^2 \, dx \, ?$$

5. *Maximizing Profits Under Dynamic Prices*

We are now in a position to solve the problem proposed in Section 3, namely that of maximizing the profit function

$$\pi = \int_{t_0}^{t_1} [py - Q(u)]\,dt\,, \tag{21}$$

where we assume that the demand, y, the supply, u, and the total cost, $Q(u)$, are given by the following formulas:

$$y = -ap(t) + b + cp'(t)\,, \quad u = \alpha p(t) - \beta + \gamma p'(t)\,,$$

$$Q(u) = Au^2 + Bu + C\,.$$

It will be recalled that the parameters are assumed to be positive quantities.

In order to determine the price under which the integral will be maximized we first compute the Euler condition. By simple differentiation of the integrand, $F = py - Q(u)$, we first compute

$$\frac{\partial F}{\partial p} = b - B\alpha + 2A\alpha\beta - (2a + 2A\alpha^2)p + (c - 2A\alpha\gamma)p'\,,$$

$$\frac{\partial F}{\partial p'} = -\gamma B + 2A\beta\gamma + (c - 2A\alpha\gamma)p - 2A\gamma^2 p'\,,$$

$$\frac{d}{dt}\frac{\partial F}{\partial p'} = (c - 2A\alpha\gamma)p' - 2A\gamma^2 p''\,.$$

Substituting these values in the Euler equation, equation (17) of the preceding section, we obtain the differential equation

$$p''(t) - \lambda^2 p(t) = -\lambda^2 p_0\,, \tag{22}$$

where we employ the abbreviations

$$\lambda^2 = \frac{(a + A\alpha^2)}{A\gamma^2}\,, \qquad p_0 = \frac{[A\alpha\beta - \tfrac{1}{2}(B\alpha - b)]}{a + A\alpha^2}\,.$$

The solution of (22) is easily seen to equal

$$p(t) = p_0 + C_1 e^{\lambda(t-t_0)} + C_2 e^{-\lambda(t-t_0)}\,, \tag{23}$$

where C_1 and C_2 are arbitrary constants.

This solution is observed to furnish a maximum value to π, since $R = \partial^2 F/\partial p'^2 = -2A\gamma^2$, and by hypothesis $A > 0$. From assumptions as to the positive character of the parameters, it is clear that λ is a real positive number. Consequently $p(t)$ will increase exponentially with time unless $C_1 = 0$. In this case $p(t)$ will approach the constant value p_0 as time increases. Neither of these appear to be realistic conclusions. We shall return to a discussion of this problem in Section 8.

PROBLEMS

1. Given the profit integral

$$\pi = \int_{t_0}^{t_1} [py - Q(u)]\, dt,$$

where we define $y = b + cp'(t)$, $u = -\beta + \gamma\, p'(t)$, $Q(u) = Au^2$, prove that the integral is a maximum when prices are a quadratic function of the time.

2. Under the assumptions: $u = 7 - p(t) + 15p'(t)$, $Q(u) = 5 - 0.3u + 0.005\, u^2$, compute the extremals for the integral

$$\pi = \int_{t_0}^{t_1} [pu - Q(u)]\, dt.$$

3. If δ is the force of interest (see Chapter 13) and if $P(t)$ is a principal continuously invested over a period of time from $t = 0$ to $t = n$, then the total accumulation at the end of the period is given by the integral

$$S = \int_0^n e^{\delta t}\, P(t)\, dt.$$

A man finds that the amount of income from his business which he can invest is related to prices by the following formula:

$$P(t) = ap^2 - bp'^2, \quad a, b > 0.$$

Determine what the equation of prices must be in order that he may make a maximum accumulation.

6. *Extensions of the Elementary Problem of the Calculus of Variations*

The elementary problem in the calculus of variations which we discussed in Section 4 can be extended in two ways useful to us in studying problems in dynamic economics.

The first of these is called the *parametric* problem, since we assume that the extremal curve is to be given in terms of a parameter; that is, it appears in the form

$$x = x(t), \qquad y = y(t).$$

We are thus required to maximize or minimize the integral

$$I = \int_a^b F(x, y, x', y')\, dt, \tag{24}$$

where the functions $x(t)$ and $y(t)$ satisfy the conditions imposed in the preceding discussion.

The derivation of Euler's condition proceeds just as in the

simpler problem, but now the condition appears in the form of the following two equations which must be satisfied simultaneously by $x(t)$ and $y(t)$:

$$(25) \qquad \frac{\partial F}{\partial x} - \frac{d}{dt}\frac{\partial F}{\partial x'} = 0 \,, \qquad \frac{\partial F}{\partial y} - \frac{d}{dt}\frac{\partial F}{\partial y'} = 0 \,.$$

Example. As an example, let us consider the problem previously solved, namely the determination of the shortest distance between two points. The integral to be minimized now has the form

$$I = \int_a^b (x'^2 + y'^2)^{\frac{1}{2}} \, dt \,.$$

Solution. Equations (25) yield the conditions

$$x'(x'^2 + y'^2)^{-\frac{1}{2}} = c \,, \qquad y'(x'^2 + y'^2)^{-\frac{1}{2}} = d \,.$$

Solving for x' and y', we obtain $x' = k$, $y' = m$, which yield at once the parametric functions

$$x = kt + p \,, \qquad y = mt + q \,.$$

These are seen to be the parametric equations of a straight line.

The second useful generalization is the *isoperimetric problem* mentioned in Section 4. This problem consists in determining the function $y(x)$, which is an extremal for the integral

$$(26) \qquad I = \int_a^b F(x, y, y') \, dx \,,$$

but which also satisfies the auxiliary integral condition

$$(27) \qquad J = \int_a^b G(x, y, y') \, dx \,,$$

where J is a given constant.

An example in point is Dido's problem, mentioned in Section 4, where we are required to maximize the area

$$I = \tfrac{1}{2} \int_a^b (yx' - xy') \, dt \,,$$

subject to the condition that the length of the perimeter is a given constant; that is,

$$(28) \qquad J = \int_a^b (x'^2 + y'^2)^{\frac{1}{2}} \, dt \,.$$

The Euler condition for this problem appears as before in the form of two equations,

$$(29) \qquad \frac{\partial H}{\partial x} - \frac{d}{dt}\frac{\partial H}{\partial x'} = 0 \,, \qquad \frac{\partial H}{\partial y} - \frac{d}{dt}\frac{\partial H}{\partial y'} = 0 \,,$$

where H is the function $F + \lambda G$, that is, $H = F + \lambda G$. The parameter λ is a constant, which must be determined from the conditions of the problem.

Example. In illustration, we shall return to Dido's problem. For this case we have

$$H = \tfrac{1}{2}(yx' - xy') + \lambda(x'^2 + y'^2)^{\frac{1}{2}}.$$

Solution. The Euler equations (29) are seen to reduce to the following:

$$\lambda x'(x'^2 + y'^2)^{-\frac{1}{2}} = -y, \qquad \lambda y'(x'^2 + y'^2)^{-\frac{1}{2}} = x.$$

Dividing the second of these equations by the first, we obtain

$$\frac{y'}{x'} = -\frac{x}{y}$$

which one immediately recognizes as the equation of the tangent to a circle. The solution then takes the form

$$x = \lambda \cos t, \qquad y = \lambda \sin t. \tag{30}$$

Since a closed perimeter is assumed, we must have $x(a) = x(b)$, $y(a) = y(b)$, which now requires that $a = 0$, $b = 2\pi$. Substituting (30) in (28), we now obtain for the determination of λ the equation

$$J = 2\pi\lambda,$$

where J is the given length of the perimeter.

PROBLEMS

1 Suppose that the profit integral

$$\pi = \int_{t_0}^{t_1} [pu - Q(u)]\, dt$$

is to be maximized under the assumptions: $u = -\beta + \gamma p'(t)$, $Q(u) = Au^2$. How is the solution modified if the integral of average costs (see Chapter 6) is to be equal to a given contant; that is, if we impose the restraint

$$\int_{t_0}^{t_1} \frac{Q(u)}{u}\, dt = J \text{ (a constant)?}$$

2. Discuss problem 1 under the assumption that total revenue is constant; that is, provided

$$\int_{t_0}^{t_1} pu\, dt = J \text{ (a constant)?}$$

3. Find the extremals for the integral

$$I = \int_{t_0}^{t_1} [x(x'^2 + y'^2)]^{\frac{1}{2}}\, dt.$$

4. Solve problem 3 under the assumption that the integral of length is a constant; that is, provided

$$\int_{t_0}^{t_1} (x'^2 + y'^2)^{\frac{1}{2}}\, dt = J \text{ (a constant).}$$

7. *Integral Demand and Supply Curves*

In Sections 1 and 2 the assumption was made that demand and supply depend not only upon the price but also upon its derivative. It is possible, however, to replace this assumption by another, which, when subjected to the final court of appeals, namely statistical analysis, may prove to be the more realistic one. This assumption states that the demand or supply of a commodity depends not only upon present prices, but also upon prices which have prevailed in the not-too-distant past. Thus, according to this assumption, we look at last month's prices and add to our inventory if the trend is up, but reduce our inventory if the trend is down. The farmer, as a producer, decides to plant more acres of wheat this year because last year's price was high, but he will reduce his acreage if last year's price was low.

This assumption, as it relates to demand, can be formulated analytically in the following equation:

$$y(t) = -ap(t) + b + \sum_{n=1}^{k} \alpha_n p(t - n\lambda) \,, \tag{31}$$

where the constants α_n form a set of weights which diminish with n; that is, $\lim \alpha_n = 0$ as $n \to \infty$. The parameter λ is some suitable time interval. For the merchant, as a wholesale buyer, it may be a month and for the miller, as a purchaser of future wheat crops, it may be a year. Obviously if all the constants α_n are zero, equation (31) reduces to the case of classical linear demand.

Analytically it is sometimes more convenient to write equation (31) in integral form. Thus we may write

$$y(t) = -ap(t) + b + \int_{-\infty}^{t} K(t, s) p(s) \, ds \,, \tag{32}$$

where we assume that

$$\lim_{s \to -\infty} K(t, s) = 0 \,. \tag{33}$$

Regarded as a definition of $p(t)$ in terms of a known demand, equation (32) will be recognized as an integral equation of Volterra type. The function $K(t, s)$ is called the *kernel* of the equation. A kernel which meets the condition imposed by (33) is given by

$$K(t, s) = K_0 \, e^{-\lambda(t-s)} \,, \tag{34}$$

where K_0 and λ are constant parameters, the latter being assumed to be positive.

It is obvious that the supply function may be formulated similarly as a function of past prices if we write

$$u(t) = \alpha p(t) - \beta + \sum \beta_n p(t - n\lambda), \tag{35}$$

or in integral form

$$u(t) = \alpha p(t) - \beta + \int_{-\infty}^{t} L(t, s) p(s) dt , \tag{36}$$

where, as before,

$$\lim_{s \to -\infty} L(t, s) = 0 . \tag{37}$$

It will be observed that the supply curve reduces to the classical case of linear supply provided the kernel, $L(t, s)$, is identically zero.

In order to see what results we may expect from the assumption of an integral demand curve, let us determine the market price for the case where supply is equal to demand, that is to say, where $y(t) = u(t)$, provided supply is the classical linear case

$$u(t) = \alpha p(t) - \beta ,$$

and demand is defined by (32) and (34).

Equating supply to demand, we obtain the integral equation

$$\alpha p(t) - \beta = -a p(t) + b + \int_{-\infty}^{t} K_0 e^{-\lambda(t-s)} p(s) ds . \tag{38}$$

By direct substitution it is easily shown that the solution of this equation is

$$p(t) = \frac{-\lambda(\beta + b)}{K_0 - \lambda(\alpha + a)} + C e^{[K_0/(\alpha+a) - \lambda] t} ,$$

where C is an arbitrary constant.

It follows at once from this that if the exponent of e is negative, that is to say, if

$$K_0 < \lambda(\alpha + a) , \tag{39}$$

then $p(t)$ approaches a limit,

$$\lim_{t \to \infty} p(t) = \frac{(\beta + b)}{(\alpha + a) - K_0/\lambda} . \tag{40}$$

If $K_0 = 0$, we get the classical price

$$p_0 = \frac{\beta + b}{\alpha + a} ,$$

as determined in (5), Section 2.

Hence, referring to (40), we see that if the demand is affected by the past behavior of prices, then the market price will be higher than p_0 when $K_0 > 0$, and lower when $K_0 < 0$.

8. Maximizing Profits with Demand Dominated by an External Variable

The statistical verification of the postulates of any dynamic formulation is naturally one of considerable complexity, since no economic time series is free from the influence of general trends and all price series are sensitive to the movements of the business cycle. It is thus difficult to appraise the various movements of production and sales as linear functionals of price without taking into account the influence of other important factors.

One elaborate study is available, however, through the work of R. H. Whitman (see *Bibliography*) who sought to test the dynamic relationships which presumably exist between the demand for steel and its price. Whitman's investigation was essentially that of determining statistically the parameters in the following four equations:

$$\text{(A)} \qquad y = a\,p(t) + b + ct\,,$$

$$\text{(B)} \qquad y = a\,p(t) + b + h\,p'(t),$$

$$\text{(C)} \qquad y = a\,p(t) + b + \sum_{n=1}^{k} a_n\,p(t-nr)\,,$$

$$\text{(D)} \qquad y = a\,p(t) + b + h\,p'(t) + \sum_{n=1}^{k} a_n\,p(t-nr)\,.$$

Recognizing the need for taking account of the general moves of the business cycle Whitman added the following fifth equation to his investigation:

$$\text{(E)} \qquad y = a\,p(t) + b + ct + h\,p'(t) + d\,I\,,$$

where I is an index of general business activity.

The interval of exploration, from 1902 to 1930 inclusive, was divided into three periods: I (1902–1915), II (1916–1920), and III (1921–1930), and the values of the parameters in the five assumed demand functionals were computed. The reader will find a résumé of the results of this analysis in Whitman's original article, or in the author's work on *The Analysis of Economic Time Series,* Chapter 8. The relative agreement between formula (A) and the data, and formula (E) and the data, however, may be seen from the graphical representation given in Figure 89.

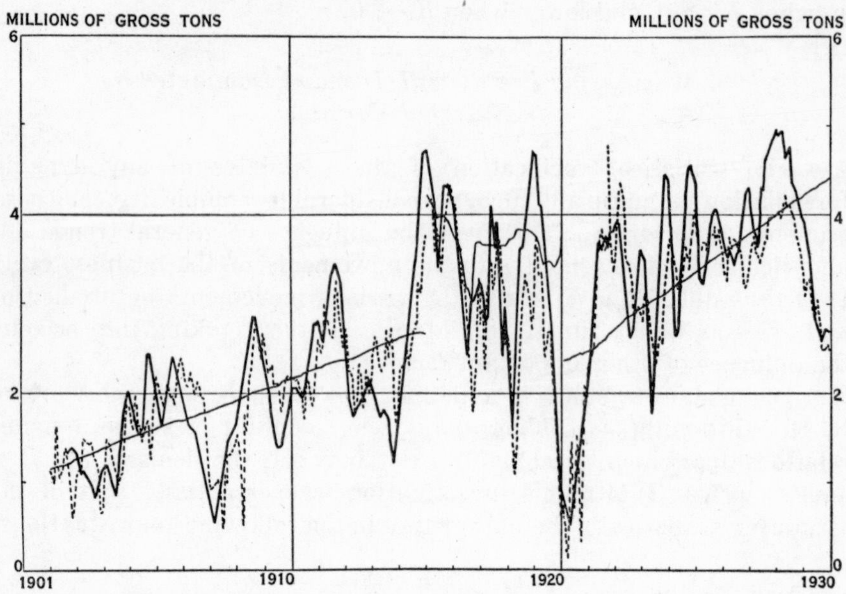

FIGURE 89.—THE DEMAND FOR STEEL. THE ORIGINAL DATA ARE REPRESENTED BY THE HEAVY LINE, THE REGRESSION (A) BY THE LIGHT LINE, AND THE REGRESSION (E) BY THE DOTTED LINE.

As one may readily surmise, the correlations observed by Whitman improved from formula (A) to formula (E). The significant thing for us to observe here is that the correlation coefficients for formula (B) in the three periods were respectively 0.66, 0.65, and 0.74, but when the index of business activity was added to obtain formula (E), these coefficients attained the significant values of 0.81, 0.88, and 0.92 respectively.

A second fact is also worthy of comment in this connection, namely, that although the signs of the parameter a were negative for the first two periods and positive for the third when formula (A) was fitted to the data, the signs are uniformly negative when (E) was fitted.

Our conclusion from this study, then, is this. In so far as steel is concerned, the price schedule has a relatively insignificant influence upon demand in comparison with the fluctuations of the general index of business. This conclusion is supported further by the observation that the demand for steel follows the movements of the stock market, the lag being in the neighborhood of three months.

With these facts before us, and with an eye to the unsatisfactory conclusions reached in Section 5 when we maximized profits under dynamic prices, let us now replace demand as given in that section by a new demand function, $Y(t)$, which takes account of the business index. That is to say, let us write

$$(41) \qquad Y(t) = y(t) + \phi(t),$$

where $y(t)$ is defined as in Section 5 and $\phi(t)$ is a term which measures the external influences derived from business itself upon the demand for steel.

Substituting the function $F = pY - Q(u)$ in Euler's equation we obtain equation (22) as before, except that there has been added another term, namely, $-\phi(t)/(2A\gamma^2)$, which we shall designate as $f(t)$. From Whitman's study we also have new light concerning the value of the constant λ^2 defined in Section 5. There it was assumed that a was a positive number, but we see from the values obtained by Whitman that a is negative. Since we also have reason to believe that A in the cost function is small for actual situations, the expression defining λ^2 is probably negative. Consequently, we shall replace λ^2 by $-m^2$, and thus we are led by this analysis to the equation

$$(42) \qquad p''(t) + m^2 p(t) = m^2 p_0 + f(t),$$

where we use the abbreviation

$$(43) \qquad f(t) = -\frac{\phi(t)}{2A\gamma^2}.$$

It may be verified by explicit substitution that the solution of equation (42) is given by the function

$$(44) \quad p(t) = p_0 + K \cos m(t+\mu) + \frac{1}{m}\int_0^t \sin m(t-s)\, f(s)\, ds,$$

where K and μ are arbitrary constants. It will be readily verified that this function will maximize profits provided A is a positive number.

The solution defined by (44) seems to fit empirical observations approximately, since it supplies an oscillatory price, the movements of which are modified by the integral of the function defining the external influences. As a matter of fact, to use the language of physics, this function acts as an *impressed force* upon the system, and can change profoundly the character of the oscillations.

For example, if $f(t)$ has the form $f(t) = f_0 \cos kt$, then the solution becomes

$$(45) \quad p(t) = p_0 + K \cos m(t + \mu) + \frac{f_0}{m^2 - k^2} (\cos kt - \cos mt) .$$

It is well known in dynamics that the phenomenon of *resonance* is observed whenever the period of the impressed force coincides with the period of the system itself, that is to say, whenever $k = m$.[1] In this case, the last term of (45) reduces to the function

$$(46) \qquad \frac{f_0 \, t \sin mt}{2m} .$$

Hence, as t increases the price is observed to oscillate with constantly increasing amplitude.

The striking difference between the character of economic time series before and after the great bull market of 1929 makes one raise the query whether or not the remarkable movements in the latter period may not indicate the existence of some such resonance phenomenon as we have described above. We shall return to this question in the next chapter.

PROBLEMS

1. Show that (46) follows as the limit of the last term of equation (45). Recall the property that if

$$\lim_{x=a} \left[\frac{u(x)}{v(x)}\right] = \frac{0}{0}, \quad \text{then} \quad \lim_{x=a} \left[\frac{u(x)}{v(x)}\right] = \lim_{x=a} \left[\frac{u'(x)}{v'(x)}\right] .$$

2. What would happen to price under the condition that $p(t)$ is defined by (44) in which we set $f(s) =$ a constant?

3. Determine the effect upon price as defined by equation (44) under the assumption that $f(s) = L\, e^{-ks}$.

4. Compute $p(t)$ as given by equation (44) provided $f(s) = a\, e^{-bs} \cos ks$.

9. The Dynamics of Automobile Demand

In the last section we have shown how the dynamics of supply and demand requires the introduction into the system of an impressed force measured by the general index of business. The realistic nature of this conclusion is argued for by other studies. One of the most interesting of these is the demand for passenger automobiles in the United States, which has been the object of three separate investiga-

[1] For a discussion of the phenomenon of resonance see A. G. Webster, *The Dynamics of Particles*, 2nd edition, 1912, p. 153.

tions. The first due to P. de Wolff,[2] the second by C. F. Roos and V. von Szeliski,[3] and the third by the National Resources Committee under the direction of G. C. Means,[4] have developed formulas to describe the sales over a period of years of passenger automobiles in the United States.

It will not be desirable here to examine the technical details of these interesting studies, but the end results, the time regressions, will be instructive. These may be briefly described as follows:

The study of de Wolff develops a formula of the type

$$R = T - 0.65\,K + 0.20\,N + 3.36\,,$$

where R is the annual new owners' sales in millions of cars, T is the logistic trend of sales, K is the average unit value of cars in hundreds of dollars, and N is the total of corporation profits in billions of dollars.

Among other formulas the second study develops the following regression:

$$S = 0.92\,I^{1.07}\,P^{-0.74}\,T^{1.10}\,,$$

where S is replacement sales, I is supernumerary income defined as the difference between national income and living costs, P is the average price per car, and T is an index measuring theoretical scrapping of cars.

The third study assumes a more complicated formula as follows:

$$S' = 0.4123\,(0.9561)^t\,(19 + I^{2.1795})^{0.6899}\,J^{1.2574}\,(0.9144 + 0.0001184N)\,,$$

where S' is the annual sale of passenger cars (in thousands), t is time measured from 1927, I is consumers' income of wage earners in billions of 1936 dollars, J is other consumer's income in billions of 1936 dollars, and N is the number of cars, in thousands, which are at least 7 years of age.

The interest for us in these three studies is found in the fact that all of the demands contain as an essential variable some quantity associated with income. In the first it is corporation profits, in the second supernumerary income, and in the third consumer's income. Since all these quantities are highly correlated with the index of business em-

[2] "The Demand for Passenger Cars in the United States," *Econometrica,* Vol. 6, 1938, pp. 113–129.

[3] *The Dynamics of Automobile Demand,* General Motors Corporation, 1939, pp. 21–95.

[4] *Patterns of Resource Use,* Washington, D. C., 1939, 149 pp. In particular, p. 133.

ployed in the study of the preceding section, we see that the dynamics of demand for automobiles requires the introduction of the same impressed force as that found necessary to describe the demand for steel.

Our final conclusion from the analysis of this chapter is then, that dynamical theories of demand and supply must introduce as a primary variable some measure of the index of business. This is true whether the theory is formulated in terms of the extremal properties of the profit integral, or whether it arises from special considerations such as those involved in the sale of automobiles. This measure then assumes the role of an impressed force in the dynamical system. Some further attention to this thesis will be given in the next chapter.

SELECTED BIBLIOGRAPHY OF FUNCTIONALS IN ECONOMIC APPLICATIONS

ALLEN, R. G. D. *Mathematical Analysis for Economists*, London, 1938, xvi + 548 pp. In particular, Chapter 20.

EVANS, G. C. (1) "A Simple Theory of Competition," *American Mathematical Monthly*, Vol. 29, 1922, pp. 371–380.

(2) "Dynamics of Monopoly," *American Mathematical Monthly*, Vol. 31, 1924, pp. 77–83.

(3) *Mathematical Introduction to Economics*, New York, 1930, xi + 177 pp. In particular, Chapter 15 and Appendix II.

HOTELLING, H. (1) "A General Mathematical Theory of Depreciation," *Journal of the American Statistical Association*, Vol. 20, 1925, pp. 340–353.

(2) "Differential Equations Subject to Error, and Population Estimates," *Journal of the American Statistical Association*, Vol. 22, 1937, pp. 283–314.

PANKRAZ, O. "Sur la loi de la demande," *Econometrica*, Vol. 4, 1936, pp. 153–156.

ROOS, C. F. (1) "A Mathematical Theory of Competition," *American Journal of Mathematics*, Vol. 57, 1925, pp. 163–175.

(2) "A Dynamical Theory of Economics," *Journal of Political Economy*, Vol. 35, 1927, pp. 632–656.

(3) "A Mathematical Theory of Depreciation and Replacement," *American Journal of Mathematics*, Vol. 50, 1928, pp. 147–157.

(4) "The Problem of Depreciation in the Calculus of Variations," *Bulletin of the American Math. Soc.*, Vol. 34, 1928, pp. 218–228.

(5) "A Mathematical Theory of Price and Production Fluctuations and Economic Crises," *Journal of Political Economy*, Vol. 38, 1930, pp. 501–522.

(6) *Dynamic Economics*, Bloomington, Ind., 1934, xvi + 275 pp.

(7) "Theoretical Studies of Demand," *Econometrica*, Vol. 2, 1934, pp. 73-90.

(8) "Economic Theory of the Shorter Work Week," *Econometrica*, Vol. 3, 1935, pp. 21–39.

TAYLOR, J. S. "A Statistical Theory of Depreciation Based on Unit Cost," *Journal of the American Statistical Association*, Vol. 18, 1923.

TINTNER, G. (1) "The Maximization of Utility over Time," *Econometrica*, Vol. 6, 1938, pp. 154–158.

(2) "The Theoretical Derivation of Dynamic Demand Curves," *Econometrica*, Vol. 6, 1938, pp. 375–380.

WHITMAN, R. H. "The Statistical Law of Demand for a Producer's Good as Illustrated by the Demand for Steel," *Econometrica*, Vol. 4, 1936, pp. 138–152.

ZINN, M. K. "A General Theory of the Correlation of Time Series of Statistics," *The Review of Economic Statistics*, Vol. 9, 1927, pp. 184–197.

CHAPTER 18

THE DYNAMICS OF ECONOMIC TIME SERIES

1. Historical Introduction

In previous chapters we have considered some of the statistical methods by means of which structure may be recognized in economic time series. We have also discussed some special classes of variables and have seen the mechanics of the function of money in economic phenomena. In these chapters we have examined certain suggestions about a dynamics of supply and demand and we have made application to the integral of profits. But in all of this we have not formulated a general principle of the dynamics of time series. It is the purpose of this chapter to advance some tentative postulates whose consequences seem to be in general statistical agreement with the behavior of many basic time series.

The problem of formulating a general system of equations for an economy is an old one. We have already discussed this question for the static case in Chapter 9, where the attempts of Walras, Pareto, and others to establish the equations of general equilibrium were set forth. The complexities of the general system appear to be so great, however, that hope of attaining a useful formulation of the equations which govern the dynamics of the economic variables from this point of view seems remote indeed. Another and simpler method must be sought for if we expect to make progress in the statistical appraisal of the dynamical problem.

Models, however, are not lacking for this attempt to formulate the dynamics of time series, as one may readily convince himself by a survey of the articles listed in the *Bibliography* at the end of this chapter. One of the most interesting of these was furnished by M. Kalecki, who sought to establish a macroscopic model in terms of the production of capital goods. The significance of this model resides partly in the fact that Kalecki attempted to evaluate the parameters in his equations and thus to justify his theory on the basis of its agreement with the observed existence of a ten year cycle in business. To the model of Kalecki R. Frisch applied the name of *macrodynamic*. He extended the system by introducing the proposition that the energy which gives the observed movement in economic time series is derived from erratic shocks. These shocks continually renew the energy dissipated by the natural damping factors of the system. Frisch attributes the origin of the idea to Knut Wicksell about whom he says:[1]

> Knut Wicksell seems to be the first who has been definitely aware of the two types of problems in economic cycle analysis—the propagation problem and the impulse problem—and also the first who has formulated explicitly the theory that the source of energy which maintains the economic cycles is erratic shocks. He conceived more or less definitely of the economic system as being pushed along irregularly, jerkingly. New innovations and exploitations do not come regularly he says. But, on the other hand, these irregular jerks may cause more or less regular cyclical movements. He illustrates it by one of those perfectly simple and yet profound illustrations: "If you hit a wooden rocking-horse with a club the movement of the horse will be very different to that of the club."

The erratic-shock theory of time series was subjected to a penetrating analysis by G. U. Yule, (see *Bibliography*) who sought to determine the nature of the periodicity in sunspot data. A similar study was made by E. Slutzky, who exhibited a remarkable similarity between an index of English business for 1855–1877 and a series formed from the moving average of a series of random numbers.[2] H. Wold in a work entitled *A Study in the Analysis of Stationary Time Series* extended the ideas to Slutzky and Yule. More recently M. M. Flood and T. Haavelmo have applied the methods suggested by the general theory to problems connected with the analysis of business cycles.[3]

But from another point of view we have seen in many places throughout this book that there has been an insistent demand that the problems of economics be formulated in terms of some extremal principle. Thus in the static theory of demand we obtained the equilibrium conditions by maximizing utility subject to the restraint of a constant budget. In the theory of monopoly the central thesis was the maximization of the profit function. In the preceding chapter the same principle was extended to the problem of profits under conditions of dynamic prices and dynamic demand.

The models which have been set up for the description of the dynamics of economic time series have, for the most part, been concerned with one or the other of these points of view. It is probable that both must be included in the final form of the theory which will have general acceptance as a realistic representation of the observed

[1] From "Propagation, Problems and Impulse Problems in Dynamic Economics," in *Economic Essays in Honor of Gustav Cassel*, 1933, 35 pp.

[2] "The Summation of Random Causes as the Source of Cyclic Processes," *Econometrica*, Vol. 5, 1937, pp. 105–146; originally printed in Russian in 1927.

[3] See *Bibliography* for these references.

phenomena. In the next three sections some attempt will be made to formulate a dynamical model which will account for cycles, a model that will include the influence of erratic shocks, and will also use the extremal principle. The theory differs somewhat from the original proposition of Wicksell and Frisch in the fact that erratic shocks are introduced essentially through an expression which takes the place of kinetic energy in ordinary mechanics. The impressed force is then expressed by a term measuring the fluctuations in inventory, which would appear to be more in agreement with the statistical analysis given in the preceding chapter. This assumption, of course, does not exclude the influence of erratic shocks from the impressed force, since obviously the accumulation, or the dissipation, of stocks of goods is greatly affected by current events. We need but witness the impulse given to manufacturing during the first months of the NRA experiment in 1933 and 1934.

2. *The Erratic-Shock Theory of Time Series*

It seems reasonable to suppose that the movements in the time series of economics may have essentially common origins with those observed in certain elastic phenomena of physics. The difference is one of complexity rather than of essential distinction. If this proposition is correct, then certain analogies between the two systems of variables, economic time series on the one hand, and elastic oscillations on the other, should be observed.

The theory of the dynamics of time series which we propose to develop here assumes that the economic system is fundamentally a stable configuration, at least for short periods of time, and if we were sufficiently wise we could characterize it by means of a set of elastic constants. The motions of the variables in such a system would possess characteristic frequencies, which depend both upon the elastic constants and upon the nature of the forces which set the variables in motion. But just as in mechanical systems the motion cannot be maintained unless energy of some kind is introduced into it, an energy which is derived from what are called *impressed forces.* Theories differ as to the nature of these impressed forces in the case of economic variation. The fundamental postulate of what has come to be called the *erratic-shock* theory of economic time series is found in the proposition that the energy is introduced into the system by means of random events, such as wars, droughts, large business failures, new inventions, etc., which occur with sufficient regularity to maintain the motion of the system.

In order to illustrate this idea, we shall assume that some basic price series is observed to have a harmonic, or almost harmonic motion, described by the equation

$$p''(t) + m^2 p(t) = f(t). \tag{1}$$

Now we have shown in Section 8 of Chapter 17 that the solution of this equation is given by the function

$$p(t) = K \cos m(t + \mu) + \frac{1}{m} \int_0^t \sin m(t - s) f(s)\, ds\,, \tag{2}$$

where K and μ are arbitrary constants.

Let us examine, first, some of the characteristics of the solution given by (2). We see by direct substitution that if $f(s)$ is constant, or almost constant, the resulting motion will have the same period (or almost the same period) as that defined by the homogeneous equation

$$p''(t) + m^2 p(t) = 0\,; \tag{3}$$

that is to say, it will have the period $T = 2\pi/m$.

Moreover, if $f(s)$ is an impulsive force, that is to say, very great for a very brief period of time, then the motion is again harmonic and the period is the same as the period of the homogeneous equation (3). It should be pointed out, however, that if the impulse is too great, so that the elastic limits which are essentially implied by equation (1) are exceeded, then the period lengthens and is given by the formula

$$T = \frac{4K(\alpha)}{m}\,, \tag{4}$$

where $K(\alpha)$ is the complete elliptic integral of first kind and depends upon the magnitude of the quantity α.[4] It is beyond the scope of this exposition to derive this formula. We need merely observe that $K(0) = \frac{1}{2}\pi$, and that $K(\alpha)$ is an increasing function of α.

Now if it is true that the energy which supplies the economic system with its movement is derived from a succession of erratic shocks not too violent in magnitude, then we should expect to find in economic time series a cyclical variation reasonably uniform in character. Such a movement is actually observed, for example, in the index

[4] A definition of this function and a description of its properties will be found in any advanced calculus. When α is not too large and if it is expressed in radians, then $\kappa(\alpha)$ can be written approximately in the form

$$\kappa(\alpha) = \tfrac{1}{2}\pi(1 + \alpha^2/16).$$

of common stocks which is graphically represented in Figure 72 of Chapter 16.

In the case of great shocks, however, such as that of the collapse of the great bull market of 1929, we should expect to find in the subsequent time interval a lengthening of the normal period of the series. Such a lengthening is actually observed in the years after 1932, as one many verify by consulting Figure 3 of Chapter 1.

3. Formulation of the Fundamental Integral

It would be interesting, indeed, if it were possible to do so, to formulate the dynamics of economic time series in terms of a variations principle, as has been done so effectively in the dynamics of physical variables. We have already discussed this problem in Chapter 17 in connection with the assumption of maximum profits under a system of dynamic prices.

There are many ways to formulate such a principle and probably, in the present state of economic theory, one way is a priori as good as another, provided the resulting equations describe statistically the observed variation in the time series. We shall indicate one path by which such a formulation can be attained.

There is something intriguing to the fancy in assuming a hedonistic postulate, that is to say, a postulate which supposes that economic activity takes place in such a manner that the happiness of the greatest number of people is maximized. From the dynamic point of view, this might be formulated in the statement that the integral of the utility function over a time interval is greater by the actual path of purchase and consumption of goods than by any other. But alas, a casual survey of the real world of exchange seems to indicate that this is not the case. Wars, inflations, depressions, disasters, droughts, and other erratic shocks, are too severe in their economic repercussions to permit the formulation of a general principle of economic behavior along this line. Rather does it seem that we try to maximize our utility function under the restraining influences of the erratic shocks which we have mentioned above.

Let us begin by assuming that there are three elements which are the major factors in determining the behavior of economic time series. The first of these is the utility function,

$$U = u(x_1, x_2, \cdots, x_n), \tag{5}$$

which we discussed in detail in Chapter 3. We shall assume here, as we did there, that this function is maximized subject to the budget equation, although now the quantities x_i and the prices p_i are functions of time. We are thus led to the fundamental equations

$$\frac{\partial U}{\partial x_i} = \lambda p_i(t) \ , \tag{6}$$

where λ is the marginal utility of money.

If the theory which we are tentatively advancing should appear to violate the generally assumed proposition that business seeks to maximize its profit function, it should be pointed out that this principle is essentially contained in equation (6). Moreover, the analysis of Chapter 17 would appear to indicate that under the conditions of economic dynamics, the maximization of the integral of profit is not entirely satisfactory to describe the behavior of prices. Agreement between fact and theory appears to require the introduction of an impressed force, which depends upon the behavior of business in general.

We shall see later in Section 6 that a model proposed by G. Tintner requires that the right hand member of equation (6) be modified by a multiplier, which depends upon the prevailing rate of interest. Sufficient for our theory, this multiplier might be written $e^{-\delta t}$, where δ is the force of interest. There is no reason why this modification should not be introduced into equation (6). Since such a term would impose a mild inflation upon prices and increase their oscillation, it is clear that the effects of this factor must be counteracted by the impressed force if we admit that observed movements in price are cyclical and undamped over considerable periods of time.

The second component of our general theory is that of the effect of the erratic shocks, the importance of which was discussed in the preceding section. The influence of these upon the economic system we shall introduce through the following bilinear form,

$$A = \sum x'_i(t) p'_i(t) \ . \tag{7}$$

The reason for assuming A as a measure of the effect of shocks will be readily seen from an observation of most economic time series in periods of world disturbance. Both variables are noticeably affected in such periods. Although there would be some advantage in measuring the effect of shocks by a bilinear form that was always certainly of one sign, it is probable that A is, for the most part, a positive function of the time. It will be observed, for example, that in periods when prices are rising, namely, where $p' > 0$, there is a tendency for people to buy, that is to say, $x' > 0$. Similarly, in periods of falling prices when $p' < 0$, business men are hesitant to increase their inventories and trade declines, that is to say, $x' < 0$. These inclinations are readily observed in the great trade expansion from 1926 to 1929, and in the subsequent collapse of business from 1929 to 1932. It is also worth noting that Irving Fisher has shown that the correlation between $p'(t)$ and the employment index is positive and of the order of 0.85.

The third factor which must be introduced into our system is that of the effects of overproduction. This influence we shall measure by the non-negative function

$$B = \sum (x_i - u_i)^2 , \tag{8}$$

where the x_i are the amounts of goods purchased and u_i the amounts manufactured. When u_i greatly exceeds x_i, then we meet the situation where inventories are too high, farm carryovers are excessive, etc. This is recognized by business men as an undesirable condition, since major panics have, for the most part, developed in years which followed periods of unusual trade expansion.

In order to set up our dynamical model, we shall now introduce the assumption that over a period of time the general tendency of people is to maximize their utility, while at the same time they attempt to minimize the effects of erratic shocks and of excessive inventories. In mathematical terms, we shall assume that in the processes of trade, people as a whole strive to maximize the integral

$$J = \int_{t_0}^{t_1} (U - \kappa A - \nu B)\, dt , \tag{9}$$

where κ and ν are positive quantities.

If, then, we designate the integrand of (9) by F and evaluate the derivatives of the Euler condition

$$\frac{\partial F}{\partial x_i} - \frac{d}{dt}\frac{\partial F}{\partial x'_i} = 0 , \tag{10}$$

we shall obtain, on noting (6), the following:

$$\frac{\partial F}{\partial x_i} = \frac{\partial U}{\partial x_i} - \kappa \frac{\partial A}{\partial x_i} - \nu \frac{\partial B}{\partial x_i} = \lambda p_i - \nu \sum (x_i - u_i) ,$$

$$\frac{\partial F}{\partial x'_i} = \frac{\partial U}{\partial x'_i} - \kappa \frac{\partial A}{\partial x'_i} - \nu \frac{\partial B}{\partial x'_i} = - \kappa p'_i .$$

When these quantities are substituted in equation (10), we obtain the following relationship:

(11) $$\kappa p''_i + \lambda p_i = \nu \sum (x_i - u_i) ,$$

which thus becomes the fundamental equation in the dynamical theory of prices.

Without loss of generality, we can set $\kappa = 1$. Since the right hand member is a function of time, let us replace it by the function $U(t)$. Equation (11) then assumes the compact form

(12) $$p''_i + \lambda p_i = U(t) .$$

It is clear that the function $U(t)$ will be a fluctuating quantity, perhaps periodic in character, which varies about some mean value which is the difference between the mean value of consumption and the mean value of inventory.

If we assume that consumption and production are essentially in equilibrium, then $U(t)$ will be a constant, which, without essential loss of generality, can be set equal to zero. Equation (12) is then replaced by

(13) $$p''_i + \lambda p_i = 0 .$$

It λ is a constant, this equation will define a simple harmonic motion of period equal to $2\pi/\sqrt{\lambda}$. Moreover, we know from the theory of differential equations, that even when λ varies, if this variation differs sufficiently little from a constant, over a given period of time, the motion defined by equation (13) will still be nearly periodic.

The nature of λ, which we recall is the marginal utility of money, is still obscure. However, if we assume Bernoulli's formula given in Chapter 3, we might argue tentatively that λ is inversely proportional to available money and directly proportional to the velocity of this money. This very rough approximation is based upon the proposition that the denominator of Bernoulli's formula is measured by the available supply of money, and that the numerator, the propensity to spend, is measured by the velocity of money.

It is amusing, at least, to follow the consequences of this hazardous speculation. For this purpose let us write $\lambda = c^2 V/M$, where c^2 is a constant, V the velocity of the money, and M the quantity of money. The period of the movement of prices as defined by equation (13) then becomes

(14) $$T = \frac{2\pi}{c}\sqrt{\frac{M}{V}} .$$

From this formula we should assume that in normal times, as, for example, in the years between 1900 and 1914 when both M and V were relatively constant, the value of T would remain constant. An observation of Figure 72 in Chapter 16 shows that this was, indeed, the case. But in disruptive times, as, for example, the years between 1932 and 1940 when M increased and V declined, we should expect a material lengthening of the observed period. That the period did, indeed, increase in these years is readily observed in Figure 3 of Chapter 1.

4. The Resonance Theory of Crises

By an *economic crisis* we shall mean the existence of an abnormal displacement of the elements of an economic time series from its normal trend. The magnitude of the crisis can be measured by the ratio of the extreme displacement to the standard deviation of the series in normal periods.

One of the most remarkable crises in the history of economics was the great bull market of 1929. In the years prior to this market the standard error of the Cowles Commission–Standard Statistics industrial stock price index, with trend removed, was $\sigma_1 = 5.98$. Before 1929 the deviation from trend had been normal, the largest, perhaps, being that in 1919 when the deviation was as great as 23.1. The ratio between this and σ_1 is seen to be approximately 3.8, a large value, but not an abnormal one. But in September, 1929 the index showed the fantastic deviation from trend of 143.0 , which was approximately 24 times σ_1 as estimated from the preceding period of stable prices. The magnitude of the movement is graphically portrayed in Figure 3 of Chapter 1.

If we regard the liquidation ratio of this inflation as the ratio between the highest and lowest points attained by the index, then the stock values in September, 1929, with an index of 216.1, were liquidated in June of 1932 at a level of 33.7, that is, at ratio of 15 per cent.

Such phenomena are rare in history, although they occasionally occur. The tulip mania in Holland between 1634 and 1637 was one of these events, in which the speculative fever developed around the value of tulip bulbs. Liquidation appears to have taken place at from five to ten per cent of the speculative values.

Another example is found in the simultaneous inflations in France and England, which occurred around 1720. The French inflation is now known as the Mississippi Scheme and that in England as the South Sea Bubble. Liquidation in the French inflation was, in one extreme case, as low as two per cent. In England the liquidation ratio, computed from the maximum quotation of 1050 in June, 1720, and the minimum of 135 in November of that year, is seen to be around 13 per cent.

On what dynamical principle can we account for such violent inflationary and deflationary movements? The author can find only one physical analogy to these, namely, that of *resonance*. This phenomenon, which we have described briefly in Section 8 of Chapter 17, can be more adequately explained as follows:

Let us consider the solution of the following differential equation:

$$A \frac{d^2u}{dt^2} + B \frac{du}{dt} + Cu = E \cos qt , \tag{15}$$

where A, B, C, E, and q are constants.

This equation describes the behavior of many variable quantities in physics. Thus, u may be the displacement of the pendulum of a clock from its position of equilibrium, or the displacement of a bead on an elastic wire from its initial position, or the electric charge of a simple, conducting circuit containing inductance, resistance, and capacity. The quantity B represents the frictional coefficient, and the function $E \cos qt$ is the driving, or impressed force, which keeps the system in motion. The remaining parameters, A and C, are coefficients, which represent the inertia and the spring potential of the system.

The general solution of equation (15) can be written in the form

$$u = Ke^{-\lambda t} \sin \left(\frac{2\pi}{T} t + \omega \right) + L \cos (qt - \alpha) , \tag{16}$$

where K and ω are arbitrary constants, and where the other quantities are defined by the relationships

$$\lambda = \frac{B}{2A} , \quad T = \frac{4\pi A}{\sqrt{4AC - B^2}} , \quad \tan \alpha = \frac{Bq}{C - Aq^2} , \tag{17}$$

$$L = \frac{E}{\sqrt{(C - Aq^2) + B^2q^2}} .$$

Since λ is always a positive quantity in all physical systems, it is clear that in time the first term of (16) will damp out and u will consist of the single term $L \cos (qt - \alpha)$. This conclusion is usually stated in the form of the theorem, *that oscillating physical systems tend to assume the period of the impressed force.*

It is upon the coefficient of this last term that we shall now focus our attention. We see that if the damping factor is small, that is to say, if B is small, and if $C - Aq^2 = 0$, then the value of L in (17) becomes large, since it is now given by $L = E/(Bq)$.

But from (17) we see that if B is small, then we have

$$\frac{2\pi}{T} \sim \frac{C}{A} = q \, . \tag{18}$$

From this we may conclude that if the damping coefficient is small, and if the period of the impressed force equals the natural period of the system, then L increases and the amplitude of the vibrations of u become large. This phenomenon is called *resonance.* It is the phenomenon observed when vessels roll heavily in a comparatively gentle sea, or when bridges vibrate, and even break down, under the march of troops across them.

Let us now observe that the phenomenon of resonance in physical systems is strikingly similar to the phenomenon observed in the bull market of 1929. If we examine Figure 3 of Chapter 1, we note the inflationary peak rising from a regular sinusoidal movement about the line of trend. The great decline, which followed the bull market, and the secondary inflation, which reached its top in 1937, are characteristic features of a resonance phenomenon.

The mass psychology of an inflationary movement is instructive to observe. During the period of major activity the volume of sales on the New York stock exchange increased greatly. The public, observing the phenomenon, sought in great numbers to profit by it. Poverty seemed to be well on the way to extermination, and many people held paper fortunes in their hands. Were those who speculated in this great inflation any wiser than their predecessors of the tulip mania? Let those who think so consider whether a commentator on the year 1929 might not have used aptly the words of the wag of the seventeenth century who spoke of "the wonderful year 1637, when one fool hatched another; the people were rich without property, and wise without understanding."

The thesis which we have advanced above may be made plausible by considering the values of the constants which are obtained when the equation

$$Au'' + Bu' + Cu + D \cos qt = 0 \, , \quad q = 2\pi/41 \, , \tag{19}$$

is fitted to the Dow Jones industrial stock price averages, represented by u, and their first two derivatives, u' and u''. The period employed in the analysis is from 1897 to 1914.

Determining the constants by the method of least squares, we obtain the equation

$$u'' + 0.00004u' + 0.01744u = 0.07032 \cos qt \,, \tag{20}$$

the solution of which is found to be

$$u = K \sin \left(\frac{2\pi t}{47.6} + \omega\right) + 11.6424 \cos qt \,. \tag{21}$$

From this we see that the natural period of the system appears to be about 48 months, and that the damping coefficient is approximately zero. Both of these facts are in accord with the resonance postulate.

We next observe that $|C - q^2| = 0.00604$, and hence a very small change in either of the constants would lead to the phenomenon of resonance.

As we have just said, the crisis of 1929 was created undoubtedly by a great increase of interest in speculation on the part of many people. The velocity of money in New York expanded rapidly, and this, as we might surmise from the relationship developed in Section 3 of this chapter, that is, equation (14), would tend to decrease the natural period of the system. Such a decrease is actually observed in the interval from 1915 to 1925.

PROBLEMS

1. If in the motion described by equation (3) we assume that T is normally 40 months, compute the value of m. Now from Figure 3 of Chapter 1 estimate the value of T in the period from 1929 to 1940. Then from formula (4) compute $K(\alpha)$ and hence, from a table of elliptic integrals, find α.

2. Assume that the value of T in formula (14) is normally 40 months. Using for M the average per capita value of circulating deposits in the period 1919 to 1926 and for V the average velocity of these deposits in the same period (secure data from Chapter 12), compute c. Now using for M the average circulating deposits in the period 1930 to 1937 and for V the average velocity of money, compute T. How does this value compare with the estimate which you made for T in problem 1 for the period from 1929 to 1930?

3. What would be the effect on prices if we always had a constant surplus?

4. Find the solution of equation (12) if $U = p_0 + A \cos mt$.

5. If $p(t)$ is observed to have a period of 40 months can λ be computed, or is the value of λ modified by the nature of the function $U(t)$?

6. Employing the data given in problem 4 of Chapter 1, discuss in the light of this chapter the behavior of prices in Paris during the Mississippi Scheme.

5. The Macrodynamic Theory of Production

Because of its mathematical as well as its economic interest we shall give a brief résumé of what R. Frisch has called the *macrodynamic* theory, a terminology adopted to apply to those "processes connected with the functioning of the economic system as a whole, disregarding the details of disproportionate development of special parts of that system."

Kalecki's original theory, as well as the modification made by Frisch, is designed to explain the observed oscillations in business by means of the average lag between the volume of orders for capital goods and the delivery of the finished goods, a lag represented by the symbol θ. Thus, if $I(t)$ is the total volume of orders per unit of time at the time t, and if $L(t)$ is the corresponding volume of deliveries, then the relationship between these quantities is expressed by the equation

$$L(t) = I(t-\theta). \tag{22}$$

To this equation we then add another connecting $L(t)$ with the rate of change per unit of time of the total volume of industrial equipment existing at the time t. Thus, if $K(t)$ represents this total volume of equipment, and if U, assumed constant, is the demand made per unit of time upon production for the restoration of the industrial mechanism, we have the second relationship

$$K'(t) = L(t) - U. \tag{23}$$

We further define $A(t)$ as the volume of orders per unit of time which is completed over a length of time equal to the lag θ, that is to say, from an actual time $t - \theta$ to time t. This quantity is obviously connected with $I(t)$ by the relationship

$$A(t) = \frac{1}{\theta} \int_{t-\theta}^{t} I(s)\, ds. \tag{24}$$

The fundamental postulate is now introduced that $I(t)$ is a linear function of $K(t)$ and $A(t)$; that is to say, we assume that

$$I(t) = mC + m\,A(t) - n\,K(t), \tag{25}$$

where m, n, and C are constants, the latter being "the constant part of the consumption of capitalists."

If we employ the convenient abbreviation, $J(t) = I(t) - U$, we may show without difficulty that $J(t)$ satisfies the following difference-differential equation, which is the distinguishing feature of Kalecki's theory:

$$(26) \qquad J'(t) = \frac{m}{\theta}\,[J(t) - J(t-\theta)] - n\,J(t-\theta)\,.$$

Assuming a solution of the form

$$(27) \qquad J(t) = J(0)\,e^{rt},$$

we are led for the determination of r to the characteristic equation:

$$(28) \qquad (m + n\theta)\,e^{-r\theta} = m - r\theta\,.$$

Since the observed economic time series are oscillatory in character, and since the movements for the most part appear to have no damping factor, Kalecki assumed that r was a pure imaginary. This necessitated restrictions upon m and n. Since the details of the computation thus involve highly restrictive assumptions, we shall not repeat them here but refer the reader to the original article or to the author's work on *The Analysis of Economic Time Series,* Chapter 8, where they are given in detail. It is interesting to observe, however, that with an estimate of 0.6 for θ, the unit being a year, Kalecki found that the characteristic motion was a cycle with a period of 10 years.

The theory of Frisch, while similar to that of Kalecki, has certain variations which make it possible for him to account for cycles other than the long cycle explained by Kalecki.

Employing the notation given above, we may write the two fundamental postulates of Frisch in the following form:

$$(29) \qquad \begin{aligned} I(t) &= m\,X(t) + \mu\,X'(t), \\ X'(t) &= c - \lambda[r\,X(t) + s\,A(t)]\,, \end{aligned}$$

where $X(t)$ is the volume of consumption goods per unit of time, and m, μ, c, λ, r, and s are constants. The first of these equations is derived from the assumption that the orders for capital goods, $I(t)$, depend, first upon consumption and, second, upon the rate of consumption, and that this dependence is linear. The second equation states that the rate of change in the volume of consumers' goods diminishes proportionately to what Frisch, borrowing the term from Walras, calls the *encaisse désirée* (the need for cash). Neither proposition has been determined by statistical means.

Adjoining then, to this system, Kalecki's equation (24) above, Frisch determines as his characteristic equation the following:

$$\frac{\theta\,\rho}{1 - e^{-\rho\theta}} = -\,\lambda\, s\, \frac{m + \mu\,\rho}{r\lambda + \rho}\,. \tag{30}$$

Frisch assumes that ρ may be written $-\beta + i\,\alpha$, where i is the imaginary unit, and does not impose the restriction that β, the damping coefficient, is zero. Instead of this, he assumes that the energy of the system is supplied by erratic shocks, and when the effect of one impulse has damped away, another comes to take its place. He thus avoids the restrictive character of the Kalecki theory, but replaces it by a kind of continuity of impulses.

Since the details of Frisch's computation are somewhat involved and the determination of the constants empirical, we shall merely summarize his results. Thus, assuming the following values for the parameters:

$$\theta = 3\,,\quad \mu = 10\,,\quad m = 0.5\,,\quad \lambda = 0.05\,,\quad r = 2,\quad \text{and } s = 1\,,$$

Frisch discovers an oscillatory motion the first three cycles of which possess the following characteristics:

Characteristics	First Cycle	Second Cycle	Third Cycle
Frequency: (α)	0.73355	1.79775	2.8533
Period: $T = 2\pi/\alpha$	8.5654	3.4950	2.2021
Damping exponent: (β)	0.37134	0.5157	0.59105

The engaging feature of this analysis is found in the observation that it accounts for periods in the business cycle of 8.57, 3.50, and 2.2 years, all of which have been observed, as we shall see in the next chapter. Perhaps the most vulnerable point is the assumption of a lag between orders and delivery of 3 years, a lag six times as long as that assumed by Kalecki.

6. *Other Theories*

A résumé of the theories sketched in Section 5 and a description of a number of other systems which have been proposed will be found in an admirable survey published in 1935 by J. Tinbergen (see *Bibliography*).

Tinbergen himself has formulated several systems, one of which contained as many as 22 equations. Since the complexity increases rapidly with the number of variables used, the major problem in this type of analysis is to construct a system which accounts with sufficient accuracy for the major movements of the business cycle and yet does not involve so many variables that it becomes statistically unmanageable. The solution of such a problem then must depend upon the, as yet unproved, assumption that a few dominating variables exist, which can account for most of the existing movement.

In one such system Tinbergen employed the following variables: (1) Price of finished consumer's goods, $P + p(t)$; (2) The number of products started (consumer's goods), $Z + z(t)$; (3) The number of products sold (consumer's goods), $Y + y(t)$; (4) Income spent by consumers, $X + x(t)$; (5) Increase of stocks of products, $V + v(t)$.

Assuming a system of linear relationships between these variables, Tinbergen found that the elimination of all but $z(t)$ led to the following equation in this variable:

$$z(t) - 2a\, z(t-1) + b\, z(t-2\eta) = 0, \tag{31}$$

where a, b, and η are empirical constants. If $\eta = 1$, then the condition that oscillatory solutions exist reduces to $a^2 < b$.

The use of difference equations of the type represented by (31) in problems connected with the dynamics of time series has been common since the work of G. U. Yule, to which reference has already been made in Section 1. Thus, in his analysis of the variation in sunspot numbers, Yule introduced the difference equation

$$\Delta^2 u(t) + \mu\, u(t+1) = \phi(t), \tag{32}$$

where $u(t)$ is the value at time t of the oscillation to be described, $\Delta^2 u(t) = u(t+2) - 2\, u(t+1) + u(t)$, and $\phi(t)$ is an impressed force consisting for the most part of small erratic fluctuations.

This method of approach to dynamic problems has an especial appeal since one can connect it easily with the autocorrelation function described in Section 5 of Chapter 16. Thus, let us assume that u_x is the deviation of some variable from its trend, and that u_x is related to preceding values by the equation

$$u_x = g_1\, u_{x-1} + g_2\, u_{x-2} + \cdots + g_s\, u_{x-s}\,. \tag{33}$$

If u_x is normalized by division by its standard deviation, σ, and if the series is sufficiently long so that neither the correlation coefficients nor the standard deviation are essentially altered by the omission of a few terms, then we shall have

$$\frac{1}{2a}\int_{-a}^{a} u_x\, u_{x+t}\, dx = r(t) = g_1\, r(t-1) + g_2\, r(t-2) + \cdots + g_s\, r(t-s). \tag{34}$$

We thus see that the autocorrelation function $r(t)$ is a solution of the original differential equation, and consequently the harmonic characteristics of u_x can be inferred directly from it. This same conclusion was reached in another way in Chapter 16. The analyses of economic time series made by Wold, Flood, and Haavelmo, to which we have referred earlier, are connected with this method.

It will be observed that a direct use of difference equations, that is to say, the determination by the method of least squares of the parameters g_1, g_2, etc., obviates the necessity of formulating a set of relationships between presumably connected variates such as those given above by Tinbergen. The use of models, however, seems highly desirable in connection with this method, since otherwise its status is merely that of a descriptive statistical device for which a priori justification is lacking.

Adopting a somewhat different rationale, L. Amoroso has followed the model of classical mechanics, deriving equations similar to those of Lagrange. It will be recalled that the Lagrangian system is derived from the first variation of the integral over time of the difference between kinetic and potential energy. Hence, with his eye upon the classical model, Amoroso first introduces the difference

$$H = T - \theta \,, \tag{35}$$

where T and θ are defined by the sums:

$$T = e^{-\delta t} \sum_m p_m z_m \,; \qquad \theta = e^{-\delta t} \sum_{r,s} q_s x_{rs} \,. \tag{36}$$

In these expressions z_m is the quantity of the product m manufactured in unit time, p_m the price of the product m at time t, x_{rs} the quantity, per unit of time, of the factor of production s employed in manufacturing the product r, q_s the price of the factor of production s, and δ the force of interest.

The first variation of the integral of H over time, leads immediately to the following equations:

$$\frac{\partial H}{\partial x_{rs}} = \frac{d}{dt}\left(\frac{\partial H}{\partial x'_{rs}}\right), \tag{37}$$

where r is taken over the range $1, 2, \cdots, m$, and s over the range $1, 2, \cdots, n$. With this classical formulation before him, Amoroso is then able to find analogies between kinetic energy, the principle of the conservation of energy, etc. and certain economic quantities.

From yet another point of view G. Tintner in a series of papers has generalized the static demand theory, in particular that formulation of it associated with the names of J. R. Hicks and R. G. D. Allen, to the dynamic case. This study is designed to "give a somewhat firmer theoretical foundation to the dynamical demand theory of the Econometrists, especially G. C. Evans and C. F. Roos." Although it will be impossible to survey the various results of this formulation of the dynamics problem, the following may be cited as characteristic of Tintner's study.

In Chapter 3 we found that the fundamental relationship between the utility function $U(x_1, x_2, \cdots, x_n)$ and the prices, $p_1, p_2, \cdots, p_n$, which prevail in a static economy, is given by the following system:

$$\frac{\partial U}{\partial x_i} = \lambda p_i , \qquad i = 1, 2, 3, \cdots, n , \tag{38}$$

where λ is the marginal utility of money.

In Tintner's scheme this fundamental relationship is modified in economic dynamics by the rates of interest which prevail over the intervals of time which make up the range of the variation. Hence equation (38) is replaced by the following:

$$\frac{\partial U}{\partial x_i} = \frac{\lambda_1 p_i(t)}{(1+i_1)(1+i_2)\cdots(1+i_{t-1})} , \tag{39}$$

where i_1, i_2, etc. are the rates of interest prevailing in the range prior to the time t, λ_1 is the initial marginal utility of money, and $p_i(t)$ is the variable price of the commodity $x_i(t)$.

PROBLEMS

1. Assuming Kalecki's values: $m = 0.95$, $n = 0.121$, $\theta = 0.06$, show that $r = 0.378i$ is a solution of equation (28). Hence, discuss the nature of the solution of equation (26) and find the period of the motion.

2. Using the values of Frisch, estimate the values of ρ which satisfy equation (30).

3. Show that to a first approximation the roots of the equation

$$\tan \theta\alpha = \theta\alpha ,$$

yield values of α which satisfy the imaginary part of equation (30).

4. Given $a = 1$, $b = 2$, $\eta = 1$, solve equation (31) and show that the solution is oscillatory. *Hint*: Assume a solution of the form $z(t) = A\,B^t$.

5. If in equation (32), $\mu = 4 \sin^2 s$, $s = \pi h/T$, and $\phi(t) = f(t + 2h)$, show that a solution is given by

$$u(t) = A \sin\frac{2\pi}{T}(t+\tau) + f(t) + \frac{\sin 4s}{\sin 2s} f(t-h) + \frac{\sin 6s}{\sin 2s} f(t-2h) + \cdots .$$

6. Given the following difference equation

$$u_x = 3.35\, u_{x-1} - 4.43\, u_{x-2} + 2.71\, u_{x-3} - 0.64\, u_{x-4} ,$$

show that the following autocorrelation function is a solution:

$$r(t) = 0.19\, e^{-0.0408t} \cos \frac{2\pi t}{12} + 0.15\, e^{-0.0202t} + 0.66\, e^{-0.3425t} .$$

For the significance of this problem see illustrative Example 2 of Section 6, Chapter 16.

7. Writing Tintner's equation (39) in the form

$$\frac{\partial U}{\partial x_i} = \lambda\, e^{-\delta t}\, p_i(t) ,$$

and assuming that this replaces equation (6) of Section 3, show that equation (12) now has the form

$$p''_i + \lambda\, e^{-\delta t}\, p_i = U(t) .$$

8. Prove that the solution of the equation

$$p''(t) + \lambda\, e^{-\delta t}\, p(t) = 0 ,$$

is given by the function

$$p(t) = A\, J_0(z) + B\, Y_0(z) , \qquad z = \frac{2\sqrt{\lambda}}{\delta}\, e^{-\frac{1}{2}\delta t},$$

where $J_0(z)$ and $Y_0(z)$ are Bessel functions of zero order satisfying the equation

$$\frac{d^2u}{dz^2} + \frac{1}{z}\frac{du}{dz} + u = 0 .$$

9. In problem 8, assuming that $A = 10$, $B = 0$, $\lambda = 1$, $\delta = 0.04$, discuss explicitly the motion of prices using a table of Bessel functions. Prove the statement made in Section 3 that the introduction of the discount term increases the oscillations and tends to inflate prices.

SELECTED BIBLIOGRAPHY OF THE DYNAMICS OF TIME SERIES

AMOROSO, L. "The Transformation of Value in the Productive Process," *Econometrica*, Vol. 8, 1940, pp. 1–11.

DRESCH, F. W. "A Simplified Economic System with Dynamic Elements," *Report of the Fifth Annual Research Conference of the Cowles Commission*, 1939, pp. 18–21.

FLOOD, M. M. "Recursive Methods in Business-Cycle Analysis," *Econometrica*, Vol. 8, 1940, pp. 333–353.

FRISCH, R. "Propagation Problems and Impulse Problems in Dynamic Economics," in *Economic Essays in Honor of Gustav Cassel*, 1933, 35 pp.

HAAVELMO, T. "The Inadequacy of Testing Dynamic Theory by Comparing Theoretical Solutions and Observed Cycles," *Econometrica*, Vol. 8, 1940, pp. 312–321.

HOTELLING, H. "Differential Equations Subject to Error and Population Estimates," *Journal of the American Statistical Association*, Vol. 22, 1927, pp. 283–314.

KALECKI M. "A Macrodynamic Theory of Business Cycles," *Econometrica*, Vol. 3, 1935, pp. 327–344.

KNIGHT, F. H. *Risk, Uncertainty, and Profit.* Reprint, London, 1933.

ROOS, C. F. (1) "A Mathematical Theory of Competition," *American Journal of Mathematics*, Vol. 47, 1925, pp. 163–175.

(2) *Dynamic Economics,* Bloomington, Ind., 1934, xvi + 275 pp.

SAVAGE, L. J. [see A. Smithies (2)].

SMITHIES, A. (1) "The Maximization of Profits over Time with Changing Cost and Demand Functions," *Econometrica,* Vol. 7, 1939, pp. 312–318.

(2) (with L. J. SAVAGE) "A Dynamical Problem in Duopoly," *Econometrica,* Vol 8, 1940, pp. 130–143.

TINBERGEN, J. (1) "Annual Survey: Suggestions on Quantitative Business Cycle Theory," *Econometrica,* Vol. 3, 1935, pp. 241–308.

(2) *An Economic Approach to Business Cycle Problems.* Paris, 1937, 75 pp.

TINTNER, G. (1) "A Note on Distribution of Income over Time," *Econometrica,* Vol. 4, 1936, pp. 60–66.

(2) "Monopoly over Time," *Econometrica,* Vol. 5, 1937, pp. 160–170.

(3) "Maximization of Utility over Time," *Econometrica,* Vol. 6, 1938, pp. 154–158.

(4) "The Theoretical Derivation of Dynamic Demand Curves," *Econometrica,* Vol. 6, 1938, pp. 375–380.

WOLD, H. *A Study in the Analysis of Stationary Time Series.* Uppsala, 1938, vi + 211 pp.

YULE, G. U. (1) "Why do we Sometimes Get Nonsense Correlations Between Time Series?", *Journal of the Royal Statistical Society,* Vol. 89, 1929, pp. 1–64.

(2) "On a Method of Investigating Periodicities in Disturbed Series, with Special Reference to Wolfer's Sunspot Numbers," *Philosophical Transactions of the Royal Society,* Vol. 226 (A), 1927, pp. 267–298.

CHAPTER 19

The Theory of Business Cycles

1. *History of Business Cycles*

As we have said in the first chapter, the expression *business cycles* is a term applied to the more or less periodic alternations of business between prosperity and depression. It is clear that a business cycle is not a cycle in the mathematical sense of the word, but it is a movement which may be reasonably well represented by the sum of several harmonic terms.

The study of business cycles in any modern sense began with the present century, since an adequate description of the movements required a competent theory of index numbers, better statistical information about the component time series which comprise a business index, and perfected statistical techniques to cope with the intricacies of the problem.

Probably the origin of the theory of business cycles should be ascribed to the notable work of J. C. L. de Sismondi (1773–1842) entitled the *Nouveaux principes d'économie politique,* published in 1819. This work called attention to the problem of commercial crises and suggested reasons for them.

But the problem was not systematically studied until half a century later, when the advancing pace of commerce and the increasing demands of industrial activity began to make insistent demands for a more adequate interpretation of economic time series. The publication in 1860 of Clement Juglar's work entitled *Des crises commerciales et leur retour périodique,* called attention to the roughly periodic character of business.

Two years later there appeared also a work of W. S. Jevons (1835–1882) under the title *On the Study of Periodic Commercial Fluctuations.* Jevons was the father of index numbers. He wrote on secular trends and seasonal variations. His extensive study of English prices was a landmark in the statistical analysis of economic time series.

From the time of Juglar and Jevons the progress of investigation was uninterrupted. J. H. Poynting, the eminent British physicist, wrote on secular trends in 1884 and this study was continued by R. H. Hooker in 1901. In 1914 H. L. Moore published his classical study on

Economic Cycles: Their Law and Cause. Warren Persons made the first of his business barometers in 1915 and two years later began his work at Harvard on business cycles, which has exerted so wide an influence both at home and abroad.

The study of business cycles was accelerated by the World War, which stimulated the collection of data referring to many of the components of the general business index. From the problems presented by that great struggle, it became apparent that the complex economic system of modern society cannot be understood properly without a better knowledge of past experience. When we compare the meager and imperfect data available to Jevons and his contemporaries with the vast wealth of such data which we possess today, we can begin to appreciate our own fortunes. This comparison makes it easier for us to understand the slow progress made in earlier years in the analysis and interpretation of economic time series.

2. Types of Cycles

The most important inquiry with which to begin a discussion of business cycles is to question the actual existence of such cycles in the sense of the existence of periodic, or near-periodic, variations in the data of time series. This important question has been variously answered, although the general opinion inclines to the belief that cycles of a more or less permanent character are observed in many economic time series.

In order to have a precise method for the description of the harmonic characteristics of a time series let us refer to Section 4 of Chapter 16 in which we discussed the technique of constructing a Schuster periodogram. It is easily established that if $R_1^2, R_2^2, R_3^2, \cdots$ are the squares of the ordinates of the periodogram constructed over the following sequence of periods:

$$(1) \qquad T = \frac{2a}{1}, \frac{2a}{2}, \frac{2a}{3}, \frac{2a}{4}, \cdots, \frac{2a}{n}, \cdots,$$

where $2a$ is the range of the data, then the variance of the data, σ^2, is connected with the sequence of the R_i^2 by the following equation:

$$(2) \qquad R_1^2 + R_2^2 + R_3^2 + R_4^2 + \cdots = 2\sigma^2 .$$

It seems reasonable, therefore, to adopt as a measure of the cyclical character of an economic time series the ratio

$$(3) \qquad E = \frac{R^2(T_1) + R^2(T_2) + \cdots + R^2(T_p)}{2\sigma^2},$$

where T_1, T_2, $\cdots$, T_p are the characteristic periods, that is to say, the spectrum, of the time series. It is obvious that this measure will be only an approximate one unless the characteristic periods belong to the sequence defined by (1). But in the usual case the value of $2a$ is much longer than any of the characteristic periods, and since the values of T defined by (1) tend to cluster about the lower end of the range, the characteristic periods in (3) can be approximated by appropriately selected values in (1).

In most economic series the value of E for the two or three significant harmonic terms revealed by the periodogram seldom exceeds 0.25. That is to say, not more than 25 per cent of the variance is accounted for by strictly harmonic components. At first sight this might appear to indicate the tenuous nature of business cycles. That this is not the case, however, is illustrated by many series. Although the significance of E depends upon the length of the series analyzed, it is readily proved by methods somewhat too technical to discuss in this book, that a cycle is readily discernible in any series where E is as large as 0.25, provided the range of the series is sufficiently long to include five or more of the dominant cycles.[1] In the case of well-defined seasonal variations, such as those visible in Figure 90, the value of E is 0.12. An instructive example is found in astronomy where the existence of a sun spot cycle with a period equal to 11.25 years is accepted without reservation, although the nature and cause of the phenomenon is unknown. An analysis of the cycle over a century and a half from 1750 to 1900 shows the value of E is slightly less than 0.35, although for recent years it has been much higher. For the series used in example 2 of Section 4, Chapter 16, the value of E reaches the rather unusual magnitude of 0.46. The highest value ever observed by the author in an economic time series was $E(33) + E(44) = 0.73$ in the monthly Dow-Jones industrial stock price averages, corrected for trend, over the period 1914 to 1924.

It will be impossible here to summarize the statistical evidence relating to the existence of cycles in economic time series, but the final conclusion seems to be that certain cyclical patterns can be observed, and that these patterns are reasonably stable ones. The cycles thus recognized may be summarized as follows:

(a) A seasonal variation with a period of 12 months.

(b) The 22-month cycle, usually associated with textile manufacturing.

[1] See Chapter 5 in the author's *Analysis of Economic Time Series*. For the results of harmonic analyses of economic data see also Chapter 7 of that work.

(c) The 40-month cycle, called the short business cycle, which is found consistently in manufacturing indexes, industrial production, industrial stock prices, and other business series.

(d) The 60-month cycle, frequently found associated with the 40-month cycle, though of less importance. A cycle of this length is found in European data with a greater amplitude than in American data.

(e) The long business cycle of from 9 to 11 years in length.

(f) The building cycle of from 15 to 20 years in length.

(g) The war cycle of approximately 50 years, associated with major fluctuations in the price index.

The seasonal cycle is found in many economic time series. A typical example is shown in Figure 90, where we observe the seasonal variation in freight car loadings over the period from 1919 to 1932. The variation is definite and regular, being discernible through boom years and bear years alike. The second graph in Figure 90 shows the

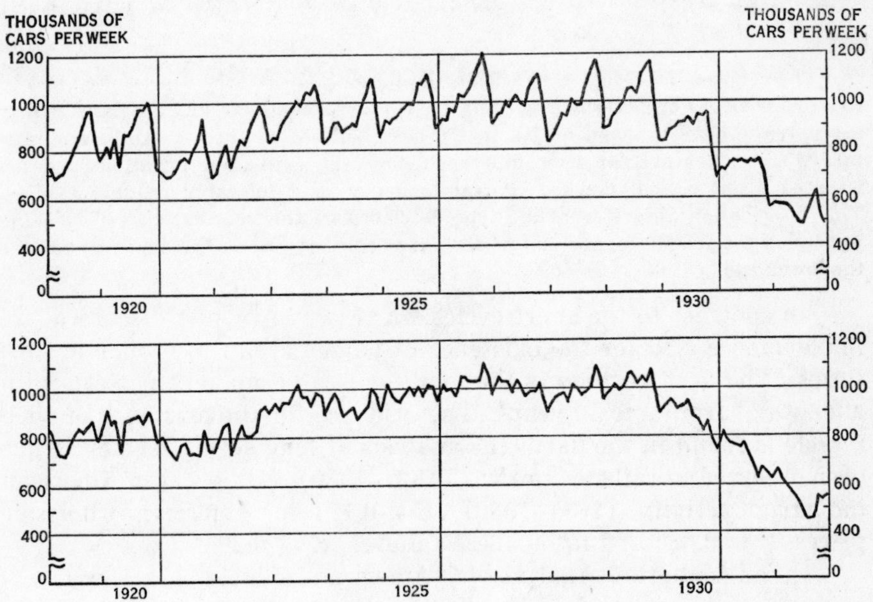

FIGURE 90. — SEASON VARIATION SHOWN BY MONTHLY AVERAGES OF MEAN WEEKLY FREIGHT-CAR LOADINGS.

The first chart shows the actual data and the second chart the series obtained by removing the seasonal factor.

appearance of the series after the seasonal factor has been removed. This series also has a minor component of 6 months. From 15 to 20 per cent of the variance of a time series with a well defined seasonal variation can be accounted for by this factor.

Three short cycles are commonly observed in economic time series which relate to business, industrial production, stock prices, and the like. The first has a period of around 22 months and is most pronounced in data pertaining to the textile industry. The second, which varies from 35 to 43 months in American data, is often a very prominent characteristic of the movement. An excellent example is furnished by the index of industrial stock prices, which is graphically portrayed in Figure 72 of Chapter 16. As we have said above approximately 46 per cent of the variance is accounted for by the single harmonic term with a period equal to 41 months. A third component with a period roughly equal to five years is often observed in the patterns of business. This cycle, however, appears to be more characteristic of European than of American data.

Commenting upon the short business cycle, W. C. Mitchell in his treatise on *Business Cycles, The Problem and its Setting* (p. 343) says:

> The conclusion is clear that within the period and country represented by our indexes, business cycles, while varying in length from a year and a half to nearly seven years, have a modal length in the neighborhood of three to three and one-half years. They are far from uniform in duration, but their durations are distributed about a well marked central tendency in a tolerably regular fashion. This distribution differs from the type described by the "normal curve" in being prolonged toward the upper end of the time scale somewhat further than toward the lower end.

In contrast to the short cycles which we have just discussed, we find evidence also for the existence of longer cycles in economic time series. The first of these is the more or less permanent pattern with a length of from 9 to 10 years. The evidence for the existence of such a cycle is found in the harmonic analysis of long series. The cycle has been observed in rail stock prices (1831–1930), $E = 0.11$; in American industrial activity (1831–1930), $E = 0.17$; in American wholesale prices, $E = 0.08$; and in business failures, $E = 0.20$.

In an elaborate analysis of American industrial activity, expressed as a per cent of normal by months over the period from January, 1790 to December, 1929 inclusive, a total of 1680 months, E. B. Wilson constructed the periodogram shown in Figure 91.[2] Wilson divided the range into three overlapping periods of 840 months as follows: I (1790–1859); II (1825–1894); III (1860–1929). The period-

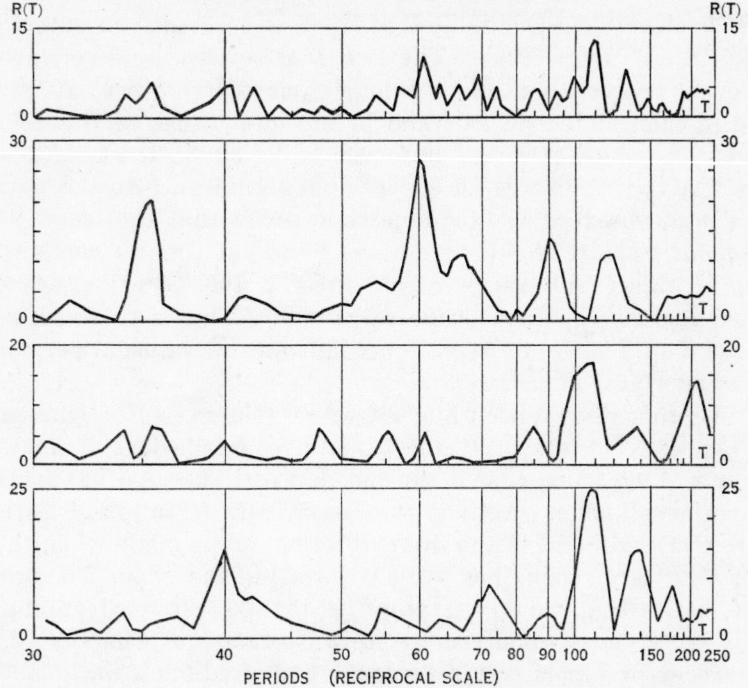

FIGURE 91. — WILSON'S PERIODOGRAM OF BUSINESS ACTIVITY.

The top curve refers to the period 1790–1929; the second curve to the period 1790–1859; the third curve to the period 1825–1894; and the fourth curve to the period 1860–1929.

ograms of each of these sections of the data, as well as that for the entire period, are shown in the accompanying figure. The scale for T, it will be observed, is reciprocal.

From Wilson's data we find the following significant values:

Period	I(1790–1859)		II(1825–1894)		III(1890–1929)		1790–1929	
T	R^2	$E(T)$	R^2	$E(T)$	R^2	$E(T)$	R^2	$E(T)$
35	19.6	.1292	......	....	......	....	......	....
40	......	....	......	....	14.8	.1092	......	....
60	27.5	.1813	......	....	......	....	......	....
61	......	....	......	....	......	....	10.0	.0696
90	14.3	.0943	......	....	......	....	......	....
106	......	....	17.9	.1607	......	....	......	....
108	......	....	......	....	25.4	.1873	......	....
110	......	....	......	....	......	....	12.5	.0870
120	12.5	.0824	......	....	......	....	......	....
138	......	....	......	....	14.8	.1092	......	....
216	......	....	15.7	.1410	......	....	......	....

[2] The data were compiled by L. P. Ayres for the Cleveland Trust Company.

It is clear from this table that there is no great concentration of energy in any single cycle. The two short cycles, however, are conspicuously represented, and the long cycle of from 8 to 10 years is found in each of the periods and in the total range of the data. Although the values of E are observed to be small, the length of the series analyzed indicates an exceptional significance to the patterns. It has been observed in economic time series that the length of the cycle tends to shift slightly from one period of time to another. The result of this is to cause interference in the periodogram and a marked decrease in the average value of R^2. Thus a value as high as 0.09 for E in a series of 1680 items indicates an unusual permanence in the underlying structure.

With this view Wilson himself would take exception since he has said [see *Bibliography,* Wilson (2)]: "When the test of Schusters' was applied we found that it showed that oscillations of Ayres' Index of American Business Activity was essentially fortuitous." The point of difference is found in the interpretations to be made when the values of $E(T)$ are as small as those recorded in the table. The possibility of forecasting would certainly be highly restricted as one may readily see from the analysis given in Section 9 of Chapter 16. The standard error bands would be large and prediction uncertain as a consequence. But when we add to the evidence of the periodogram other observations about the cyclical structure visible in different component series of business activity, then we may speak with somewhat more conviction about the existence and permanence of the patterns suggested by the original analysis.

In the Wilson periodogram we observe in the period from 1825 to 1894 a component for which $T = 216$ months, that is to say, 18 years. This is the famous building cycle, the influence of which has been observed in other economic time series for more than a century. The length of the cycle varies from around 16 years to 20 years. A composite index of building activity over the period from 1830 to 1936 has been constructed by G. F. Warren and F. A. Pearson by combining (a) an index of building permits per capita by J. R. Riggleman, (b) an index of annual volume of new building, prepared by R. Wenzlick, and (c) an index of the monthly volume of construction per capita in 120 cities in the United States. This composite index is graphically represented in Figure 92. It will be observed that the peaks of construction came 17, 18, 19, 19, and 16 years apart and averaged 18 years. The same structure has also been observed in European data.

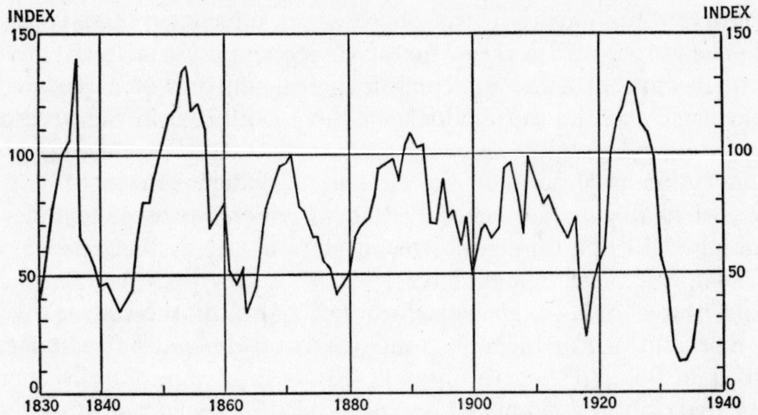

FIGURE 92. — COMPOSITE INDEX OF BUILDING ACTIVITY IN THE UNITED STATES

The longest period that has been observed in American data is the 50-year war cycle, about which we have commented in Chapter 1. The great inflationary peaks fifty years apart are strikingly apparent in Figure 1. The value of E for the single harmonic term of period equal to 50 years reaches the astonishing value of 0.59, although statistical belief in the permanence of this unusual pattern must be cautiously stated since only three cycles are contained within the range of the data.

3. *The Significance of Cycles*

In engineering, physics, astronomy, and other applied sciences, the significance of periodic phenomena is found to a large extent in their repetitive character and in the consequent forecasting of the future behavior of the system of variables to which they pertain. The computation of the tables of the ephemeris is based upon the observed cycles of the heavenly bodies, cycles, let it be added, that in some respects are as complex as those observed in economic time series, although, after more than two centuries of investigation, their errors have been reduced to insignificant values.

So also in economics the observation of real cyclical phenomena in time series should lead to the same forecasting power which distinguishes an exact science from an inexact one. Unfortunately, as we have observed above, the proportion of the total variance which can be attributed to pure harmonic terms in economic data is small even in the most regular of the series. And also, in contrast to the exact sciences, there exist only tenuous and largely unverified theories as to the origin and the nature of the cycles which have been observed. The erratic element is still a large factor in economic variation.

But in spite of these difficulties, the recognition of a few persistent patterns, such as those which we have exhibited in the preceding section, makes it possible to reach certain tentative conclusions about the underlying structure of the economic system. In the following sections we shall consider several patterns which, however tenuous the supporting data may appear to be in view of the deductions derived from them, are at least suggestive.

The first of these concerns the relationship of the business cycle to the distributions of income as measured by the concentration ratio described in Section 7 of Chapter 2. Since the value of total income and its distribution among the classes of the economic system are probably the two most important variables in the determination of economic well-being, the significance of such a study will be apparent.

The second problem considers the possibility of interpreting the phenomena of political history by observing the behavior of the fundamental economic series. One of the most interesting periods for this analysis is found in the century and a half which followed the discovery of America. Fortunately we now have exceptional data relating to the economy of Spain so that such a deduction is possible. We shall find that the century from 1500 to 1600 was characterized by one of the most spectacular advances in trade that was ever observed in economic history. The ensuing fifty years, at the top of the trade logistic, were featured by large cyclical movements not unlike those which we have observed in the economy of the United States in recent years.

Our third and concluding study will be a macroscopic analysis of certain historical episodes in the political development of the United States as they may be interpreted from economic data. Over a period exceeding a century in length we now possess the most extensive and reliable data ever assembled for any large economic system. The political events over this fruitful century and more may now be associated with the concurrent economic movements. The scrutiny which we are proposing to make is both objective and tentative in character, however, since categorical conclusions are not yet justified in a science as new and as untested as the present one. The reader is warned to reflect occasionally on the conversation between Alice and the White King, who remarked to her: ". . . And I haven't sent the two Messengers, either. They've both gone to town. Just look along the road, and tell me if you can see either of them." "I see nobody on the road," said Alice. "I only wish *I* had such eyes," the King remarked in a fretful tone. "To be able to see Nobody! And at that distance, too! Why, it's as much as I can do to see real people, by this light!"

4. Business Cycles and the Distribution of Incomes

In Chapter 2 we discussed the distribution of incomes in an economic system as a static problem, and we found a certain function which would graduate satisfactorily the observed data for any given annual period. If, however, we examine the Johnson diagram, Figure 6 of Chapter 2, we are struck by the fact that annual distributions of income vary considerably from one another. For example, we observe in the Johnson diagram that the points at the lower end of the successive lines of distribution show a large variation which tends to follow the business cycle, whereas, those at the upper end exhibit the variation to a much less degree. It will be instructive to have an interpretation of this phenomenon.

If we had a strictly Paretean economy, namely, one in which the parameter ν was always equal to 1.5, then we see from the analysis of Section 9, Chapter 2, that the number of people, N_z, who are in the income class z or higher, is given by the formula

$$N_z = 0.25273N(I/Nz)^{1.5}, \tag{4}$$

where I is the total income and N is the total number of income recipients.

If N is proportional to I, then clearly N_z would vary directly as I, a conclusion that is not substantiated by the Johnson diagram. But we have observed also in Chapter 2 that ν varies with the business cycle, the tendency being for ν to increase in periods of depression and to diminish in times of prosperity. This variation is conspicuously shown in the following table of the concentration ratios, ρ, in connection with which we give the number of people, N, who had incomes equal to or in excess of half a million dollars:

CONCENTRATION RATIO, ρ, AND NUMBER OF INCOMES, N, NOT LESS THAN $500,000

Year	ρ	N	Year	ρ	N	Year	ρ	N	Year	ρ	N
1914	0.481	......	1919	0.413	254	1924	0.427	317	1929	0.543	1489
1915	0.556	......	1920	0.379	156	1925	0.481	686	1930	0.446	468
1916	0.595	......	1921	0.357	84	1926	0.476	699	1931	0.413	226
1917	0.505	456	1922	0.413	228	1927	0.490	847	1932	0.397	106
1918	0.435	245	1923	0.407	215	1928	0.543	1494	1933	0.417	131

Hence the assumption that the distribution of incomes remains Paretean during swings of the business cycle is not a valid one. We also observe the high correlation which exists between the concentration ratio and the number of people with high incomes.

Referring again to Chapter 2 we see that the number of people, N_z, who are in the income class z or higher, can be written in the general case as follows:

$$N_z = \frac{\kappa(\nu)}{z^\nu} N\,(I/N)^\nu, \tag{5}$$

where $\kappa(\nu)$ has the values $\kappa(1.3) = 0.1741$, $\kappa(1.5) = 0.2527$, $\kappa(1.9) = 0.4038$. But if I and N are assumed to be fixed, it can be readily shown that N_z is extremely sensitive to changes in ν provided z is sufficiently large. For example, if $z = \$500{,}000$, then when $\nu = 1.3$, there will be nearly 10 times as many people in this high income class as when ν has the Paretean value 1.5. Similarly, when $\nu = 1.9$ there will be slightly less than one per cent of the Paretean number who have incomes in excess of half a million dollars. Although such extreme variation is not observed in the table given above, yet the percentage change between 1921 and 1928 was approximately equal to 1800.

But we must next observe that I itself is not an invariant quantity, since it depends upon the level of prices. For example, I was 74.3 billions dollars in 1920 and 60.1 billion dollars in 1931. But the actual purchasing power of the income in 1931 was greater than in 1920, since the price level in the first year was 1.93, while the price level was 1.50 in the second. Dividing the two incomes by their respective price indexes, we obtain 38.5 billion as the real income in 1920 and 40.1 as the real income in 1931. Since the comparison of real incomes is clearly more significant than the comparison of nominal or dollar incomes, we shall use as the fundamental variable in our analysis the total real annual income defined by the ratio

$$I = I'/P, \tag{6}$$

where I' is the total annual nominal income, and P the general index of prices.

We shall now introduce the assumption that N_z, the number of people who are in the income class z or higher, is given by the formula

$$N_z = \kappa\, I\, \gamma\, z^{-\nu}, \tag{7}$$

where κ and γ are statistical parameters.

In order to test this formula we use the following data over the period from 1917 to 1934 inclusive, where I' is the total income (in billions), I, the total real income (in billions), P the general price index (1913=1.00), N_1 the number of people having incomes over \$1,000,000, N_2 the number having incomes over \$500,000, N_3 the number having incomes over \$300,000, N_4 the number having incomes over \$150,000, and N_5 the number having incomes over \$100,000.

Year	I'	P	$I=I'/P$	log I	N_1	N_2	N_3	N_4	N_5
1917	53.2	1.39	38.3	1.583	141	456	1015	3362	6664
1918	60.2	1.57	38.3	1.583	67	245	627	2141	4499
1919	67.4	1.73	39.0	1.591	65	254	679	2543	5526
1920	74.3	1.93	38.5	1.585	33	156	395	1458	3649
1921	52.6	1.63	32.2	1.508	21	84	246	985	2352
1922	61.7	1.58	39.1	1.592	67	228	537	1860	4031
1923	69.8	1.65	42.3	1.626	74	215	542	1843	4182
1924	69.6	1.66	41.9	1.622	75	317	774	2650	5715
1925	77.1	1.70	45.4	1.657	207	686	1578	4801	9560
1926	78.5	1.71	45.9	1.662	231	699	1591	4858	9582
1927	77.2	1.71	45.1	1.654	290	847	1988	5861	11122
1928	80.5	1.76	45.7	1.660	511	1494	3250	8928	15977
1929	79.1	1.79	44.2	1.645	513	1489	3130	8440	14816
1930	77.2	1.68	46.0	1.663	150	468	1020	3091	6202
1931	60.1	1.50	40.1	1.603	77	226	494	1500	3184
1932	46.5	1.32	35.2	1.547	20	106	246	841	1836
1933	44.4	1.29	34.4	1.537	50	131	272	867	2051
1934	50.4	1.37	36.8	1.566	33	119	235	925	1907

Without giving the details of the calculation, which is a simple problem in correlation, we may state the results. Designating by r_{In} the correlation coefficient between log I and log N_n, and by γ_n the value of γ obtained from the data for log N_n, we observe the following values:

n	1	2	3	4	5
r_{In}	0.8538	0.8657	0.8602	0.8494	0.8495
γ_n	7.7683	6.9691	6.7024	5.8491	5.3374

From this table we see that the assumption of a dependence between N_z and I as given in equation (7) is statistically justified. The observed correlations are high and significant. The relationship between log I and log N_2 is graphically portrayed in Figure 93.

We notice also from the table just given that there is a tendency for the values of γ_n to decrease as lower income levels are introduced, a fact in keeping with the observation that the line of upper points

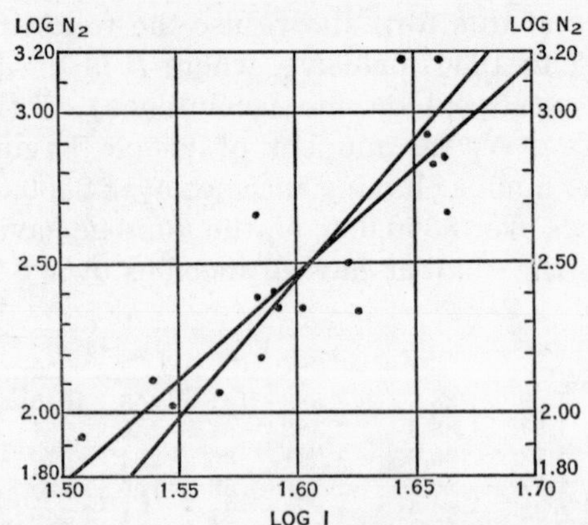

FIGURE 93. — CORRELATION BETWEEN LOG I AND LOG N_2, WHERE I IS TOTAL REAL INCOME AND N_2 IS THE NUMBER OF PEOPLE HAVING INCOMES IN EXCESS OF $500,000.

on the Johnson diagram exhibits a much smaller variation than the line of points at the lower end of the lines of distribution.

We next inquire as to the variation of N, the total number of income recipients, with the total real income I. We shall assume that N varies as some power of I, namely, that

$$N = k_1 I^\delta , \tag{8}$$

where δ is a parameter to be determined.

Unfortunately there exist few reliable data to test this relationship, but the following table for the years 1929 to 1935 inclusive may be used to obtain an approximate determination of δ:[3]

Year	log I	N	log N
1929	1.645	43,979,000	7.643
1930	1.663	41,880,000	7.622
1931	1.603	38,529,000	7.586
1932	1.547	34,986,000	7.543
1933	1.537	35,200,000	7.547
1934	1.566	37,306,000	7.572
1935	1.579	38,139,000	7.581

Correlating log N with log I, we obtain $\delta = 0.7273$. Since the table is very short for a reliable correlation, there is undoubtedly considerable error in this value of δ. However, since it is reasonable to suppose that N varies approximately linearly with I, the value of δ is certainly of the right order of magnitude.

[3] These data are from *National Income in the United States, 1929–35*, by the U. S. Dept. of Commerce, Bureau of Foreign and Domestic Commerce, 1936, p. 31.

Our conclusion from this study may be stated briefly. Large variations in the cycle of business are reflected in corresponding variations in the concentration ratio of income. The effect which the cycle imposes upon different income groups is non-linear, varying as the first power of total real income for the group of income receivers as a whole, and as the fifth and higher powers of total real income for those in income ranges equal to, or exceeding $100,000.

5. *The Economic Theory of History*

The first suggestion that the principal variable in the interpretation of historical movements depended upon economic facts rather than upon political ideology is found in H. T. Buckle's *History of Civilization*, published in 1857, and in the *Misère de la philosophie* of Karl Marx, which appeared ten years earlier, but which gained little currency until the argument was repeated and extended in the third volume of *Das Kapital*, published in 1894. Unfortunately neither of these writers, nor their interpreters, have been able to furnish adequate statistical evidence for this interesting and important theory.

It will be impossible here to give more than a cursory examination of one or two problems which tend to substantiate the proposition that economic variation is closely associated with historical movements. A more extensive account will be found in the author's work on *The Analysis of Economic Time Series*.

We shall examine first, because of its intimate connection with the material given in Chapter 12 on the equation of exchange, the very interesting century and a half from 1500 to 1650. In this period we find the origin of our present level of prices and the beginnings of the scientific movement which finally resulted in the great industrial revolution of the nineteenth and twentieth centuries.

Data over the period in question are from three reliable sources. We have a record of wheat prices in England by J. E. T. Rogers, previously referred to in Section 7 of Chapter 12, an admirable index of Spanish commodity prices compiled by E. J. Hamilton, also previously mentioned in Chapter 12, and a table showing the total importation of gold and silver into Spain in terms of a standard peso, data provided by Hamilton.[4] To these we may add the estimates of the world's production of gold and silver from 1493 to 1890 made by Adolph Soet-

[4] "Imports of American Gold and Silver into Spain, 1503–1660," *Quarterly Journal of Economics*, Vol. 43, 1929.

beer, whose studies on this question are generally accepted as the most reliable and authoritative.[5]

The accompanying tables give (1) Hamilton's index of Spanish prices, and (2) the total imports of treasure into Spain expressed in

INDEX OF SPANISH PRICES, 1501–1650

Year	Index of Prices	Year	Index of Prices	Year	Index of Prices	Year	Index of Prices	Year	Index of Prices
1501	33.26	1531	57.06	1561	86.83	1591	112.73	1621	133.93
1502	36.41	1532	54.99	1562	91.49	1592	117.12	1622	136.05
1503	37.34	1533	51.36	1563	89.66	1593	113.43	1623	137.67
1504	38.15	1534	53.81	1564	88.67	1594	114.24	1624	142.04
1505	40.59	1535	48.95	1565	92.38	1595	114.08	1625	143.09
1506	46.89	1536	53.94	1566	90.29	1596	116.61	1626	162.17
1507	46.42	1537	53.21	1567	90.91	1597	123.75	1627	169.43
1508	44.78	1538	57.05	1568	92.44	1598	132.55	1628	166.65
1509	39.33	1539	56.41	1569	90.18	1599	134.92	1629	166.51
1510	38.76	1540	58.20	1570	93.84	1600	137.24	1630	160.84
1511	39.78	1541	56.02	1571	97.53	1601	143.56	1631	158.94
1512	37.92	1542	60.49	1572	97.32	1602	138.16	1632	163.95
1513	39.41	1543	58.06	1573	99.94	1603	139.73	1633	159.52
1514	40.48	1544	60.09	1574	98.29	1604	142.25	1634	156.85
1515	41.16	1545	59.48	1575	103.71	1605	144.34	1635	154.83
1516	40.55	1546	64.75	1576	95.65	1606	139.63	1636	160.54
1517	40.18	1547	62.64	1577	94.00	1607	135.64	1637	169.74
1518	43.46	1548	66.32	1578	97.84	1608	136.12	1638	169.51
1519	43.24	1549	70.63	1579	107.77	1609	129.61	1639	161.71
1520	42.06	1550	69.05	1580	102.77	1610	132.86	1640	161.80
1521	46.48	1551	69.40	1581	103.95	1611	127.92	1641	170.75
1522	50.51	1552	71.32	1582	106.57	1612	127.53	1642	186.07
1523	48.84	1553	70.24	1583	108.51	1613	128.77	1643	172.25
1524	49.24	1554	71.77	1584	110.36	1614	133.85	1644	171.71
1525	50.39	1555	71.02	1585	111.35	1615	130.41	1645	168.36
1526	49.83	1556	72.28	1586	106.62	1616	135.40	1646	173.98
1527	53.12	1557	79.74	1587	111.31	1617	136.72	1647	175.00
1528	51.20	1558	80.92	1588	107.62	1618	136.41	1648	183.14
1529	53.49	1559	77.86	1589	113.09	1619	131.23	1649	188.03
1530	56.78	1560	79.09	1590	113.97	1620	134.77	1650	198.47

terms of a standard peso, equivalent to 42.29 grams of pure silver. Hamilton's index, base = 1571–1580, is not given directly by him, but may be obtained by dividing his index of money wages by his index of real wages.

[5] For data from 1493 to 1880 see Soetbeer, *Materialien zur Erläuterung und Beurteilung der wirtschaftlichen Edelmetallverhältnisse und der Währungsfrage.* Zweite Vervöllstandigte Ausgabe, Berlin, 1886. For data from 1881 to 1890 see Soetbeer: "Edelmetallgewinnung und Verwendung in den Jahren 1881 bis 1890," *Hildebrand's Jahrbücher für Nationalökonomie und Statistik,* Vol. 56, 1891, pp. 537, 538, 561. Soetbeer's estimates, together with their equivalents in dollars are given by J. D. Magee, "The World's Production of Gold and Silver from 1493 to 1905," *Journal of Political Economy,* Vol. 18, 1910, pp. 50–58.

If we convert the total importation reported by Hamilton into equivalent ounces of gold, using 12 arbitrarily as the silver equivalent of gold, we obtain 50,740,000 ounces as the total importation. This is approximately 35 per cent of the total of 147,562,228 ounces for all of Europe as estimated by Soetbeer.

It will be necessary for us to have some estimate of the total amount of circulating treasure in Europe prior to the great price inflation which began in 1500. This can be estimated from the observed price rise itself, but we are fortunate in having a comprehensive study of the question of treasure in Europe made by W. Jacob early in the nineteenth century.[6] From this investigation Jacob concluded "that no very great increase or decrease in the stock of precious metals occurred during those centuries (between the time of the Norman Conquest and that of the discovery of America) ; or it may be presumed that the supply from the mines was nearly equal to the consumption by friction on the circulation, and to that portion which either had been lost from being buried in the ground and not again found, or that had been lost by shipwrecks."

TOTAL IMPORTS OF TREASURE INTO SPAIN IN PESOS

Years	Amount	Years	Amount	Years	Amount
1503–1505	371,056	1556–1560	7,998,999	1611–1615	24,528,121
1506–1510	816,237	1561–1565	11,207,536	1616–1620	30,112,460
1511–1515	1,195,554	1566–1570	14,141,216	1621–1625	27,010,679
1516–1520	993,197	1571–1575	11,906,610	1626–1630	24,954,527
1521–1525	134,171	1576–1580	17,251,942	1631–1635	17,110,855
1526–1530	1,038,438	1581–1585	29,374,612	1636–1640	16,314,602
1531–1535	1,650,232	1586–1590	23,832,631	1641–1645	13,763,803
1536–1540	3,937,892	1591–1595	35,184,863	1646–1650	11,770,548
1541–1545	4,954,006	1596–1600	34,428,501	1651–1655	7,293,767
1546–1550	5,508,712	1601–1605	24,403,329	1656–1660	3,361,111
1551–1555	9,865,532	1606–1610	31,405,207	Total	447,820,951

Jacob estimated that the amount of circulating treasure which existed in Europe in the year 806 was equivalent to £33,674,256. Using this figure we see that the prices of the Middle Ages were maintained by a circulating coinage equivalent approximately to 8,500,000 ounces of gold. Since, however, the arts and industry may be assumed to have absorbed another amount of treasure approximately equal to that used in coinage,[7] we are probably not far wrong in estimating that

[6] *An Historical Inquiry into the Production and Consumption of Precious Metals*, London, 1831, Vol. 1, xvi + 380 pp.; Vol. 2, xi + 415 pp.

[7] The average amount of gold production added to monetary stock from 1850 to 1929 was 56%. See G. F. Warren and F. A. Pearson, *Gold and Prices*, New York, 1935, p. 125.

there existed at the beginning of the sixteenth century in Europe a treasure of precious metals approximately equal to 17,000,000 ounces of gold.

With this tentative figure before us we can now proceed to the formation of an index of money in Spain for the century and a half under consideration. As a base for our index we shall assume the period from 1570 to 1580, the average being set equal to 100.

We shall assume as the index of money the following ratio

$$I(x) = 100\left[\frac{M_x + X}{M + X}\right] = 100\left[\frac{X}{M + X} + \frac{M_x}{M + X}\right], \tag{9}$$

where X is the amount of treasure in Spain prior to 1500, M is the average of the treasure which had been accumulated within the decade between 1570 and 1580 since the beginning of the century, and M_x is the treasure accumulated from 1500 to the year x.

In this formula the values of M and M_x are accurately known from Hamilton's data for Spain and from Soetbeer's data for Europe. The difficulty lies in estimating X. Lacking other evidence we shall employ the value given above based upon Jacob's study. That this cannot be far from the correct value can be checked in other ways. In the first place, we know that the amount of treasure in Europe remained essentially unchanged over the many centuries between the fall of Rome and the beginning of the sixteenth century. The careful study of J. E. T. Rogers on English prices during the Middle Ages, which we have cited in Chapter 12, is eloquent evidence of a stable and unchanging money supply in Western Europe. In the second place, the reader may verify for himself by a simple application of the equation of exchange that if X is assumed to be as large as 32,000,000 ounces of gold, the conclusion inevitably follows that trade did not increase in Europe during the first 80 years of the sixteenth century, and thereafter advanced very moderately. Since all evidence is to the contrary, we thus see that an upper bound can thus be set for the value of X. In similar fashion, it can be demonstrated that to assume a smaller value for X than that given above will imply a greater increase in trade than one might reasonably expect from the number of registered vessels sailing to and from the Indies from the ports of Spain during the first half of the century.

Since there is no way to know how much of this original supply of treasure was in Spain, our analysis may now proceed as follows: We first assume the decade between 1570 and 1580 as base (= 100), and using Soetbeer's estimates compute $I(x)$ for the year 1500. According to Soetbeer the average amount of treasure imported into Europe at the base period was equivalent to 53,200,000 ounces of gold. This is our value of M, and hence we obtain

$$(10) \qquad I(0) = \left[\frac{17{,}000{,}000}{53{,}200{,}000 + 17{,}000{,}000}\right] = 22.22 \, .$$

Since we are interested in Spanish trade, rather than that of Europe as a whole, we now shift to the data of Hamilton. Still using Soetbeer's figures we compute $I(5) = 26.00$, and this we shall assume is the treasure index for Spain as well as for Europe in the year 1505. From Hamilton's data the average accumulation of treasure into Spain from 1505 to the middle of the base period was equal to 83,974,303 pesos. The value of X in formula (9), which now refers to 1505, is readily found from the equation $100X/(M + X) = 26.00$. We thus obtain $X = 29{,}504{,}480$ pesos, and consequently the sum, $M + X = 113{,}478{,}780$ pesos. Introducing this value into (9), we see that we can compute $I(x)$ for any year ending a five year period, and hence, by linear interpolation, for any intermediate year. The results of this computation are given in the accompanying table.

Since our principal objective in this computation is the computation of an index of trade for Spain, we consider next the equation of exchange, which we can write in the form

$$(11) \qquad I(x) = K\,P(x)\,T(x),$$

where K is a parameter, which includes the velocity of money for which no estimates are available, and a factor, which takes care of the fact that $I(x)$ is an index number rather than the actual quantity of money itself.

We shall now assume that K is relatively constant. In an economy, which does not have the elasticity of a banking system, but which employs a hand-to-hand exchange of money, the velocity of money presumably varies little from one period to another. The relative stability of prices in the years prior to 1500 would also argue that the variation in K was relatively small.

An index of trade, referring to the period 1571–1580 as base, is then given approximately by the formula

$$(12) \qquad T(x) = 100\,\frac{I(x)}{P(x)} \, .$$

Using this formula, and the data already assembled, we then compute the values of the trade index over the century and a half under

Money and Trade Indexes for Spain, 1505–1650

Year	Money	Trade	Year	Money	Trade	Year	Money	Trade	Year	Money	Trade
1505	26.00	64.06	1542	36.35	60.10	1579	104.56	97.02	1616	291.94	215.61
1506	26.14	55.76	1543	37.23	64.11	1580	107.60	104.70	1617	297.24	217.41
1507	26.29	56.63	1544	38.10	63.40	1581	112.78	108.49	1618	302.55	221.79
1508	26.43	59.03	1545	38.97	65.52	1582	117.96	110.68	1619	307.86	234.59
1509	26.58	67.57	1546	39.94	61.69	1583	123.13	113.48	1620	313.16	232.37
1510	26.72	68.94	1547	40.91	65.31	1584	128.31	116.26	1621	317.92	237.38
1511	26.93	67.70	1548	41.88	63.15	1585	133.49	119.88	1622	322.68	237.18
1512	27.14	71.48	1549	42.85	60.68	1586	137.69	129.14	1623	327.45	237.85
1513	27.35	69.40	1550	43.83	63.47	1587	141.89	127.47	1624	332.21	233.88
1514	27.56	68.09	1551	45.56	65.65	1588	146.09	135.74	1625	336.97	235.49
1515	27.77	67.48	1552	47.30	66.33	1589	150.29	132.89	1626	341.36	210.50
1516	27.95	68.92	1553	49.04	69.82	1590	154.49	135.55	1627	345.76	204.07
1517	28.12	69.99	1554	50.78	70.75	1591	160.69	142.54	1628	350.16	210.12
1518	28.30	65.11	1555	52.52	73.95	1592	166.89	142.50	1629	354.56	212.94
1519	28.47	65.85	1556	53.93	74.61	1593	173.09	152.60	1630	358.96	223.18
1520	28.65	68.11	1557	55.34	69.40	1594	179.30	156.95	1631	361.97	227.74
1521	28.67	61.69	1558	56.75	70.13	1595	185.50	162.60	1632	364.99	222.62
1522	28.70	56.81	1559	58.16	74.70	1596	191.57	164.28	1633	368.00	230.69
1523	28.72	58.80	1560	59.57	75.32	1597	197.63	159.70	1634	371.02	236.54
1524	28.74	58.37	1561	61.54	70.88	1598	203.70	153.68	1635	374.04	241.58
1525	28.77	57.09	1562	63.52	69.43	1599	209.77	155.47	1636	376.91	234.78
1526	28.95	58.10	1563	65.49	73.05	1600	215.83	157.27	1637	379.79	223.75
1527	29.13	54.84	1564	67.47	76.09	1601	220.13	153.34	1638	382.66	225.75
1528	29.32	57.26	1565	69.44	75.17	1602	224.44	162.45	1639	385.54	238.41
1529	29.50	55.15	1566	71.94	79.67	1603	228.74	163.70	1640	388.41	240.06
1530	29.68	52.27	1567	74.43	81.87	1604	233.04	163.82	1641	390.84	228.89
1531	29.97	52.53	1568	76.92	83.21	1605	237.34	164.43	1642	393.26	211.35
1532	30.26	55.03	1569	79.41	88.06	1606	242.87	173.94	1643	395.69	229.72
1533	30.55	59.49	1570	81.91	87.28	1607	248.41	183.14	1644	398.12	231.85
1534	30.84	57.32	1571	84.00	86.13	1608	253.94	186.56	1645	400.54	237.91
1535	31.14	63.61	1572	86.10	88.47	1609	259.48	200.20	1646	404.49	232.49
1536	31.83	59.01	1573	88.20	88.25	1610	265.01	199.47	1647	408.45	233.40
1537	32.52	57.01	1574	90.30	91.87	1611	269.34	210.55	1648	412.40	225.18
1538	33.22	58.23	1575	92.40	89.09	1612	273.66	214.58	1649	416.35	221.43
1539	33.91	60.12	1576	95.44	99.78	1613	277.98	215.87	1650	420.30	207.04
1540	34.61	59.46	1577	98.48	104.77	1614	282.31	210.91	1651		
1541	35.48	63.33	1578	101.52	103.76	1615	286.63	219.79	1652		

consideration. These computations are recorded in the accompanying table and they are graphically shown in Figure 94.

We now have before us the elements for an economic interpretation of history. The prosperity of Spain, which carried with it the prosperity of much of Western Europe, was a phenomenon of trade rather than of price. Great fortunes were undoubtedly made and the well-being of people generally was raised. The struggle for existence was ameliorated and leisure for contemplation and artistic creation resulted as a consequence. An examination of the remarkable curve shown in Figue 94 tells us better than pages of history why there was great sterility during the Middle Ages and an astonishing burst of creative enterprise at the beginning of the Renaissance. Do we wonder that Cervantes in Spain and Shakespeare in England were contemporaries, or that Tycho Brahe in Denmark, Galileo in Italy, and Kepler in Germany flourished in the second half of the sixteenth century? P. A. Sorokin, who has devoted considerable attention to this problem in his analysis of cultural dynamics, reaches the conclusion: "So far as the Graeco-Roman and the Western cultures are concerned, we discover the existence of a definite association between the rise and fall of economic well-being and the type of the dominant culture."[8]

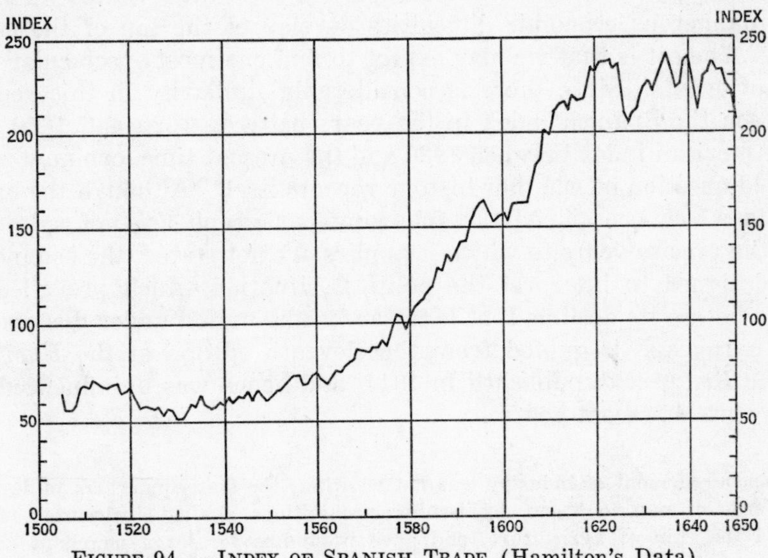

FIGURE 94. — INDEX OF SPANISH TRADE (Hamilton's Data).

The defeat of the Spanish Armada in 1588 has been heralded as the dramatic event which marked, perhaps, the beginning of the downfall of the Spanish empire. But we see from Figure 94 that the effect of this defeat was a comparatively insignificant matter compared with events that came after. The great trade advance was only temporarily halted and continued almost without interruption to its peak in the decade between 1620 and 1630. There it was, rather than in 1588, that disaster befell the Spanish empire. Thus history says about Philip IV, who succeeded to the Spanish throne at the death of his father in 1621, that "his reign, after a few passing years of bar-

[8] See *Social and Cultural Dynamics*, Vol. 3, New York, 1937, Chapter 8.

ren successes, was a long story of political and military decay and disaster. The king has been held responsible for the fall of Spain, which was, however, due in the main to internal causes beyond the control of the most despotic ruler, however capable he had been." Our history ends in 1650, but the ominous depression which was in full course by that date gives eloquent evidence as to the political instability which prevailed when the effects of the magnificent trade advance of the sixteenth century had begun to wane. The student will find it an interesting exercise to locate the exact historical events which are associated with the major movements in the index.

From recent events in the economy of the United States we know that dangerous economic difficulties develop at the top of the trade cycle. Then it is that we may expect to find our most spectacular historical events. Since there is considerable similarity in this regard between the Spanish index in the years between 1620 and 1650 and the American index between 1920 and the present time, one may raise the old question of whether history repeats itself. Although the exact events which occasioned the following paragraph are not specified, and the precise years to which it applies are not stated, the comments are designed to interpret the political situation which prevailed in Spain before its decline, that is to say, in the period under discussion. The paragraph is quoted from the eleventh edition of the *Encyclopaedia Britannica*, published in 1911, and hence was uninfluenced by the events of recent years:

> Encouragement of industry was not wanting; the state undertook to develop the herds of merino sheep, by issuing prohibitions against inclosures, which proved the ruin of agriculture, and gave premiums for large merchant ships, which ruined the owners of small vessels and reduced the merchant navy of Spain to a handful of galleons. *Tasas*, fixed prices, were placed on everything. The weaver, the fuller, the armourer, the potter, the shoemaker were told exactly how to do their own work. All this did not bear its full fruit during the reign of the Catholic sovereigns but by the end of the 16th century it had reduced Spain to a state of byzantine regulation in which every kind of work had to be done under the eye and subject to the interference of a vast swarm of government officials, all ill paid, and often not paid, all therefore necessitous and corrupt. When the New World was opened, commerce with it was limited to Seville in order that the supervision of the state might be more easily exercised. The great resource of the treasury was the *alcabalas* or excises — taxes (farmed by contractors) of 5 or 10% on an article every time it was sold — on the ox when sold to the butcher, on the hide when sold to the tanner, on the dressed hide sold to the shoemaker and on his shoes. All this also did not bear its full fruit until later times, but by the 17th century it had made Spain one of the two "most beggardly nations in Europe" — the other being Portugal.

6. The Role of Cycles in American History

Since we now possess so many long series relating to basic economic variables, it will be an interesting and perhaps instructive exercise to examine the correlation between great historical movements in American history and the corresponding variations observable in the time series themselves. We shall comment briefly on a few of the most conspicuous patterns.

Referring to Figure 95, we have five basic series shown in their relationship to one another and to some of the most important events in the history of the United States. Since our history is taught as a series of events connected with the administrations of the presidents, the names of these and the lengths of their terms of office are shown at the top of the figure.

The first and most conspicuous observations is that war is the great inflator, as we have had occasion to remark earlier in the book. In American history these price inflations have occurred at intervals of 50 years. The exact dates of the three maxima in the curve of prices are respectively November, 1814, August, 1864, and May, 1920. The intervals are thus 49 years and 8 months, and 55 years and 7 months respectively. The relative significance of these three major conflicts is shown by the fact that the effects of the Mexican War (1846–1848) and of the Spanish-American war (1898) are almost negligible.

A tentative deduction may be made from this, that the magnitude of a war in relation to its effect upon the economic system of the conflicting powers can be measured roughly by means of an index of the following form:

$$W(t) = \frac{P(t) - P_0}{P_0}, \tag{13}$$

where $P(t)$ is the index of prices at time t, defined as the date at the end of the price inflation created by the war, and P_0 is the general level of prices which prevailed in the period before the conflict. Since a country may not actually be involved in a war and yet be affected by it, the index may be used to measure these secondary influences.

The value of $W(t)$ for some conflicts for which data are available are given in the table on page 443.

From this table we see that the War of 1812 was much less severe in its effects than were the two later conflicts. Although the inflationary peak in 1814 compares in height with the other two, one readily notes that it arose from a considerably higher initial plateau of prices.

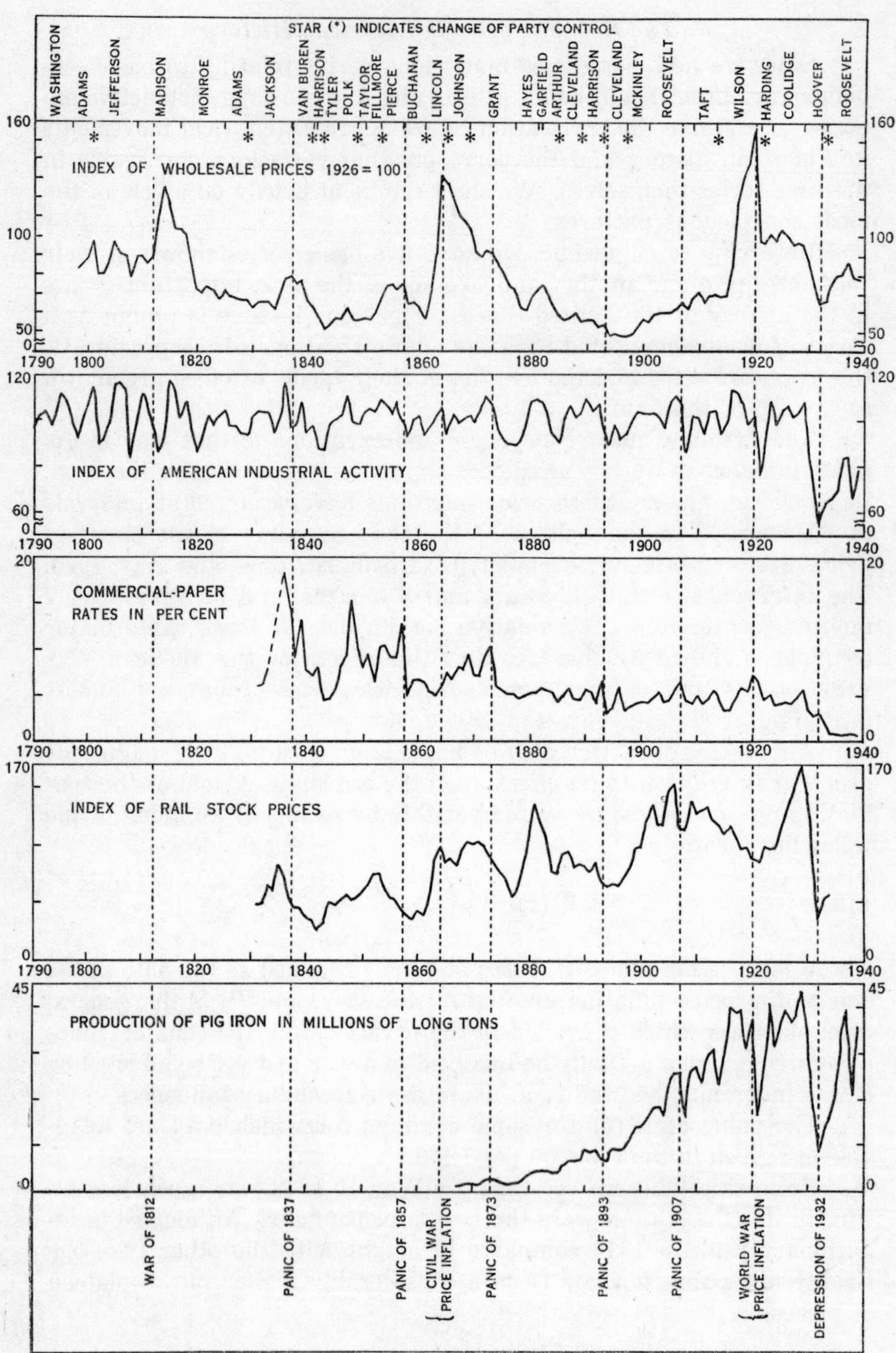

FIGURE 95. — INTERACTIONS BETWEEN POLITICAL EVENTS AND ECONOMIC VARIATIONS.

War	Country	Date (t)	$W(t)$
Napoleonic	England	1815	0.49
War of 1812	United States	1814	0.45
Franco-Prussian	Germany	1871	0.30
	England	1871	0.16
U. S. Civil War	United States	1864	1.13
World War	United States	1920	1.23
	England	1921	1.95
	France	1926	7.03
	Germany	1923	∞
Sino-Japanese	China	Mar., 1938	0.61
	Japan	Mar., 1938	0.35

It is probably much more than a coincidence that the decline of the price index after each of the three war inflations is observed to follow much the same pattern. First there is a rapid drop, largely in the price of farm commodities, from which comes the farm problem. From this decline there ensues a short respite, which in the decade of the twenties was called the period of the Coolidge prosperity. Then comes a second drop which is long and severe. The one following the Civil War was initiated by the panic of 1873, and the one following the World War by the collapse of stock prices in 1929. This decline finally stops and there ensues a period of mild inflation, which terminates once more in panic and hard times. Thus the inflation which began in the administration of Andrew Jackson ended with the panic of 1837, and that which began in the administration of Hayes terminated with the panic of 1884. The bottom of this final decline was reached in one case in 1843 and in the other in 1895. During the intervening years there is business pessimism, industrial unrest, and general hard times. The ensuing period, however, is one of advancing prosperity. Business increases, the tempo of industrial life improves, minor crises like the rich man's panic of 1907 are easily overcome, and prosperity returns. Alas, this promising period, the most prosperous one in the nation's history, terminates again with another war inflation and the fatal cycle repeats itself. Such appear to be the principal characteristics of the war cycle.

We also notice from Figure 95 that the movement of prices appears to have a great influence upon party politics as it prevails in the United States. Thus we observe that changes in the control of political parties have occurred for the most part at the bottom of a severe drop in prices or during a protracted decline. Of the 14 such changes, excluding the changes occasioned by the deaths of William Henry Harrison and Lincoln, 10 occurred during or at the bottom of such depression periods. It will be observed also that four of the most thoroughly repudiated American presidents, Van Buren, Buchanan, Johnson, and Hoover, had the misfortune of holding office during severe declines of the price index. Van Buren and Hoover were rejected by electoral votes of 60 to 234 and 59 to 472 respectively. Neither Buchanan nor Johnson was renominated.

The curious failure of the Democratic party to gain control after the spectacular decline of prices during Grant's administration needs explanation. This is found in the confusion which surrounded the election of Hayes. In the electoral college Tilden, his opponent, had 184 uncontested votes, one short of election, to 163 for Hayes. Two conflicting ballots were sent in by the states of South Carolina, Florida, Oregon, and Louisiana. The "Electoral Commission," appointed to settle the controversy, decided each contested ballot by a vote of 7 to 8 for Hayes. By so close a margin as this was the expected economic reversal of party defeated in 1877.

The reversals of party control in 1853 and 1913, contrary to the economic forecast, also have historical explanations. The first was undoubtedly due to the shadow of the coming conflict, economic in large part, between the slavery and the anti-slavery interests. Favoring compromise in slavery, Fillmore failed to get the nomination and Pierce was chosen by an electoral vote of 254 to 42. In 1913 the split in the Republican party, occasioned by the feud between Theodore Roosevelt and Taft, allowed the minority party to win. The popular vote of Roosevelt and Taft was 7,610,000; that for Wilson was 6,286,000. The electoral vote was 435 for Wilson, 88 for Roosevelt, and 8 for Taft.

The re-election of Monroe in 1821, during a period of price deflation, is a curious incident since it was nearly unanimous, one electoral vote only being cast against him. His second term was called the era of good feeling. But it is clear from the curve of industrial production that the country by 1821 was emerging rapidly from the effects of the deflation in prices. Trade was expanding and not unlikely the financial difficulties occasioned by the price decline were offset by the rapidly enlarging economic invasion of western territory.

The great increase in the wealth, prestige, and well-being of the United States since 1880 is told more eloquently by the production curve of pig iron than by any description of special incidents. No period in history, with the possible exceptions of the age of Pericles in Athens, the age of Augustus in Rome, the sixteenth century in Spain, and the nineteenth century in England, has shown so remarkable an advance in culture and general standard of living as has taken place in the United States from 1880 to 1930. The golden age of science, accelerated by the founding and development of a great public school system, will undoubtedly be attributed by history to this period.

This brief survey of the possibilities of throwing new light upon the facts of American history can do no more than indicate the problem and its setting. But there is no doubt that in the secular trend of the time series of rail stock prices we can see the drama of the development of the railroads and the opening of the western empire of the United States. What drama also lies behind the great fluctuations of interest rates during the administration of Jackson and the period of the California gold rush!

7. *Conclusion*

In this chapter we have surveyed briefly some of the evidence which has been presented to show the existence of cycles in economic time series. To a certain extent the nature of this evidence is similar to that introduced in problems in *inverse probability*. The reader will recall that inverse probability attempts to state the chance that, if an event is known to have proceeded from n mutually exclusive causes, it proceeded from a specified one of these causes.

To illustrate, let us suppose that the evidence of the periodogram shows that for a certain period, T, there exists a maximum value of R. Let us assume further that we know the distribution of the values of R as a frequency function, $y = F(R)$, where $\int_0^\infty F(R)\, dR = 1$. Then the probability that R will have a value between R_0 and $R_0 + dR$ is given by $F(R_0)\,dR$, and the probability that R will exceed R_0 in value is

$$P = 1 - \int_0^{R_0} F(R)\, dR \,. \tag{14}$$

This probability may be regarded as giving us a measure of our belief in the reality of the structure through the observation of a value of R in the periodogram which exceeds R_0.

Let us assume that P is very small for some observed value of R, and we are asked, as a result of this evidence, whether or not the corresponding value of T may be regarded as a permanent characteristic of the time series. Clearly we may assume either that it is such a permanent characteristic, or that it is not. What probability shall we assign to these two mutually exclusive propositions? In the language of inverse probability we may say: An event (the observation of the improbable value of R) is known to have proceeded from two mutually exclusive causes (either the cycle of period T is a permanent characteristic of the time series, or it is not). What is the probability, p, that the event proceeded from the first cause?

The well known formula in inverse probability may then be written

$$p = \frac{(1-P)P_1}{(1-P)P_1 + P(1-P_1)}, \tag{15}$$

where P is obtained from (14) and P_1 is the probability of the first assumed cause of the observation, namely, that the cycle is a permanent characteristic of the series.

Now values as large as 0.995 for $1 - P$ are not infrequently observed directly from the periodograms of economic time series. But what value shall we give to P_1? If we invoke the principle of insufficient reason we may set $P_1 = \frac{1}{2}$, and thus obtain $p = 1 - P = 0.995$.

But a personal inquiry into our belief in this figure shows that it is far from realistic. No one who has worked intimately with the data will believe that the chances are 995 in 1000 that any cycle revealed by a periodogram over some period of time will persist through the suceeding period. It is thus clear that the principle of insufficient reason is an unsatisfactory postulate, and that personal estimates of p are essentially easier to make than direct estimates of P_1 itself. Hence, it is more satisfactory to solve (15) for P_1 in terms of p. We thus obtain

$$P_1 = \frac{pP}{(1-p)(1-P) + pP}. \tag{16}$$

If we now set $p = \frac{1}{2}$, we get $P = 0.005$, which states that, in spite of the unusual size of the observed value of R in the periodogram, and in spite of our half measure of belief that it is evidence of a permanent structure, if such a structure actually exists, the probability that the observed value of R actually came from such a permanent pattern is only 0.005.

From this analysis we see the great importance which must be attached to quests for a satisfactory theory of the origin of cycles, such a theory, for example, as one of those discussed in Chapter 18. How much greater, thus, would be our confidence in the 10-year cycle of business as shown in the periodogram, if we could rely on an analysis similar to that introduced by Kalecki!

But if we are willing to assume that certain structures are observed in economic time series, and if we grant that these structures are reasonably repetitive and permanent, then there are conclusions which can be derived from the fact of their existence. Some of these have been tentatively set forth in the preceding section of this chapter. Whether the reader believes that we have been dealing with fact or fancy must depend to a large extent upon his personal reaction to the evidence that has been presented.

PROBLEMS

1. Represent graphically the values of ρ in the table of Section 4. What conclusions can you draw from the cyclical variation of this ratio?

2. Find the serial correlation between ρ and total income I' as given in Section 4. What inference do you draw from this relationship?

3. Estimate the length of the Spanish trade cycle as shown in the data from 1620 to 1650.

4. Estimate the value of R^2 for the Spanish trade cycle. Compute σ^2 from the data and evaluate $E(T)$.

5. The following table shows the number of registered vessels sailing to and from the Indies from the ports of Spain from 1506 to 1555 inclusive:[9]

Year	No. of Vessels	Year	No. of Vessels	Year	No. of Vessels	Year	No. of Vessels	Year	No. of Vessels	Year	No. of Vessels
1506	34	1515	63	1524	70	1532	84	1540	126	1548	162
1507	51	1516	52	1525	110	1533	97	1541	139	1549	174
1508	67	1517	94	1526	96	1534	121	1542	150	1550	157
1509	47	1518	98	1527	109	1535	128	1543	128	1551	162
1510	27	1519	92	1528	72	1536	151	1544	76	1552	125
1511	34	1520	108	1529	104	1537	70	1545	135	1553	79
1512	54	1521	64	1530	112	1538	104	1546	144	1554	27
1513	61	1522	43	1531	87	1539	116	1547	158	1555	109
1514	76	1523	54								

Represent these data graphically and compare with the index of Spanish trade over this period. Compare also with the money index. What would you infer about trade with the Indies after 1555?

6. Soetbeer's estimates show that the total treasure accumulated by Europe from 1500 to 1650 expressed in ounces of gold was as follows:

Year	Ounces of Gold	Year	Ounces of Gold
1501	327,000	1600	85,529,028
1525	8,980,685	1625	119,059,588
1550	25,208,698	1650	147,562,228
1575	52,668,808		

[9] Data from Appendix 8 of C. H. Harding's *Trade and Navigation Between Spain and the Indies in the Time of the Hapsburgs*. Cambridge, Mass., 1918, xxvii + 371 pp. The author says: "The figures in these tables were secured from a volume in the Archivo de Indias (30.2.1/3) entitled: 'Libro de registros de las naos que han ido y venido á las Indias desde el año de 1504 en adelante'. It seems to be a sort of index or calendar of the registers which passed through the Casa de Contratación. Whether the list is complete or not there is no means of knowing."

Compare these estimates with the Spanish importation as reported by Hamilton. If prices rose in other countries as rapidly as they did in Spain, how rapidly did their trade increase?

7. If we had assumed as the initial treasure in Spain an amount just half as great as that actually assumed, what would the trade have been by 1550? by 1650?

8. Answer problem 7 on the assumption that the initial treasure in Spain was twice as great as that actually assumed.

9. From some history of Spain attempt to find the events which led to the trade declines of 1625, 1641, and 1646.

10. Black Friday according to the dictionary is "any of various Fridays on which disastrous events occurred as in the U. S., Sept. 24, 1869, and Sept. 19, 1873." Are these dates in evidence in any of the curves shown in Figure 95?

11. Find from history the causes of the rises in the curve of wholesale prices for the United States around the years 1837, 1855, and 1882.

SELECTED BIBLIOGRAPHY ON THE THEORY OF BUSINESS CYCLES

BRATT, E. C. *Business Cycles and Forecasting.* Chicago, 1937, xiii + 501 pp.

COWDEN, D. J. (See F. E. Croxton).

CROXTON, F. E. (with D. J. COWDEN). *Applied General Statistics.* New York, 1939, xviii + 944 pp. In particular, Chapters 17, 18, and 19.

DAVIS, H. T. *The Analysis of Economic Time Series.* Principia Press, 1941.

FISHER, I. *Booms and Depressions.* New York, 1932, xxi + 258 pp.

HABERLER, G. VON. *Prosperity and Depression.* New edition, Geneva, 1939.

JEVONS, W. S. "On the Study of Periodic Commercial Fluctuations," 1862.

KEYNES, J. M. *The General Theory of Employment, Interest, and Money.* London, 1936, xii + 403 pp.

MITCHELL, W. C. (1) *Business Cycles, The Problem and its Setting.* New York, 1927, xxii + 489 pp.
(2) (See W. L. Thorp).

MOORE, H. L. *Economic Cycles: Their Law and Cause.* New York, 1914, viii + 149 pp.

PERSONS, W. H. *Forecasting Business Cycles.* New York, 1931, xiv + 295 pp.

SCHUMPETER, J. A. *Business Cycles, A Theoretical, Historical, and Statistical Analysis of the Capitalistic Processes.* Two volumes, New York, 1939, xvi + 1095 pp.

SELIGMAN, E. R. A. "The Economic Interpretation of History," *American Economic Association Publications,* Series 3, Vol. 3, 1902, pp. 369–397.

SNYDER, C. (1) *Capitalism the Creator.* New York, 1940, xii + 473 pp.
(2) *Business Cycles and Business Measurements.* New York, 1927, 326 pp.

THORP, W. L. (with W. C. MITCHELL). *Business Annals.* National Bureau of Economic Research, New York, 1926, 380 pp.

TINTNER, G. *Prices in the Trade Cycle.* Vienna, 1935, xii + 203 pp. + 2 sets of graphs.

WILSON, E. B. (1) "The Periodogram of American Business Activity," *Quarterly Journal of Economics,* Vol. 48, 1933–34, pp. 375–417.
(2) "Are there Periods in American Business Activity," *Science,* Vol. 80, 1934, pp. 193–199.

CHAPTER 20

International Exchange

1. *Historical Note*

The first mathematical treatment of the theory of foreign exchange was made by A. A. Cournot in the third chapter of his classical treatise on *The Theory of Wealth,* published in 1838. In this work Cournot makes the assumption that "all commercial peoples have adopted the same monetary unit, for instance, one gram of fine silver, or, what amounts to the same thing, that the ratio of each monetary unit to a gram of fine silver be permanently established."

Unfortunately Cournot's assumption holds very tenuously in a realistic world. The impact of wars and of great commercial crises from time to time cause extraordinary changes in national currencies. The loss of gold reserves will force a nation to abandon the gold standard and from that time on the currency will be subjected to the buffets of every commercial storm. The stabilization of currencies seems to be a dream the fulfillment of which appears today to be very remote. D. Ricardo (1772–1823) many years ago appraised the situation accurately when he said that "the exchange accurately measures the depreciation of the currency."[1]

The reason for the existence of a gold standard in international trade is precisely to accomplish the stability of currencies postulated by Cournot. In periods of economic calm it has worked with reasonable satisfaction. But in periods of economic stress the gold standard has failed completely as a mechanism of currency stabilization. Prior to 1933 the American dollar was defined as 23.22 grains of fine gold, the English pound as 113.00 grains. On January 1, 1934 an abrupt change was made by fiat in these values and the dollar became equal to $13\frac{5}{7}$ grains; the pound has freed itself entirely from the gold definition. Because of the favorable ratio between the American dollar and gold as a result of this abrupt change, there ensued a steady flow of gold toward the United States until this country has accumulated in its vaults 75 per cent of the entire stock of monetary gold in the world. This abnormal accumulation has resulted in essential abandonment of the gold standard by most of the other countries.

[1] *Letters of Ricardo to Malthus,* edited by J. Bonar, 1887, p. 15.

The problems of international trade have intrigued the imagination of many economists and numerous works are available on the subject, a few of which are referred to in the selected *Bibliography* at the end of this chapter. A number of theories have been advanced to account for the existence of foreign trade, to explain the fluctuations in the ratios of different currencies, and to compare the advantages of free trade with that restrained by protective tariffs. Many of the theories are still conjectural and the subject is replete with controversy, as one might well believe where comprehensive data are scanty and hypotheses numerous. Of recent treatises one of the most adequate is that by G. von Haberler, published in 1933 in German, but made available in an English translation in 1936. This work has the advantage of surveying the problem from the background of the chaotic Germany economy, which passed through an infinite inflation and emerged with one of the most stable currencies in Europe. More recently the extensive studies of J. Viner have reached fruition in a comprehensive treatise published in 1937 (see *Bibliography*). This work is definitive of the present status of the problem.

Mathematical theories have been advanced by F. Y. Edgeworth, V. Pareto, and T. O. Yntema. Edgeworth in a series of elaborate papers attempted to explain the variations in international trade in terms of the Marshallian theory by maximizing a composite utility function for two countries, taking account of the disutility which measures the work expended in creating the goods exchanged. Pareto, on the other hand, extended his equilibrium theory to include the conditions of international trade. He did not go beyond the point of enumerating variables and expressing them in terms of a sufficient number of equations to make their evaluation determinate. The equations of general equilibrium serve also as the basis of the discussion of the problem made by Yntema. His theory extends the demand and supply relationships of the ordinary theory to the problem of international trade.

Extensive discussions have also been made by J. W. Angell, G. Cassel, F. W. Taussig, A. C. Pigou and others. These writers, however, produced their works in the decade between 1920 and 1930, just at a time when spectacular events were taking place which were to shed new light upon the mechanism of international trade. That we yet have a full comprehension of the meaning of these events is doubtful, but that the phenomena of recent years promise to provide a factual background for some of the perplexing problems is clearly demonstrated.

The construction of an adequate theory is also complicated by the nature of the international medium of exchange. At the time when Cournot wrote his *Theory of Wealth,* this medium was principally silver because of its relative abundance, but by 1870 the substantial increase in the production of gold had made possible the adoption of this metal as an international standard. A history of this interesting change will be found in a recent publication by D. H. Leavens on *Silver Money* (see *Bibliography*). During the sixteenth century the value of gold in terms of silver was in the ratio approximately of 12 to 1. This ratio fluctuated so slightly over the intervening years that in 1896 W. J. Bryan ran for the presidency of the United States on a free silver platform advocating a bimetallism in the ratio of 16 to 1. Can we wonder at the perplexities of international monetary experts when we observe that this ratio in recent years has reached the fantastic figure of 100 to 1?

A partial, if not a complete, breakdown in the gold standard for international trade has come about through the vast increase in the gold holdings of the United States. As we have said earlier, the value of gold in terms of the dollar was increased 69 per cent by fiat, and at the same time gold was demonetized as a medium of internal trade in the United States. As a result of this and of the urgent needs of Europe, a great flow of gold has taken place into the United States until 75 per cent or more of the total monetary gold of the world lies fallow in the vaults of the United States Treasury. The result of this unparalleled movement has been to throw most of the world's currencies onto a non-metallic basis. Adopting a current euphemism, we now speak of these systems as *managed currencies.*

2. The Problem of International Exchange

In the preceding section we have given some indication of the complexity of the problem of international trade. We shall now consider one aspect of it, namely the question of international exchange. By this we mean the problem of determining the ratios between the currencies of different countries having trade with one another.

In order to realize the complexities of the situation, let us examine the data given in the following table which shows the exchange ratios between the United States dollar, the English pound, the French franc, and the German mark. In 1914 the parities in terms of the dollar were respectively \$4.8665, \$0.1929, and \$0.2382, which, it will be observed from the table, were essentially equal to the actual quotations for the year in question. For the sake of ready comparison the

EXCHANGE RATIOS EXPRESSED AS DOLLARS AND AS INDEX NUMBERS

Year	Pound	%	Franc	%	Mark	%	Year	Pound	%	Franc	%	Mark	%
1914	$4.905	100	$0.1952	100	$0.2346	100	1927	$4.861	99	$0.0392	20	$0.2376	101
1915	4.751	97	0.1798	92	0.2061	88	1928	4.866	99	0.0392	20	0.2386	102
1916	4.759	97	0.1697	87	0.1817	77	1929	4.857	99	0.0391	20	0.2381	101
1917	4.754	97	0.1730	89	0.1572	67	1930	4.862	99	0.0393	20	0.2385	102
1918	4.755	97	0.1780	91	0.1718	73	1931	4.532	92	0.0392	20	0.2363	101
1919	4.431	90	0.1441	64	0.0670	29	1932	3.504	71	0.0393	20	0.2375	101
1920	3.659	75	0.0702	36	0.0175	7	1933	4.201	86	0.0501	26	0.3037	129
1921	3.852	79	0.0746	38	0.0121	5	1934	5.039	103	0.0657	34	0.3938	168
1922	4.429	90	0.0819	42	0.0023	1	1935	4.902	100	0.0660	34	0.4026	172
1923	4.574	93	0.0607	31	....	......	1936	4.971	101	0.0612	31	0.4030	172
1924	4.418	90	0.0523	27	0.2380	101	1937	4.945	101	0.0405	21	0.4021	171
1925	4.829	98	0.0477	24	0.2380	101	1938	4.890	100	0.0288	15	0.4016	171
1926	4.858	99	0.0325	17	0.2380	101	1939	4.435	90	0.0251	13	0.4006	171

exchange values are reduced to index numbers, 1914 = 100.

The index numbers given in the table are graphically represented in Figure 96 about which certain instructive observations may be made. The repercussions of the World War upon the currencies of European nations are clearly seen in the violent fluctuations of the ratios in the deflationary period from 1918 to 1926, and again in the depression period from 1930 to 1935. The most striking phenomenon, perhaps, is the history of the German mark. This monetary unit declined to zero in 1923; it was recreated the next year to its prewar parity, and then gained added stature in the gold revaluation of 1934. The increase of 69 per cent, exactly accounted for by the 69 per cent increase in the value of gold referred to the dollar, was maintained during the subsequent years in spite of the fact that Germany had

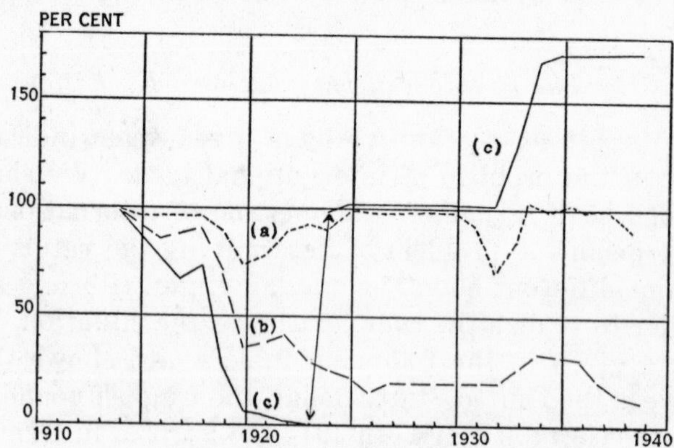

FIGURE 96.—VALUES OF THE RATIOS OF EXCHANGE IN TERMS OF DOLLARS, REDUCED TO PER CENT OF 1914 VALUES: (a) THE POUND; (b) THE FRANC; (c) THE MARK.

less than 0.8 of one per cent of the world's gold in 1933 and less than 0.2 of one per cent in 1936.

The extreme variability of the franc throughout the period embraced by the table, and its decline to new lows after the temporary effect of the gold revaluation had been expended, is in striking contrast to that of the mark. The English pound, to which many currencies have been tied in international exchange, also had an unstable history. It succeeded in recovering from the great war deflation of 1920. The second decline of the pound, which began in 1931, was reversed by the revaluation of gold in 1934, and the pound exceeded its 1914 value for the first time in 20 years. But this prosperous level was short-lived, a third decline being ushered in by the conflict which began in 1939.

This history of fluctuations in European currencies, which we have just described, is in great contrast to the history of stable international exchange which prevailed for many years in the period prior to 1914. The explanation of these contrasting phenomena is essentially the problem of international exchange.

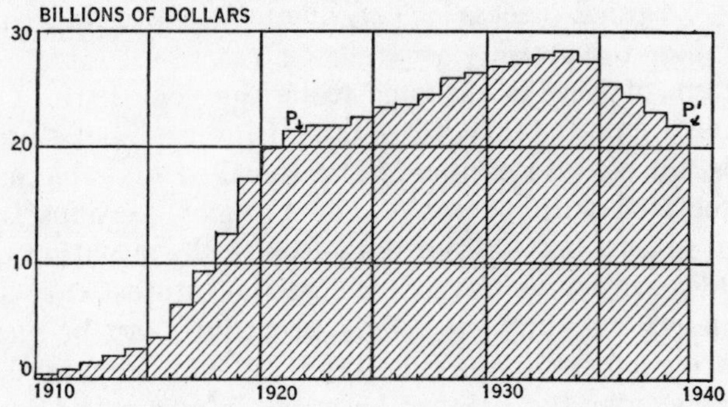

FIGURE 97.—ACCUMULATION OF THE EXCESS OF MERCHANDISE + GOLD + SILVER IN THE FOREIGN TRADE OF THE UNITED STATES IN BILLIONS OF DOLLARS.

At the point P the war debt was 9.6 billions and at the point P' the debt was 13.1 billions.

It would be very satisfactory, indeed, if we could deduce the change in the money ratios from the statistics of the balance of trade between the nations involved. By the term *balance of trade,* economists generally mean the difference between the amount of goods exported and the amount imported. If this difference is positive, then the trade balance is said to be favorable, but if the difference is negative, then the balance is unfavorable. In considering the balance of trade some disagreement prevails among economists as to whether imports and exports of gold and silver should be included in the balance. Adam Smith argued that treasure was a commodity like any other goods classified as mercantile. But others have held that treasure functions as an international money, and hence the movements of gold and silver should be regarded separately. Since the significance of the hoard of gold recently amassed by the United States is still a highly controversial subject, one may incline to either opinion. However, it must be observed that the most significant change in the ratios of exchange was caused by the fiat devaluation of gold in 1934.

In order to see how difficult would be the problem of accounting for the exchange ratios from the point of view of the balance of trade, let us examine this balance from the point of view of the United States. In Figure 97 there is shown the value of the integral

$$y(t) = \int_0^t E(t)\, dt ,$$

where we use the abbreviation

$E(t)$ = *Annual excess of merchandise + gold + silver exported over that imported.*

The origin of time is assumed to be the year 1910. Clearly this sum should be accumulated at some rate of interest, but since the trade balance does not contain explicitly the so-called invisible exports and imports associated with payments for services, perhaps the unaccumulated sum gives a better approximation to the situation than otherwise. In other words, we have cancelled the interest rate against the invisible exports and imports. This procedure can be justified statistically since good estimates exist from 1919 of these invisible items. Thus, if we consider the balance between shipping and freight services, tourist expenditures, immigrant remittances, interest and dividend payments, war debt receipts, balance of government transactions, and miscellaneous commodity and service items, the value of $y(t)$ is reduced from 1919 to 1936 by a matter of 5,156.0 millions of dollars. This difference can be compensated for by accumulating $y(t)$ for 1918 at a force of interest slightly less than 2 per cent per annum. The values of $y(t)$ and $E(t)$ over the period in question are given in the table on page 455.

We observe from the table that the value of $y(t)$ reached a maximum value in excess of 28 billion dollars in 1933. But in the following year the gold devaluation started a flood of treasure toward the United States and by 1938 the accumulation in the balance had been

EXCESS OF MERCHANDISE + GOLD + SILVER AND ITS ACCUMULATION
(Unit = $1,000,000)

Year	$E(t)$	$y(t)$	Year	$E(t)$	$y(t)$	Year	$E(t)$	$y(t)$
1910	273.3	273.3	1920	2,880.1	20,010.1	1930	513.6	27,115.5
1911	489.8	763.1	1921	1,296.9	21,307.0	1931	186.2	27,301.7
1912	577.3	1,340.4	1922	472.7	21,779.7	1932	728.7	28,030.4
1913	691.8	2,032.2	1923	79.4	21,859.1	1933	357.7	28,388.1
1914	540.8	2,573.0	1924	758.9	22,618.0	1934	−728.7	27,645.8
1915	1,090.9	3,663.9	1925	852.2	23,470.2	1935	−1,839.4	25,806.4
1916	2,599.1	6,263.0	1926	302.6	23,772.8	1936	−1,254.0	24,552.4
1917	3,131.3	9,394.3	1927	695.1	24,467.9	1937	−1,399.8	23,152.6
1918	3,278.4	12,672.7	1928	1,448.0	25,915.9	1938	−1,063.0	22,089.6
1919	4,457.3	17,130.0	1929	686.0	26,601.9	1939		

reduced by six billion dollars. It would thus appear, as we have said before, that the net result of the Gold Reserve Act of 1934 has been to siphon most of the monetary metal out of the treasuries of other nations and into the treasury of the United States. In the process the exchange ratios of other currencies in terms of the dollar were benefited, but in varying degrees. Thus, from their values in 1939, the pound-dollar ratio increased a matter of 32 per cent, the franc-dollar ratio 14 per cent, and the mark-dollar ratio 71 per cent. But the fact that the ratios were thus affected by such different amounts indicates that the problem of international exchange cannot be explained on the basis of the value of gold and its relationship to the accumulated excess measured by $y(t)$.

Although the existence of a great international debt between nations must have some influence upon the stability of international prices, since these are certainly affected by international credits, the mere existence of the debt does not necessarily affect the ratios of exchange directly. The enormous increase in $y(t)$ since 1910 is partially accounted for by the credits extended to European countries during the World War. This international indebtedness to the United States reached the considerable figure of 9,597.5 millions of dollars by November 15, 1921 and had increased to 13,119.3 millions of dollars by March 1, 1939. But the movements of the exchange ratios are in no manner accounted for by this debt, since the variation of the debt has always been in a positive direction, whereas the ratios have changed in both directions over the period under examination.

3. International Exchange and Internal Prices

Although as we have seen that the problem presented by the variation in the ratios of exchange is a very complex one, the most satisfactory explanation of large secular movements is to be found in the behavior of internal prices.

We shall not attempt to give a full account here, but it is instructive to examine the relationship between the pound and the dollar from the point of view of the fluctuations of the internal prices of these two countries. In the following table we give the values of the indexes of wholesale prices (1926 = 100) in England and the United States and the ratio of the pound to the dollar, reduced to an index over the period from 1920 to 1938.

WHOLESALE PRICE INDEXES FOR ENGLAND AND THE UNITED STATES AND THEIR RATIO (1926 = 100)

Year	English Index	U. S. Index	Ratio	Year	English Index	U. S. Index	Ratio	Year	English Index	U. S. Index	Ratio
1920	207.8	154.4	75	1927	95.5	95.4	100	1934	71.1	75.0	106
1921	135.9	97.6	72	1928	94.7	96.7	102	1935	71.8	80.0	111
1922	107.1	96.7	90	1929	92.2	95.3	103	1936	76.2	80.8	106
1923	107.4	100.6	93	1930	80.8	86.4	107	1937	87.1	86.3	99
1924	112.2	98.1	88	1931	70.3	73.0	104	1938	81.2	77.1	95
1925	107.8	103.5	96	1932	68.9	64.9	94	1939	......	78.6	......
1926	100.0	100.0	100	1933	69.2	66.0	95	1940			

The ratio between the wholesale prices of England and the United States and the ratio of the pound to the dollar, reduced to an index number with 1926 = 100, are graphically shown in Figure 98. From this we see that there is a general agreement between the two series. The greatest variation is found in the period around 1932 and 1933, when the international gold situation had become acute.

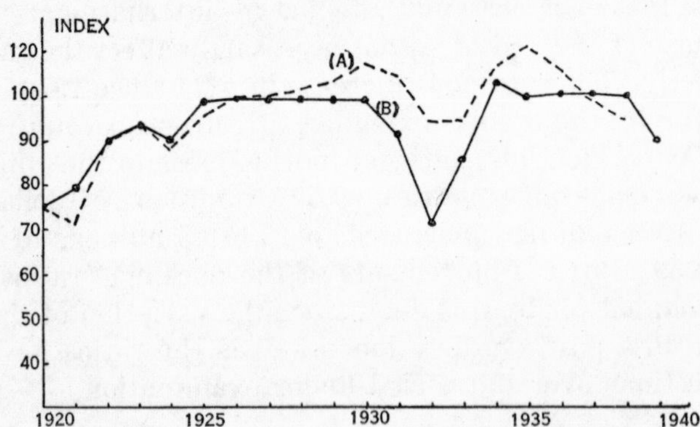

FIGURE 98.—RELATIONSHIP BETWEEN EXCHANGE RATIOS AND RATIOS OF INTERNAL PRICES. (A) RATIO OF AMERICAN WHOLESALE PRICE INDEX TO BRITISH WHOLESALE PRICE INDEX; (B) POUND-DOLLAR EXCHANGE RATIO. (1926 = 100).

From this discussion it will be learned that, although there is a high correlation between the ratio of internal prices and the ratio of

Balance of trade = Goods sold – goods bought + treasure exported – treasure imported = $E(t)$

$\int_{1910}^{t} E(t)\,dt$

exchange between two countries, the entire variation is not to be accounted for so simply. The reason is not difficult to find. The ratio of exchange is not a simple function of two economies, but it is related also to the economies of all other countries. Some indication of this connection will be developed in the next section.

PROBLEMS

1. The following data show the index number of wholesale prices in Germany from 1914 to 1922 inclusive (1913 = 100), as given by C. Bresciani-Turroni in *The Economics of Inflation*, English edition, 1937:

	1914	1915	1916	1917	1918	1919	1920	1921	1922
Jan.	96	126	150	156	204	262	1260	1440	3670
Feb.	96	133	151	158	198	270	1680	1380	4100
March	96	139	148	159	198	274	1710	1340	5430
April	95	142	149	163	204	286	1571	1330	6350
May	97	139	151	163	203	297	1510	1310	6460
June	99	139	152	165	209	308	1380	1370	7030
July	99	150	161	172	208	339	1370	1430	10060
Aug.	109	146	159	203	235	422	1450	1920	19200
Sept.	111	145	154	199	230	493	1500	2070	28700
Oct.	118	147	153	201	234	562	1470	2460	56600
Nov.	123	147	151	203	234	678	1510	3420	115400
Dec.	125	149	151	203	245	803	1440	3490	147500

Using these data together with the values of the general price index for the United States as they are given in Section 7 of Chapter 12, estimate the dollar-mark exchange rate over the period from 1914 to 1922 inclusive. Compare your estimates with the annual averages given in Section 2 of this chapter.

2. Employing the data on the dollar-franc exchange rate over the period from 1914 to 1926 inclusive as given in Section 2 of this chapter, estimate from the general price index for the United States as given in Section 7 of Chapter 12, the extent of the French inflation.

3. From June, 1931 to April, 1933 inclusive the monthly average of the dollar-yen exchange rate correlated 0.8551 with the value of imports from Japan. What conclusion would you draw from this fact?

4. *The Equations of the Rates of Exchange*

In preceding sections we have discussed the problem of the secular changes in the rates of exchange caused by large dislocations in internal prices and by excessive movements of gold from one or more countries to another. We shall now consider the problem from a more restrictive point of view, namely, on the basis of an exchange of credits between financial centers in different countries over short periods of time. Although Cournot, who first discussed the problem, considered the transactions as annual exchanges, we shall assume that the movements of money take place within shorter intervals of time. The theory thus attempts to account, first, for the existence of comparatively stable exchange ratios over short periods of time, and, second, for the equilibrium maintained between them.

Adopting Cournot's notation, we shall say that m_{ij} is the total of the sums for which the center (i) is indebted to center (j) over some fixed interval of time, and that m_{ij} is the sum for which center (j) is indebted to center (i). Let us represent by c_{ij} the rate of exchange between the currency of center (i) and the currency of center (j). It is obvious that c_{ji} will be the reciprocal of c_{ij}; that is to say;

$$(1) \qquad c_{ij} = \frac{1}{c_{ji}} .$$

If we consider the case of r centers, then the subscripts i and j must be permuted among the numbers $1, 2, 3, \cdots, r$, excepting only that $i \neq j$. We thus see that there will be $r(r-1)$ such permutations. But because of the relationship noted in equation (1), the number of independent ratios reduces to $\frac{1}{2}r(r-1)$.

But the number of independent ratios can be further reduced since the following relationship must also prevail between them:

$$(2) \qquad c_{ik} = c_{ij}\, c_{jk} .$$

This is readily established by noting that a dollar is worth c_{12} pounds in London and c_{13} francs in France, while a pound is worth c_{23} francs in France. If, then, c_{13} were less than the product $c_{12}\, c_{23}$ it would be advantageous in the exchange of dollars into francs to buy a draft on London, and with this to buy a draft on Paris. Conversely, if c_{13} were greater than $c_{12}\, c_{23}$, it would pay a trader in France to buy dollars in New York through a London draft.

The reader may verify that the number of relationships of the form given by (2) is equal to the following sum:

$$(3) \qquad (r-2) + (r-3) + \cdots + 2 + 1 = \tfrac{1}{2}(r-1)(r-2) .$$

The system which gives the equilibrium between centers at the time of settlement is given by the following

$$(4) \qquad \begin{aligned} m_{12} + m_{13} + \cdots + m_{1r} &= m_{21}\, c_{21} + m_{31}\, c_{31} + \cdots + m_{r1}\, c_{r1} , \\ m_{21} + m_{23} + \cdots + m_{2r} &= m_{12}\, c_{12} + m_{32}\, c_{32} + \cdots + m_{r2}\, c_{r2} , \\ m_{31} + m_{32} + \cdots + m_{3r} &= m_{13}\, c_{13} + m_{23}\, c_{23} + \cdots + m_{r3}\, c_{r3} , \\ &\cdots\cdots\cdots\cdots\cdots\cdots \\ m_{r1} + m_{r2} + \cdots + m_{r,r-1} &= m_{1r}\, c_{1r} + m_{2r}\, c_{2r} + \cdots + m_{r-1,r}\, c_{r-1,r} . \end{aligned}$$

In this system we have r equations in the $\frac{1}{2}r(r-1)$ unknown quantities c_{ij}. But from (2) and (3) we see that the actual number of unknown quantities is equal to $\frac{1}{2}r(r-1) - \frac{1}{2}(r-1)(r-2) = r-1$. We thus appear to have an over determination of the ratios of exchange since there are r equations in $r-1$ unknown quantities.

But if the equations in (4) after the first are multiplied successively by $c_{21}, c_{31}, \cdots, c_{r1}$, if the products of $c_{ij}\, c_{jk}$ are replaced by c_{ik}, noting that $c_{ii} = 1$, and if the resulting equations added, then the first equation of the system is obtained. Hence, in general, we have exactly $r - 1$ independent equations for the determination of the $r-1$ unknown ratios of exchange.

Example. Let us determine the ratios of exchange for the case of three financial centers.

Solution: In this case the system (4) assumes the form

$$
\begin{aligned}
m_{12} + m_{13} &= m_{21}c_{21} + m_{31}c_{31}, \\
m_{21} + m_{23} &= m_{12}c_{12} + m_{32}c_{32}, \\
m_{31} + m_{32} &= m_{13}c_{13} + m_{23}c_{23}.
\end{aligned} \tag{5}
$$

Multiplying the second equation by c_{21} and the third by c_{31}, and taking account of (2) we get the following system:

$$
\begin{aligned}
m_{21}c_{21} + \qquad\qquad m_{31}c_{31} &= m_{12} + m_{13}, \\
(m_{21} + m_{23})c_{21} - \qquad m_{32}c_{31} &= m_{12}, \\
m_{23}c_{21} - (m_{31} + m_{32})c_{31} &= -m_{13}.
\end{aligned}
$$

The solution of this system is immediately found from any two of these equations to be the following:

$$
\begin{aligned}
c_{21} &= \frac{m_{31}m_{12} + m_{12}m_{32} + m_{13}m_{32}}{m_{21}m_{31} + m_{21}m_{32} + m_{31}m_{23}}, \\
c_{31} &= \frac{m_{21}m_{13} + m_{12}m_{23} + m_{13}m_{23}}{m_{21}m_{31} + m_{21}m_{32} + m_{31}m_{23}}.
\end{aligned} \tag{6}
$$

The third ratio, c_{32}, is then obtained from these values from the relationship: $c_{32} = c_{31}/c_{21}$.

Commenting upon the result which we have just obtained, Cournot makes the following remark:

> The composition of the values c_{21}, c_{31}, and c_{32} in this particular case, shows clearly enough how the ratio of m_{12} to m_{21} can vary considerably, without causing great variation in the value of c_{21}, or, in other words, how the interconnection of centers of exchange diminishes the variation in the rate of exchange from one place to another.

It is interesting to examine the case where the denominators of the fractions in (6) vanish. Since the m_{ij} are positive or zero, these denominators vanish only when two of the values vanish. For example, this would be the case for any one of the following:

$$m_{21}=m_{31}=0\,, \qquad m_{21}=m_{23}=0\,, \qquad m_{31}=m_{32}=0\,.$$

If the first case is assumed to hold, then we shall have from (5)

$$m_{12}+m_{13}=0\,,$$

which means that $m_{12}=m_{13}=0$. Hence we obtain

$$c_{32}=\frac{m_{23}}{m_{32}}\,, \qquad c_{23}=\frac{m_{32}}{m_{23}}\,.$$

But this is the case of two markets only. Hence, we reach the conclusion that if the determinants are zero, then the markets are separated and there exists no exchange between (2) and (1) or (3) and (1).

The conclusion which we have reached for three markets can be extended without difficulty to r markets. This problem has been considered in detail by H. E. Bray (see *Bibliography*), who has determined the conditions under which the r centers break up into s sets of separate markets between members of which the ratios of exchange are determinate. He has also found conditions under which centers not included in the s sets of markets are bankrupt, and he has proved that "whereas the credit of each of them at any solvent market is zero, some of them have debit balances with at least one of the solvent markets."

PROBLEMS

1. Consider the case of three markets in which $m_{21}=m_{23}=0$, and show that the second market has no trade with the other two.

2. In system (4) let $r=4$. Multiply the second system by c_{31} and the second by c_{41}. Employing (2), show that these transformed equations together with the first equation give the following system:

$$m_{21}c_{21}+m_{31}c_{31}+m_{41}c_{41}=m_{12}+m_{13}+m_{14}\,,$$
$$(m_{12}+m_{23}+m_{24})c_{21}-m_{32}c_{31}-m_{42}c_{41}=m_{12}\,,$$
$$-m_{23}c_{21}+(m_{31}+m_{32}+m_{34})c_{13}-m_{43}c_{41}=m_{13}\,.$$

3. Solve the system in problem 2 for c_{21}, c_{31}, and c_{41}.

4. Determine conditions under which the first market would have no trade with the other three.

5. Determine conditions under which the four markets of problem 2 would break up into two independent systems of two markets each.

5. *Concluding Remarks*

We come finally to the end of this long task in which many economic theories have been surveyed. Wherever possible these theories have been subjected to review by that final court of appeals, the statistical data. There is evidence, alas, that in many instances we must think again, and certainly this is the case with the problem so cursorily surveyed in this brief chapter.

When the economic problems of a large and wealthy nation like the United States are difficult to solve, how immeasurably more complex become the problems of international trade! Standards of living vary among nations almost as much as they do among individuals. The desire for raw materials and the struggle to acquire the factors of production to fabricate them into useful commodities must necessarily create frictions between nations seeking to maintain, or better, their standards of living.

International trade is complicated by these national frictions and the free flow of commerce is frequently disrupted in one part of the world or another by wars. In spite of notable attempts to create a stabilizing union, as, for example, the Hague Tribunal established in 1899 and the League of Nations in 1920, there appears to be little prospect at the present time that the world will achieve an artificial mechanism for the successful operation of international trade. The suspicion among nations, which is never absent, prevents the establishment of anything resembling an international clearing house for international trade balances. The course of history supports this conclusion. In earlier times barter was the accepted method of exchange. In what we have believed to be more enlightened times, barter yielded to the use of gold and silver as a means of settling international balances, but this device in its turn has failed for the simple reason that one nation has obtained a monopoly on treasure.

Tariff walls between countries have prevented the free flow of goods from one place to another. The reasons for the existence of such walls are found, of course, in the different standards of living which prevail in different countries. Even in a country as homogeneous as the United States the existence of a sales tax in one state has created friction with adjoining states, where no such tax, or, perhaps, a lower tax, exists. The appearance of *ports of entry* in certain places has been a consequence, and but for the free-trade clause in the national Constitution, there would soon develop an intolerable situation in interstate commerce which could readily lead to conflict.

It seems fairly clear, however, from the great commercial success of the United States, in contrast to that of Europe, which has been interrupted by constant strife among its many separate nations, that the creation of superstates, where large areas might be free to trade with one another, would tend to reduce international friction, stabilize prices, and standardize conditions of living. But whether this is so, and how it is to be accomplished only the god of history knows.

SELECTED BIBLIOGRAPHY ON INTERNATIONAL EXCHANGE

ANGELL, J. W. *The Theory of International Prices.* Cambridge, Mass., 1926.

BRAY, H. E. "Rates of Exchange," *American Mathematical Monthly,* Vol. 29, 1922, pp. 365–371.

BROWN, W. A. JR. *The International Gold Standard Reinterpreted, 1914-1934.* New York, National Bureau of Economic Research, 1940, 2 vols., 1420 pp.

CASSEL, G. *Money and Foreign Exchange After 1914.* New York, 1923, vi + 287 pp.

COURNOT, A. A. *Mathematical Principles of the Theory of Wealth.* 1838, Chapter 3.

EDGEWORTH, F. Y. "The Theory of International Values," *Economic Journal,* Vol. 4, 1894, pp. 35–50, 424–443, 606–638. See also his *Papers Relating to Political Economy,* Vol. 2, London, 1925, pp. 3–60.

EVANS, G. C. *Mathematical Introduction to Economics.* New York, 1930, Chapter 7.

HABERLER, G. VON. *The Theory of International Trade.* London, 1936, xv + 408 pp.

LEAVENS, D. H. *Silver Money.* Cowles Commission Monograph No. 4, Principia Press, 1939, xix + 439 pp.

MOSAK, J. L. "A Mathematical Restatement of the Theory of International Trade," Doctor's Dissertation, University of Chicago, 1941.

PARETO, V. (1) "Teoria matematica dei cambi forestieri," *Giornale degli Econo misti,* Vol. 8, 1894, pp. 142–173.

(2) "Teoria matematica del commercio internazionale," *Ibid.,* Vol. 10, 1895, pp. 476–498.

PIGOU, A. C. (with D. H. ROBERTSON). *Economic Essays and Addresses.* London, 1931, vii + 215 pp.

RICARDO, D. *Letters of Ricardo to Malthus.* Edited by J. Bonar, 1887.

ROBERTSON, D. H. (see A. C. PIGOU).

TAUSSIG, F. W. *International Trade.* New York, 1927.

VINCI, F. "The Mean External Appreciation of Money and a New Definition of So-called External Prices," *Report of the Third Annual Conference of the Cowles Commission,* 1937, pp. 96–98.

VINER, J. (1) *Canada's Balance of International Indebtedness, 1900–1913.* Cambridge, Mass, 1924.

(2) *Studies in the Theory of International Trade.* New York, 1937, xv + 650 pp.

WHITAKER, A. C. *Foreign Exchange.* New York, 1919, xiv + 647 pp.

WICKSELL, K. *Lectures on Political Economy.* Vol. 2, New York, 1935, vi + 238 pp. In particular, pp. 102–126.

YNTEMA, T. O. (1) "The Influence of Dumping on Monopoly Prices," *Journal of Political Economy,* Vol. 36, 1928, pp. 686–698.

(2) *A Mathematical Reformulation of the General Theory of International Trade.* Chicago, 1932, xii + 120 pp.

TABLES

TABLE I. $s_n = (1 + i)^n$. (AMOUNT OF 1 AT COMPOUND INTEREST)

n	1%	1½%	2%	3%	4%	5%	6%	7%
1	1.0100	1.0150	1.0200	1.0300	1.0400	1.0500	1.0600	1.0700
2	1.0201	1.0302	1.0404	1.0609	1.0816	1.1025	1.1236	1.1449
3	1.0303	1.0457	1.0612	1.0927	1.1249	1.1576	1.1910	1.2250
4	1.0406	1.0614	1.0824	1.1255	1.1699	1.2155	1.2625	1.3108
5	1.0510	1.0773	1.1041	1.1593	1.2167	1.2763	1.3382	1.4026
6	1.0615	1.0934	1.1262	1.1941	1.2653	1.3401	1.4185	1.5007
7	1.0721	1.1098	1.1487	1.2299	1.3159	1.4071	1.5036	1.6058
8	1.0829	1.1265	1.1717	1.2668	1.3686	1.4775	1.5938	1.7182
9	1.0937	1.1434	1.1951	1.3048	1.4233	1.5513	1.6895	1.8385
10	1.1046	1.1605	1.2190	1.3439	1.4802	1.6289	1.7908	1.9672
11	1.1157	1.1779	1.2434	1.3842	1.5395	1.7103	1.8983	2.1049
12	1.1268	1.1956	1.2682	1.4258	1.6010	1.7959	2.0122	2.2522
13	1.1381	1.2136	1.2936	1.4685	1.6651	1.8856	2.1329	2.4098
14	1.1495	1.2318	1.3195	1.5126	1.7317	1.9799	2.2609	2.5785
15	1.1610	1.2502	1.3459	1.5580	1.8009	2.0789	2.3966	2.7590
16	1.1726	1.2690	1.3728	1.6047	1.8730	2.1829	2.5404	2.9522
17	1.1843	1.2880	1.4002	1.6528	1.9479	2.2920	2.6928	3.1588
18	1.1961	1.3073	1.4282	1.7024	2.0258	2.4066	2.8543	3.3799
19	1.2081	1.3270	1.4568	1.7535	2.1068	2.5270	3.0256	3.6165
20	1.2202	1.3469	1.4859	1.8061	2.1911	2.6533	3.2071	3.8697
21	1.2324	1.3671	1.5157	1.8603	2.2788	2.7860	3.3996	4.1406
22	1.2447	1.3876	1.5460	1.9161	2.3699	2.9253	3.6035	4.4304
23	1.2572	1.4084	1.5769	1.9736	2.4647	3.0715	3.8197	4.7405
24	1.2697	1.4295	1.6084	2.0328	2.5633	3.2251	4.0489	5.0724
25	1.2824	1.4509	1.6406	2.0938	2.6658	3.3864	4.2919	5.4274
26	1.2953	1.4727	1.6734	2.1566	2.7725	3.5557	4.5494	5.8074
27	1.3082	1.4948	1.7069	2.2213	2.8834	3.7335	4.8223	6.2139
28	1.3213	1.5172	1.7410	2.2879	2.9987	3.9201	5.1117	6.6488
29	1.3345	1.5400	1.7758	2.3566	3.1187	4.1161	5.4184	7.1143
30	1.3478	1.5631	1.8114	2.4273	2.2434	4.3219	5.7435	7.6123
31	1.3613	1.5865	1.8476	2.5001	3.3731	4.5380	6.0881	8.1451
32	1.3749	1.6103	1.8845	2.5751	3.5081	4.7649	6.4534	8.7153
33	1.3887	1.6345	1.9222	2.6523	3.6484	5.0032	6.8406	9.3253
34	1.4026	1.6590	1.9607	2.7319	3.7943	5.2533	7.2510	9.9781
35	1.4166	1.6839	1.9999	2.8139	3.9461	5.5160	7.6861	10.6766
36	1.4308	1.7091	2.0399	2.8983	4.1039	5.7918	8.1473	11.4239
37	1.4451	1.7348	2.0807	2.9852	4.2681	6.0814	8.6361	12.2236
38	1.4595	1.7608	2.1223	3.0748	4.4388	6.3855	9.1543	13.0793
39	1.4741	1.7872	2.1647	3.1670	4.6164	6.7048	9.7035	13.9948
40	1.4889	1.8140	2.2080	3.2620	4.8010	7.0400	10.2857	14.9745
41	1.5038	1.8412	2.2522	3.3599	4.9931	7.3920	10.9029	10.0227
42	1.5188	1.8688	2.2972	3.4607	5.1928	7.7616	11.5570	17.1443
43	1.5340	1.8969	2.3432	3.5645	5.4005	8.1497	12.2505	18.3444
44	1.5493	1.9253	2.3901	3.6715	5.6165	8.5572	12.9855	19.6285
45	1.5648	1.9542	2.4379	3.7816	5.8412	8.9850	13.7646	21.0025
46	1.5805	1.9835	2.4866	3.8950	6.0748	9.4343	14.5905	22.4726
47	1.5963	2.0133	2.5363	4.0119	6.3178	9.9060	15.4659	24.0457
48	1.6122	2.0435	2.5871	4.1323	6.5705	10.4013	16.3939	25.7289
49	1.6283	2.0741	2.6388	4.2562	6.8333	10.9213	17.3775	27.5299
50	1.6446	2.1052	2.6916	4.3839	7.1067	11.4674	18.4202	29.4570

TABLE II. $v^n = (1 + i)^{-n}$. (PRESENT VALUE OF 1 AT COMPOUND INTEREST)

n	1%	1½%	2%	3%	4%	5%	6%	7%
1	0.9901	0.9852	0.9804	0.9709	0.9615	0.9524	0.9434	0.9346
2	0.9803	0.9707	0.9612	0.9426	0.9246	0.9070	0.8900	0.8734
3	0.9706	0.9563	0.9423	0.9151	0.8890	0.8638	0.8396	0.8163
4	0.9610	0.9422	0.9238	0.8885	0.8548	0.8227	0.7921	0.7629
5	0.9515	0.9283	0.9057	0.8626	0.8219	0.7835	0.7473	0.7130
6	0.9420	0.9145	0.8880	0.8375	0.7903	0.7462	0.7050	0.6663
7	0.9327	0.9010	0.8706	0.8131	0.7599	0.7107	0.6651	0.6227
8	0.9235	0.8877	0.8535	0.7894	0.7307	0.6768	0.6274	0.5820
9	0.9143	0.8746	0.8368	0.7664	0.7026	0.6446	0.5919	0.5439
10	0.9053	0.8617	0.8203	0.7441	0.6756	0.6139	0.5584	0.5083
11	0.8963	0.8489	0.8043	0.7224	0.6496	0.5847	0.5268	0.4751
12	0.8874	0.8364	0.7885	0.7014	0.6246	0.5568	0.4970	0.4440
13	0.8787	0.8240	0.7730	0.6810	0.6006	0.5303	0.4688	0.4150
14	0.8700	0.8119	0.7579	0.6611	0.5775	0.5051	0.4423	0.3878
15	0.8613	0.7999	0.7430	0.6419	0.5553	0.4810	0.4173	0.3624
16	0.8528	0.7880	0.7284	0.6232	0.5339	0.4581	0.3936	0.3387
17	0.8444	0.7764	0.7142	0.6050	0.5134	0.4363	0.3714	0.3166
18	0.8360	0.7649	0.7002	0.5874	0.4936	0.4155	0.3503	0.2959
19	0.8277	0.7536	0.6864	0.5703	0.4746	0.3957	0.3305	0.2765
20	0.8195	0.7425	0.6730	0.5537	0.4564	0.3769	0.3118	0.2584
21	0.8114	0.7315	0.6598	0.5375	0.4388	0.3589	0.2942	0.2415
22	0.8034	0.7207	0.6468	0.5219	0.4220	0.3418	0.2775	0.2257
23	0.7954	0.7100	0.6342	0.5067	0.4057	0.3256	0.2618	0.2109
24	0.7876	0.6995	0.6217	0.4919	0.3901	0.3101	0.2470	0.1971
25	0.7798	0.6892	0.6095	0.4776	0.3751	0.2953	0.2330	0.1842
26	0.7720	0.6790	0.5976	0.4637	0.3607	0.2812	0.2198	0.1722
27	0.7644	0.6690	0.5859	0.4502	0.3468	0.2678	0.2074	0.1609
28	0.7568	0.6591	0.5744	0.4371	0.3335	0.2551	0.1956	0.1504
29	0.7493	0.6494	0.5631	0.4243	0.3207	0.2429	0.1846	0.1406
30	0.7419	0.6398	0.5521	0.4120	0.3083	0.2314	0.1741	0.1314
31	0.7346	0.6313	0.5412	0.4000	0.2965	0.2204	0.1643	0.1228
32	0.7273	0.6210	0.5306	0.3883	0.2851	0.2099	0.1550	0.1147
33	0.7201	0.6118	0.5202	0.3770	0.2741	0.1999	0.1462	0.1072
34	0.7130	0.6028	0.5100	0.3660	0.2636	0.1904	0.1379	0.1002
35	0.7059	0.5939	0.5000	0.3554	0.2534	0.1813	0.1301	0.0937
36	0.6989	0.5851	0.4902	0.3450	0.2437	0.1727	0.1227	0.0875
37	0.6920	0.5764	0.4806	0.3350	0.2343	0.1644	0.1158	0.0818
38	0.6852	0.5679	0.4712	0.3252	0.2253	0.1566	0.1092	0.0765
39	0.6784	0.5595	0.4619	0.3158	0.2166	0.1491	0.1031	0.0715
40	0.6717	0.5513	0.4529	0.3066	0.2083	0.1420	0.0972	0.0668
41	0.6650	0.5431	0.4440	0.2976	0.2003	0.1353	0.0917	0.0624
42	0.6584	0.5351	0.4353	0.2890	0.1926	0.1288	0.0865	0.0583
43	0.6519	0.5272	0.4268	0.2805	0.1852	0.1227	0.0816	0.0545
44	0.6454	0.5194	0.4184	0.2724	0.1780	0.1169	0.0770	0.0509
45	0.6391	0.5117	0.4102	0.2644	0.1712	0.1113	0.0727	0.0476
46	0.6327	0.5042	0.4022	0.2567	0.1646	0.1060	0.0685	0.0445
47	0.6265	0.4967	0.3943	0.2493	0.1583	0.1009	0.0647	0.0416
48	0.6203	0.4894	0.3865	0.2420	0.1522	0.0961	0.0610	0.0389
49	0.6141	0.4821	0.3790	0.2350	0.1463	0.0916	0.0575	0.0363
50	0.6080	0.4750	0.3715	0.2281	0.1407	0.0872	0.0543	0.0339

TABLE III. $s_{\overline{n|}} = \frac{(1+i)^n - 1}{i}$. (Amount of an Annuity of 1)

n	1%	1½%	2%	3%	4%	5%	6%	7%
1	1.0000	1.0000	1.0000	1.0000	1.0000	1.0000	1.0000	1.0000
2	2.0100	2.0150	2.0200	2.0300	2.0400	2.0500	2.0600	2.0700
3	3.0301	3.0452	3.0604	3.0909	3.1216	3.1525	3.1836	3.2149
4	4.0604	4.0909	4.1216	4.1836	4.2465	4.3101	4.3746	4.4399
5	5.1010	5.1523	5.2040	5.3091	5.4163	5.5256	5.6371	5.7507
6	6.1520	6.2296	6.3081	6.4684	6.6330	6.8019	6.9753	7.1533
7	7.2135	7.3230	7.4343	7.6625	7.8983	8.1420	8.3938	8.6540
8	8.2857	8.4328	8.5830	8.8923	9.2142	9.5491	9.8975	10.2598
9	9.3685	9.5593	9.7546	10.1591	10.5828	11.0266	11.4913	11.9780
10	10.4622	10.7027	10.9497	11.4639	12.0061	12.5779	13.1808	13.8164
11	11.5668	11.8633	12.1687	12.8078	13.4864	14.2068	14.9716	15.7836
12	12.6825	13.0412	13.4121	14.1920	15.0258	15.9171	16.8699	17.8885
13	13.8093	14.2368	14.6803	15.6178	16.6268	17.7130	18.8821	20.1406
14	14.9474	15.4504	15.9739	17.0863	18.2919	19.5986	21.0151	22.5505
15	16.0970	16.6821	17.2934	18.5989	20.0236	21.5786	23.2760	25.1290
16	17.2579	17.9324	18.6393	20.1569	21.8249	23.6575	25.6725	27.8881
17	18.4304	19.2014	20.0121	21.7616	23.6975	25.8404	28.2129	30.8402
18	19.6147	20.4894	21.4123	23.4144	25.6454	28.1324	30.9057	33.9990
19	20.8109	21.7967	22.8406	25.1169	27.6712	30.5390	33.7600	37.3790
20	22.0190	23.1237	24.2974	26.8704	29.7781	33.0660	36.7856	40.9955
21	23.2392	24.4705	25.7833	28.6765	31.9692	35.7193	39.9927	44.8652
22	24.4716	25.8376	27.2990	30.5368	34.2480	38.5052	43.3923	49.0057
23	25.7163	27.2251	28.8450	32.4529	36.6179	41.4305	46.9958	53.4361
24	26.9735	28.6335	30.4219	34.4265	39.0826	44.5020	50.8156	58.1767
25	28.2432	30.0630	32.0303	36.4593	41.6459	47.7271	54.8645	63.2490
26	29.5256	31.5140	33.6709	38.5530	44.3117	51.1135	59.1564	68.6765
27	30.8209	32.9867	35.3443	40.7096	47.0842	54.6691	63.7058	74.4838
28	32.1291	34.4815	37.0512	42.9309	49.9676	58.4026	68.5281	80.6977
29	33.4504	35.9987	38.7922	45.2189	52.9663	62.3227	73.6398	87.3465
30	34.7849	37.5387	40.5681	47.5754	56.0849	66.4388	79.0582	94.4608
31	36.1327	39.1018	42.3794	50.0027	59.3283	70.7608	84.8017	102.0730
32	37.4941	40.6883	44.2270	52.5028	62.7015	75.2988	90.8898	110.2182
33	38.8690	42.2986	46.1116	55.0778	66.2095	80.0638	97.3432	118.9334
34	40.2577	43.9331	48.0338	57.7302	69.8579	85.0670	104.1838	128.2588
35	41.6603	45.5921	49.9945	60.4621	73.6522	90.3203	111.4348	138.2369
36	43.0769	47.2760	51.9944	63.2759	77.5983	95.8363	119.1209	148.9135
37	44.5076	48.9851	54.0343	66.1742	81.7022	101.6281	127.2681	160.3374
38	45.9527	50.7199	56.1149	69.1594	85.9703	107.7095	135.9042	172.5610
39	47.4123	52.4807	58.2372	72.2342	90.4091	114.0950	145.0585	185.6403
40	48.8864	54.2679	60.4020	75.4013	95.0255	120.7998	154.7620	199.6351
41	50.3752	56.0819	62.6100	78.6633	99.8265	127.8398	165.0477	214.6096
42	51.8790	57.9231	64.8622	82.0232	104.8196	135.2318	175.9505	230.6322
43	53.3978	59.7920	67.1595	85.4839	110.0124	142.9933	187.5076	247.7765
44	54.9318	61.6889	69.5027	89.0484	115.4129	151.1430	199.7580	266.1209
45	56.4811	63.6142	71.8927	92.7199	121.0294	159.7002	212.7435	285.7493
46	58.0459	65.5684	74.3306	96.5015	126.8706	168.6852	226.5081	306.7518
47	59.6263	67.5519	76.8172	100.3965	132.9454	178.1194	241.0986	329.2244
48	61.2226	69.5652	70.3535	104.4084	139.2632	188.0254	256.5645	353.2701
49	62.8348	71.6087	81.9406	108.5406	145.8337	198.4267	272.9584	378.9990
50	64.4632	73.6828	84.5794	112.7969	152.6671	209.3480	290.3359	406.5289

TABLE IV. $a_{\overline{n|}} = \dfrac{1 - v^n}{i}$. (PRESENT VALUE OF AN ANNITY OF 1)

n	1%	1½%	2%	3%	4%	5%	6%	7%
1	0.9901	0.9852	0.9804	0.9709	0.9615	0.9524	0.9434	0.9346
2	1.9704	1.9559	1.9416	1.9135	1.8861	1.8594	1.8334	1.8080
3	2.9410	2.9122	2.8839	2.8286	2.7751	2.7232	2.6730	2.6243
4	3.9020	3.8544	3.8077	3.7171	3.6299	3.5460	3.4651	3.3872
5	4.8534	4.7826	4.7135	4.5797	4.4518	4.3295	4.2124	4.1002
6	5.7955	5.6972	5.6014	5.4172	5.2421	5.0757	4.9173	4.7665
7	6.7282	6.5982	6.4720	6.2303	6.0021	5.7864	5.5824	5.3893
8	7.6517	7.4859	7.3255	7.0197	6.7327	6.4632	6.2098	5.9713
9	8.5660	8.3605	8.1622	7.7861	7.4353	7.1078	6.8017	6.5152
10	9.4713	9.2222	8.9826	8.5302	8.1109	7.7217	7.3601	7.0236
11	10.3676	10.0711	9.7868	9.2526	8.7605	8.3064	7.8869	7.4987
12	11.2551	10.9075	10.5753	9.9540	9.3851	8.8633	8.3838	7.9427
13	12.1337	11.7315	11.3484	10.6350	9.9856	9.3936	8.8527	8.3577
14	13.0037	12.5434	12.1062	11.2961	10.5631	9.8986	9.2950	8.7455
15	13.8651	13.3432	12.8493	11.9379	11.1184	10.3797	9.7122	9.1079
16	14.7179	14.1313	13.5777	12.5611	11.6523	10.8378	10.1059	9.4466
17	15.5623	14.9076	14.2919	13.1661	12.1657	11.2741	10.4773	9.7632
18	16.3983	15.6726	14.9920	13.7535	12.6593	11.6896	10.8276	10.0591
19	17.2260	16.4262	15.6785	14.3238	13.1339	12.0853	11.1581	10.3356
20	18.0456	17.1686	16.3514	14.8775	13.5903	12.4622	11.4699	10.5940
21	18.8570	17.9001	17.0112	15.4150	14.0292	12.8212	11.7641	10.8355
22	19.6604	18.6208	17.6580	15.9369	14.4511	13.1630	12.0416	11.0612
23	20.4558	19.3309	18.2922	16.4436	14.8568	13.4886	12.3034	11.2722
24	21.2434	20.0304	18.9139	16.9355	15.2470	13.7986	12.5504	11.4693
25	22.0232	20.7196	19.5235	17.4134	15.6221	14.0939	12.7834	11.6536
26	22.7952	21.3986	20.1210	17.8768	15.9828	14.3752	13.0032	11.8258
27	23.5596	22.0676	20.7069	18.3270	16.3296	14.6430	13.2105	11.9867
28	24.3164	22.7267	21.2813	18.7641	16.6631	14.8981	13.4062	12.1371
29	25.0658	23.3761	21.8444	19.1885	16.9837	15.1411	13.5907	12.2777
30	25.8077	24.0158	22.3965	19.6004	17.2920	15.3725	13.7648	12.4090
31	26.5423	24.6461	22.9377	20.0004	17.5885	15.5928	13.9291	12.5318
32	27.2696	25.2671	23.4683	20.3888	17.8736	15.8027	14.0840	12.6466
33	27.9897	25.8790	23.9886	20.7658	18.1476	16.0025	14.2302	12.7538
34	28.7027	26.4817	24.4986	21.1318	18.4112	16.1929	14.3681	12.8540
35	29.4086	27.0756	24.9986	21.4872	18.6646	16.3742	14.4982	12.9477
36	30.1075	27.6607	25.4888	21.8323	18.9083	16.5469	14.6210	13.0352
37	30.7995	28.2371	25.9695	22.1672	19.1426	16.7113	14.7368	13.1170
38	31.4847	28.8051	26.4406	22.4925	19.3679	16.8679	14.8460	13.1935
39	32.1630	29.3646	26.9026	22.8082	19.5845	17.0170	14.9491	13.2649
40	32.8347	29.9158	27.3555	23.1148	19.7928	17.1591	15.0463	13.3317
41	33.4997	30.4590	27.7995	23.4124	19.9931	17.2944	15.1380	13.3941
42	34.1581	30.9941	28.2348	23.7014	20.1856	17.4232	15.2245	13.4524
43	34.8100	31.5212	28.6616	23.9819	20.3708	17.5459	15.3062	13.5070
44	35.4555	32.0406	29.0800	24.2543	205488	17.6628	15.3832	13.5579
45	36.0945	32.5523	29.4902	24.5187	20.7200	19.7741	15.4558	13.6055
46	36.7272	33.0565	29.8923	24.7754	20.8847	18.8801	15.5244	13.6500
47	37.3537	33.5532	30.2866	25.0247	21.0429	17.9810	15.5890	13.6916
48	37.9740	34.0426	30.6731	25.2667	21.1951	18.0772	15.6500	13.7305
49	38.5881	34.5247	31.0521	25.5017	21.3415	18.1687	15.7076	13.7668
50	39.1961	34.9997	31.4236	25.7298	21.4822	18.2559	15.7619	13.8007

TABLE V. American Experience Table of Mortality

x	l_x	d_x	q_x	p_x	x	l_x	d_x	q_x	p_x
10	100 000	749	.007 490	.992 510	53	66 797	1091	.016 333	.983 667
11	99 251	746	.007 516	.992 484	54	65 706	1143	.017 396	.982 604
12	98 505	743	.007 543	.992 457	55	64 563	1199	.018 571	.981 429
13	97 762	740	.007 569	.992 431	56	63 364	1260	.019 885	.980 115
14	97 022	737	.007 596	.992 404	57	62 104	1325	.021 335	.978 665
15	96 285	735	.007 634	.992 366	58	60 779	1394	.022 936	.977 064
16	95 550	732	.007 661	.992 339	59	59 385	1468	.024 720	.975 280
17	94 818	729	.007 688	.992 312	60	57 917	1546	.026 693	.973 307
18	94 089	727	.007 727	.992 273	61	56 371	1628	.028 880	.971 120
19	93 362	725	.007 765	.992 235	62	54 743	1713	.031 292	.968 708
20	92 637	723	.007 805	.992 195	63	53 030	1800	.033 943	.966 057
21	91 914	722	.007 855	.992 145	64	51 230	1889	.036 873	.963 127
22	91 192	721	.007 906	.992 094	65	49 341	1980	.040 129	.959 871
23	90 471	720	.007 958	.992 042	66	47 361	2070	.043 707	.956 293
24	89 751	719	.008 011	.991 989	67	45 291	2158	.047 647	.952 353
25	89 032	718	.008 065	.991 935	68	43 133	2243	.052 002	.947 998
26	88 314	718	.008 130	.991 870	69	40 890	2321	.056 762	.943 238
27	87 596	718	.008 197	.991 803	70	38 569	2391	.061 993	.938 007
28	86 878	718	.008 264	.991 736	71	36 178	2448	.067 665	.932 335
29	86 160	719	.008 345	.991 655	72	33 730	2487	.073 733	.926 267
30	85 441	720	.008 427	.991 573	73	31 243	2505	.080 178	.919 822
31	84 721	721	.008 510	.991 490	74	28 738	2501	.087 028	.912 972
32	84 000	723	.008 607	.991 393	75	26 237	2476	.094 371	.905 629
33	83 277	726	.008 718	.991 282	76	23 761	2431	.102 311	.897 689
34	82 551	729	.008 831	.991 169	77	21 330	2369	.111 064	.888 936
35	81 822	732	.008 946	.991 054	78	18 961	2291	.120 827	.879 173
36	81 090	737	.009 089	.990 911	79	16 670	2196	.131 734	.868 266
37	80 353	742	.009 234	.990 766	80	14 474	2091	.144 466	.855 534
38	79 611	749	.009 408	.990 592	81	12 383	1964	.158 605	.841 395
39	78 862	756	.009 586	.990 414	82	10 419	1816	.174 297	.825 703
40	78 106	765	.009 794	.990 206	83	8 603	1648	.191 561	.808 439
41	77 341	774	.010 008	.989 992	84	6 955	1470	.211 359	.788 641
42	76 567	785	.010 252	.989 748	85	5 485	1292	.235 552	.764 448
43	75 782	797	.010 517	.989 483	86	4 193	1114	.265 681	.734 319
44	74 985	812	.010 829	.989 171	87	3 079	933	.303 020	.696 980
45	74 173	828	.011 163	.988 837	88	2 146	744	.346 692	.653 308
46	73 345	848	.011 562	.988 438	89	1 402	555	.395 863	.604 137
47	72 497	870	.012 000	.988 000	90	847	385	.454 545	.545 455
48	71 627	896	.012 509	.987 491	91	462	246	.532 466	.467 534
49	70 731	927	.013 106	.986 894	92	216	137	.634 259	.365 741
50	69 804	962	.013 781	.986 219	93	79	58	.734 177	.265 823
51	68 842	1001	.014 541	.985 459	94	21	18	.857 143	.142 857
52	67 841	1044	.015 389	.984 611	95	3	3	1.000 000	.000 000

TABLE VI. Commutation Columns

American Experience—Interest = 3½%

x	D_x	N_x	M_x	x	D_x	N_x	M_x
10	70 891.9	1 575 535.3	17 612.91	53	10 787.4	145 915.7	5 853.095
11	67 891.5	1 504 643.4	17 099.89	54	10.252.4	135 128.2	5 682.861
12	65 189.0	1 436 661.9	16 606.20	55	9 733.40	124 875.8	5 510.544
13	62 509.4	1 371 472.9	16 131.12	56	9 229.60	115 542.4	5 335.898
14	59 938.4	1 308 963.5	15 673.96	57	8 740.17	105 912.8	5 158.573
15	57 471.6	1 249 025.0	15 234.05	58	8 264.44	97 172.64	4 978.405
16	55 104.2	1 191 553.4	14 810.17	59	7 801.82	88 908.20	4 795.266
17	52 832.9	1 136 449.2	14 402.30	60	7 351.65	81 106.38	4 608.926
18	50 653.9	1 083 616.2	14 009.83	61	6 913.44	73 754.73	4 419.322
19	48 562.8	1 032 962.4	13 631.68	62	6 486.75	66 841.28	4 226.413
20	46 556.2	984 399.6	13 267.32	63	6 071.27	60 354.54	4 030.296
21	44 630.8	937 843.4	12 916.25	64	5 666.85	54 283.27	3 831.187
22	42 782.8	893 212.6	12 577.53	65	5 273.33	48 616.41	3 629.300
23	41 009.2	850 429.9	12 250.71	66	4 890.55	43 343.08	3 424.843
24	39 307.1	809 420.6	11 935.38	67	4 518.65	38 452.53	3 218.321
25	37 673.6	770 113.6	11 631.14	68	4 157.82	33 933.88	3 010.299
26	36 106.1	732 439.9	11 337.59	69	3 808.32	29 776.06	2 801.396
27	34 601.5	696 333.8	11 053.97	70	3 470.67	25 967.74	2 592.538
28	33 157.4	661 732.4	10 779.94	71	3 145.43	22 497.07	2 384.657
29	31 771.3	628 575.0	10 515.18	72	2 833.42	19 351.64	2 179.018
30	30 440.8	596 803.6	10 259.02	73	2 535.75	16 518.22	1 977.167
31	29 163.5	566 362.9	10 011.17	74	2 253.57	13 982.47	1 780.731
32	27 937.5	537 199.3	9 771.375	75	1 987.87	11 728.90	1 591.240
33	26 760.5	509 261.8	9 539.044	76	1 739.39	9 741.028	1 409.988
34	25 630.1	482 501.3	9 313.638	77	1 508.63	8 001.633	1 238.047
35	24 544.7	456 871.2	9 094.955	78	1 295.73	6 492.999	1 076.158
36	23 502.5	432 326.5	8 882.798	79	1 100.65	5 197.271	924.8937
37	22 501.4	408 824.0	8 676.415	80	923.338	4 096.624	784.8046
38	21 539.7	386 322.6	8 475.658	81	763.234	3 173.286	655.9245
39	20 615.5	364 782.9	8 279.860	82	620.465	2 410.052	538.9657
40	19 727.4	344 167.4	8 088.915	83	494.995	1 789.587	434.4776
41	18 873.6	324 440.0	7 902.231	84	386.641	1 294.592	342.8624
42	18 052.9	305 566.3	7 719.738	85	294.610	907.9513	263.9059
43	17 263.6	287 513.4	7 540.910	86	217.598	613.3417	196.8569
44	16 504.4	270 249.8	7 365.489	87	154.383	395.7438	141.0003
45	15 773.6	253 745.5	7 192.809	88	103.963	241.3609	95.80107
46	15 070.0	237 971.9	7 022.682	89	65.6231	137.3978	60.97682
47	14 392.1	222 901.9	6 854.337	90	38.3047	71.77470	35.87752
48	13 738.5	208 509.8	6 687.466	91	20.1869	33.47001	19.05509
49	13 107.9	194 771.3	6 521.419	92	9.11889	13.28309	8.669695
50	12 498.6	181 663.4	6 355.436	93	3.22236	4.16421	3.081545
51	11 909.6	169 164.7	6 189.012	94	0.827611	0.94184	0.795762
52	11 339.5	157 255.2	6 021.696	95	0.114232	0.11423	0.110369

TABLE VII. COEFFICIENTS FOR FITTING A STRAIGHT LINE TO DATA

(The numbers in parentheses denote the number of ciphers between the decimal point and the first significant figure.)

p	A	A'	p
1	.333 3333 333	.500 0000 000	1
2	.200 0000 000	.100 0000 000	2
3	.142 8571 429	.(1) 357 1428 571	3
4	.111 1111 111	.(1) 166 6666 667	4
5	.(1) 909 0909 091	.(2) 909 0909 091	5
6	.(1) 769 2307 692	.(2) 549 4505 495	6
7	.(1) 666 6666 667	.(2) 357 1428 571	7
8	.(1) 588 2352 941	.(2) 245 0980 392	8
9	.(1) 526 3157 895	.(2) 175 4385 965	9
10	.(1) 476 1904 762	.(2) 129 8701 299	10
11	.(1) 434 7826 087	.(3) 988 1422 925	11
12	.(1) 400 0000 000	.(3) 769 2307 692	12
13	.(1) 370 3703 704	.(3) 610 5006 105	13
14	.(1) 344 8275 862	.(3) 492 6108 374	14
15	.(1) 322 5806 452	.(3) 403 2258 064	15
16	.(1) 303 0303 030	.(3) 334 2245 989	16
17	.(1) 285 7142 857	.(3) 280 1120 448	17
18	.(1) 270 2702 703	.(3) 237 0791 844	18
19	.(1) 256 4102 564	.(3) 202 4291 498	19
20	.(1) 243 9024 390	.(3) 174 2160 279	20
21	.(1) 232 5581 395	.(3) 151 0117 789	21
22	.(1) 222 2222 222	.(3) 131 7523 057	22
23	.(1) 212 7659 574	.(3) 115 6336 725	23
24	.(1) 204 0816 327	.(3) 102 0408 163	24
25	.(1) 196 0784 314	(4) 904 9773 756	25
26	.(1) 188 6792 453	.(4) 806 3215 610	26
27	.(1) 181 8181 818	.(4) 721 5007 215	27
28	.(1) 175 4385 965	.(4) 648 1721 545	28
29	.(1) 169 4915 254	.(4) 584 4535 359	29
30	.(1) 163 9344 262	.(4) 528 8207 298	30
31	.(1) 158 7301 587	.(4) 480 0307 220	31
32	.(1) 153 8461 538	.(4) 437 0629 371	32
33	.(1) 149 2537 313	.(4) 399 0741 480	33
34	.(1) 144 9275 362	.(4) 365 3635 367	34
35	.(1) 140 8450 704	.(4) 335 3454 058	35
36	.(1) 136 9863 014	.(4) 308 5277 058	36
37	.(1) 133 3333 333	.(4) 284 4950 213	37
38	.(1) 129 8701 299	.(4) 262 8949 997	38
39	.(1) 126 5822 785	.(4) 243 4274 586	39
40	.(1) 123 4567 901	.(4) 225 8355 917	40
41	.(1) 120 4819 277	.(4) 209 8988 288	41
42	.(1) 117 6470 588	.(4) 195 4270 080	42
43	.(1) 114 9425 287	.(4) 182 2555 952	43
44	.(1) 112 3595 506	.(4) 170 2417 433	44
45	.(1) 109 8901 099	.(4) 159 2610 288	45
46	.(1) 107 5268 817	.(4) 149 2047 387	46
47	.(1) 105 2631 579	.(4) 139 9776 036	47
48	.(1) 103 0927 835	.(4) 131 4958 973	48
49	.(1) 101 0101 010	.(4) 123 6858 380	49
50	.(2) 990 0990 099	.(4) 116 4822 365	50

INDEX OF NAMES

INDEX OF SUBJECTS